# EXPERIMENTAL RESEARCHES IN ELECTRICITY

## by MICHAEL FARADAY

*in three volumes bound as two*

*Volumes I and II*

NEW YORK

DOVER PUBLICATIONS, INC.

Published in Canada by General Publishing Company, Ltd., 30 Lesmill Road, Don Mills, Toronto, Ontario.

Published in the United Kingdom by Constable and Company, Ltd., 10 Orange Street, London W. C. 2.

This Dover edition, first published in 1965, is an unabridged and unaltered republication of the work originally published in three volumes. Volumes I and III were originally published by Taylor and Francis in 1839 and 1855, respectively, and Volume II was originally published by Richard and John Edward Taylor in 1844.

*Library of Congress Catalog Card Number: 63-19490*

Manufactured in the United States of America

Dover Publications, Inc.
180 Varick Street
New York 14, N.Y.

# CONTENTS

# EXPERIMENTAL RESEARCHES IN ELECTRICITY

## by MICHAEL FARADAY

*Volume I*

# PREFACE.

I HAVE been induced by various circumstances to collect in One Volume the Fourteen Series of Experimental Researches in Electricity, which have appeared in the Philosophical Transactions during the last seven years : the chief reason has been the desire to supply at a moderate price the whole of these papers, with an Index, to those who may desire to have them.

The readers of the volume will, I hope, do me the justice to remember that it was not written as a *whole*, but in parts ; the earlier portions rarely having any known relation at the time to those which might follow. If I had rewritten the work, I perhaps might have considerably varied the form, but should not have altered much of the real matter : it would not, however, then have been considered a faithful reprint or statement of the course and results of the whole investigation, which only I desired to supply.

I may be allowed to express my great satisfaction at finding, that the different parts, written at intervals during seven years, harmonize so well as they do. There would have been nothing particular in this, if the parts had related only to matters well ascertained before any of them were written :—but as each professes to contain something of original discovery, or of correction of received views, it does surprise even my partiality, that they should have the degree of consistency and apparent general accuracy which they seem to me to present.

I have made some alterations in the text, but they have been altogether of a typographical or grammatical character; and even where greatest, have been intended to explain the sense, not to alter it. I have often added Notes at the bottom of the page, as to paragraphs 59, 360, 439, 521, 552, 555, 598, 657, 883, for the correction of errors, and also the purpose of illustration: but these are all distinguished from the Original Notes of the Researches by the date of *Dec.* 1838.

The date of a scientific paper containing any pretensions to discovery is frequently a matter of serious importance, and it is a great misfortune that there are many most valuable communications, essential to the history and progress of science, with respect to which this point cannot now be ascertained. This arises from the circumstance of the papers having no dates attached to them individually, and of the journals in which they appear having such as are inaccurate, *i. e.* dates of a period earlier than that of publication. I may refer to the note at the end of the First Series, as an illustration of the kind of confusion thus produced. These circumstances have induced me to affix a date at the top of every other page, and I have thought myself justified in using that placed by the Secretary of the Royal Society on each paper as it was received. An author has no right, perhaps, to claim an earlier one, unless it has received confirmation by some public act or officer.

Before concluding these lines I would beg leave to make a reference or two ; first, to my own Papers on Electro-magnetic Rotations in the Quarterly Journal of Science, 1822., xii. 74. 186. 283. 416. and also to my Letter on Magneto-electric Induction in the Annales de Chimie, li. p. 404. These might, as to the matter, very properly have appeared in this volume, but they would have interfered with it as a simple reprint of the "Experimental Researches" of the Philosophical Transactions.

Then I wish to refer, in relation to the Fourth Series on a new law of Electric Conduction, to Franklin's experiments on the non-conduction of ice, which have been very properly separated and set forth by Professor Bache, (Journal of the Franklin Institute, 1836. xvii. 183). These, which I did not at all remember as to the extent of the effect, though they in no way anticipate the expression of the law I state as to the general effect of liquefaction on electrolytes, still should never be forgotten when speaking of that law as applicable to the case of water.

There are two papers which I am anxious to refer to, as corrections or criticisms of parts of the Experimental Researches. The first of these is one by Jacobi, (Philosophical Magazine, 1838, xiii. 401) relative to the possible production of a spark on completing the junction of the two metals of a single pair of plates (915.). It is an excellent paper, and though I have not repeated the experiments, the description of them convinces me that I must have been in error. The second is by that excellent philosopher, Marianini, (Memoria della Societa Italiana di Modena, xxi. 205), and is a critical and experimental examination of

Series viii, and of the question whether metallic contact is or is not *productive* of a part of the electricity of the voltaic pile. I see no reason as yet to alter the opinion I have given; but the paper is so very valuable, comes to the question so directly, and the point itself is of such great importance, that I intend at the first opportunity renewing the inquiry, and, if I can, rendering the proofs either on the one side or the other undeniable to all.

Other parts of these researches have received the honor of critical attention from various philosophers, to all of whom I am obliged, and some of whose corrections I have acknowledged in the foot notes. There are, no doubt, occasions on which I have not felt the force of the remarks, but time and the progress of science will best settle such cases; and, although I cannot honestly say that I *wish* to be found in error, yet I do fervently hope that the progress of science in the hands of its many zealous present cultivators will be such, as by giving us new and other developments, and laws more and more general in their applications, will even make me think that what is written and illustrated in these experimental researches, belongs to the by-gone parts of science.

                    MICHAEL FARADAY.

Royal Institution,
    March, 1839.

# CONTENTS.

# EXPERIMENTAL RESEARCHES

## IN

# ELECTRICITY.

———◆———

## FIRST SERIES.

§ 1. *On the Induction of Electric Currents.* § 2. *On the Evolution of Electricity from Magnetism.* § 3. *On a new Electrical Condition of Matter.* § 4. *On* Arago's *Magnetic Phenomena.*

[Read November 24, 1831.]

1. THE power which electricity of tension possesses of causing an opposite electrical state in its vicinity has been expressed by the general term Induction; which, as it has been received into scientific language, may also, with propriety, be used in the same general sense to express the power which electrical currents may possess of inducing any particular state upon matter in their immediate neighbourhood, otherwise indifferent. It is with this meaning that I purpose using it in the present paper.

2. Certain effects of the induction of electrical currents have already been recognised and described: as those of magnetization; Ampère's experiments of bringing a copper disc near to a flat spiral; his repetition with electro-magnets of Arago's extraordinary experiments, and perhaps a few others. Still it appeared unlikely that these could be all the effects which induction by currents could produce; especially as, upon dispensing with iron, almost the whole of them disappear, whilst yet an infinity of bodies, exhibiting definite phenomena of in-

duction with electricity of tension, still remain to be acted upon
by the induction of electricity in motion.

3. Further : Whether Ampère's beautiful theory were adopted, or any other, or whatever reservation were mentally made,
still it appeared very extraordinary, that as every electric current was accompanied by a corresponding intensity of magnetic
action at right angles to the current, good conductors of electricity, when placed within the sphere of this action, should
not have any current induced through them, or some sensible
effect produced equivalent in force to such a current.

4. These considerations, with their consequence, the hope
of obtaining electricity from ordinary magnetism, have stimulated me at various times to investigate experimentally the inductive effect of electric currents. I lately arrived at positive
results ; and not only had my hopes fulfilled, but obtained a
key which appeared to me to open out a full explanation of
Arago's magnetic phenomena, and also to discover a new state,
which may probably have great influence in some of the most
important effects of electric currents.

5. These results I purpose describing, not as they were obtained, but in such a manner as to give the most concise view
of the whole.

## § 1. *Induction of Electric Currents.*

6. About twenty-six feet of copper wire one twentieth of an
inch in diameter were wound round a cylinder of wood as a
helix, the different spires of which were prevented from touching by a thin interposed twine. This helix was covered with
calico, and then a second wire applied in the same manner. In
this way twelve helices were superposed, each containing an
average length of wire of twenty-seven feet, and all in the same
direction. The first, third, fifth, seventh, ninth, and eleventh
of these helices were connected at their extremities end to
end, so as to form one helix ; the others were connected in a
similar manner ; and thus two principal helices were produced,
closely interposed, having the same direction, not touching anywhere, and each containing one hundred and fifty-five feet in
length of wire.

7. One of these helices was connected with a galvanometer,
the other with a voltaic battery of ten pairs of plates four inches

square, with double coppers and well charged; yet not the slightest sensible deflection of the galvanometer needle could be observed.

8. A similar compound helix, consisting of six lengths of copper and six of soft iron wire, was constructed. The resulting iron helix contained two hundred and fourteen feet of wire, the resulting copper helix two hundred and eight feet; but whether the current from the trough was passed through the copper or the iron helix, no effect upon the other could be perceived at the galvanometer.

9. In these and many similar experiments no difference in action of any kind appeared between iron and other metals.

10. Two hundred and three feet of copper wire in one length were coiled round a large block of wood; other two hundred and three feet of similar wire were interposed as a spiral between the turns of the first coil, and metallic contact everywhere prevented by twine. One of these helices was connected with a galvanometer, and the other with a battery of one hundred pairs of plates four inches square, with double coppers, and well charged. When the contact was made, there was a sudden and very slight effect at the galvanometer, and there was also a similar slight effect when the contact with the battery was broken. But whilst the voltaic current was continuing to pass through the one helix, no galvanometrical appearances nor any effect like induction upon the other helix could be perceived, although the active power of the battery was proved to be great, by its heating the whole of its own helix, and by the brilliancy of the discharge when made through charcoal.

11. Repetition of the experiments with a battery of one hundred and twenty pairs of plates produced no other effects; but it was ascertained, both at this and the former time, that the slight deflection of the needle occurring at the moment of completing the connexion, was always in one direction, and that the equally slight deflection produced when the contact was broken, was in the other direction.; and also, that these effects occurred when the first helices were used (6. 8.).

12. The results which I had by this time obtained with magnets led me to believe that the battery current through one wire, did, in reality, induce a similar current through the other

wire, but that it continued for an instant only, and partook more of the nature of the electrical wave passed through from the shock of a common Leyden jar than of the current from a voltaic battery, and therefore might magnetise a steel needle, although it scarcely affected the galvanometer.

13. This expectation was confirmed; for on substituting a small hollow helix, formed round a glass tube, for the galvanometer, introducing a steel needle, making contact as before between the battery and the inducing wire (7. 10.), and then removing the needle before the battery contact was broken, it was found magnetised.

14. When the battery contact was first made, then an unmagnetised needle introduced into the small indicating helix (13.), and lastly the battery contact broken, the needle was found magnetised to an equal degree apparently as before; but the poles were of the contrary kind.

15. The same effects took place on using the large compound helices first described (6. 8.).

16. When the unmagnetised needle was put into the indicating helix, before contact of the inducing wire with the battery, and remained there until the contact was broken, it exhibited little or no magnetism; the first effect having been nearly neutralised by the second (13. 14.). The force of the induced current upon making contact was found always to exceed that of the induced current at breaking of contact; and if therefore the contact was made and broken many times in succession, whilst the needle remained in the indicating helix, it at last came out not unmagnetised, but a needle magnetised as if the induced current upon making contact had acted alone on it. This effect may be due to the accumulation (as it is called) at the poles of the unconnected pile, rendering the current upon first making contact more powerful than what it is afterwards, at the moment of breaking contact.

17. If the circuit between the helix or wire under induction and the galvanometer or indicating spiral was not rendered complete *before* the connexion between the battery and the inducing wire was completed or broken, then no effects were perceived at the galvanometer. Thus, if the battery communications were first made, and then the wire under induction connected with the indicating helix, no magnetising power was

there exhibited. But still retaining the latter communications, when those with the battery were broken, a magnet was formed in the helix, but of the second kind (14.), *i. e.* with poles indicating a current in the same direction to that belonging to the battery current, or to that always induced by that current at its cessation.

18. In the preceding experiments the wires were placed near to each other, and the contact of the inducing one with the battery made when the inductive effect was required; but as the particular action might be supposed to be exerted only at the moments of making and breaking contact, the induction was produced in another way. Several feet of copper wire were stretched in wide zigzag forms, representing the letter W, on one surface of a broad board; a second wire was stretched in precisely similar forms on a second board, so that when brought near the first, the wires should everywhere touch, except that a sheet of thick paper was interposed. One of these wires was connected with the galvanometer, and the other with a voltaic battery. The first wire was then moved towards the second, and as it approached, the needle was deflected. Being then removed, the needle was deflected in the opposite direction. By first making the wires approach and then recede, simultaneously with the vibrations of the needle, the latter soon became very extensive; but when the wires ceased to move from or towards each other, the galvanometer-needle soon came to its usual position.

19. As the wires approximated, the induced current was in the *contrary* direction to the inducing current. As the wires receded, the induced current was in the *same* direction as the inducing current. When the wires remained stationary, there was no induced current (54.).

20. When a small voltaic arrangement was introduced into the circuit between the galvanometer (10.) and its helix or wire, so as to cause a permanent deflection of 30° or 40°, and then the battery of one hundred pairs of plates connected with the inducing wire, there was an instantaneous action as before (11.); but the galvanometer-needle immediately resumed and retained its place unaltered, notwithstanding the continued contact of the inducing wire with the trough: such was the case in whichever way the contacts were made (33.).

21. Hence it would appear that collateral currents, either in the same or in opposite directions, exert no permanent inducing power on each other, affecting their quantity or tension.

22. I could obtain no evidence by the tongue, by spark, or by heating fine wire or charcoal, of the electricity passing through the wire under induction; neither could I obtain any chemical effects, though the contacts with metallic and other solutions were made and broken alternately with those of the battery, so that the second effect of induction should not oppose or neutralize the first (13. 16.).

23. This deficiency of effect is not because the induced current of electricity cannot pass fluids, but probably because of its brief duration and feeble intensity; for on introducing two large copper plates into the circuit on the induced side (20.), the plates being immersed in brine, but prevented from touching each other by an interposed cloth, the effect at the indicating galvanometer or helix occurred as before. The induced electricity could also pass through a voltaic trough (20.). When, however, the quantity of interposed fluid was reduced to a drop, the galvanometer gave no indication.

24. Attempts to obtain similar effects by the use of wires conveying ordinary electricity were doubtful in the results. A compound helix similar to that already described, containing eight elementary helices (6.), was used. Four of the helices had their similar ends bound together by wire, and the two general terminations thus produced connected with the small magnetising helix containing an unmagnetised needle (13.). The other four helices were similarly arranged, but their ends connected with a Leyden jar. On passing the discharge, the needle was found to be a magnet; but it appeared probable that a part of the electricity of the jar had passed off to the small helix, and so magnetised the needle. There was indeed no reason to expect that the electricity of a jar possessing as it does great tension, would not diffuse itself through all the metallic matter interposed between the coatings.

25. Still it does not follow that the discharge of ordinary electricity through a wire does not produce analagous phenomena to those arising from voltaic electricity; but as it appears impossible to separate the effects produced at the moment when the discharge begins to pass, from the equal and contrary effects

produced when it ceases to pass (16.), inasmuch as with ordinary electricity these periods are simultaneous, so there can be
scarcely any hope that in this form of the experiment they can
be perceived.

26. Hence it is evident that currents of voltaic electricity
present phenomena of induction somewhat analagous to those
produced by electricity of tension, although, as will be seen hereafter, many differences exist between them.   The result is the
production of other currents, (but which are only momentary,)
parallel, or tending to parallelism, with the inducing current.
By reference to the poles of the needle formed in the indicating
helix (13. 14.) and to the deflections of the galvanometer-
needle (11.), it was found in all cases that the induced current,
produced by the first action of the inducing current, was in
the contrary direction to the latter, but that the current produced by the cessation of the inducing current was in the same
direction (19.).   For the purpose of avoiding periphrasis, I
propose to call this action of the current from the voltaic battery *volta-electric induction*.   The properties of the second
wire, after induction has developed the first current, and whilst
the electricity from the battery continues to flow through its
inducing neighbour (10. 18.), constitute a peculiar electric condition, the consideration of which will be resumed hereafter
(60.).   All these results have been obtained with a voltaic apparatus consisting of a single pair of plates.

## § 2. *Evolution of Electricity from Magnetism.*

27. A welded ring was made of soft round bar-iron, the
metal being seven eighths of an inch in thickness, and the ring
six inches in external diameter.   Three helices were put round
one part of this ring, each containing about twenty-four feet of
copper wire one twentieth of an inch thick ; they were insulated from the iron and each other, and superposed in the manner
before described (6.), occupying about nine inches in length
upon the ring.   They could be used separately or conjointly ;
the group may be distinguished by the letter A (Pl. I. fig. 1.).
On the other part of the ring about sixty feet of similar copper
wire in two pieces were applied in the same manner, forming a
helix B, which had the same common direction with the helices

of A, but being separated from it at each extremity by about half an inch of the uncovered iron.

28. The helix B was connected by copper wires with a galvanometer three feet from the ring. The helices of A were connected end to end so as to form one common helix, the extremities of which were connected with a battery of ten pairs of plates four inches square. The galvanometer was immediately affected, and to a degree far beyond what has been described when with a battery of tenfold power helices *without iron* were used (10.) ; but though the contact was continued, the effect was not permanent, for the needle soon came to rest in its natural position, as if quite indifferent to the attached electro-magnetic arrangement. Upon breaking the contact with the battery, the needle was again powerfully deflected, but in the contrary direction to that induced in the first instance.

29. Upon arranging the apparatus so that B should be out of use, the galvanometer be connected with one of the three wires of A (27.), and the other two made into a helix through which the current from the trough (28.) was passed, similar but rather more powerful effects were produced.

30. When the battery contact was made in one direction, the galvanometer-needle was deflected on the one side ; if made in the other direction, the deflection was on the other side. The deflection on breaking the battery contact was always the reverse of that produced by completing it. The deflection on making a battery contact always indicated an induced current in the opposite direction to that from the battery ; but on breaking the contact the deflection indicated an induced current in the same direction as that of the battery. No making or breaking of the contact at B side, or in any part of the galvanometer circuit, produced any effect at the galvanometer. No continuance of the battery current caused any deflection of the galvanometer-needle. As the above results are common to all these experiments, and to similar ones with ordinary magnets to be hereafter detailed, they need not be again particularly described.

31. Upon using the power of one hundred pairs of plates (10.) with this ring, the impulse at the galvanometer, when

contact was completed or broken, was so great as to make the needle spin round rapidly four or five times, before the air and terrestial magnetism could reduce its motion to mere oscillation.

32. By using charcoal at the ends of the B helix, a minute *spark* could be perceived when the contact of the battery with A was completed. This spark could not be due to any diversion of a part of the current of the battery through the iron to the helix B; for when the battery contact was continued, the galvanometer still resumed its perfectly indifferent state (28.). The spark was rarely seen on breaking contact. A small platina wire could not be ignited by this induced current; but there seems every reason to believe that the effect would be obtained by using a stronger original current or a more powerful arrangement of helices.

33. A feeble voltaic current was sent through the helix B and the galvanometer, so as to deflect the needle of the latter 30° or 40°, and then the battery of one hundred pairs of plates connected with A; but after the first effect was over, the galvanometer-needle resumed exactly the position due to the feeble current transmitted by its own wire. This took place in whichever way the battery contacts were made, and shows that here again (20.) no permanent influence of the currents upon each other, as to their quantity and tension, exists.

34. Another arrangement was then employed connecting the former experiments on volta-electric induction (6—26.) with the present. A combination of helices like that already described (6.) was constructed upon a hollow cylinder of pasteboard: there were eight lengths of copper wire, containing altogether 220 feet; four of these helices were connected end to end, and then with the galvanometer (7.); the other intervening four were also connected end to end, and the battery of one hundred pairs discharged through them. In this form the effect on the galvanometer was hardly sensible (11.), though magnets could be made by the induced current (13.). But when a soft iron cylinder seven eighths of an inch thick, and twelve inches long, was introduced into the pasteboard tube, surrounded by the helices, then the induced current affected the galvanometer powerfully, and with all the phenomena just described (30.). It possessed also the power of making mag-

nets with more energy, apparently, than when no iron cylinder was present.

35. When the iron cylinder was replaced by an equal cylinder of copper, no effect beyond that of the helices alone was produced. The iron cylinder arrangement was not so powerful as the ring arrangement already described (27.).

36. Similar effects were then produced by *ordinary magnets :* thus the hollow helix just described (34.) had all its elementary helices connected with the galvanometer by two copper wires, each five feet in length ; the soft iron cylinder was introduced into its axis ; a couple of bar magnets, each twenty-four inches long, were arranged with their opposite poles at one end in contact, so as to resemble a horse-shoe magnet, and then contact made between the other poles and the ends of the iron cylinder, so as to convert it for the time into a magnet (fig. 2.) : by breaking the magnetic contacts, or reversing them, the magnetism of the iron cylinder could be destroyed or reversed at pleasure.

37. Upon making magnetic contact, the needle was deflected ; continuing the contact, the needle became indifferent, and resumed its first position ; on breaking the contact, it was again deflected, but in the opposite direction to the first effect, and then it again became indifferent. When the magnetic contacts were reversed the deflections were reversed.

38. When the magnetic contact was made, the deflection was such as to indicate an induced current of electricity in the opposite direction to that fitted to form a magnet, having the same polarity as that really produced by contact with the bar magnets. Thus when the marked and unmarked poles were placed as in fig. 3, the current in the helix was in the direction represented, P being supposed to be the end of the wire going to the positive pole of the battery, or that end towards which the zinc plates face, and N the negative wire. Such a current would have converted the cylinder into a magnet of the opposite kind to that formed by contact with the poles A and B ; and such a current moves in the opposite direction to the currents which in M. Ampère's beautiful theory are considered as constituting a magnet in the position figured [*].

[*] The relative position of an electric current and a magnet is by most persons found very difficult to remember, and three or four helps to the memory

39. But as it might be supposed that in all the preceding experiments of this section, it was by some peculiar effect taking place during the formation of the magnet, and not by its mere virtual approximation, that the momentary induced current was excited, the following experiment was made. All the similar ends of the compound hollow helix (34.) were bound together by copper wire, forming two general terminations, and these were connected with the galvanometer. The soft iron cylinder (34.) was removed, and a cylindrical magnet, three quarters of an inch in diameter and eight inches and a half in length, used instead. One end of this magnet was introduced into the axis of the helix (fig. 4.), and then, the galvanometer-needle being stationary, the magnet was suddenly thrust in; immediately the needle was deflected in the same direction as if the magnet had been formed by either of the two preceding processes (34. 36.). Being left in, the needle resumed its first position, and then the magnet being withdrawn the needle was deflected in the opposite direction. These effects were not great; but by introducing and withdrawing the magnet, so that the impulse each time should be added to those previously communicated to the needle, the latter could be made to vibrate through an arc of 180° or more.

40. In this experiment the magnet must not be passed entirely through the helix, for then a second action occurs. When the magnet is introduced, the needle at the galvanometer is deflected in a certain direction; but being in, whether it be pushed quite through or withdrawn, the needle is deflected in a direction the reverse of that previously produced. When the magnet is passed in and through at one continuous motion,

have been devised by M. Ampère and others. I venture to suggest the following as a very simple and effectual assistance in these and similar latitudes. Let the experimenter think he is looking down upon a dipping needle, or upon the pole of the earth, and then let him think upon the direction of the motion of the hands of a watch, or of a screw moving direct; currents in that direction round a needle would make it into such a magnet as the dipping needle, or would themselves constitute an electro-magnet of similar qualities; or if brought near a magnet would tend to make it take that direction; or would themselves be moved into that position by a magnet so placed; or in M. Ampère's theory are considered as moving in that direction in the magnet. These two points of the position of the dipping-needle and the motion of the watch hands being remembered, any other relation of the current and the magnet can be at once deduced from it.

the needle moves one way, is then suddenly stopped, and finally moves the other way.

41. If such a hollow helix as that described (34.) be laid east and west (or in any other constant position), and a magnet be retained east and west, its marked pole always being one way; then whichever end of the helix the magnet goes in at, and consequently whichever pole of the magnet enters first, still the needle is deflected the same way: on the other hand, whichever direction is followed in withdrawing the magnet, the deflection is constant, but contrary to that due to its entrance.

42. These effects are simple consequences of the *law* hereafter to be described (114.).

43. When the eight elementary helices were made one long helix, the effect was not so great as in the arrangement described. When only one of the eight helices was used, the effect was also much diminished. All care was taken to guard against any direct action of the inducing magnet upon the galvanometer, and it was found that by moving the magnet in the same direction, and to the same degree on the outside of the helix no effect on the needle was produced.

44. The Royal Society are in possession of a large compound magnet formerly belonging to Dr. Gowin Knight, which, by permission of the President and Council, I was allowed to use in the prosecution of these experiments : it is at present in the charge of Mr. Christie, at his house at Woolwich, where, by Mr. Christie's kindness, I was at liberty to work; and I have to acknowledge my obligations to him for his assistance in all the experiments and observations made with it. This magnet is composed of about 450 bar magnets, each fifteen inches long, one inch wide, and half an inch thick, arranged in a box so as to present at one of its extremities two external poles (fig. 5.). These poles projected horizontally six inches from the box, were each twelve inches high and three inches wide. They were nine inches apart; and when a soft iron cylinder, three quarters of an inch in diameter and twelve inches long, was put across from one to the other, it required a force of nearly one hundred pounds to break the contact. The pole to the left in the figure is the marked pole*.

* To avoid any confusion as to the poles of the magnet, I shall designate the

45. The indicating galvanometer, in all experiments made with this magnet, was about eight feet from it, not directly in front of the poles, but about 16° or 17° on one side. It was found that on making or breaking the connexion of the poles by soft iron, the instrument was slightly affected ; but all error of observation arising from this cause was easily and carefully avoided.

46. The electrical effects exhibited by this magnet were very striking. When a soft iron cylinder thirteen inches long was put through the compound hollow helix, with its ends arranged as two general terminations (39.), these connected with the galvanometer, and the iron cylinder brought in contact with the two poles of the magnet (fig. 5.), so powerful a rush of electricity took place that the needle whirled round many times in succession*.

47. Notwithstanding this great power, if the contact was continued, the needle resumed its natural position, being entirely uninfluenced by the position of the helix (30.). But on breaking the magnetic contact, the needle was whirled round in the opposite direction with a force equal to the former.

48. A piece of copper plate wrapped *once* round the iron cylinder like a socket, but with interposed paper to prevent contact, had its edges connected with the wires of the galvanometer. When the iron was brought in contact with the poles the galvanometer was strongly affected.

49. Dismissing the helices and sockets, the galvanometer wire was passed over, and consequently only half round the iron cylinder (fig. 6.) ; but even then a strong effect upon the needle was exhibited, when the magnetic contact was made or broken.

50. As the helix with its iron cylinder was brought towards the magnetic poles, but *without making contact,* still powerful effects were produced. When the helix, without the iron cylinder, and consequently containing no metal but copper, was approached to, or placed between the poles (44.), the needle

pole pointing to the north as the marked pole ; I may occasionally speak of the north and south ends of the needle, but do not mean thereby north and south poles. That is by many considered the true north pole of a needle which points to the south ; but in this country it is often called the south pole.

* A soft iron bar in the form of a lifter to a horse-shoe magnet, when supplied with a coil of this kind round the middle of it, becomes, by juxtaposition with a magnet, a ready source of a brief but determinate current of electricity.

was thrown 80°, 90°, or more, from its natural position. The inductive force was of course greater, the nearer the helix, either with or without its iron cylinder, was brought to the poles; but otherwise the same effects were produced, whether the helix, &c. was or was not brought into contact with the magnet; *i. e.* no permanent effect on the galvanometer was produced; and the effects of approximation and removal were the reverse of each other (30.).

51. When a bolt of copper corresponding to the iron cylinder was introduced, no greater effect was produced by the helix than without it. But when a thick iron wire was substituted, the magneto-electric induction was rendered sensibly greater.

52. The direction of the electric current produced in all these experiments with the helix, was the same as that already described (38.) as obtained with the weaker bar magnets.

53. A spiral containing fourteen feet of copper wire, being connected with the galvanometer, and approximated directly towards the marked pole in the line of its axis, affected the instrument strongly; the current induced in it was in the reverse direction to the current theoretically considered by M. Ampère as existing in the magnet (38.), or as the current in an electro-magnet of similar polarity. As the spiral was withdrawn, the induced current was reversed.

54. A similar spiral had the current of eighty pairs of 4-inch plates sent through it so as to form an electro-magnet, and then the other spiral connected with the galvanometer (53.) approximated to it; the needle vibrated, indicating a current in the galvanometer spiral the reverse of that in the battery spiral (18. 26.). On withdrawing the latter spiral, the needle passed in the opposite direction.

55. Single wires, approximated in certain directions towards the magnetic pole, had currents induced in them. On their removal, the currents were inverted. In such experiments the wires should not be removed in directions different to those in which they were approximated; for then occasionally complicated and irregular effects are produced, the causes of which will be very evident in the fourth part of this paper.

56. All attempts to obtain chemical effects by the induced current of electricity failed, though the precautions before described (22.), and all others that could be thought of, were em-

ployed.   Neither was any sensation on the tongue, or any convulsive effect upon the limbs of a frog, produced.   Nor could
charcoal or fine wire be ignited (133.).   But upon repeating
the experiments more at leisure at the Royal Institution, with
an armed loadstone belonging to Professor Daniell and capable
of lifting about thirty pounds, a frog was *very powerfully convulsed* each time magnetic contact was made.   At first the
convulsions could not be obtained on breaking magnetic contact; but conceiving the deficiency of effect was because of
the comparative slowness of separation, the latter act was effected by a blow, and then the frog was convulsed strongly.
The more instantaneous the union or disunion is effected, the
more powerful the convulsion.   I thought also I could perceive
the *sensation* upon the tongue and the *flash* before the eyes;
but I could obtain no evidence of chemical decomposition.

57. The various experiments of this section prove, I think,
most completely the production of electricity from ordinary
magnetism.   That its intensity should be very feeble and quantity small, cannot be considered wonderful, when it is remembered that like thermo-electricity it is evolved entirely within
the substance of metals retaining all their conducting power.
But an agent which is conducted along metallic wires in the
manner described; which, whilst so passing possesses the peculiar magnetic actions and force of a current of electricity;
which can agitate and convulse the limbs of a frog; and which,
finally, can produce a spark* by its discharge through charcoal
(32.), can only be electricity.   As all the effects can be produced by ferruginous electro-magnets (34.), there is no doubt
that arrangements like the magnets of Professors Moll, Henry,
Ten Eyke, and others, in which as many as two thousand
pounds have been lifted, may be used for these experiments;
in which case not only a brighter spark may be obtained, but
wires also ignited, and, as the current can pass liquids (23.),
chemical action be produced.   These effects are still more
likely to be obtained when the magneto-electric arrangements
to be explained in the fourth section are excited by the powers
of such apparatus.

* For a mode of obtaining the spark from the common magnet which I
have found effectual, see the Philosophical Magazine for June 1832, p. 5.   In
the same Journal for November 1834, vol. v. p. 349, will be found a method
of obtaining the magneto-electric spark, still simpler in its principle, the use
of soft iron being dispensed with altogether.—*Dec.* 1838.

58. The similarity of action, almost amounting to identity, between common magnets and either electro-magnets or volta-electric currents, is strikingly in accordance with and confirmatory of M. Ampère's theory, and furnishes powerful reasons for believing that the action is the same in both cases ; but, as a distinction in language is still necessary, I propose to call the agency thus exerted by ordinary magnets, *magneto-electric* or *magnelectric* induction (26.).

59. The only difference which powerfully strikes the attention as existing between volta-electric and magneto-electric induction, is the suddenness of the former, and the sensible time required by the latter : but even in this early state of investigation there are circumstances which seem to indicate, that upon further inquiry this difference will, as a philosophical distinction, disappear (68.) *.

### § 3. *New Electrical State or Condition of Matter* †.

60. Whilst the wire is subject to either volta-electric or magneto-electric induction, it appears to be in a peculiar state ; for it resists the formation of an electrical current in it, whereas, if in its common condition, such a current would be produced ; and when left uninfluenced it has the power of originating a current, a power which the wire does not possess under common circumstances. This electrical condition of matter has not hitherto been recognised, but it probably exerts a very important influence in many if not most of the phenomena produced by currents of electricity. For reasons which will immediately appear (71.), I have, after advising with several learned friends, ventured to designate it as the *electro-tonic* state.

61. This peculiar condition shows no known electrical effects whilst it continues ; nor have I yet been able to discover any

* For important additional phenomena and developments of the induction of electrical currents, see now the ninth series, 1048–1118.—*Dec.* 1838.

† This section having been read at the Royal Society and reported upon, and having also, in consequence of a letter from myself to M. Hachette, been noticed at the French Institute, I feel bound to let it stand as part of the paper ; but later investigations (intimated 73. 76. 77.) of the laws governing these phenomena, induce me to think that the latter can be fully explained without admitting the electro-tonic state. My views on this point will appear in the second series of these researches.—M. F.

peculiar powers exerted, or properties possessed, by matter whilst retained in this state.

62. It shows no reaction by attractive or repulsive powers. The various experiments which have been made with powerful magnets upon such metals as copper, silver, and generally those substances not magnetic, prove this point; for the substances experimented upon, if electrical conductors, must have acquired this state; and yet no evidence of attractive or repulsive powers has been observed. I have placed copper and silver discs, very delicately suspended on torsion balances in vacuo near to the poles of very powerful magnets, yet have not been able to observe the least attractive or repulsive force.

63. I have also arranged a fine slip of gold-leaf very near to a bar of copper, the two being in metallic contact by mercury at their extremities. These have been placed in vacuo, so that metal rods connected with the extremities of the arrangement should pass through the sides of the vessel into the air. I have then moved powerful magnetic poles, about this arrangement, in various directions, the metallic circuit on the outside being sometimes completed by wires, and sometimes broken. But I never could obtain any sensible motion of the gold-leaf, either directed to the magnet or towards the collateral bar of copper, which must have been, as far as induction was concerned, in a similar state to itself.

64. In some cases it has been supposed that, under such circumstances, attractive and repulsive forces have been exhibited, *i. e.* that such bodies have become slightly magnetic. But the phenomena now described, in conjunction with the confidence we may reasonably repose in M. Ampère's theory of magnetism, tend to throw doubt on such cases; for if magnetism depend upon the attraction of electrical currents, and if the powerful currents at first excited, both by volta-electric and magneto-electric induction, instantly and naturally cease (12. 28. 47.), causing at the same time an entire cessation of magnetic effects at the galvanometer needle, then there can be little or no expectation that any substances not partaking of the peculiar relation in which iron, nickel, and one or two other bodies, stand, should exhibit magneto-attractive powers. It seems far more probable, that the extremely feeble permanent effects ob-

served have been due to traces of iron, or perhaps some other unrecognized cause not magnetic.

65. This peculiar condition exerts no retarding or accelerating power upon electrical currents passing through metal thus circumstanced (20. 33.). Neither could any such power upon the inducing current itself be detected ; for when masses of metal, wires, helices, &c. were arranged in all possible ways by the side of a wire or helix, carrying a current measured by the galvanometer (20.), not the slightest permanent change in the indication of the instrument could be perceived. Metal in the supposed peculiar state, therefore, conducts electricity in all directions with its ordinary facility, or, in other words, its conducting power is not sensibly altered by it.

66. All metals take on the peculiar state. This is proved in the preceding experiments with copper and iron (9.), and with gold, silver, tin, lead, zinc, antimony, bismuth, mercury, &c. by experiments to be described in the fourth part (132.), admitting of easy application. With regard to iron, the experiments prove the thorough and remarkable independence of these phenomena of induction, and the ordinary magnetical appearances of that metal.

67. This state is altogether the effect of the induction exerted, and ceases as soon as the inductive force is removed. It is the same state, whether produced by the collateral passage of voltaic currents (26.), or the formation of a magnet (34. 36.), or the mere approximation of a magnet (39. 50.) ; and is a strong proof in addition to those advanced by M. Ampère, of the identity of the agents concerned in these several operations. It probably occurs, momentarily, during the passage of the common electric spark (24.), and may perhaps be obtained hereafter in bad conductors by weak electrical currents or other means (74. 76.).

68. The state appears to be instantly assumed (12.), requiring hardly a sensible portion of time for that purpose. The *difference* of time between volta-electric and magneto-electric induction, rendered evident by the galvanometer (59.), may probably be thus explained. When a voltaic current is sent through one of two parallel wires, as those of the hollow helix (34.), a current is produced in the other wire, as brief in its

continuance as the time required for a single action of this kind, and which, by experiment, is found to be inappreciably small. The action will seem still more instantaneous, because, as there is an accumulation of power in the poles of the battery before contact, the first rush of electricity in the wire of communication is greater than that sustained after the contact is completed; the wire of induction becomes at the moment electrotonic to an equivalent degree, which the moment after sinks to the state in which the continuous current can sustain it, but in sinking, causes an opposite induced current to that at first produced. The consequence is, that the first induced wave of electricity more resembles that from the discharge of an electric jar, than it otherwise would do.

69. But when the iron cylinder is put into the same helix (34.), previous to the connexion being made with the battery, then the current from the latter may be considered as active in inducing innumerable currents of a similar kind to itself in the iron, rendering it a magnet. This is known by experiment to occupy time; for a magnet so formed, even of soft iron, does not rise to its fullest intensity in an instant, and it may be because the currents within the iron are successive in their formation or arrangement. But as the magnet can induce, as well as the battery current, the combined action of the two continues to evolve induced electricity, until their joint effect is at a maximum, and thus the existence of the deflecting force is prolonged sufficiently to overcome the inertia of the galvanometer needle.

70. In all those cases where the helices or wires are advanced towards or taken from the magnet (50. 55.), the direct or inverted current of induced electricity continues for the time occupied in the advance or recession; for the electro-tonic state is rising to a higher or falling to a lower degree during that time, and the change is accompanied by its corresponding evolution of electricity; but these form no objections to the opinion that the electro-tonic state is instantly assumed.

71. This peculiar state appears to be a state of tension, and may be considered as *equivalent* to a current of electricity, at least equal to that produced either when the condition is induced or destroyed. The current evolved, however, first or last, is not to be considered a measure of the degree of tension

to which the electro-tonic state has risen; for as the metal retains its conducting powers unimpaired (65.), and as the electricity evolved is but for a moment, (the peculiar state being
instantly assumed and lost (68.),) the electricity which may be
led away by long wire conductors, offering obstruction in their
substance proportionate to their small lateral and extensive
linear dimensions, can be but a very small portion of that really
evolved within the mass at the moment it assumes this condition. Insulated helices and portions of metal instantly assumed the state; and no traces of electricity could be discovered in them, however quickly the contact with the electrometer was made, after they were put under induction, either
by the current from the battery or the magnet. A single drop
of water or a small piece of moistened paper (23. 56.) was obstacle sufficient to stop the current through the conductors,
the electricity evolved returning to a state of equilibrium
through the metal itself, and consequently in an unobserved
manner.

72. The tension of this state may therefore be comparatively
very great. But whether great or small, it is hardly conceivable
that it should exist without exerting a reaction upon the
original inducing current, and producing equilibrium of some
kind. It might be anticipated that this would give rise to a
retardation of the original current; but I have not been able
to ascertain that this is the case. Neither have I in any other
way as yet been able to distinguish effects attributable to such
a reaction.

73. All the results favour the notion that the electro-tonic
state relates to the particles, and not to the mass, of the wire
or substance under induction, being in that respect different
to the induction exerted by electricity of tension. If so, the
state may be assumed in liquids when no electrical current is
sensible, and even in non-conductors; the current itself, when
it occurs, being as it were a contingency due to the existence
of conducting power, and the momentary propulsive force exerted by the particles during their arrangement. Even when
conducting power is equal, the currents of electricity, which as
yet are the only indicators of this state, may be unequal, because of differences as to number, size, electrical condition, &c.
&c. in the particles themselves. It will only be after the laws

which govern this new state are ascertained, that we shall be able to predict what is the true condition of, and what are the electrical results obtainable from, any particular substance.

74. The current of electricity which induces the electrotonic state in a neighbouring wire, probably induces that state also in its own wire; for when by a current in one wire a collateral wire is made electro-tonic, the latter state is not rendered any way incompatible or interfering with a current of electricity passing through it (62.). If, therefore, the current were sent through the second wire instead of the first, it does not seem probable that its inducing action upon the second would be less, but on the contrary more, because the distance between the agent and the matter acted upon would be very greatly diminished. A copper bolt had its extremities connected with a galvanometer, and then the poles of a battery of one hundred pairs of plates connected with the bolt, so as to send the current through it; the voltaic circuit was then suddenly broken, and the galvanometer observed for any indications of a return current through the copper bolt due to the discharge of its supposed electro-tonic state. No effect of the kind was obtained, nor indeed, for two reasons, ought it to be expected; for first, as the cessation of induction and the discharge of the electro-tonic condition are simultaneous, and not successive, the return current would only be equivalent to the neutralization of the last portion of the inducing current, and would not therefore show any alteration of direction; or assuming that time did intervene, and that the latter current was really distinct from the former, its short, sudden character (12. 26.) would prevent it from being thus recognized.

75. No difficulty arises, I think, in considering the wire thus rendered electro-tonic by its own current more than by any external current, especially when the apparent non-interference of that state with currents is considered (62. 71.). The simultaneous existence of the conducting and electro-tonic states finds an analogy in the manner in which electrical currents can be passed through magnets, where it is found that both the currents passed, and those of the magnets, preserve all their properties distinct from each other, and exert their mutual actions.

76. The reason given with regard to metals extends also to fluids and all other conductors, and leads to the conclusion that when electric currents are passed through them they also

assume the electro-tonic state.  Should that prove to be the
case, its influence in voltaic decomposition, and the transference
of the elements to the poles, can hardly be doubted.  In the
electro-tonic state the homogeneous particles of matter appear
to have assumed a regular but forced electrical arrangement
in the direction of the current, which if the matter be undecomposable, produces, when relieved, a return current ; but in
decomposable matter this forced state may be sufficient to make
an elementary particle leave its companion, with which it is in
a constrained condition, and associate with the neighbouring
similar particle, in relation to which it is in a more natural condition, the forced electrical arrangement being itself discharged
or relieved, at the same time, as effectually as if it had been
freed from induction.  But as the original voltaic current is
continued, the electro-tonic state may be instantly renewed,
producing the forced arrangement of the compound particles,
to be as instantly discharged by a transference of the elementary particles of the opposite kind in opposite directions, but
parallel to the current.  Even the differences between common
and voltaic electricity, when applied to effect chemical decomposition, which Dr. Wollaston has pointed out *, seem explicable by the circumstances connected with the induction of
electricity from these two sources (25.).  But as I have reserved
this branch of the inquiry, that I might follow out the investigations contained in the present paper, I refrain (though much
tempted) from offering further speculations.

77. Marianini has discovered and described a peculiar affection of the surfaces of metallic discs, when, being in contact
with humid conductors, a current of electricity is passed through
them ; they are then capable of producing a reverse current of
electricity, and Marianini has well applied the effect in explanation of the phenomena of Ritter's piles †.  M. A. de la Rive
has described a peculiar property acquired by metallic conductors, when being immersed in a liquid as poles, they have
completed, for some time, the voltaic circuit, in consequence
of which, when separated from the battery and plunged into
the same fluid, they by themselves produce an electric current ‡.
M. A. Van Beek has detailed cases in which the electrical relation of one metal in contact with another has been preserved

* Philosophical Transactions, 1801, p. 247.
† Annales de Chimie, XXXVIII. 5.        ‡ Ibid. XXVIII. 190.

after separation, and accompanied by its corresponding chemical effects *. These states and results appear to differ from the electro-tonic state and its phenomena; but the true relation of the former to the latter can only be decided when our knowledge of all these phenomena has been enlarged.

78. I had occasion in the commencement of this paper (2.) to refer to an experiment by Ampère, as one of those dependent upon the electrical induction of currents made prior to the present investigation, and have arrived at conclusions which seem to imply doubts of the accuracy of the experiment (62. &c.) : it is therefore due to M. Ampère that I should attend to it more distinctly. When a disc of copper (says M. Ampère) was suspended by a silk thread and surrounded by a helix or spiral, and when the charge of a powerful voltaic battery was sent through the spiral, a strong magnet at the same time being presented to the copper disc, the latter turned at the moment to take a position of equilibrium, exactly as the spiral itself would have turned had it been free to move. I have not been able to obtain this effect, nor indeed any motion; but the cause of my failure in the *latter* point may be due to the momentary existence of the current not allowing time for the inertia of the plate to be overcome (11. 12.). M. Ampère has perhaps succeeded in obtaining motion from the superior delicacy and power of his electro-magnetical apparatus, or he may have obtained only the motion due to cessation of action. But all my results tend to invert the sense of the proposition stated by M. Ampère, " that a current of electricity tends to put the electricity of conductors near which it passes in motion in the same direction," for they indicate an opposite direction for the produced current (26. 53.) ; and they show that the effect is momentary, and that it is also produced by magnetic induction, and that certain other extraordinary effects follow thereupon.

79. The momentary existence of the phenomena of induction now described is sufficient to furnish abundant reasons for the uncertainty or failure of the experiments, hitherto made to obtain electricity from magnets, or to effect chemical decomposition or arrangement by their means †.

* Annales de Chimie, XXXVIII. 49.
† The Lycée, No. 36, for January 1st, has a long and rather premature article, in which it endeavours to show anticipations by French philosophers of my researches. It however mistakes the erroneous results of MM. Fresnel and Am-

80. It also appears capable of explaining fully the remarkable phenomena observed by M. Arago between metals and magnets when either are moving (120.), as well as most of the results obtained by Sir John Herschel, Messrs. Babbage, Harris, and others, in repeating his experiments ; accounting at the same time perfectly for what at first appeared inexplicable ; namely, the non-action of the same metals and magnets when at rest. These results, which also afford the readiest means of obtaining electricity from magnetism, I shall now proceed to describe.

### § 4. *Explication of Arago's Magnetic Phenomena.*

81. If a plate of copper be revolved close to a magnetic needle, or magnet, suspended in such a way that the latter may rotate in a plane parallel to that of the former, the magnet tends to follow the motion of the plate ; or if the magnet be revolved, the plate tends to follow its motion ; and the effect is so powerful, that magnets or plates of many pounds weight may be thus carried round.    If the magnet and plate be at rest relative to each other, not the slightest effect, attractive or repulsive, or of any kind, can be observed between them (62.).    This is the phenomenon discovered by M. Arago ; and he states that the effect takes place not only with all metals, but with solids, liquids, and even gases, *i. e.* with all substances (130.).

82. Mr. Babbage and Sir John Herschel, on conjointly repeating the experiments in this country *, could obtain the effects only with the metals, and with carbon in a peculiar state (from gas retorts), *i. e.* only with excellent conductors of electricity.    They refer the effect to magnetism induced in the plate by the magnet ; the pole of the latter causing an opposite pole in the nearest part of the plate, and  round  this  a  more diffuse

père for true ones, and then imagines my true results are like those erroneous ones.  I notice it here, however, for the purpose of doing honour to Fresnel in a much higher degree than would have been merited by a feeble anticipation of the present investigations.    That great philosopher, at the same time with myself and fifty other persons, made experiments which the present paper proves could give no expected result.    He was deceived for the moment, and published his imaginary success ; but on more carefully repeating his trials, he could find no proof of their accuracy ; and, in the high and pure philosophic desire to remove error as well as discover truth, he recanted his first statement. The example of Berzelius regarding the first Thorina is another instance of this fine feeling ; and as occasions are not rare, it would be to the dignity of science if such examples were more frequently followed.—February 10th, 1832.

* Philosophical Transactions, 1825, p. 467.

polarity of its own kind (120.). The essential circumstance in producing the rotation of the suspended magnet is, that the substance revolving below it shall acquire and lose its magnetism in sensible time, and not instantly (124.). This theory refers the effect to an attractive force, and is not agreed to by the discoverer, M. Arago, nor by M. Ampère, who quote against it the absence of all attraction when the magnet and metal are at rest (62. 123.), although the induced magnetism should still remain ; and who, from experiments made with a long dipping needle, conceive the action to be always repulsive (125.).

83. Upon obtaining electricity from magnets by the means already described (36. 46.), I hoped to make the experiment of M. Arago a new source of electricity ; and did not despair, by reference to terrestrial magneto-electric induction, of being able to construct a new electrical machine. Thus stimulated, numerous experiments were made with the magnet of the Royal Society at Mr. Christie's house, in all of which I had the advantage of his assistance. As many of these were in the course of the investigation superseded by more perfect arrangements, I shall consider myself at liberty to rearrange them in a manner calculated to convey most readily what appears to me to be a correct view of the nature of the phenomena.

84. The magnet has been already described (44.). To concentrate the poles, and bring them nearer to each other, two iron or steel bars, each about six or seven inches long, one inch wide, and half an inch thick, were put across the poles as in fig. 7, and being supported by twine from slipping, could be placed as near to or far from each other as was required. Occasionally two bars of soft iron were employed, so bent that when applied, one to each pole, the two smaller resulting poles were vertically over each other, either being uppermost at pleasure.

85. A disc of copper, twelve inches in diameter, and about one fifth of an inch in thickness, fixed upon a brass axis, was mounted in frames so as to allow of revolution either vertically or horizontally, its edge being at the same time introduced more or less between the magnetic poles (fig. 7). The edge of the plate was well amalgamated for the purpose of obtaining a good but moveable contact, and a part round the axis was also prepared in a similar manner.

86. Conductors or electric collectors of copper and lead were constructed so as to come in contact with the edge of the copper disc (85.), or with other forms of plates hereafter to be described (101.). These conductors were about four inches long, one third of an inch wide, and one fifth of an inch thick ; one end of each was slightly grooved, to allow of more exact adaptation to the somewhat convex edge of the plates, and then amalgamated. Copper wires, one sixteenth of an inch in thickness, attached, in the ordinary manner, by convolutions to the other ends of these conductors, passed away to the galvanometer.

87. The galvanometer was roughly made, yet sufficiently delicate in its indications. The wire was of copper covered with silk, and made sixteen or eighteen convolutions. Two sewing-needles were magnetized and fixed on to a stem of dried grass parallel to each other, but in opposite directions, and about half an inch apart ; this system was suspended by a fibre of unspun silk, so that the lower needle should be between the convolutions of the multiplier, and the upper above them. The latter was by much the most powerful magnet, and gave terrestrial direction to the whole ; fig. 8 represents the direction of the wire and of the needles when the instrument was placed in the magnetic meridian : the ends of the wires are marked A and B for convenient reference hereafter. The letters S and N designate the south and north ends of the needle when affected merely by terrestrial magnetism ; the end N is therefore the marked pole (44.). The whole instrument was protected by a glass jar, and stood, as to position and distance relative to the large magnet, under the same circumstances as before (45.).

88. All these arrangements being made, the copper disc was adjusted as in fig. 7, the small magnetic poles being about half an inch apart, and the edge of the plate inserted about half their width between them. One of the galvanometer wires was passed twice or thrice loosely round the brass axis of the plate, and the other attached to a conductor (86.), which itself was retained by the hand in contact with the amalgamated edge of the disc at the part immediately between the magnetic poles. Under these circumstances all was quiescent, and the galvanometer exhibited no effect. But the instant the plate moved,

the galvanometer was influenced, and by revolving the plate quickly the needle could be deflected 90° or more.

89. It was difficult under the circumstances to make the contact between the conductor and the edge of the revolving disc uniformly good and extensive; it was also difficult in the first experiments to obtain a regular velocity of rotation: both these causes tended to retain the needle in a continual state of vibration; but no difficulty existed in ascertaining to which side it was deflected, or generally, about what line it vibrated. Afterwards, when the experiments were made more carefully, a permanent deflection of the needle of nearly 45° could be sustained.

90. Here therefore was demonstrated the production of a permanent current of electricity by ordinary magnets (57.).

91. When the motion of the disc was reversed, every other circumstance remaining the same, the galvanometer needle was deflected with equal power as before; but the deflection was on the opposite side, and the current of electricity evolved, therefore, the reverse of the former.

92. When the conductor was placed on the edge of the disc a little to the right or left, as in the dotted positions fig. 9, the current of electricity was still evolved, and in the same direction as at first (88. 91.). This occurred to a considerable distance, *i. e.* 50° or 60° on each side of the place of the magnetic poles. The current gathered by the conductor and conveyed to the galvanometer was of the same kind on both sides of the place of greatest intensity, but gradually diminished in force from that place. It appeared to be equally powerful at equal distances from the place of the magnetic poles, not being affected in that respect by the direction of the rotation. When the rotation of the disc was reversed, the direction of the current of electricity was reversed also; but the other circumstances were not affected.

93. On raising the plate, so that the magnetic poles were entirely hidden from each other by its intervention, (*a.* fig. 10,) the same effects were produced in the same order, and with equal intensity as before. On raising it still higher, so as to bring the place of the poles to *c*, still the effects were produced, and apparently with as much power as at first.

94. When the conductor was held against the edge as if fixed

to it, and with it moved between the poles, even though but
for a few degrees, the galvanometer needle moved and indicated
a current of electricity, the same as that which would have
been produced if the wheel had revolved in the same direction,
the conductor remaining stationary.

95. When the galvanometer connexion with the axis was
broken, and its wires made fast to two conductors, both applied
to the edge of the copper disc, then currents of electricity were
produced, presenting more complicated appearances, but in
perfect harmony with the above results. Thus, if applied as
in fig. 11, a current of electricity through the galvanometer
was produced ; but if their place was a little shifted, as in fig.
12, a current in the contrary direction resulted; the fact being,
that in the first instance the galvanometer indicated the difference between a strong current through A and a weak one
through B, and in the second, of a weak current through A
and a strong one through B (92.), and therefore produced opposite deflections.

96. So also when the two conductors were equidistant from
the magnetic poles, as in fig. 13, no current at the galvanometer
was perceived, whichever way the disc was rotated, beyond
what was momentarily produced by irregularity of contact ;
because equal currents in the same direction tended to pass
into both. But when the two conductors were connected with
one wire, and the axis with the other wire, (fig. 14,) then the
galvanometer showed a current according with the direction of
rotation (91.) ; both conductors now acting consentaneously,
and as a single conductor did before (88).

97. All these effects could be obtained when only one of the
poles of the magnet was brought near to the plate ; they were
of the same kind as to direction, &c., but by no means so
powerful.

98. All care was taken to render these results independent
of the earth's magnetism, or of the mutual magnetism of the
magnet and galvanometer needles. The contacts were made
in the magnetic equator of the plate, and at other parts ; the
plate was placed horizontally, and the poles vertically ; and
other precautions were taken. But the absence of any interference of the kind referred to, was readily shown by the want
of all effect when the disc was removed from the poles, or the

poles from the disc; every other circumstance remaining the same.

99. The *relation of the current* of electricity produced, to the magnetic pole, to the direction of rotation of the plate, &c. &c., may be expressed by saying, that when the unmarked pole (44. 84.) is beneath the edge of the plate, and the latter revolves horizontally, screw-fashion, the electricity which can be collected at the edge of the plate nearest to the pole is positive. As the pole of the earth may mentally be considered the unmarked pole, this relation of the rotation, the pole, and the electricity evolved, is not difficult to remember. Or if, in fig. 15, the circle represent the copper disc revolving in the direction of the arrows, and *a* the outline of the unmarked pole placed beneath the plate, then the electricity collected at *b* and the neighbouring parts is positive, whilst that collected at the centre *c* and other parts is negative (88.). The currents in the plate are therefore from the centre by the magnetic poles towards the circumference.

100. If the marked pole be placed above, all other things remaining the same, the electricity at *b*, fig. 15, is still positive. If the marked pole be placed below, or the unmarked pole above, the electricity is reversed. If the direction of revolution in any case is reversed, the electricity is also reversed.

101. It is now evident that the rotating plate is merely another form of the simpler experiment of passing a piece of metal between the magnetic poles in a rectilinear direction, and that in such cases currents of electricity are produced at right angles to the direction of the motion, and crossing it at the place of the magnetic pole or poles. This was sufficiently shown by the following simple experiment: A piece of copper plate one-fifth of an inch thick, one inch and a half wide, and twelve inches long, being amalgamated at the edges, was placed between the magnetic poles, whilst the two conductors from the galvanometer were held in contact with its edges; it was then drawn through between the poles of the conductors in the direction of the arrow, fig. 16; immediately the galvanometer needle was deflected, its north or marked end passed eastward, indicating that the wire A received negative and the wire B positive electricity; and as the marked pole was above,

the result is in perfect accordance with the effect obtained by the rotatory plate (99.).

102. On reversing the motion of the plate, the needle at the galvanometer was deflected in the opposite direction, showing an opposite current.

103. To render evident the character of the electrical current existing in various parts of the moving copper plate, differing in their relation to the inducing poles, one collector (86.) only was applied at the part to be examined near to the pole, the other being connected with the end of the plate as the most neutral place : the results are given at figs. 17—20, the marked pole being above the plate.   In fig. 17, B received positive electricity; but the plate moving in the same direction, it received on the opposite side, fig. 18, negative electricity; reversing the motion of the latter, as in fig. 20, B received positive electricity ; or reversing the motion of the first arrangement, that of fig. 17 to fig. 19, B received negative electricity.

104. When the plates were previously removed sideways from between the magnets, as in fig. 21, so as to be quite out of the polar axis, still the same effects were produced, though not so strongly.

105. When the magnetic poles were in contact, and the copper plate was drawn between the conductors near to the place, there was but very little effect produced.   When the poles were opened by the width of a card, the effect was somewhat more, but still very small.

106. When an amalgamated copper wire, one eighth of an inch thick, was drawn through between the conductors and poles (101.), it produced a very considerable effect, though not so much as the plates.

107. If the conductors were held permanently against any particular parts of the copper plates, and carried between the magnetic poles with them, effects the same as those described were produced, in accordance with the results obtained with the revolving disc (94.).

108. On the conductors being held against the ends of the plates, and the latter then passed between the magnetic poles, in a direction transverse to their length, the same effects were

produced (fig. 22.).   The parts of the plates towards the end
may be considered either as mere conductors, or as portions of
metal in which the electrical current is excited, according to
their distance and the strength of the magnet ; but the results
were in perfect harmony with those before obtained.   The effect was as strong as when the conductors were held against
the sides of the plate (101.).

109. When a mere wire, connected with the galvanometer
so as to form a complete circuit, was passed through between
the poles, the galvanometer was affected; and upon moving
the wire to and fro, so as to make the alternate impulses produced correspond with the vibrations of the needle, the latter
could be increased to 20° or 30° on each side the magnetic
meridian.

110. Upon connecting the ends of a plate of metal with the
galvanometer wires, and then carrying it between the poles
from end to end (as in fig. 23.), in either direction, no effect
whatever was produced upon the galvanometer.   But the moment the motion became transverse, the needle was deflected.

111. These effects were also obtained from *electro-magnetic
poles,* resulting from the use of copper helices or spirals, either
alone or with iron cores (34. 54.).   The directions of the motions were precisely the same ; but the action was much greater
when the iron cores were used, than without.

112. When a flat spiral was passed through edgewise between the poles, a curious action of the galvanometer resulted ;
the needle first went strongly one way, but then suddenly
stopped, as if it struck against some solid obstacle, and immediately returned.   If the spiral were passed through from
above downwards, or from below upwards, still the motion of
the needle was in the same direction, then suddenly stopped,
and then was reversed.   But on turning the spiral half-way
round, *i. e.* edge for edge, then the directions of the motions
were reversed, but still were suddenly interrupted and inverted
as before.   This double action depends upon the halves of the
spiral (divided by a line passing through its centre perpendicular to the direction of its motion) acting in opposite directions ;
and the reason why the needle went to the same side, whether
the spiral passed by the poles in the one or the other direction,
was the circumstance, that upon changing the motion, the di-

rection of the wires in the approaching half of the spiral was changed also. The effects, curious as they appear when witnessed, are immediately referable to the action of single wires (40. 109.).

113. Although the experiments with the revolving plate, wires, and plates of metal, were first successfully made with the large magnet belonging to the Royal Society, yet they were all ultimately repeated with a couple of bar magnets two feet long, one inch and a half wide, and half an inch thick; and, by rendering the galvanometer (87.) a little more delicate, with the most striking results. Ferro-electro-magnets, as those of Moll, Henry, &c. (57.), are very powerful. It is very essential, when making experiments on different substances, that thermo-electric effects (produced by contact of the fingers, &c.) be avoided, or at least appreciated and accounted for; they are easily distinguished by their permanency, and their independence of the magnets, or of the direction of the motion.

114. The relation which holds between the magnetic pole, the moving wire or metal, and the direction of the current evolved, *i. e. the law* which governs the evolution of electricity by magneto-electric induction, is very simple, although rather difficult to express. If in fig. 24. PN represent a horizontal wire passing by a marked magnetic pole, so that the direction of its motion shall coincide with the curved line proceeding from below upwards; or if its motion parallel to itself be in a line tangential to the curved line, but in the general direction of the arrows; or if it pass the pole in other directions, but so as to cut the magnetic curves * in the same general direction, or on the same side as they would be cut by the wire if moving along the dotted curved line;—then the current of electricity in the wire is from P to N. If it be carried in the reverse directions, the electric current will be from N to P. Or if the wire be in the vertical position, figured P′ N′, and it be carried in similar directions, coinciding with the dotted horizontal curve so far, as to cut the magnetic curves on the same side with it, the current will be from P′ to N′. If the wire be considered a tangent to the curved surface of the cylindrical mag-

---

* By magnetic curves I mean the lines of magnetic forces, however modified by the juxtaposition of poles, which would be depicted by iron filings; or those to which a very small magnetic needle would form a tangent.

net, and it be carried round that surface into any other position, or if the magnet itself be revolved on its axis, so as to
bring any part opposite to the tangential wire,—still, if afterwards the wire be moved in the directions indicated, the current of electricity will be from P to N ; or if it be moved in the
opposite direction, from N to P; so that as regards the motions of the wire past the pole, they may be reduced to two,
directly opposite to each other, one of which produces a current from P to N, and the other from N to P.

115. The same holds true of the unmarked pole of the magnet, except that if it be substituted for the one in the figure,
then, as the wires are moved in the direction of the arrows, the
current of electricity would be from N to P, and when they
move in the reverse direction, from P to N.

116. Hence the current of electricity which is excited in
metal when moving in the neighbourhood of a magnet, depends
for its direction altogether upon the relation of the metal to the
resultant of magnetic action, or to the magnetic curves, and
may be expressed in a popular way thus : Let A B (fig. 25.)
represent a cylinder magnet, A being the marked pole, and B
the unmarked pole; let P N be a silver knife-blade resting
across the magnet with its edge upward, and with its marked
or notched side towards the pole A ; then in whatever direction
or position this knife be moved edge foremost, either about
the marked or the unmarked pole, the current of electricity
produced will be from P to N, provided the intersected curves
proceeding from A abut upon the notched surface of the knife,
and those from B upon the unnotched side. Or if the knife
be moved with its back foremost, the current will be from N
to P in every possible position and direction, provided the intersected curves abut on the same surfaces as before. A little
model is easily constructed, by using a cylinder of wood for a
magnet, a flat piece for the blade, and a piece of thread connecting one end of the cylinder with the other, and passing
through a hole in the blade, for the magnetic curves : this
readily gives the result of any possible direction.

117. When the wire under induction is passing by an electro-
magnetic pole, as for instance one end of a copper helix traversed by the electric current (34.), the direction of the current
in the approaching wire is the same with that of the current

in the parts or sides of the spirals nearest to it, and in the receding wire the reverse of that in the parts nearest to it.

118. All these results show that the power of inducing
electric currents is circumferentially exerted by a magnetic
resultant or axis of power, just as circumferential magnetism
is dependent upon and is exhibited by an electric current.

119. The experiments described combine to prove that when
a piece of metal (and the same may be true of all conducting
matter (213.) ) is passed either before a single pole, or between
the opposite poles of a magnet, or near electro-magnetic poles,
whether ferruginous or not, electrical currents are produced
across the metal transverse to the direction of motion; and
which therefore, in Arago's experiments, will approximate
towards the direction of radii.  If a single wire be moved like
the spoke of a wheel near a magnetic pole, a current of electricity is determined through it from one end towards the
other.  If a wheel be imagined, constructed of a great number of these radii, and this revolved near the pole, in the
manner of the copper disc (85.), each radius will have a current produced in it as it passes by the pole.  If the radii
be supposed to be in contact laterally, a copper disc results,
in which the directions of the currents will be generally the
same, being modified only by the coaction which can take
place between the particles, now that they are in metallic contact.

120. Now that the existence of these currents is known,
Arago's phenomena may be accounted for without considering
them as due to the formation in the copper of a pole of the
opposite kind to that approximated, surrounded by a diffuse
polarity of the same kind (82.) ; neither is it essential that the
plate should acquire and lose its state in a finite time; nor on
the other hand does it seem necessary that any repulsive force
hould be admitted as the cause of the rotation (82.).

121. The effect is precisely of the same kind as the electro-
magnetic rotations which I had the good fortune to discover
some years ago*.  According to the experiments then made,
which have since been abundantly confirmed, if a wire (P N
fig. 26.) be connected with the positive and negative ends of a
voltaic battery, so that the positive electricity shall pass from

* Quarterly Journal of Science, vol. xii. pp. 74, 186, 416, 283.

P to N, and a marked magnetic pole N be placed near the
wire between it and the spectator, the pole will move in a direction tangential to the wire, *i. e.* towards the right, and the
wire will move tangentially towards the left, according to the
directions of the arrows.   This is exactly what takes place in
the rotation of a plate beneath a magnetic pole; for let N (fig.
27.) be a marked pole above the circular plate, the latter being
rotated in the direction of the arrow: immediately currents of
positive electricity set from the central parts in the general direction of the radii by the pole to the parts of the circumference *a* on the other side of that pole (99. 119.), and are
therefore exactly in the same relation to it as the current in
the wire (P N, fig. 26), and therefore the pole in the same
manner moves to the right hand.

122. If the rotation of the disc be reversed, the electric currents are reversed (91.), and the pole therefore moves to the
left hand.   If the contrary pole be employed, the effects are
the same, *i. e.* in the same direction, because currents of electricity, the reverse of those described, are produced, and by
reversing both poles and currents, the visible effects remain
unchanged.   In whatever position the axis of the magnet be
placed, provided the same pole be applied to the same side
of the plate, the electric current produced is in the same direction, in consistency with the law already stated (114, &c.) ;
and thus every circumstance regarding the direction of the motion may be explained.

123. These currents are *discharged or return* in the parts
of the plate on each side of and more distant from the place of
the pole, where, of course, the magnetic induction is weaker :
and when the collectors are applied, and a current of electricity
is carried away to the galvanometer (88.), the deflection there
is merely a repetition, by the same current or part of it, of the
effect of rotation in the magnet over the plate itself.

124. It is under the point of view just put forth that I have
ventured to say it is not necessary that the plate should acquire and lose its state in a finite time (120.) ; for if it were
possible for the current to be fully developed the instant *before*
it arrived at its state of nearest approximation to the vertical
pole of the magnet, instead of opposite to or a little beyond
it, still the relative motion of the pole and plate would be the

same, the resulting force being in fact tangential instead of direct.

125. But it is possible (though not necessary for the rotation) that *time* may be required for the development of the maximum current in the plate, in which case the resultant of all the forces would be in advance of the magnet when the plate is rotated, or in the rear of the magnet when the latter is rotated, and many of the effects with pure electro-magnetic poles tend to prove this is the case. Then, the tangential force may be resolved into two others, one parallel to the plane of rotation, and the other perpendicular to it : the former would be the force exerted in making the plate revolve with the magnet, or the magnet with the plate ; the latter would be a repulsive force, and is probably that, the effects of which M. Arago has also discovered (82.).

126. The extraordinary circumstance accompanying this action which has seemed so inexplicable, namely, the cessation of all phenomena when the magnet and metal are brought to rest, now receives a full explanation (82.) ; for then the electrical currents which cause the motion cease altogether.

127. All the effects of solution of metallic continuity, and the consequent diminution of power described by Messrs. Babbage and Herschel\*, now receive their natural explanation, as well also as the resumption of power when the cuts were filled up by metallic substances, which, though conductors of electricity, were themselves very deficient in the power of influencing magnets. And new modes of cutting the plate may be devised, which shall almost entirely destroy its power. Thus, if a copper plate (81.) be cut through at about a fifth or sixth of its diameter from the edge, so as to separate a ring from it, and this ring be again fastened on, but with a thickness of paper intervening (fig. 29), and if Arago's experiment be made with this compound plate so adjusted that the section shall continually travel opposite the pole, it is evident that the magnetic currents will be greatly interfered with, and the plate probably lose much of its effect †.

---

\* Philosophical Transactions, 1825, p. 481.

† This experiment has actually been made by Mr. Christie, with the results here described, and is recorded in the Philosophical Transactions for 1827, p. 82.

An elementary result of this kind was obtained by using two pieces of thick copper, shaped as in fig. 28. When the two neighbouring edges were amalgamated and put together, and the arrangement passed between the poles of the magnet, in a direction parallel to these edges, a current was urged through the wires attached to the outer angles, and the galvanometer became strongly affected; but when a single film of paper was interposed, and the experiment repeated, no sensible effect could be produced.

128. A section of this kind could not interfere much with the induction of magnetism, supposed to be of the nature ordinarily received by iron.

129. The effect of rotation or deflection of the needle, which M. Arago obtained by ordinary magnets, M. Ampère succeeded in procuring by electro-magnets. This is perfectly in harmony with the results relative to volta-electric and magneto-electric induction described in this paper. And by using flat spirals of copper wire, through which electric currents were sent, in place of ordinary magnetic poles (111.), sometimes applying a single one to one side of the rotating plate, and sometimes two to opposite sides, I obtained the induced currents of electricity from the plate itself, and could lead them away to, and ascertain their existence by, the galvanometer.

130. The cause which has now been assigned for the rotation in Arago's experiment, namely, the production of electrical currents, seems abundantly sufficient in all cases where the metals, or perhaps even other conductors, are concerned; but with regard to such bodies as glass, resins, and, above all, gases, it seems impossible that currents of electricity, capable of producing these effects, should be generated in them. Yet Arago found that the effects in question were produced by these and by all bodies tried (81.). Messrs. Babbage and Herschel, it is true, did not observe them with any substance not metallic, except carbon, in a highly conducting state (82.). Mr. Harris has ascertained their occurrence with wood, marble, freestone and annealed glass, but obtained no effect with sulphuric acid and saturated solution of sulphate of iron, although these are better conductors of electricity than the former substances.

131. Future investigations will no doubt explain these diffi-

culties, and decide the point whether the retarding or dragging action spoken of is always simultaneous with electric currents*. The existence of the action in metals, only whilst the currents exist, *i. e.* whilst motion is given (82. 88.), and the explication of the repulsive action observed by M. Arago (82. 125.), are powerful reasons for referring it to this cause ; but it may be combined with others which occasionally act alone.

132. Copper, iron, tin, zinc, lead, mercury, and all the metals tried, produced electrical currents when passed between the magnetic poles : the mercury was put into a glass tube for the purpose. The dense carbon deposited in coal gas retorts, also produced the current, but ordinary charcoal did not. Neither could I obtain any sensible effects with brine, sulphuric acid, saline solutions, &c., whether rotated in basins, or inclosed in tubes and passed between the poles.

133. I have never been able to produce any sensation upon the tongue by the wires connected with the conductors applied to the edges of the revolving plate (88.) or slips of metal (101.). Nor have I been able to heat a fine platina wire, or produce a spark, or convulse the limbs of a frog. I have failed also to produce any chemical effects by electricity thus evolved (22. 56.).

134. As the electric current in the revolving copper plate occupies but a small space, proceeding by the poles and being discharged right and left at very small distances comparatively (123.) ; and as it exists in a thick mass of metal possessing almost the highest conducting power of any, and consequently offering extraordinary facility for its production and discharge ; and as, notwithstanding this, considerable currents may be drawn off which can pass through narrow wires, forty, fifty, sixty, or even one hundred feet long ; it is evident that the current existing in the plate itself must be a very powerful one, when the rotation is rapid and the magnet strong. This is also abundantly proved by the obedience and readiness with which a magnet ten or twelve pounds in weight follows the

* Experiments which I have since made convince me that this particular action is always due to the electrical currents formed; and they supply a test by which it may be distinguished from the action of ordinary magnetism, or any other cause, including those which are mechanical or irregular, producing similar effects (254.).

motion of the plate and will strongly twist up the cord by which it is suspended.

135. Two rough trials were made with the intention of constructing *magneto-electric machines.* In one, a ring one inch and a half broad and twelve inches external diameter, cut from a thick copper plate, was mounted so as to revolve between the poles of the magnet and represent a plate similar to those formerly used (101.), but of interminable length ; the inner and outer edges were amalgamated, and the conductors applied one to each edge, at the place of the magnetic poles. The current of electricity evolved did not appear by the galvanometer to be stronger, if so strong, as that from the circular plate (88.).

136. In the other, small thick discs of copper or other metal, half an inch in diameter, were revolved rapidly near to the poles, but with the axis of rotation out of the polar axis ; the electricity evolved was collected by conductors applied as before to the edges (86.). Currents were procured, but of strength much inferior to that produced by the circular plate.

137. The latter experiment is analogous to those made by Mr. Barlow with a rotating iron shell, subject to the influence of the earth*. The effects obtained by him have been referred by Messrs. Babbage and Herschel to the same cause as that considered as influential in Arago's experiment† ; but it would be interesting to know how far the electric current which might be produced in the experiment would account for the deflexion of the needle. The mere inversion of a copper wire six or seven times near the poles of the magnet, and isochronously with the vibrations of the galvanometer needle connected with it, was sufficient to make the needle vibrate through an arc of 60° or 70°. The rotation of a copper shell would perhaps decide the point, and might even throw light upon the more permanent, though somewhat analogous effects obtained by Mr. Christie.

138. The remark which has already been made respecting iron (66.), and the independence of the ordinary magnetical phenomena of that substance, and the phenomena now described of magneto-electric induction in that and other metals, was fully confirmed by many results of the kind detailed in this

* Philosophical Transactions, 1825, p. 317.        † Ibid. 1825, p. 485.

section.   When an iron plate similar to the copper one formerly described (101.) was passed between the magnetic poles, it gave a current of electricity like the copper plate, but decidedly of less power; and in the experiments upon the induction of electric currents (9.), no difference in the kind of action between iron and other metals could be perceived.   The power therefore of an iron plate to drag a magnet after it, or to intercept magnetic action, should be carefully distinguished from the similar power of such metals as silver, copper, &c. &c., inasmuch as in the iron by far the greater part of the effect is due to what may be called ordinary magnetic action. There can be no doubt that the cause assigned by Messrs. Babbage and Herschel in explication of Arago's phenomena is the true one, when iron is the metal used.

139. The very feeble powers which were found by those philosophers to belong to bismuth and antimony, when moving, of affecting the suspended magnet, and which has been confirmed by Mr. Harris, seem at first disproportionate to their conducting powers; whether it be so or not must be decided by future experiment (73.) *.   These metals are highly crystalline, and probably conduct electricity with different degrees of facility in different directions; and it is not unlikely that where a mass is made up of a number of crystals heterogeneously associated, an effect approaching to that of actual division may occur (127.) ; or the currents of electricity may become more suddenly deflected at the confines of similar crystalline arrangements, and so be more readily and completely discharged within the mass.

* I have since been able to explain these differences, and prove, with several metals, that the effect is in the order of the conducting power; for I have been able to obtain, by magneto-electric induction, currents of electricity which are proportionate in strength to the conducting power of the bodies experimented with (211.).

*Royal Institution, November* 1831.

---

*Note.*—In consequence of the long period which has intervened between the reading and printing of the foregoing paper, accounts of the experiments have been dispersed, and, through a letter of my own to M. Hachette, have reached France and Italy.   That letter was translated (with some errors), and read to the Academy of Sciences at Paris, 26th December, 1831.   A copy of it in *Le Temps* of the 28th December quickly reached Signor Nobili, who, with Signor

Antinori, immediately experimented upon the subject, and obtained many of the results mentioned in my letter; others they could not obtain or understand, because of the brevity of my account. These results by Signori Nobili and Antinori have been embodied in a paper dated 31st January 1832, and printed and published in the number of the *Antologia* dated November 1831, (according at least to the copy of the paper kindly sent me by Signor Nobili). It is evident the work could not have been then printed; and though Signor Nobili, in his paper, has inserted my letter as the text of his experiments, yet the circumstance of back date has caused many here who have heard of Nobili's experiments by report only, to imagine his results were anterior to, instead of being dependent upon, mine.

I may be allowed under these circumstances to remark, that I experimented on this subject several years ago, and have published results. (See Quarterly Journal of Science for July 1825, p. 338.) The following also is an extract from my note-book, dated November 28, 1825: " Experiments on induction by connecting wire of voltaic battery :—a battery of four troughs, ten pairs of plates, each arranged side by side—the poles connected by a wire about four feet long, parallel to which was another similar wire separated from it only by two thicknesses of paper, the ends of the latter were attached to a galvanometer: —exhibited no action, &c. &c. &c.—Could not in any way render any induction evident from the connecting wire." The cause of failure at that time is now evident (79).—M. F., April 1832.

# SECOND SERIES.

## THE BAKERIAN LECTURE.

§ 5. *Terrestrial Magneto-electric Induction.* § 6. *Force and Direction of Magneto-electric Induction generally.*

Read January 12, 1832.

### § 5. *Terrestrial Magneto-electric Induction.*

140. WHEN the general facts described in the former paper were discovered, and the *law* of magneto-electric induction relative to direction was ascertained (114.), it was not difficult to perceive that the earth would produce the same effect as a magnet, and to an extent that would, perhaps, render it available in the construction of new electrical machines. The following are some of the results obtained in pursuance of this view.

141. The hollow helix already described (6.) was connected with a galvanometer by wires eight feet long; and the soft iron cylinder (34.) after being heated red hot and slowly cooled, to remove all traces of magnetism, was put into the helix so as to project equally at both ends, and fixed there. The combined helix and bar were held in the magnetic direction or line of dip, and (the galvanometer needle being motionless) were then inverted, so that the lower end should become the upper, but the whole still correspond to the magnetic direction; the needle was immediately deflected. As the latter returned to its first position, the helix and bar were again inverted; and by doing this two or three times, making the inversions and vibrations to coincide, the needle swung through an arc of 150° or 160°.

142. When one end of the helix, which may be called A, was uppermost at first (B end consequently being below), then it mattered not in which direction it proceeded during the inversion, whether to the right hand or left hand, or through any other course; still the galvanometer needle passed in the same direction. Again, when B end was uppermost, the inversion of the helix and bar in any direction always caused the needle

to be deflected one way; that way being the opposite to the course of the deflection in the former case.

143. When the helix with its iron core in any given position was inverted, the effect was as if a magnet with its marked pole downwards had been introduced from above into the inverted helix. Thus, if the end B were upwards, such a magnet introduced from above would make the marked end of the galvanometer needle pass west. Or the end B being downwards, and the soft iron in its place, inversion of the whole produced the same effect.

144. When the soft iron bar was taken out of the helix and inverted in various directions within four feet of the galvanometer, not the slightest effect upon it was produced.

145. These phenomena are the necessary consequence of the inductive magnetic power of the earth, rendering the soft iron cylinder a magnet with its marked pole downwards. The experiment is analogous to that in which two bar magnets were used to magnetize the same cylinder in the same helix (36.), and the inversion of position in the present experiment is equivalent to a change of the poles in that arrangement. But the result is not less an instance of the evolution of electricity by means of the magnetism of the globe.

146. The helix alone was then held permanently in the magnetic direction, and the soft iron cylinder afterwards introduced; the galvanometer needle was instantly deflected; by withdrawing the cylinder as the needle returned, and continuing the two actions simultaneously, the vibrations soon extended through an arc of 180°. The effect was precisely the same as that obtained by using a cylinder magnet with its marked pole downwards; and the direction of motion, &c. was perfectly in accordance with the results of former experiments obtained with such a magnet (39.). A magnet in that position being used, gave the same deflection, but stronger. When the helix was put at right angles to the magnetic direction or dip, then the introduction or removal of the soft iron cylinder produced no effect at the needle. Any inclination to the dip gave results of the same kind as those already described, but increasing in strength as the helix approximated to the direction of the dip.

147. A cylinder magnet, although it has great power of affecting the galvanometer when moving into or out of the helix,

has no power of continuing the deflection (39.) ; and therefore, though left in, still the magnetic needle comes to its usual place of rest.  But upon repeating (with the magnet) the experiment of inversion in the direction of the dip (141.), the needle was affected as powerfully as before; the disturbance of the magnetism in the steel magnet, by the earth's inductive force upon it, being thus shown to be nearly, if not quite, equal in amount and rapidity to that occurring in soft iron.  It is probable that in this way magneto-electrical arrangements may become very useful in indicating the disturbance of magnetic forces, where other means will not apply ; for it is not the whole magnetic power which produce the visible effect, but only the difference due to the disturbing causes.

148. These favourable results led me to hope that the direct magneto-electric induction of the earth might be rendered sensible ; and I ultimately succeeded in obtaining the effect in several ways.  When the helix just referred to (141. 6.) was placed in the magnetic dip, but without any cylinder of iron or steel, and was then inverted, a feeble action at the needle was observed.  Inverting the helix ten or twelve times, and at such periods that the deflecting forces exerted by the currents of electricity produced in it should be added to the momentum of the needle (39.), the latter was soon made to vibrate through an arc of 80° or 90°.  Here, therefore, currents of electricity were produced by the direct inductive power of the earth's magnetism, without the use of any ferruginous matter, and upon a metal not capable of exhibiting any of the ordinary magnetic phenomena.  The experiment in everything represents the effects produced by bringing the same helix to one or both poles of any powerful magnet (50.).

149. Guided by the law already expressed (114.), I expected that all the electric phenomena of the revolving metal plate could now be produced without any other magnet than the earth.  The plate so often referred to (85.) was therefore fixed so as to rotate in a horizontal plane.  The magnetic curves of the earth (114. *note*), *i. e.* the dip, passes though this plane at angles of about 70°, which it was expected would be an approximation to perpendicularity, quite enough to allow of magneto-electric induction sufficiently powerful to produce a current of electricity.

150. Upon rotation of the plate, the currents ought, according to the law (114. 121.), to tend to pass in the direction of the radii, through *all* parts of the plate, either from the centre to the circumference, or from the circumference to the centre, as the direction of the rotation of the plate was one way or the other.   One of the wires of the galvanometer was therefore brought in contact with the axis of the plate, and the other attached to a leaden collector or conductor (86.), which itself was placed against the amalgamated edge of the disc.   On rotating the plate there was a distinct effect at the galvanometer needle; on reversing the rotation, the needle went in the opposite direction; and by making the action of the plate coincide with the vibrations of the needle, the arc through which the latter passed soon extended to half a circle.

151.   Whatever part of the edge of the plate was touched by the conductor, the electricity was the same, provided the direction of rotation continued unaltered.

152. When the plate revolved *screw-fashion,* or as the hands of a watch, the current of electricity (150.) was from the centre to the circumference; when the direction of rotation was *unscrew,* the current was from the circumference to the centre. These directions are the same with those obtained when the unmarked pole of a magnet was placed beneath the revolving plate (99.).

153. When the plate was in the magnetic meridian, or in any other plane *coinciding* with the magnetic dip, then its rotation produced no effect upon the galvanometer.   When inclined to the dip but a few degrees, electricity began to appear upon rotation.   Thus when standing upright in a plane perpendicular to the magnetic meridian, and when consequently its own plane was inclined only about 20° to the dip, revolution of the plate evolved electricity.   As the inclination was increased, the electricity became more powerful until the angle formed by the plane of the plate with the dip was 90°, when the electricity for a given velocity of the plate was a maximum.

154. It is a striking thing to observe the revolving copper plate become thus a *new electrical machine*; and curious results arise on comparing it with the common machine.   In the one, the plate is of the best non-conducting substance that can be applied; in the other, it is the most perfect conductor: in the one,

insulation is essential; in the other it is fatal. In comparison of the quantities of electricity produced, the metal machine does not at all fall below the glass one; for it can produce a constant current capable of deflecting the galvanometer needle, whereas the latter cannot. It is quite true that the force of the current thus evolved has not as yet been increased so as to render it available in any of our ordinary applications of this power; but there appears every reasonable expectation that this may hereafter be effected; and probably by several arrangements. Weak as the current may seem to be, it is as strong as, if not stronger than, any thermo-electric current; for it can pass fluids (23.), agitate the animal system, and in the case of an electro-magnet has produced sparks (32.).

155. A disc of copper, one fifth of an inch thick and only one inch and a half in diameter, was amalgamated at the edge; a square piece of sheet lead (copper would have been better) of equal thickness had a circular hole cut in it, into which the disc loosely fitted; a little mercury completed the metallic communication of the disc and its surrounding ring; the latter was attached to one of the galvanometer wires, and the other wire dipped into a little metallic cup containing mercury, fixed upon the top of the copper axis of the small disc. Upon rotating the disc in a horizontal plane, the galvanometer needle could be affected, although the earth was the only magnet employed, and the radius of the disc but three quarters of an inch; in which space only the current was excited.

156. On putting the pole of a magnet under the revolving disc, the galvanometer needle could be permanently deflected.

157. On using copper wires one sixth of an inch in thickness instead of the smaller wires (86.) hitherto constantly employed, far more powerful effects were obtained. Perhaps if the galvanometer had consisted of fewer turns of thick wire instead of many convolutions of thinner, more striking effects would have been produced.

158. One form of apparatus which I purpose having arranged, is to have several discs superposed; the discs are to be metallically connected, alternately at the edges and at the centres, by means of mercury; and are then to be revolved alternately in opposite directions, *i. e.* the first, third, fifth, &c. to the right hand, and the second, fourth, sixth, &c. to the

left hand; the whole being placed so that the discs are perpendicular to the dip, or intersect most directly the magnetic curves of powerful magnets. The electricity will be from the centre to the circumference in one set of discs, and from the circumference to the centre in those on each side of them; thus the action of the whole will conjoin to produce one combined and more powerful current.

159. I have rather, however, been desirous of discovering new facts and new relations dependent on magneto-electric induction, than of exalting the force of those already obtained; being assured that the latter would find their full development hereafter.

———————

160. I referred in my former paper to the probable influence of terrestrial magneto-electric induction (137.) in producing, either altogether or in part, the phenomena observed by Messrs. Christie and Barlow*, whilst revolving ferruginous bodies; and especially those observed by the latter when rapidly rotating an iron shell, which were by that philosopher referred to a change in the ordinary disposition of the magnetism of the ball. I suggested also that the rotation of a copper globe would probably insulate the effects due to electric currents from those due to mere derangement of magnetism, and throw light upon the true nature of the phenomena.

161. Upon considering the law already referred to (114.), it appeared impossible that a metallic globe could revolve under natural circumstances, without having electric currents produced within it, circulating round the revolving globe in a plane at right angles to the plane of revolution, provided its axis of rotation did not coincide with the dip; and it appeared that the current would be most powerful when the axis of revolution was perpendicular to the dip of the needle: for then all those parts of the ball below a plane passing through its centre and perpendicular to the dip, would in moving cut the magnetic curves in one direction, whilst all those parts above that plane would intersect them in the other direction: currents therefore would exist in these moving parts, proceeding from one pole of rotation to the other; but the currents above would

* Christie, Phil. Trans. 1825, pp. 58, 347, &c.   Barlow, Phil. Trans. 1825, p. 317.

be in the reverse direction to those below, and in conjunction with them would produce a continued circulation of electricity.

162. As the electric currents are nowhere interrupted in the ball, powerful effects were expected, and I endeavoured to obtain them with simple apparatus. The ball I used was of brass; it had belonged to an old electrical machine, was hollow, thin (too thin), and four inches in diameter; a brass wire was screwed into it, and the ball either turned in the hand by the wire, or sometimes, to render it more steady, supported by its wire in a notched piece of wood, and motion again given by the hand. The ball gave no signs of magnetism when at rest.

163. A compound magnetic needle was used to detect the currents. It was arranged thus: a sewing-needle had the head and point broken off, and was then magnetized; being broken in halves, the two magnets thus produced were fixed on a stem of dried grass, so as to be perpendicular to it, and about four inches asunder; they were both in one plane, but their similar poles in contrary directions. The grass was attached to a piece of unspun silk about six inches long, the latter to a stick passing through a cork in the mouth of a cylindrical jar; and thus a compound arrangement was obtained, perfectly sheltered from the motion of the air, but little influenced by the magnetism of the earth, and yet highly sensible to magnetic and electric forces, when the latter were brought into the vicinity of the one or the other needle.

164. Upon adjusting the needles to the plane of the magnetic meridian; arranging the ball on the outside of the glass jar to the west of the needles, and at such a height that its centre should correspond horizontally with the upper needle, whilst its axis was in the plane of the magnetic meridian, but perpendicular to the dip; and then rotating the ball, the needle was immediately affected. Upon inverting the direction of rotation, the needle was again affected, but in the opposite direction. When the ball revolved from east over to west, the marked pole went eastward; when the ball revolved in the opposite direction, the marked pole went westward or towards the ball. Upon placing the ball to the east of the needles, still the needle was deflected in the same way; *i. e.* when the ball revolved from east over to west, the marked pole went eastward (or to-

wards the ball) ; when the rotation was in the opposite direction, the marked pole went westward.

165. By twisting the silk of the needles, the latter were brought into a position perpendicular to the plane of the magnetic meridian ; the ball was again revolved, with its axis parallel to the needles ; the upper was affected as before, and the deflection was such as to show that both here and in the former case the needle was influenced solely by currents of electricity existing in the brass globe.

166. If the upper part of the revolving ball be considered as a wire moving from east to west, over the unmarked pole of the earth, the current of electricity in it should be from north to south (99. 114. 150.) ; if the under part be considered as a similar wire, moving from west to east over the same pole, the electric current should be from south to north ; and the circulation of electricity should therefore be from north above to south, and below back to north, in a metal ball revolving from east above to west in these latitudes. Now these currents are exactly those required to give the directions of the needle in the experiments just described ; so that the coincidence of the theory from which the experiments were deduced with the experiments themselves, is perfect.

167. Upon inclining the axis of rotation considerably, the revolving ball was still found to affect the magnetic needle ; and it was not until the angle which it formed with the magnetic dip was rendered small, that its effects, even upon this apparatus, were lost (153.). When revolving with its axis parallel to the dip, it is evident that the globe becomes analogous to the copper plate ; electricity of one kind might be collected at its equator, and of the other kind at its poles.

168. A current in the ball, such as that described above (161.), although it ought to deflect a needle the same way whether it be to the right or the left of the ball and of the axis of rotation, ought to deflect it the contrary way when above or below the ball ; for then the needle is, or ought to be, acted upon in a contrary direction by the current. This expectation was fulfilled by revolving the ball beneath the magnetic needle, the latter being still inclosed in its jar. When the ball was revolved from east over to west, the marked pole of the needle, instead of passing eastward, went westward ;

and when revolved from west over to east, the marked pole went eastward.

169. The deflections of the magnetic needle thus obtained with a brass ball are exactly in the same direction as those observed by Mr. Barlow in the revolution of the iron shell; and from the manner in which iron exhibits the phenomena of magneto-electric induction like any other metal, and distinct from its peculiar magnetic phenomena (132.), it is impossible but that electric currents must have been excited, and become active in those experiments. What proportion of the whole effect obtained is due to this cause, must be decided by a more elaborate investigation of all the phenomena.

170. These results, in conjunction with the general law, before stated (114.) suggested an experiment of extreme simplicity, which yet, on trial, was found to answer perfectly. The exclusion of all extraneous circumstances and complexity of arrangement, and the distinct character of the indications afforded, render this single experiment an epitome of nearly all the facts of magneto-electric induction.

171. A piece of common copper wire, about eight feet long, and one twentieth of an inch in thickness, had one of its ends fastened to one of the terminations of the galvanometer wire, and the other end to the other termination; thus it formed an endless continuation of the galvanometer wire: it was then roughly adjusted into the shape of a rectangle, or rather of a loop, the upper part of which could be carried to and fro over the galvanometer, whilst the lower part, and the galvanometer attached to it, remained steady (Plate II. fig. 30.). Upon moving this loop over the galvanometer from right to left, the magnetic needle was immediately deflected; upon passing the loop back again, the needle passed in the contrary direction to what it did before; upon repeating these motions of the loop in accordance with the vibrations of the needle (39.), the latter soon swung through 90° or more.

172. The relation of the current of electricity produced in the wire, to its motion, may be understood by supposing the convolutions of the galvanometer away, and the wire arranged as a rectangle, with its lower edge horizontal and in the plane of the magnetic meridian, and a magnetic needle suspended above and over the middle part of this edge, and directed by

the earth (fig. 30.).   On passing the upper part of the rectangle from west to east in the position represented by the
dotted line, the marked pole of the magnetic needle went west ;
the electric current was therefore from north to south in the
part of the wire passing under the needle, and from south to
north in the moving or upper part of the parallelogram.   On
passing the upper part of the rectangle from east to west over
the galvanometer, the marked pole of the needle went east,
and the current of electricity was therefore the reverse of the
former.

173. When the rectangle was arranged in a plane east and
west, and the magnetic needle made parallel to it, either by
the torsion of its suspension thread or the action of a magnet,
still the general effects were the same.   On moving the upper
part of the rectangle from north to south, the marked pole
of the needle went north ; when the wire was moved in the
opposite direction, the marked pole went south.   The same
effect took place when the motion of the wire was in any
other azimuth of the line of dip ; the direction of the current always being conformable to the law formerly expressed
(114.), and also to the directions obtained with the rotating
ball (164.).

174. In these experiments it is not necessary to move the
galvanometer or needle from its first position.   It is quite sufficient if the wire of the rectangle is distorted where it leaves
the instrument, and bent so as to allow the moving upper part
to travel in the desired direction.

175. The moveable part of the wire was then arranged
*below* the galvanometer, but so as to be carried across the dip.
It affected the instrument as before, and in the same direction ;
*i. e.* when carried from west to east under the instrument, the
marked end of the needle went west, as before.   This should,
of course be the case ; for when the wire is cutting the magnetic dip in a certain direction, an electric current also in a
certain direction should be induced in it.

176. If in fig. 31. $dp$ be parallel to the dip, and B A be considered as the upper part of the rectangle (171.), with an arrow $c$ attached to it, both these being retained in a plane perpendicular to the dip,—then, however B A with its attached
arrow is moved upon $d\,p$ as an axis, if it afterwards proceed

in the direction of the arrow, a current of electricity will move along it from B towards A.

177. When the moving part of the wire was carried up or down parallel to the dip, no effect was produced on the galvanometer. When the direction of motion was a little inclined to the dip, electricity manifested itself; and was at a maximum when the motion was perpendicular to the magnetic direction.

178. When the wire was bent into other forms and moved, equally strong effects were obtained, especially when instead of a rectangle a double catenarian curve was formed of it on one side of the galvanometer, and the two single curves or halves were swung in opposite directions at the same time; their action then combined to affect the galvanometer: but all the results were reducible to those above described.

179. The longer the extent of the moving wire, and the greater the space through which it moves, the greater is the effect upon the galvanometer.

180. The facility with which electric currents are produced in metals when moving under the influence of magnets, suggests that henceforth precautions should always be taken, in experiments upon metals and magnets, to guard against such effects. Considering the universality of the magnetic influence of the earth, it is a consequence which appears very extraordinary to the mind, that scarcely any piece of metal can be moved in contact with others, either at rest, or in motion with different velocities or in varying directions, without an electric current existing within them. It is probable that amongst arrangements of steam-engines and metal machinery, some curious accidental magneto-electric combinations may be found, producing effects which have never been observed, or, if noticed, have never as yet been understood.

---

181. Upon considering the effects of terrestrial magneto-electric induction which have now been described, it is almost impossible to resist the impression that similar effects, but infinitely greater in force, may be produced by the action of the globe, as a magnet, upon its own mass, in consequence of its diurnal rotation. It would seem that if a bar of metal be laid in these latitudes on the surface of the earth parallel to the mag-

netic meridian, a current of electricity tends to pass through it from south to north, in consequence of the travelling of the bar from west to east (172.), by the rotation of the earth; that if another bar in the same direction be connected with the first by wires, it cannot discharge the current of the first, because it has an equal tendency to have a current in the same direction induced within itself: but that if the latter be carried from east to west, which is equivalent to a diminution of the motion communicated to it from the earth (172.), then the electric current from south to north is rendered evident in the first bar, in consequence of its discharge, at the same time, by means of the second.

182. Upon the supposition that the rotation of the earth tended, by magneto-electro induction, to cause currents in its own mass, these would, according to the law (114.) and the experiments, be, upon the surface at least, from the parts in the neighbourhood of or towards the plane of the equator, in opposite directions to the poles; and if collectors could be applied at the equator and at the poles of the globe, as has been done with the revolving copper plate (150.), and also with magnets (220.), then negative electricity would be collected at the equator, and positive electricity at both poles (222.). But without the conductors, or something equivalent to them, it is evident these currents could not exist, as they could not be discharged.

183. I did not think it impossible that some natural difference might occur between bodies, relative to the intensity of the current produced or tending to be produced in them by magneto-electric induction, which might be shown by opposing them to each other; especially as Messrs. Arago, Babbage, Herschel, and Harris, have all found great differences, not only between the metals and other substances, but between the metals themselves, in their power of receiving motion from or giving it to a magnet in trials by revolution (130.). I therefore took two wires, each one hundred and twenty feet long, one of iron and the other of copper. These were connected with each other at their ends, and then extended in the direction of the magnetic meridian, so as to form two nearly parallel lines, nowhere in contact except at the extremities. The copper wire was then divided in the middle, and examined

by a delicate galvanometer, but no evidence of an electrical current was obtained.

184. By favour of His Royal Highness the President of the Society, I obtained the permission of His Majesty to make experiments at the lake in the gardens of Kensington-palace, for the purpose of comparing, in a similar manner, water and metal. The basin of this lake is artificial; the water is supplied by the Chelsea Company; no springs run into it, and it presented what I required, namely, a uniform mass of still pure water, with banks ranging nearly from east to west, and from north to south.

185. Two perfectly clean bright copper plates, each exposing four square feet of surface, were soldered to the extremities of a copper wire; the plates were immersed in the water, north and south of each other, the wire which connected them being arranged upon the grass of the bank. The plates were about four hundred and eighty feet from each other, in a right line; the wire was probably six hundred feet long. This wire was then divided in the middle, and connected by two cups of mercury with a delicate galvanometer.

186. At first, indications of electric currents were obtained; but when these were tested by inverting the direction of contact, and in other ways, they were found to be due to other causes than the one sought for. A little difference in temperature; a minute portion of the nitrate of mercury used to amalgamate the wires, entering into the water employed to reduce the two cups of mercury to the same temperature; was sufficient to produce currents of electricity, which affected the galvanometer, notwithstanding they had to pass through nearly five hundred feet of water. When these and other interfering causes were guarded against, no effect was obtained; and it appeared that even such dissimilar substances as water and copper, when cutting the magnetic curves of the earth with equal velocity, perfectly neutralized each other's action.

187. Mr. Fox of Falmouth has obtained some highly important results respecting the electricity of metalliferous veins in the mines of Cornwall, which have been published in the Philosophical Transactions*. I have examined the paper with a view to ascertain whether any of the effects were pro-

* 1830, p. 399.

bably referable to magneto-electric induction ; but, though unable to form a very strong opinion, believe they are not. When parallel veins running east and west were compared, the general tendency of the electricity *in the wires* was from north to south ; when the comparison was made between parts towards the surface and at some depth, the current of electricity in the wires was from above downwards. If there should be any natural difference in the force of the electric currents produced by magneto-electric induction in different substances, or substances in different positions moving with the earth, and which might be rendered evident by increasing the masses acted upon, then the wires and veins experimented with by Mr. Fox might perhaps have acted as dischargers to the electricity of the mass of strata included between them, and the directions of the currents would agree with those observed as above.

188. Although the electricity obtained by magneto-electric induction in a few feet of wire is of but small intensity, and has not yet been observed except in metals, and carbon in a particular state, still it has power to pass through brine (23.) ; and, as increased length in the substance acted upon produces increase of intensity, I hoped to obtain effects from extensive moving masses of water, though quiescent water gave none. I made experiments therefore (by favour) at Waterloo Bridge, extending a copper wire nine hundred and sixty feet in length upon the parapet of the bridge, and dropping from its extremities other wires with extensive plates of metal attached to them to complete contact with the water. Thus the wire and the water made one conducting circuit ; and as the water ebbed or flowed with the tide, I hoped to obtain currents analogous to those of the brass ball (161.).

189. I constantly obtained deflections at the galvanometer, but they were very irregular, and were, in succession, referred to other causes than that sought for. The different condition of the water as to purity on the two sides of the river ; the difference in temperature ; slight differences in the plates, in the solder used, in the more or less perfect contact made by twisting or otherwise ; all produced effects in turn : and though I experimented on the water passing through the middle arches only ; used platina plates instead of copper ; and took every other precaution, I could not after three days obtain any satisfactory results.

190. Theoretically, it seems a necessary consequence, that where water is flowing, there electric currents should be formed: thus, if a line be imagined passing from Dover to Calais through the sea, and returning through the land beneath the water to Dover, it traces out a circuit of conducting matter, one part of which, when the water moves up or down the channel, is cutting the magnetic curves of the earth, whilst the other is relatively at rest. This is a repetition of the wire experiment (171.), but with worse conductors. Still there is every reason to believe that electric currents do run in the general direction of the circuit described, either one way or the other, according as the passage of the water is up or down the channel. Where the lateral extent of the moving water is enormously increased, it does not seem improbable that the effect should become sensible; and the gulf stream may thus, perhaps, from electric currents moving across it, by magneto-electric induction from the earth, exert a sensible influence upon the forms of the lines of magnetic variation*.

191. Though positive results have not yet been obtained by the action of the earth upon water and aqueous fluids, yet, as the experiments are very limited in their extent, and as such fluids do yield the current by artificial magnets (23.), (for transference of the current is proof that it may be produced (213.),) the supposition made that the earth produces these induced currents within itself (181.) in consequence of its diurnal rotation, is still highly probable (222. 223.); and when it is considered that the moving masses extend for thousands of miles across the magnetic curves, cutting them in various directions within its mass, as well as at the surface, it is possible the electricity may rise to considerable intensity.

192. I hardly dare venture, even in the most hypothetical form, to ask whether the Aurora Borealis and Australis may not be the discharge of electricity, thus urged towards the poles of the earth, from whence it is endeavouring to return by natural and appointed means above the earth to the equatorial regions. The non-occurrence of it in very high latitudes

* Theoretically, even a ship or a boat when passing on the surface of the water, in northern or southern latitudes, should have currents of electricity running through it directly across the line of her motion; or if the water is flowing past the ship at anchor, similar currents should occur.

is not at all against the supposition; and it is remarkable that Mr. Fox, who observed the deflections of the magnetic needle at Falmouth, by the Aurora Borealis, gives that direction of it which perfectly agrees with the present view. He states that all the variations at night were towards the east [*], and this is what would happen if electric currents were setting from south to north in the earth under the needle, or from north to south in space above it.

§ 6. *General remarks and illustrations of the Force and Direction of Magneto-electric induction.*

193. In the repetition and variation of Arago's experiment by Messrs. Babbage, Herschel, and Harris, these philosophers directed their attention to the differences of force observed amongst the metals and other substances in their action on the magnet. These differences were very great[†], and led me to hope that by mechanical combinations of various metals important results might be obtained (183). The following experiments were therefore made, with a view to obtain, if possible, any such difference of the action of two metals.

194. A piece of soft iron bonnet-wire covered with cotton was laid bare and cleaned at one extremity, and there fastened by metallic contact with the clean end of a copper wire. Both wires were then twisted together like the strands of a rope, for eighteen or twenty inches; and the remaining parts being made to diverge, their extremities were connected with the wires of the galvanometer. The iron wire was about two feet long, the continuation to the galvanometer being copper.

195. The twisted copper and iron (touching each other nowhere but at the extremity) were then passed between the poles of a powerful magnet arranged horse-shoe fashion (fig. 32.); but not the slightest effect was observed at the galvanometer, although the arrangement seemed fitted to show any electrical difference between the two metals relative to the action of the magnet.

196. A soft iron cylinder was then covered with paper at the middle part, and the twisted portion of the above compound wire coiled as a spiral around it, the connexion with the galva-

* Philosophical Transactions, 1831, p. 202.   † Ibid. 1825, p. 472; 1831, p. 78.

nometer still being made at the ends A B.   The iron cylinder was then brought in contact with the poles of a powerful
magnet capable of raising thirty pounds ; yet no signs of electricity appeared at the galvanometer.   Every precaution was
applied in making and breaking contact to accumulate effect,
but no indications of a current could be obtained.

197.  Copper and tin, copper and zinc, tin and zinc, tin and
iron, and zinc and iron, were tried against each other in a similar manner (194), but not the slightest sign of electric currents
could be procured.

198.  Two flat spirals, one of copper and the other of iron,
containing each eighteen inches of wire were connected with
each other and with the galvanometer, and then put face to
face so as to be in contrary directions.   When brought up to
the magnetic pole (53.), no electrical indications at the galvanometer were observed.   When one was turned round so that
both were in the same direction, the effect at the galvanometer
was very powerful.

199.  The compound helix of copper and iron wire formerly
described (8.) was arranged as a double helix, one of the helices
being all iron and containing two hundred and fourteen feet,
the other all copper and containing two hundred and eight
feet.   The two similar ends A A of the copper and iron helix
were connected together, and the other ends B B of each helix
connected with the galvanometer ; so that when a magnet was
introduced into the centre of the arrangement, the induced
currents in the iron and copper would tend to proceed in contrary directions.   Yet when a magnet was inserted, or a soft
iron bar within made a magnet by contact with poles, no effect
at the needle was produced.

200.  A glass tube about fourteen inches long was filled with
strong sulphuric acid. Twelve inches of the end of a clean
copper wire were bent up into a bundle and inserted into the
tube, so as to make good superficial contact with the acid, and
the rest of the wire passed along the outside of the tube and
away to the galvanometer.   A wire similarly bent up at the
extremity was immersed in the other end of the sulphuric acid,
and also connected with the galvanometer, so that the acid and
copper wire were in the same parallel relation to each other in
this experiment as iron and copper were in the first (194).

When this arrangement was passed in a similar manner between the poles of the magnet, not the slightest effect at the galvanometer could be perceived.

201. From these experiments it would appear, that when metals of different kinds connected in one circuit are equally subject in every circumstance to magneto-electric induction, they exhibit exactly equal powers with respect to the currents which either are formed, or tend to form, in them. The same even appears to be the case with regard to fluids, and probably all other substances.

202. Still it seemed impossible that these results could indicate the relative inductive power of the magnet upon the different metals; for that the effect should be in some relation to the conducting power seemed a necessary consequence (139), and the influence of rotating plates upon magnets had been found to bear a general relation to the conducting power of the substance used.

203. In the experiments of rotation (81.), the electric current is excited and discharged in the same substance, be it a good or bad conductor; but in the experiments just described the current excited in iron could not be transmitted but through the copper, and that excited in copper had to pass through iron; *i. e.* supposing currents of dissimilar strength to be formed in the metals proportionate to their conducting power, the stronger current had to pass through the worst conductor, and the weaker current through the best.

204. Experiments were therefore made in which different metals insulated from each other were passed between the poles of the magnet, their opposite ends being connected with the same end of the galvanometer wire, so that the currents formed and led away to the galvanometer should oppose each other; and when considerable lengths of different wires were used, feeble deflections were obtained.

205. To obtain perfectly satisfactory results a new galvanometer was constructed, consisting of two independent coils, each containing eighteen feet of silked copper wire. These coils were exactly alike in shape and number of turns, and were fixed side by side with a small interval between them, in which a double needle could be hung by a fibre of silk exactly as in the former instrument (87.) The coils may be distinguished by

the letters K L, and when electrical currents were sent through them in the same direction, acted upon the needle with the sum of their powers; when in opposite directions, with the difference of their powers.

206. The compound helix (199. 8.) was now connected, the ends A and B of the iron with A and B ends of galvanometer coil K, and the ends A and B of the copper with B and A ends of galvanometer coil L, so that the currents excited in the two helices should pass in opposite directions through the coils K and L. On introducing a small cylinder magnet within the helices, the galvanometer needle was powerfully deflected. On disuniting the iron helix, the magnet caused with the copper helix alone still stronger deflection in the same direction. On reuniting the iron helix, and unconnecting the copper helix, the magnet caused a moderate deflection in the contrary direction. Thus it was evident that the electric current induced by a magnet in a copper wire was far more powerful than the current induced by the same magnet in an equal iron wire.

207. To prevent any error that might arise from the greater influence, from vicinity or other circumstances, of one coil on the needle beyond that of the other, the iron and copper terminations were changed relative to the galvanometer coils K L, so that the one which before carried the current from the copper now conveyed that from the iron, and vice versâ. But the same striking superiority of the copper was manifested as before. This precaution was taken in the rest of the experiments with other metals to be described.

208. I then had wires of iron, zinc, copper, tin, and lead, drawn to the same diameter (very nearly one twentieth of an inch), and I compared exactly equal lengths, namely sixteen feet, of each in pairs in the following manner: The ends of the copper wire were connected with the ends A and B of galvanometer coil K, and the ends of the zinc wire with the terminations A and B of the galvanometer coil L. The middle part of each wire was then coiled six times round a cylinder of soft iron covered with paper, long enough to connect the poles of Daniell's horse-shoe magnet (56,) (fig. 33.), so that similar helices of copper and zinc, each of six turns, surrounded the bar at two places equidistant from each other and from the poles of the magnet; but these helices were purposely arranged

so as to be in contrary directions, and therefore send contrary currents through the galvanometer coils K and L.

209. On making and breaking contact between the soft iron bar and the poles of the magnet, the galvanometer was strongly affected; on detaching the zinc it was still more strongly affected in the same direction. On taking all the precautions before alluded to (207.), with others, it was abundantly proved that the current induced by the magnet in copper was far more powerful than in zinc.

210. The copper was then compared in a similar manner with tin, lead, and iron, and surpassed them all, even more than it did zinc. The zinc was then compared experimentally with the tin, lead, and iron, and found to produce a more powerful current than any of them. Iron in the same manner proved superior to tin and lead. Tin came next, and lead the last.

211. Thus the order of these metals is copper, zinc, iron, tin, and lead. It is exactly their order with respect to conducting power for electricity, and, with the exception of iron, is the order presented by the magneto-rotation experiments of Messrs. Babbage, Herschel, Harris, &c. The iron has additional power in the latter kind of experiments, because of its ordinary magnetic relations, and its place relative to magneto-electric action of the kind now under investigation cannot be ascertained by such trials. In the manner above described it may be correctly ascertained.*

212. It must still be observed that in these experiments the whole effect between different metals is not obtained; for of the thirty-four feet of wire included in each circuit, eighteen feet are copper in both, being the wire of the galvanometer coils; and as the whole circuit is concerned in the resulting force of the current, this circumstance must tend to diminish the difference which would appear between the metals if the circuits were of the same substances throughout. In the present case the difference obtained is probably not more than

* Mr. Christie, who being appointed reporter upon this paper, had it in his hands before it was complete, felt the difficulty (202.); and to satisfy his mind, made experiments upon iron and copper with the large magnet (44.), and came to the same conclusions as I have arrived at. The two sets of experiments were perfectly independent of each other, neither of us being aware of the other's proceedings.

a half of that which would be given if the whole of each circuit were of one metal.

213. These results tend to prove that the currents produced by magneto-electric induction in bodies is proportional to their conducting power. That they are *exactly* proportional to and altogether dependent upon the conducting power, is, I think, proved by the perfect neutrality displayed when two metals or other substances, as acid, water, &c. &c. (201. 186.), are opposed to each other in their action. The feeble current which tends to be produced in the worse conductor, has its transmission favoured in the better conductor, and the stronger current which tends to form in the latter has its intensity diminished by the obstruction of the former ; and the forces of generation and obstruction are so perfectly balanced as to neutralize each other exactly. Now as the obstruction is inversely as the conducting power, the tendency to generate a current must be directly as that power to produce this perfect equilibrium.

214. The cause of the equality of action under the various circumstances described, where great extent of wire (183.) or wire and water (184.) were connected together, which yet produced such different effects upon the magnet, is now evident and simple.

215. The effects of a rotating substance upon a needle or magnet ought, where ordinary magnetism has no influence, to be directly as the conducting power of the substance ; and I venture now to predict that such will be found to be the case ; and that in all those instances where non-conductors have been supposed to exhibit this peculiar influence, the motion has been due to some interfering cause of an ordinary kind ; as mechanical communication of motion through the parts of the apparatus, or otherwise (as in the case Mr. Harris has pointed out *) ; or else to ordinary magnetic attractions. To distinguish the effects of the latter from those of the induced electric currents, I have been able to devise a most perfect test, which shall be almost immediately described (243.).

216. There is every reason to believe that the magnet or magnetic needle will become an excellent measurer of the conducting power of substances rotated near it ; for I have found

* Philosophical Transactions, 1831, p. 68.

by careful experiment, that when a constant current of electricity was sent successively through a series of wires of copper, platina, zinc, silver, lead, and tin, drawn to the same diameter; the deflection of the needle was exactly equal by them all. It must be remembered that when bodies are rotated in a horizontal plane, the magnetism of the earth is active upon them. As the effect is general to the whole of the plate, it may not interfere in these cases; but in some experiments and calculations may be of important consequence.

217. Another point which I endeavoured to ascertain, was, whether it was essential or not that the moving part of the wire should, in cutting the magnetic curves, pass into positions of greater or lesser magnetic force; or whether, always intersecting curves of equal magnetic intensity, the mere motion was sufficient for the production of the current. That the latter is true, has been proved already in several of the experiments on terrestrial magneto-electric induction. Thus the electricity evolved from the copper plate (149.), the currents produced in the rotating globe (161, &c.), and those passing through the moving wire (171.), are all produced under circumstances in which the magnetic force could not but be the same during the whole experiments.

218. To prove the point with an ordinary magnet, a copper disc was cemented upon the end of a cylinder magnet, with paper intervening; the magnet and disc were rotated together, and collectors (attached to the galvanometer) brought in contact with the circumference and the central part of the copper plate. The galvanometer needle moved as in former cases, and the *direction* of motion was the *same* as that which would have resulted, if the copper only had revolved, and the magnet been fixed. Neither was there any apparent difference in the quantity of deflection. Hence, rotating the magnet causes no difference in the results; for a rotatory and a stationary magnet produce the same effect upon the moving copper.

219. A copper cylinder, closed at one extremity, was then put over the magnet, one half of which it inclosed like a cap; it was firmly fixed, and prevented from touching the magnet anywhere by interposed paper. The arrangement was then floated in a narrow jar of mercury, so that the lower edge of the

copper cylinder touched the fluid metal ; one wire of the galvanometer dipped into this mercury, and the other into a little
cavity in the centre of the end of the copper cap.   Upon rotating the magnet and its attached cylinder, abundance of electricity passed through the galvanometer, and in the same direction as if the cylinder had rotated only, the magnet being
still.   The results therefore were the same as those with the
disc (218.).

220. That the metal of the magnet itself might be substituted
for the moving cylinder, disc, or wire, seemed an inevitable
consequence, and yet one which would exhibit the effects of
magneto-electric induction in a striking form.   A cylinder magnet had therefore a little hole made in the centre of each end
to receive a drop of mercury, and was then floated pole upwards in the same metal contained in a narrow jar.   One wire
from the galvanometer dipped into the mercury of the jar,
and the other into the drop contained in the hole at the upper
extremity of the axis.   The magnet was then revolved by a
piece of string passed round it, and the galvanometer-needle
immediately indicated a powerful current of electricity.   On
reversing the order of rotation, the electrical current was reversed.   The direction of the electricity was the same as if the
copper cylinder (219.) or a copper wire had revolved round the
fixed magnet in the same direction as that which the magnet
itself had followed.   Thus a *singular independence* of the magnetism and the bar in which it resides is rendered evident.

221. In the above experiment the mercury reached about
half way up the magnet; but when its quantity was increased
until within one eighth of an inch of the top, or diminished
until equally near the bottom, still the same effects and the
*same direction* of electrical current was obtained.   But in those
extreme proportions the effects did not appear so strong as
when the surface of the mercury was about the middle, or
between that and an inch from each end.   The magnet was
eight inches and a half long, and three quarters of an inch in
diameter.

222. Upon inversion of the magnet, and causing rotation
in the same direction, *i. e.* always screw or always unscrew,
then a contrary current of electricity was produced.   But when
the motion of the magnet was continued in a direction constant

in relation to its *own axis*, then electricity of the same kind was collected at both poles, and the opposite electricity at the equator, or in its neighbourhood, or in the parts corresponding to it. If the magnet be held parallel to the axis of the earth, with its unmarked pole directed to the pole star, and then rotated so that the parts at its southern side pass from west to east in conformity to the motion of the earth; then positive electricity may be collected at the extremities of the magnet, and negative electricity at or about the middle of its mass.

223. When the galvanometer was very sensible, the mere spinning of the magnet in the air, whilst one of the galvanometer wires touched the extremity, and the other the equatorial parts, was sufficient to evolve a current of electricity and deflect the needle.

224. Experiments were then made with a similar magnet, for the purpose of ascertaining whether any return of the electric current could occur at the central or axial parts, they having the same angular velocity of rotation as the other parts (259.); the belief being that it could not.

225. A cylinder magnet, seven inches in length, and three quarters of an inch in diameter, had a hole pierced in the direction of its axis from one extremity, a quarter of an inch in diameter, and three inches deep. A copper cylinder, surrounded by paper and amalgamated at both extremities, was introduced so as to be in metallic contact at the bottom of the hole, by a little mercury, with the middle of the magnet; insulated at the sides by the paper; and projecting about a quarter of an inch above the end of the steel. A quill was put over the copper rod, which reached to the paper, and formed a cup to receive mercury for the completion of the circuit. A high paper edge was also raised round that end of the magnet and mercury put within it, which however had no metallic connexion with that in the quill, except through the magnet itself and the copper rod (fig. 34.). The wires A and B from the galvanometer were dipped into these two portions of mercury; any current through them could, therefore, only pass down the magnet towards its equatorial parts, and then up the copper rod; or vice versâ.

226. When thus arranged and rotated screw fashion, the marked end of the galvanometer needle went west, indicating

that there was a current through the instrument from A to B, and consequently from B through the magnet and copper rod to A (fig. 34.).

227. The magnet was then put into a jar of mercury (fig. 35.) as before (219.); the wire A left in contact with the copper axis, but the wire B dipped in the mercury of the jar, and therefore in metallic communication with the equatorial parts of the magnet instead of its polar extremity.   On revolving the magnet screw fashion, the galvanometer needle was deflected in the same direction as before, but far more powerfully.   Yet it is evident that the parts of the magnet from the equator to the pole were out of the electric circuit.

228. Then the wire A was connected with the mercury on the extremity of the magnet, the wire B still remaining in contact with that in the jar (fig. 36.), so that the copper axis was altogether out of the circuit.   The magnet was again revolved screw fashion, and again caused the same deflection of the needle, the current being as strong as it was in the last trial (227.), and much stronger than at first (226.).

229. Hence it is evident that there is no discharge of the current at the centre of the magnet, for the current, now freely evolved, is up through the magnet ; but in the first experiment (226.), it was down.   In fact, at that time, it was only the part of the moving metal equal to a little disc extending from the end of the wire B in the mercury to the wire A that was efficient, *i. e.* moving with a different angular velocity to the rest of the circuit (258.) ; and for that portion the direction of the current is consistent with the other results.

230. In the two after experiments, the *lateral* parts of the magnet or of the copper rod are those which move relative to the other parts of the circuit, *i. e.* the galvanometer wires ; and being more extensive, intersecting more curves, or moving with more velocity, produce the greater effect.   For the discal part, the direction of the induced electric current is the same in all, namely, from the circumference towards the centre.

---

231. The law under which the induced electric current excited in bodies moving relatively to magnets, is made dependent on the intersection of the magnetic curves by the metal (114.) being thus rendered more precise and definite (217. 220. 224.),

seem now even to apply to the cause in the first section of the former paper (26.) ; and by rendering a perfect reason for the effects produced, take away any for supposing that peculiar condition, which I ventured to call the electro-tonic state (60.).

232. When an electrical current is passed through a wire, that wire is surrounded at every part by magnetic curves, diminishing in intensity according to their distance from the wire, and which in idea may be likened to rings situated in planes perpendicular to the wire or rather to the electric current within it. These curves, although different in form, are perfectly analogous to those existing between two contrary magnetic poles opposed to each other; and when a second wire, parallel to that which carries the current, is made to approach the latter (18.), it passes through magnetic curves exactly of the same kind as those it would intersect when carried between opposite magnetic poles (109.) in one direction; and as it recedes from the inducing wire, it cuts the curves around it in the same manner that it would do those between the same poles if moved in the other direction.

233. If the wire N P (fig. 40.) have an electric current passed through it in the direction from P to N, then the dotted ring may represent a magnetic curve round it, and it is in such a direction that if small magnetic needles be placed as tangents to it, they will become arranged as in the figure, *n* and *s* indicating north and south ends (44. *note*).

234. But if the current of electricity were made to cease for a while, and magnetic poles were used instead to give direction to the needles, and make them take the same position as when under the influence of the current, then they must be arranged as at fig. 41 ; the marked and unmarked poles *a b* above the wire, being in opposite directions to those *a' b'* below. In such a position therefore the magnetic curves between the poles *a b* and *a' b'* have the same general direction with the corresponding parts of the ring magnetic curve surrounding the wire N P carrying an electric current.

235. If the second wire *p n* (fig. 40.) be now brought towards the principal wire, carrying a current, it will cut an infinity of magnetic curves, similar in direction to that figured, and consequently similar in direction to those between the poles *a b* of the magnets (fig. 41.), and it will intersect

these current curves in the same manner as it would the magnet curves, if it passed from above between the poles downwards.   Now, such an intersection would, with the magnets,
induce an electric current in the wire from $p$ to $n$ (114.); and
therefore as the curves are alike in arrangement, the same effect ought to result from the intersection of the magnetic
curves dependent on the current in the wire N P; and such is
the case, for on approximation the induced current is in the
opposite direction to the principal current (19.).

236. If the wire $p'$ $n'$ be carried up from below, it will pass
in the opposite direction between the magnetic poles; but then
also the magnetic poles themselves are reversed (fig. 41.), and
the induced current is therefore (114.) still in the same direction as before.   It is also, for equally sufficient and evident
reasons, in the same direction, if produced by the influence of
the curves dependent upon the wire.

237. When the second wire is retained at rest in the vicinity
of the principal wire, no current is induced through it, for it is
intersecting no magnetic curves.   When it is removed from
the principal wire, it intersects the curves in the opposite direction to what it did before (235.); and a current in the opposite direction is induced, which therefore corresponds with
the direction of the principal current (19.).   The same effect
would take place if by inverting the direction of motion of the
wire in passing between either set of poles (fig. 41.), it were
made to intersect the curves there existing in the opposite direction to what it did before.

238. In the first experiments (10. 13.), the inducing wire
and that under induction were arranged at a fixed distance
from each other, and then an electric current sent through the
former.   In such cases the magnetic curves themselves must
be considered as moving (if I may use the expression) across
the wire under induction, from the moment at which they begin
to be developed until the magnetic force of the current is at its
utmost; expanding as it were from the wire outwards, and
consequently being in the same relation to the fixed wire under
induction, as if *it* had moved in the opposite direction across
them, or towards the wire carrying the current.   Hence the first
current induced in such cases was in the contrary direction to
the principal current (17. 235.).   On breaking the battery con-

tact, the magnetic curves (which are mere expressions for arranged magnetic forces) may be conceived as contracting upon and returning towards the failing electrical current, and therefore move in the opposite direction across the wire, and cause an opposite induced current to the first.

239. When, in experiments with ordinary magnets, the latter, in place of being moved past the wires, were actually made near them (27. 36.), then a similar progressive development of the magnetic curves may be considered as having taken place, producing the effects which would have occurred by motion of the wires in one direction ; the destruction of the magnetic power corresponds to the motion of the wire in the opposite direction.

240. If, instead of intersecting the magnetic curves of a straight wire carrying a current, by approximating or removing a second wire (235.), a revolving plate be used, being placed for that purpose near the wire, and, as it were, amongst the magnetic curves, then it ought to have continuous electric currents induced within it ; and if a line joining the wire with the centre of the plate were perpendicular to both, then the induced current ought to be, according to the law (114.), directly across the plate, from one side to the other, and at right angles to the direction of the inducing current.

241. A single metallic wire one twentieth of an inch in diameter had an electric current passed through it, and a small copper disc one inch and a half in diameter revolved near to and under, but not in actual contact with it (fig. 39.). Collectors were then applied at the opposite edges of the disc, and wires from them connected with the galvanometer. As the disc revolved in one direction, the needle was deflected on one side ; and when the direction of revolution was reversed, the needle was inclined on the other side, in accordance with the results anticipated.

242. Thus the reasons which induce me to suppose a particular state in the wire (60.) have disappeared ; and though it still seems to me unlikely that a wire at rest in the neighbourhood of another carrying a powerful electric current is entirely indifferent to it, yet I am not aware of any distinct *facts* which authorize the conclusion that it is in a particular state.

243. In considering the nature of the cause assigned in these

papers to account for the mutual influence of magnets and moving metals (120.), and comparing it with that heretofore admitted, namely, the induction of a feeble magnetism like that produced in iron, it occurred to me that a most decisive experimental test of the two views could be applied (215.).

244. No other known power has like direction with that exerted between an electric current and a magnetic pole; it is tangential, while all other forces, acting at a distance, are direct. Hence, if a magnetic pole on one side of a revolving plate follow its course by reason of its obedience to the tangential force exerted upon it by the very current of electricity which it has itself caused, a similar pole on the opposite side of the plate should immediately set it free from this force; for the currents which tend to be formed by the action of the two poles are in opposite directions; or rather no current tends to be formed, or no magnetic curves are intersected (114.); and therefore the magnet should remain at rest. On the contrary, if the action of a north magnetic pole were to produce a southness in the nearest part of the copper plate, and a diffuse northness elsewhere (82.), as is really the case with iron; then the use of another north pole on the opposite side of the same part of the plate should double the effect instead of destroying it, and double the tendency of the first magnet to move with the plate.

245. A thick copper plate (85.) was therefore fixed on a vertical axis, a bar magnet was suspended by a plaited silk cord, so that its marked pole hung over the edge of the plate, and a sheet of paper being interposed, the plate was revolved; immediately the magnetic pole obeyed its motion and passed off in the same direction. A second magnet of equal size and strength was then attached to the first, so that its marked pole should hang *beneath* the edge of the copper plate in a corresponding position to that above, and at an equal distance (fig. 37.). Then a paper sheath or screen being interposed as before, and the plate revolved, the poles were found entirely indifferent to its motion, although either of them alone would have followed the course of rotation.

246. On turning one magnet round, so that *opposite* poles were on each side of the plate, then the mutual action of the poles and the moving metal was a maximum.

247. On suspending one magnet so that its axis was level

with the plate, and either pole opposite its edge, the revolution of the plate caused no motion of the magnet. The electrical currents dependent upon induction would now tend to be produced in a vertical direction across the thickness of the plate, but could not be so discharged, or at least only to so slight a degree as to leave all effects insensible; but ordinary magnetic induction, or that on an iron plate, would be equally if not more powerfully developed in such a position (251.).

248. Then, with regard to the production of electricity in these cases :—whenever motion was communicated by the plate to the magnets, currents existed; when it was not communicated, they ceased. A marked pole of a large bar magnet was put under the edge of the plate; collectors (86.) applied at the axis and edge of the plate as on former occasions (fig. 38.), and these connected with the galvanometer; when the plate was revolved, abundance of electricity passed to the instrument. The unmarked pole of a similar magnet was then put over the place of the former pole, so that contrary poles were above and below; on revolving the plate, the electricity was more powerful than before. The latter magnet was then turned end for end, so that marked poles were both above and below the plate, and then, upon revolving it, scarcely any electricity was procured. By adjusting the distance of the poles so as to correspond with their relative force, they at last were brought so perfectly to neutralize each other's inductive action upon the plate, that no electricity could be obtained with the most rapid motion.

249. I now proceeded to compare the effect of similar and dissimilar poles upon iron and copper, adopting for the purpose Mr. Sturgeon's very useful form of Arago's experiment. This consists in a circular plate of metal supported in a vertical plane by a horizontal axis, and weighted a little at one edge or rendered excentric so as to vibrate like a pendulum. The poles of the magnets are applied near the side and edges of these plates, and then the number of vibrations, required to reduce the vibrating are a certain constant quantity, noted. In the first description of this instrument* it is said that opposite poles produced the greatest retarding effect, and similar poles none; and yet within a page of the place the

* Edin. Phil. Journal, 1825, p. 124.

effect is considered as of the same kind with that produced in iron.

250. I had two such plates mounted, one of copper, one of iron. The copper plate alone gave sixty vibrations, in the average of several experiments, before the arc of vibration was reduced from one constant mark to another. On placing opposite magnetic poles near to, and on each side of, the same place, the vibrations were reduced to fifteen. On putting similar poles on each side of it, they rose to fifty; and on placing two pieces of wood of equal size with the poles equally near, they became fifty-two. So that, when similar poles were used, the magnetic effect was little or none (the obstruction being due to the confinement of the air, rather), whilst with opposite poles it was the greatest possible. When a pole was presented to the edge of the plate, no retardation occurred.

251. The iron plate alone made thirty-two vibrations, whilst the arc of vibration diminished a certain quantity. On presenting a magnetic pole to the edge of the plate (247.), the vibrations were diminished to eleven; and when the pole was about half an inch from the edge, to five.

252. When the marked pole was put at the side of the iron plate at a certain distance, the number of vibrations was only five. When the marked pole of the second bar was put on the opposite side of the plate at the same distance (250.), the vibrations were reduced to two. But when the second pole was an unmarked one, yet occupying exactly the same position, the vibrations rose to twenty-two. By removing the stronger of these two opposite poles a little way from the plate, the vibrations increased to thirty-one, or nearly the original number. But on removing it *altogether*, they fell to between five and six.

253. Nothing can be more clear, therefore, than that with iron, and bodies admitting of ordinary magnetic induction, *opposite* poles on opposite sides of the edge of the plate neutralize each other's effect, whilst *similar* poles exalt the action; a single pole end on is also sufficient. But with copper, and substances not sensible to ordinary magnetic impressions, *similar* poles on opposite sides of the plate neutralize each other; *opposite* poles exalt the action; and a single pole at the edge or end on does nothing.

254. Nothing can more completely show the thorough inde-pendence of the effects obtained with the metals by Arago, and those due to ordinary magnetic forces ; and henceforth, there-fore, the application of two poles to various moving substances will, if they appear at all magnetically affected, afford a proof of the nature of that affection.  If opposite poles produce a greater effect than one pole, the result will be due to electric currents.  If similar poles produce more effect than one, then the power is *not* electrical ; it is not like that active in the metals and carbon when they are moving, and in most cases will probably be found to be not even magnetical, but the re-sult of irregular causes not anticipated and consequently not guarded against.

255. The result of these investigations tends to show that there are really but very few bodies that are magnetic in the manner of iron.  I have often sought for indications of this power in the common metals and other substances ; and once in illustration of Arago's objection (82.), and in hopes of ascer-taining the existence of currents in metals by the momentary approach of a magnet, suspended a disc of copper by a single fibre of silk in an excellent vacuum, and approximated power-ful magnets on the outside of the jar, making them approach and recede in unison with a pendulum that vibrated as the disc would do : but no motion could be obtained ; not merely, no in-dication of ordinary magnetic powers, but none of *any electric current* occasioned in the metal by the approximation and re-cession of the magnet.  I therefore venture to arrange sub-stances in three classes as regards their relation to magnets ; first, those which are affected when at rest, like iron, nickel, &c., being such as possess ordinary magnetic properties ; then, those which are affected when in motion, being conductors of electricity in which are produced electric currents by the in-ductive force of the magnet ; and, lastly, those which are per-fectly indifferent to the magnet, whether at rest or in motion.

256. Although it will require further research, and probably close investigation, both experimental and mathematical, before the exact mode of action between a magnet and metal moving relatively to each other is ascertained ; yet many of the results appear sufficiently clear and simple to allow of expression in a

somewhat general manner.—If a terminated wire move so as to cut a magnetic curve, a power is called into action which tends to urge an electric current through it ; but this current cannot be brought into existence unless provision be made at the ends of the wire for its discharge and renewal.

257. If a second wire move in the same direction as the first, the same power is exerted upon it, and it is therefore unable to alter the condition of the first : for there appear to be no natural differences among substances when connected in a series, by which, when moving under the same circumstances relative to the magnet, one tends to produce a more powerful electric current in the whole circuit than another (201. 214.).

258. But if the second wire move with a different velocity, or in some other direction, then variations in the force exerted take place ; and if connected at their extremities, an electric current passes through them.

259. Taking, then, a mass of metal or an endless wire, and referring to the pole of the magnet as a centre of action, (which though perhaps not strictly correct may be allowed for facility of expression, at present,) if all parts move in the same direction, and with the same angular velocity, and through magnetic curves of constant intensity, then no electric currents are produced. This point is easily observed with masses subject to the earth's magnetism, and may be proved with regard to small magnets ; by rotating them, and leaving the metallic arrangements stationary, no current is produced.

260. If one part of the wire or metal cut the magnetic curves, whilst the other is stationary, then currents are produced. All the results obtained with the galvanometer are more or less of this nature, the galvanometer extremity being the fixed part. Even those with the wire, galvanometer, and earth (170.), may be considered so without any error in the result.

261. If the motion of the metal be in the same direction, but the angular velocity of its parts relative to the pole of the magnet different, then currents are produced. This is the case in Arago's experiment, and also in the wire subject to the earth's induction (172.), when it was moved from west to east.

262. If the magnet moves not directly to or from the arrangement, but laterally, then the case is similar to the last.

263. If different parts move in opposite directions across

the magnetic curves, then the effect is a maximum for equal velocities.

264. All these in fact are variations of one simple condition, namely, that all parts of the mass shall not move in the same direction across the curves, and with the same angular velocity. But they are forms of expression which, being retained in the mind, I have found useful when comparing the consistency of particular phenomena with general results.

*Royal Institution,*
  *December* 21, 1831.

## THIRD SERIES.

§ 7. *Identity of Electricities derived from different sources.*
§ 8. *Relation by measure of common and voltaic Electricity.*

[Read January 10th and 17th, 1833.]

§ 7. *Identity of Electricities derived from different sources.*

265. THE progress of the electrical researches which I have had the honour to present to the Royal Society, brought me to a point at which it was essential for the further prosecution of my inquiries that no doubt should remain of the identity or distinction of electricities excited by different means. It is perfectly true that Cavendish *, Wollaston †, Colladon ‡, and others, have in succession removed some of the greatest objections to the acknowledgement of the identity of common, animal, and voltaic electricity, and I believe that most philosophers consider these electricities as really the same. But on the other hand it is also true, that the accuracy of Wollaston's experiments have been denied §; and also that one of them, which really is no proper proof of chemical decomposition by common electricity (309. 327.), has been that selected by several experimenters as the test of chemical action (336. 346.). It is a fact, too, than many philosophers are still drawing distinctions between the electricities of different sources; or at least doubting whether their identity is proved. Sir Humphry Davy, for instance, in his paper on the Torpedo ‖, thought it

---

* Phil. Trans. 1776, p. 196.     † Ibid. 1801, p. 434.
‡ Annales de Chimie, 1826, p. 62, &c.    § Phil. Trans. 1832, p. 282, note.
‖ Phil. Trans. 1829, p. 17. " Common electricity is excited upon non-conductors, and is readily carried off by conductors and imperfect conductors. Voltaic electricity is excited upon combinations of perfect and imperfect conductors, and is only transmitted by perfect conductors or imperfect conductors of the best kind. Magnetism, if it be a form of electricity, belongs only to perfect conductors; and, in its modifications, to a peculiar class of them[1]. Animal electricity resides only in the imperfect conductors forming the organs of living animals, &c."

---

[1] Dr. Ritchie has shown this is not the case, Phil. Trans. 1832, p. 294.

probable that animal electricity would be found of a peculiar kind; and referring to it, to common electricity, voltaic electricity and magnetism, has said, " Distinctions might be established in pursuing the various modifications or properties of electricity in these different forms, &c." Indeed I need only refer to the last volume of the Philosophical Transactions to show that the question is by no means considered as settled *.

266. Notwithstanding, therefore, the general impression of the identity of electricities, it is evident that the proofs have not been sufficiently clear and distinct to obtain the assent of all those who were competent to consider the subject; and the question seemed to me very much in the condition of that which Sir H. Davy solved so beautifully,—namely, whether voltaic electricity in all cases merely eliminated, or did not in some actually produce, the acid and alkali found after its action upon water. The same necessity that urged him to decide the doubtful point, which interfered with the extension of his views, and destroyed the strictness of his reasoning, has obliged me to ascertain the identity or difference of common and voltaic electricity. I have satisfied myself that they are identical, and I hope the experiments which I have to offer, and the proofs flowing from them, will be found worthy the attention of the Royal Society.

* Phil. Trans. 1832, p. 259. Dr. Davy, in making experiments on the torpedo, obtains effects the same as those produced by common and voltaic electricity, and says that in its magnetic and chemical power it does not seem to be essentially peculiar,—p. 274; but then he says, p. 275, there are other points of difference ; and after referring to them, adds, "How are these differences to be explained ? Do they admit of explanation similar to that advanced by Mr. Cavendish in his theory of the torpedo ; or may we suppose, according to the analogy of the solar ray, that the electrical power, whether excited by the common machine, or by the voltaic battery, or by the torpedo, is not a simple power, but a combination of powers, which may occur variously associated, and produce all the varieties of electricity with which we are acquainted ?"
At p. 279 of the same volume of Transactions is Dr. Ritchie's paper, from which the following are extracts: "Common electricity is diffused over the surface of the metal;—voltaic electricity exists within the metal. Free electricity is conducted over the surface of the thinnest gold leaf as effectually as over a mass of metal having the same surface ;—voltaic electricity requires thickness of metal for its conduction," p. 280 : and again, " The supposed analogy between common and voltaic electricity, which was so eagerly traced after the invention of the pile, completely fails in this case, which was thought to afford the most striking resemblance." p. 291.

267. The various phenomena exhibited by electricity may, for the purpose of comparison, be arranged under two heads ; namely, those connected with electricity of tension, and those belonging to electricity in motion. This distinction is taken at present not as philosophical, but merely as convenient. The effect of electricity of tension, at rest, is either attraction or repulsion at sensible distances. The effects of electricity in motion or electrical currents may be considered as 1st, Evolution of heat ; 2nd, Magnetism ; 3rd, Chemical decomposition ; 4th, Physiological phenomena ; 5th, Spark. It will be my object to compare electricities from different sources, and especially common and voltaic electricities, by their power of producing these effects.

## I. *Voltaic Electricity.*

268. *Tension.*—When a voltaic battery of 100 pairs of plates has its extremities examined by the ordinary electrometer, it is well known that they are found positive and negative, the gold leaves at the same extremity repelling each other, the gold leaves at different extremities attracting each other, even when half an inch or more of air intervenes.

269. That ordinary electricity is discharged by points with facility through air; that it is readily transmitted through highly rarefied air ; and also through heated air, as for instance a flame; is due to its high tension. I sought, therefore, for similar effects in the discharge of voltaic electricity, using as a test of the passage of the electricity either the galvanometer or chemical action produced by the arrangement hereafter to be described (312. 316.).

270. The voltaic battery I had at my disposal consisted of 140 pairs of plates four inches square, with double coppers. It was insulated throughout, and diverged a gold leaf electrometer about one third of an inch. On endeavouring to discharge this battery by delicate points very nicely arranged and approximated, either in the air or in an exhausted receiver, I could obtain no indications of a current, either by magnetic or chemical action. In this, however, was found no point of discordance between voltaic and common electricity; for when a Leyden battery (291.) was charged so as to deflect the gold leaf electrometer to the same degree, the points were found equally unable to discharge it with such effect as to produce either magnetic or chemical action. This was not because

common electricity could not produce both these effects (307. 310.), but because when of such low intensity the quantity required to make the effects visible (being enormously great (371. 375),) could not be transmitted in any reasonable time.  In conjunction with the other proofs of identity hereafter to be given, these effects of points also prove identity instead of difference between voltaic and common electricity.

271. As heated air discharges common electricity with far greater facility than points, I hoped that voltaic electricity might in this way also be discharged.  An apparatus was therefore constructed (Plate III. fig. 46.), in which A B is an insulated glass rod upon which two copper wires, C, D, are fixed firmly ; to these wires are soldered two pieces of fine platina wire, the ends of which are brought very close to each other at $e$, but without touching ; the copper wire C was connected with the positive pole of a voltaic battery, and the wire D with a decomposing apparatus (312. 316.), from which the communication was completed to the negative pole of the battery.  In these experiments only two troughs, or twenty pairs of plates, were used.

272. Whilst in the state described, no decomposition took place at the point $a$, but when the side of a spirit-lamp flame was applied to the two platina extremities at $e$, so as to make them bright red-hot, decomposition occurred ; iodine soon appeared at the point $a$, and the transference of electricity through the heated air was established.  On raising the temperature of the points $e$ by a blowpipe, the discharge was rendered still more free, and decomposition took place instantly.  On removing the source of heat, the current immediately ceased.  On putting the ends of the wires very close by the side of and parallel to each other, but not touching, the effects were perhaps more readily obtained than before.  On using a larger voltaic battery (270.), they were also more freely obtained.

273. On removing the decomposing apparatus and interposing a galvanometer instead, heating the points $e$ as the needle would swing one way, and removing the heat during the time of its return (302.), feeble deflections were soon obtained : thus also proving the current through heated air ; but the instrument used was not so sensible under the circumstances as chemical action.

274. These effects, not hitherto known or expected under this form, are only cases of the discharge which takes place through air between the charcoal terminations of the poles of a powerful battery, when they are gradually separated after contact. Then the passage is through heated air exactly as with common electricity, and Sir H. Davy has recorded that with the original battery of the Royal Institution this discharge passed through a space of at least four inches *. In the exhausted receiver the electricity would *strike* through nearly half an inch of space, and the combined effects of rarefaction and heat was such upon the inclosed air as to enable it to conduct the electricity through a space of six or seven inches.

275. The instantaneous charge of a Leyden battery by the poles of a voltaic apparatus is another proof of the tension, and also the quantity of electricity evolved by the latter. Sir H. Davy says †, " When the two conductors from the ends of the combination were connected with a Leyden battery, one with the internal, the other with the external coating, the battery instantly became charged ; and on removing the wires and making the proper connexions, either a shock or a *spark* could be perceived : and the least possible time of contact was sufficient to renew the charge to its full intensity."

276. *In motion;* i. *Evolution of Heat.*—The evolution of heat in wires and fluids by the voltaic current is matter of general notoriety.

277. ii. *Magnetism.*—No fact is better known to philosophers than the power of the voltaic current to deflect the magnetic needle, and to make magnets according to *certain laws* ; and no effect can be more distinctive of an electrical current.

278. iii. *Chemical decomposition.*—The chemical powers of the voltaic current, and their subjection to *certain laws,* are also perfectly well known.

279. iv. *Physiological effects.*—The power of the voltaic current, when strong, to shock and convulse the whole animal system, and when weak to affect the tongue and the eyes, is very characteristic.

280. v. *Spark.*—The brilliant star of light produced by the

* Elements of Chemical Philosophy, p. 153.    † Ibid. p. 154.

discharge of a voltaic battery is known to all as the most beautiful light that man can produce by art.

———————

281. That these effects may be almost infinitely varied, some being exalted whilst others are diminished, is universally acknowledged; and yet without any doubt of the identity of character of the voltaic currents thus made to differ in their effect. The beautiful explication of these variations afforded by Cavendish's theory of quantity and intensity requires no support at present, as it is not supposed to be doubted.

282. In consequence of the comparisons that will hereafter arise between wires carrying voltaic and ordinary electricities, and also because of certain views of the condition of a wire or any other conducting substance connecting the poles of a voltaic apparatus, it will be necessary to give some definite expression of what is called the voltaic current, in contradistinction to any supposed peculiar state of arrangement, not progressive, which the wire or the electricity within it may be supposed to assume. If two voltaic troughs P N, P′ N′, fig. 42, be symmetrically arranged and insulated, and the ends N P′ connected by a wire, over which a magnetic needle is suspended, the wire will exert no effect over the needle; but immediately that the ends P N′ are connected by another wire, the needle will be deflected, and will remain so as long as the circuit is complete. Now if the troughs merely act by causing a peculiar arrangement in the wire either of its particles or its electricity, that arrangement constituting its electrical and magnetic state, then the wire N P′ should be in a similar state of arrangement *before* P and N′ were connected, to what it is afterwards, and should have deflected the needle, although less powerfully, perhaps to one half the extent which would result when the communication is complete throughout. But if the magnetic effects depend upon a current, then it is evident why they could not be produced in *any* degree before the circuit was complete; because prior to that no current could exist.

283. By *current*, I mean anything progressive, whether it be a fluid of electricity, or two fluids moving in opposite directions, or merely vibrations, or, speaking still more generally, progressive forces. By *arrangement*, I understand a local ad-

justment of particles, or fluids, or forces, not progressive. Many other reasons might be urged in support of the view of a *current* rather than an *arrangement*, but I am anxious to avoid stating unnecessarily what will occur to others at the moment.

## II. *Ordinary Electricity.*

284. By ordinary electricity I understand that which can be obtained from the common machine, or from the atmosphere, or by pressure, or cleavage of crystals, or by a multitude of other operations; its distinctive character being that of great intensity, and the exertion of attractive and repulsive powers, not merely at sensible but at considerable distances.

285. *Tension.* The attractions and repulsions at sensible distances, caused by ordinary electricity, are well known to be so powerful in certain cases, as to surpass, almost infinitely, the similar phenomena produced by electricity, otherwise excited. But still those attractions and repulsions are exactly of the same nature as those already referred to under the head *Tension, Voltaic electricity* (268.); and the difference in degree between them is not greater than often occurs between cases of ordinary electricity only. I think it will be unnecessary to enter minutely into the proofs of the identity of this character in the two instances. They are abundant; are generally admitted as good; and lie upon the surface of the subject : and whenever in other parts of the comparison I am about to draw, a similar case occurs, I shall content myself with a mere announcement of the similarity, enlarging only upon those parts where the great question of distinction or identity still exists.

286. The discharge of common electricity through heated air is a well-known fact. The parallel case of voltaic electricity has already been described (272, &c.).

287. *In motion.* i. *Evolution of heat.*—The heating power of common electricity, when passed through wires or other substances, is perfectly well known. The accordance between it and voltaic electricity is in this respect complete. Mr. Harris has constructed and described* a very beautiful and sensible

---

* Philosophical Transactions, 1827, p. 18. Edinburgh Transactions, 1831 Harris on a New Electrometer, &c. &c.

instrument on this principle, in which the heat produced in a wire by the discharge of a small portion of common electricity is readily shown, and to which I shall have occasion to refer for experimental proof in a future part of this paper (344.).

288. ii. *Magnetism.*—Voltaic electricity has most extraordinary and exalted magnetic powers. If common electricity be identical with it, it ought to have the same powers. In rendering needles or bars magnetic, it is found to agree with voltaic electricity, and the *direction* of the magnetism, in both cases, is the same; but in deflecting the magnetic needle, common electricity has been found deficient, so that sometimes its power has been denied altogether, and at other times distinc-tions have been hypothetically assumed for the purpose of avoiding the difficulty*.

289. M. Colladon, of Geneva, considered that the difference might be due to the use of insufficient quantities of common electricity in all the experiments before made on this head; and in a memoir read to the Academie des Sciences in 1826†, describes experiments, in which, by the use of a battery, points, and a delicate galvanometer, he succeeded in obtaining deflections, and thus establishing identity in that respect.    MM. Arago, Ampère, and Savary, are mentioned in the paper as having witnessed a successful repetition of the experiments. But as no other one has come forward in confirmation, MM. Arago, Ampère, and Savary, not having themselves published (that I am aware of) their admission of the results, and as some have not been able to obtain them, M. Colladon's conclusions have been occasionally doubted or denied; and an important point with me was to establish their accuracy, or remove them entirely from the body of received experimental research.    I am happy to say that my results fully confirm those by M. Colladon, and I should have had no occasion to describe them, but that they are essential as proofs of the accuracy of the final and general conclusions I am enabled to draw respecting the magnetic and chemical action of electricity, (360. 366. 367. 377. &c.).

290. The plate electrical machine I have used is fifty inches

* Demonferrand's Manuel d'Electricité dynamique, p. 121.
† Annales de Chimie, xxxiii. p. 62.

in diameter; it has two sets of rubbers; its prime conductor consists of two brass cylinders connected by a third, the whole length being twelve feet, and the surface in contact with air about 1422 square inches. When in good excitation, one revolution of the plate will give ten or twelve sparks from the conductors, each an inch in length. Sparks or flashes from ten to fourteen inches in length may easily be drawn from the conductors. Each turn of the machine, when worked moderately, occupies about ⅘ths of a second.

291. The electric battery consisted of fifteen equal jars. They are coated eight inches upwards from the bottom, and are twenty-three inches in circumference, so that each contains one hundred and eighty-four square inches of glass, coated on both sides; this is independent of the bottoms, which are of thicker glass, and contain each about fifty square inches.

292. A good *discharging train* was arranged by connecting metallically a sufficiently thick wire with the metallic gas pipes of the house, with the metallic gas pipes belonging to the public gas works of London; and also with the metallic water pipes of London. It was so effectual in its office as to carry off instantaneously electricity of the feeblest tension, even that of a single voltaic trough, and was essential to many of the experiments.

293. The galvanometer was one or the other of those formerly described (87. 205.), but the glass jar covering it and supporting the needle was coated inside and outside with tinfoil, and the upper part (left uncoated, that the motions of the needle might be examined,) was covered with a frame of wirework, having numerous sharp points projecting from it. When this frame and the two coatings were connected with the discharging train (292.), an insulated point or ball, connected with the machine when most active, might be brought within an inch of any part of the galvanometer, yet without affecting the needle within by ordinary electrical attraction or repulsion.

294. In connexion with these precautions it may be necessary to state that the needle of the galvanometer is very liable to have its magnetic power deranged, diminished, or even inverted by the passage of a shock through the instrument. If the needle be at all oblique, in the wrong direction, to the coils

of the galvanometer when the shock passes, effects of this kind are sure to happen.

295. It was to the retarding power of bad conductors, with the intention of diminishing its *intensity* without altering its *quantity,* that I first looked with the hope of being able to make common electricity assume more of the characters and power of voltaic electricity, than it is usually supposed to have.

296. The coating and armour of the galvanometer were first connected with the discharging train (292.) ; the end B (87.) of the galvanometer wire was connected with the outside coating of the battery, and then both these with the discharging train ; the end A of the galvanometer wire was connected with a discharging rod by a wet thread four feet long; and, finally, when the battery (291.) had been positively charged by about forty turns of the machine, it was discharged by the rod and the thread through the galvanometer.    The needle immediately moved.

297. During the time that the needle completed its vibration in the first direction and returned, the machine was worked, and the battery recharged ; and when the needle in vibrating resumed its first direction, the discharge was again made through the galvanometer.    By repeating this action a few times, the vibrations soon extended to above 40° on each side of the line of rest.

298. This effect could be obtained at pleasure.    Nor was it varied, apparently, either in direction or degree, by using a short thick string, or even four short thick strings in place of the long fine thread.    With a more delicate galvanometer, an excellent swing of the needle could be obtained by one discharge of the battery.

299. On reversing the galvanometer communications so as to pass the discharge through from B to A, the needle was equally well deflected, but in the opposite direction.

300. The deflections were in the same direction as if a voltaic current had been passed through the galvanometer, *i. e.* the positively charged surface of the electric battery coincided with the positive end of the voltaic apparatus (268.), and the negative surface of the former with the negative end of the latter.

301. The battery was then thrown out of use, and the communications so arranged that the current could be passed from the prime conductor, by the discharging rod held against it, through the wet string, through the galvanometer coil, and into the discharging train (292.), by which it was finally dispersed. This current could be stopped at any moment by removing the discharging rod, and either stopping the machine or connecting the prime conductor by another rod with the discharging train; and could be as instantly renewed. The needle was so adjusted, that whilst vibrating in moderate and small arcs, it required time equal to twenty-five beats of a watch to pass in one direction through the arc, and of course an equal time to pass in the other direction.

302. Thus arranged, and the needle being stationary, the current, direct from the machine, was sent through the galvanometer for twenty-five beats, then interrupted for other twenty-five beats, renewed for twenty-five beats more, again interrupted for an equal time, and so on continually. The needle soon began to vibrate visibly, and after several alternations of this kind the vibration increased to 40° or more.

303. On changing the direction of the current through the galvanometer, the direction of the deflection of the needle was also changed. In all cases the motion of the needle was in direction the same as that caused either by the use of the electric battery or a voltaic trough (300.).

304. I now rejected the wet string, and substituted a copper wire, so that the electricity of the machine passed at once into wires communicating directly with the discharging train, the galvanometer coil being one of the wires used for the discharge. The effects were exactly those obtained above (302.).

305. Instead of passing the electricity through the system, by bringing the discharging rod at the end of it into contact with the conductor, four points were fixed on to the rod; when the current was to pass they were held about twelve inches from the conductor, and when it was not to pass, they were turned away. Then operating as before (302.), except with this variation, the needle was soon powerfully deflected, and in perfect consistency with the former results. Points afforded the means by which Colladon, in all cases, made his discharges.

306. Finally, I passed the electricity first through an ex-

hausted receiver, so as to make it there resemble the aurora borealis, and then through the galvanometer to the earth; and it was found still effective in deflecting the needle, and apparently with the same force as before.

307. From all these experiments, it appears that a current of common electricity, whether transmitted through water or metal, or rarefied air, or by means of points in common air, is still able to deflect the needle; the only requisite being, apparently, to allow time for its action: that it is, in fact, just as magnetic in every respect as a voltaic current, and that in this character therefore no distinction exists.

308. Imperfect conductors, as water, brine, acids, &c. &c. will be found far more convenient for exhibiting these effects than other modes of discharge, as by points or balls; for the former convert at once the charge of a powerful battery into a feeble spark discharge, or rather continuous current, and involve little or no risk of deranging the magnetism of the needles (294.).

309. iii. *Chemical decomposition.*—The chemical action of voltaic electricity is characteristic of that agent, but not more characteristic than are the *laws* under which the bodies evolved by decomposition arrange themselves at the poles. Dr. Wollaston showed* that common electricity resembled it in these effects, and "that they are both essentially the same"; but he mingled with his proofs an experiment having a resemblance, and nothing more, to a case of voltaic decomposition, which however he himself partly distinguished; and this has been more frequently referred to by some, on the one hand, to prove the occurrence of electro-chemical decomposition, like that of the pile, and by others to throw doubt upon the whole paper, than the more numerous and decisive experiments which he has detailed.

310. I take the liberty of describing briefly my results, and of thus adding my testimony to that of Dr. Wollaston on the identity of voltaic and common electricity as to chemical action, not only that I may facilitate the repetition of the experiments, but also lead to some new consequences respecting electro-chemical decomposition (376. 377.).

311. I first repeated Wollaston's fourth experiment†, in

* Philosophical Transactions, 1801, p. 427, 434.    † Ibid. 1801, p. 429.

which the ends of coated silver wires are immersed in a drop
of sulphate of copper. By passing the electricity of the machine through such an arrangement, that end in the drop which
received the electricity became coated with metallic copper.
One hundred turns of the machine produced an evident effect;
two hundred turns a very sensible one. The decomposing action was however very feeble. Very little copper was precipitated, and no sensible trace of silver from the other pole appeared in the solution.

312. A much more convenient and effectual arrangement for
chemical decompositions by common electricity, is the following.
Upon a glass plate, fig. 43, placed over, but raised above a
piece of white paper, so that shadows may not interfere, put
two pieces of tinfoil $a$, $b$; connect one of these by an insulated
wire $c$, or wire and string (301.), with the machine, and the other
$g$, with the discharging train (292.) or the negative conductor;
provide two pieces of fine platina wire, bent as in fig. 44, so
that the part $d$, $f$ shall be nearly upright, whilst the whole is
resting on the three bearing points $p$, $e$, $f$; place these as in
fig. 43; the points $p$, $n$ then become the decomposing poles. In
this way surfaces of contact, as minute as possible, can be obtained at pleasure, and the connexion can be broken or renewed
in a moment, and the substances acted upon examined with
the utmost facility.

313. A coarse line was made on the glass with solution of
sulphate of copper, and the terminations $p$ and $n$ put into it;
the foil $a$ was connected with the positive conductor of the machine by wire and wet string, so that no sparks passed: twenty
turns of the machine caused the precipitation of so much copper
on the end $n$, that it looked like copper wire; no apparent
change took place at $p$.

314. A mixture of equal parts of muriatic acid and water
was rendered deep blue by sulphate of indigo, and a large drop
put on the glass, fig. 43, so that $p$ and $n$ were immersed at opposite sides: a single turn of the machine showed bleaching
effects round $p$, from evolved chlorine. After twenty revolutions no effect of the kind was visible at $n$, but so much chlorine
had been set free at $p$, that when the drop was stirred the
whole became colourless.

315. A drop of solution of iodide of potassium mingled with

starch was put into the same position at $p$ and $n$; on turning the machine, iodine was evolved at $p$, but not at $n$.

316. A still further improvement in this form of apparatus consists in wetting a piece of filtering paper in the solution to be experimented on, and placing that under the points $p$ and $n$, on the glass: the paper retains the substance evolved at the point of evolution, by its whiteness renders any change of colour visible, and allows of the point of contact between it and the decomposing wires being contracted to the utmost degree. A piece of paper moistened in the solution of iodide of potassium and starch, or of the iodide alone, with certain precautions (322.), is a most admirable test of electro-chemical action; and when thus placed and acted upon by the electric current, will show iodide evolved at $p$ by only half a turn of the machine. With these adjustments and the use of iodide of potassium on paper, chemical action is sometimes a more delicate test of electrical currents than the galvanometer (273.). Such cases occur when the bodies traversed by the current are bad conductors, or when the quantity of electricity evolved or transmitted in a given time is very small.

317. A piece of litmus paper moistened in solution of common salt of sulphate of soda, was quickly reddened at $p$. A similar piece moistened in muriatic acid was very soon bleached at $p$. No effects of a similar kind took place at $n$.

318. A piece of turmeric paper moistened in solution of sulphate of soda was reddened at $n$ by two or three turns of the machine, and in twenty or thirty turns plenty of alkali was there evolved. On turning the paper round, so that the spot came under $p$, and then working the machine, the alkali soon disappeared, the place became yellow, and a brown alkaline spot appeared in the new part under $n$.

319. On combining a piece of litmus with a piece of turmeric paper, wetting both with solution of sulphate of soda, and putting the paper on the glass, so that $p$ was on the litmus and $n$ on the turmeric, a very few turns of the machine sufficed to show the evolution of acid at the former and alkali at the latter, exactly in the manner effected by a volta-electric current.

320. All these decompositions took place equally well, whether the electricity passed from the machine to the foil $a$, through water, or through wire only; by *contact* with the con-

ductor, or by *sparks* there; provided the sparks were not so large as to cause the electricity to pass in sparks from *p* to *n*, or towards *n*; and I have seen no reason to believe that in cases of true electro-chemical decomposition by the machine, the electricity passed in sparks from the conductor, or at any part of the current, is able to do more, because of its tension, than that which is made to pass merely as a regular current.

321. Finally, the experiment was extended into the following form, supplying in this case the fullest analogy between common and voltaic electricity. Three compound pieces of litmus and turmeric paper (319.) were moistened in solution of sulphate of soda, and arranged on a plate of glass with platina wires, as in fig. 45. The wire *m* was connected with the prime conductor of the machine, the wire *t* with the discharging train, and the wires *r* and *s* entered into the course of the electrical current by means of the pieces of moistened paper; they were so bent as to rest each on three points, *n*, *r*, *p*; *n*, *s*, *p*, the points *r* and *s* being supported by the glass, and the others by the papers: the three terminations *p*, *p*, *p* rested on the litmus, and the other three *n*, *n*, *n* on the turmeric paper. On working the machine for a short time only, acid was evolved at *all* the poles or terminations *p*, *p*, *p*, by which the electricity entered the solution, and alkali at the other poles, *n*, *n*, *n*, by which the electricity left the solution.

322. In all experiments of electro-chemical decomposition by the common machine and moistened papers (316.), it is necessary to be aware of and to avoid the following important source of error. If a spark passes over moistened litmus and turmeric paper, the litmus paper (provided it be delicate and not too alkaline,) is reddened by it; and if several sparks are passed, it becomes powerfully reddened. If the electricity pass a little way from the wire over the surface of the moistened paper, before it finds mass and moisture enough to conduct it, then the reddening extends as far as the ramifications. If similar ramifications occur at the termination *n*, on the turmeric paper, they *prevent* the occurrence of the red spot due to the alkali, which would otherwise collect there: sparks or ramifications from the points *n* will also redden litmus paper. If paper moistened by a solution of iodide of potassium (which is an admirably delicate test of electro-chemical action,) be exposed to

the sparks or ramifications, or even a feeble stream of electricity through the air from either the point *p* or *n*, iodine will be immediately evolved.

323. These effects must not be confounded with those due to the true electro-chemical powers of common electricity, and must be carefully avoided when the latter are to be observed. No sparks should be passed, therefore, in any part of the current, nor any increase of intensity allowed, by which the electricity may be induced to pass between the platina wires and the moistened papers, otherwise than by conduction; for if it burst through the air, the effect referred to above (322.) ensues.

324. The effect itself is due to the formation of nitric acid by the combination of the oxygen and nitrogen of the air, and is, in fact, only a delicate repetition of Cavendish's beautiful experiment. The acid so formed, though small in quantity, is in a high state of concentration as to water, and produces the consequent effects of reddening the litmus paper; or preventing the exhibition of alkali on the turmeric paper; or, by acting on the iodide of potassium, evolving iodine.

325. By moistening a very small slip of litmus paper in solution of caustic potassa, and then passing the electric spark over its length in the air, I gradually neutralized the alkali, and ultimately rendered the paper red; on drying it, I found that nitrate of potassa had resulted from the operation, and that the paper had become touch paper.

326. Either litmus paper or white paper, moistened in a strong solution of iodide of potassium, offers therefore a very simple, beautiful, and ready means of illustrating Cavendish's experiment of the formation of nitric acid from the atmosphere.

327. I have already had occasion to refer to an experiment (265. 309.) made by Dr. Wollaston, which is insisted upon too much, both by those who oppose and those who agree with the accuracy of his views respecting the identity of voltaic and ordinary electricity. By covering fine wires with glass or other insulating substances, and then removing only so much matter as to expose the point, or a section of the wires, and by passing electricity through two such wires, the guarded points of which were immersed in water, Wollaston found that the water could be decomposed even by the current from the machine, without sparks, and that two streams of gas arose from the points,

exactly resembling, in appearance, those produced by voltaic electricity, and, like the latter, giving a mixture of oxygen and hydrogen gases. But Dr. Wollaston himself points out that the effect is different from that of the voltaic pile, inasmuch as both oxygen and hydrogen are evolved from *each* pole ; he calls it " a very close *imitation* of the galvanic phenomena," but adds that " in fact the resemblance is not complete," and does not trust to it to establish the principles correctly laid down in his paper.

328. This experiment is neither more nor less than a re- petition, in a refined manner, of that made by Dr. Pearson in 1797*, and previously by MM. Paets Van Troostwyk and Deiman in 1789 or earlier. That the experiment should never be quoted as proving true electro-chemical decomposition, is sufficiently evident from the circumstance, that the *law* which regulates the transference and final place of the evolved bodies (278. 309.) has no influence here. The water is decomposed at both poles independently of each other, and the oxygen and hydrogen evolved at the wires are the elements of the water existing the instant before in those places. That the poles, or rather points, have no mutual decomposing dependence, may be shown by substituting a wire, or the finger, for one of them, a change which does not at all interfere with the other, though it stops all action at the changed pole. This fact may be ob- served by turning the machine for some time ; for though bub- bles will rise from the point left unaltered, in quantity sufficient to cover entirely the wire used for the other communication, if they could be applied to it, yet not a single bubble will appear on that wire.

329. When electro-chemical decomposition takes place, there is great reason to believe that the *quantity* of matter decom- posed is not proportionate to the intensity, but to the quan- tity of electricity passed (320.). Of this I shall be able to offer some proofs in a future part of this paper (375. 377.). But in the experiment under consideration, this is not the case. If, with a constant pair of points, the electricity be passed from the machine in sparks, a certain proportion of gas is evolved ; but if the sparks be rendered shorter, less gas is evolved ; and if no sparks be passed, there is scarcely a sensible portion of

* Nicholson's Journal, 4to. vol. 1. pp. 241, 299, 349.

gases set free.  On substituting solution of sulphate of soda for water, scarcely a sensible quantity of gas could be procured even with powerful sparks, and nearly none with the mere current ; yet the quantity of electricity in a given time was the same in all these cases.

330. I do not intend to deny that with such an apparatus common electricity can decompose water in a manner analogous to that of the voltaic pile ; I believe at present that it can.  But when what I consider the true effect only was obtained, the quantity of gas given off was so small that I could not ascertain whether it was, as it ought to be, oxygen at one wire and hydrogen at the other.  Of the two streams one seemed more copious than the other, and on turning the apparatus round, still the same side in relation to the machine gave the largest stream.  On substituting solution of sulphate of soda for pure water (329.), these minute streams were still observed.  But the quantities were so small, that on working the machine for half an hour I could not obtain at either pole a bubble of gas larger than a small grain of sand.  If the conclusion which I have drawn (377.) relating to the amount of chemical action be correct, this ought to be the case.

331. I have been the more anxious to assign the true value of this experiment as a test of electro-chemical action, because I shall have occasion to refer to it in cases of supposed chemical action by magneto-electric and other electric currents (336. 346.) and elsewhere.  But, independent of it, there cannot be now a doubt that Dr. Wollaston was right in his general conclusion ; and that voltaic and common electricity have powers of chemical decomposition, alike in their nature, and governed by the same law of arrangement.

332. iv. *Physiological effects.*—The power of the common electric current to shock and convulse the animal system, and when weak to affect the tongue and the eyes, may be considered as the same with the similar power of voltaic electricity, account being taken of the intensity of the one electricity and duration of the other.  When a wet thread was interposed in the course of the current of common electricity from the battery (291.) charged by eight or ten* revolutions of the machine in good action (290.) and the discharge made by platina spatulas through the tongue or the gums, the effect upon the tongue

* Or even from thirty to forty.

and eyes was exactly that of a momentary feeble voltaic circuit.

333. v. *Spark.*—The beautiful flash of light attending the discharge of common electricity is well known. It rivals in brilliancy, if it does not even very much surpass, the light from the discharge of voltaic electricity; but it endures for an instant only, and is attended by a sharp noise like that of a small explosion. Still no difficulty can arise in recognizing it to be the same spark as that from the voltaic battery, especially under certain circumstances. The eye cannot distinguish the difference between a voltaic and a common electricity spark, if they be taken between amalgamated surfaces of metal, at intervals only, and through the same distance of air.

334. When the Leyden battery (291.) was discharged through a wet string placed in some part of the circuit away from the place where the spark was to pass, the spark was yellowish, flamy, having a duration sensibly longer than if the water had not been interposed, was about three-fourths of an inch in length, was accompanied by little or no noise, and whilst losing part of its usual character had approximated in some degree to the voltaic spark. When the electricity retarded by water was discharged between pieces of charcoal, it was exceedingly luminous and bright upon both surfaces of the charcoal, resembling the brightness of the voltaic discharge on such surfaces. When the discharge of the unretarded electricity was taken upon charcoal, it was bright upon both the surfaces, (in that respect resembling the voltaic spark,) but the noise was loud, sharp, and ringing.

335. I have assumed, in accordance, I believe, with the opinion of every other philosopher, that atmospheric electricity is of the same nature with ordinary electricity (284.), and I might therefore refer to certain published statements of chemical effects produced by the former as proofs that the latter enjoys the power of decomposition in common with voltaic electricity. But the comparison I am drawing is far too rigorous to allow me to use these statements without being fully assured of their accuracy; yet I have no right to suppress them, because, if accurate, they establish what I am labouring to put on an undoubted foundation, and have priority to my results.

336. M. Bonijol of Geneva* is said to have constructed

* Bibliothèque Universelle, 1830, tome xlv. p. 213.

very delicate apparatus for the decomposition of water by common electricity. By connecting an insulated lightning rod with his apparatus, the decomposition of the water proceeded in a continuous and rapid manner even when the electricity of the atmosphere was not very powerful. The apparatus is not described; but as the diameter of the wire is mentioned as very small, it appears to have been similar in construction to that of Wollaston (327.) ; and as that does not furnish a case of true polar electro-chemical decomposition (328.), this result of M. Bonijol does not prove the identity in chemical action of common and voltaic electricity.

337. At the same page of the Bibliothèque Universelle, M. Bonijol is said to have decomposed *potash,* and also chloride of silver by putting them into very narrow tubes and passing electric sparks from an ordinary machine over them. It is evident that these offer no analogy to cases of true voltaic decomposition, where the electricity only decomposes when it is *conducted* by the body acted upon, and ceases to decompose, according to its ordinary laws, when it passes in sparks. These effects are probably partly analogous to that which takes place with water in Pearson's or Wollaston's apparatus, and may be due to very high temperature acting on minute portions of matter; or they may be connected with the results in air (322.). As nitrogen can combine directly with oxygen under the influence of the electric spark (324.), it is not impossible that it should even take it from the potassium of the potash, especially as there would be plenty of potassa in contact with the acting particles to combine with the nitric acid formed. However distinct all these actions may be from true polar electro-chemical decompositions, they are still highly important, and well worthy of investigation.

338. The late Mr. Barry communicated a paper to the Royal Society* last year, so distinct in the details, that it would seem at once to prove the identity in chemical action of common and voltaic electricity; but, when examined, considerable difficulty arises in reconciling certain of the effects with the remainder. He used two tubes, each having a wire within it passing through the closed end, as is usual for voltaic decompositions. The tubes were filled with solution of sulphate of soda, coloured with syrup of violets, and connected by a portion of the same

* Philosophical Transactions, 1831, p. 165.

solution, in the ordinary manner; the wire in one tube was connected by a *gilt thread* with the string of an insulated electrical kite, and the wire in the other tube by a similar *gilt thread* with the ground. Hydrogen soon appeared in the tube connected with the kite, and oxygen in the other, and in ten minutes the liquid in the first tube was green from the alkali evolved, and that in the other red from free acid produced. The only indication of the strength or intensity of the atmospheric electricity is in the expression, " the usual shocks were felt on touching the string."

339. That the electricity in this case does not resemble that from any ordinary source of common electricity, is shown by several circumstances. Wollaston could not effect the decomposition of water by such an arrangement, and obtain the gases in *separate* vessels, using common electricity; nor have any of the numerous philosophers, who have employed such an apparatus, obtained any such decomposition, either of water or of a neutral salt, by the use of the machine. I have lately tried the large machine (290.) in full action for a quarter of an hour, during which time seven hundred revolutions were made, without producing any sensible effects, although the shocks that it would then give must have been far more powerful and numerous than could have been taken, with any chance of safety, from an electrical kite-string; and by reference to the comparison hereafter to be made (371.), it will be seen that for common electricity to have produced the effect, the quantity must have been awfully great, and apparently far more than could have been conducted to the earth by a gilt thread, and at the same time only have produced the " usual shocks."

340. That the electricity was apparently not analogous to voltaic electricity is evident, for the " usual shocks " only were produced, and nothing like the terrible sensation due to a voltaic battery, even when it has a tension so feeble as not to strike through the eighth of an inch of air.

341. It seems just possible that the air which was passing by the kite and string, being in an electrical state sufficient to produce the " usual shocks " only, could still, when the electricity was drawn off below, renew the charge, and so continue the current. The string was 1500 feet long, and contained two double threads. But when the enormous quantity which must have been thus collected is considered (371. 376.), the expla-

nation seems very doubtful.   I charged a voltaic battery of twenty pairs of plates four inches square with double coppers very strongly, insulated it, connected its positive extremity with the discharging train (292.), and its negative pole with an apparatus like that of Mr. Barry, communicating by a wire inserted three inches into the wet soil of the ground.   This battery thus arranged produced feeble decomposing effects, as nearly as I could judge answering the description Mr. Barry has given. Its intensity was, of course, far lower than the electricity of the kite string, but the supply of quantity from the discharging train was unlimited.   It gave no shocks to compare with the " usual shocks " of a kite-string.

342. Mr. Barry's experiment is a very important one to repeat and verify.   If confirmed, it will be, as far as I am aware, the first recorded case of true electro-chemical decomposition of water by common electricity, and it will supply a form of electrical current, which, both in quantity and intensity, is exactly intermediate with those of the common electrical machine and the voltaic pile.

### III.  *Magneto-Electricity.*

343. *Tension.*—The attractions and repulsions due to the tension of ordinary electricity have been well observed with that evolved by magneto-electric induction.   M. Pixii, by using an apparatus, clever in its construction and powerful in its action\*, was able to obtain great divergence of the gold leaves of an electrometer †.

344. *In motion :* i. *Evolution of Heat.*—The current produced by magneto-electric induction can heat a wire in the manner of ordinary electricity.   At the British Association of Science at Oxford, in June of the present year, I had the pleasure, in conjunction with Mr. Harris, Professor Daniell, Mr. Duncan, and others, of making an experiment, for which the great magnet in the museum, Mr. Harris's new electrometer (287.), and the magneto-electric coil described in my first paper (34.), were put in requisition.   The latter had been modified in the manner I have elsewhere described ‡, so as to produce an electric spark when its contact with the magnet was made

* Annales de Chimie, l. p. 322.                    † Ibid. li. p. 77.
‡ Phil. Mag. and Annals, 1832, vol. xi. p. 405.

or broken.   The terminations of the spiral, adjusted so as to
have their contact with each other broken when the spark was
to pass, were connected with the wire in the electrometer, and
it was found that each time the magnetic contact was made
and broken, expansion of the air within the instrument occurred, indicating an increase, at the moment, of the temperature
of the wire.

345. ii. *Magnetism.*—These currents were discovered by
their magnetic power.

346. iii. *Chemical decomposition.*—I have made many endeavours to effect chemical decomposition by magneto-electricity, but unavailingly.   In July last I received an anonymous
letter (which has since been published\*,) describing a magneto-
electric apparatus, by which the decomposition of water was
effected.   As the term " guarded points " is used, I suppose
the apparatus to have been Wollaston's (327. &c.), in which
case the results did not indicate polar electro-chemical decomposition.   Signor Botto has recently published certain results
which he has obtained†; but they are, as at present described,
inconclusive.   The apparatus he used was apparently that of
Dr. Wollaston, which gives only fallacious indications (327.
&c.).   As magneto-electricity can produce sparks, it would be
able to show the effects proper to this apparatus.   The apparatus of M. Pixii already referred to (343.) has however, in the
hands of himself‡ and M. Hachette§, given decisive chemical results, so as to complete this link in the chain of evidence.
Water was decomposed by it, and the oxygen and hydrogen
obtained in separate tubes according to the law governing
volta-electric and machine-electric decomposition.

347. iv. *Physiological effects.*—A frog was convulsed in the
earliest experiments on these currents (56.).   The sensation
upon the tongue, and the flash before the eyes, which I at first
obtained only in a feeble degree (56.), have been since exalted
by more powerful apparatus, so as to become even disagreeable.

348. v. *Spark.*—The feeble spark which I first obtained with
these currents (32.), has been varied and strengthened by Sig-

* Lond. and Edin. Phil. Mag. and Journ. 1832, vol. i.  p. 161.
† Ibid. 1832, vol. i. p. 441.                 ‡ Annales de Chimie, li. p. 77.
§ Ibid. li. p. 72.

nori Nobili and Antinori, and others, so as to leave no doubt as to its identity with the common electric spark.

## IV. *Thermo-Electricity.*

349. With regard to thermo-electricity, (that beautiful form of electricity discovered by Seebeck,) the very conditions under which it is excited are such as to give no ground for expecting that it can be raised like common electricity to any high degree of tension ; the effects, therefore, due to that state are not to be expected. The sum of evidence respecting its analogy to the electricities already described, is, I believe, as follows :— *Tension.* The attractions and repulsions due to a certain degree of tension have not been observed. *In currents*: i. *Evolution of Heat.* I am not aware that its power of raising temperature has been observed. ii. *Magnetism.* It was discovered, and is best recognised, by its magnetic powers. iii. *Chemical decomposition* has not been effected by it. iv. *Physiological effects.* Nobili has shown * that these currents are able to cause contractions in the limbs of a frog. v. *Spark.* The spark has not yet been seen.

350. Only those effects are weak or deficient which depend upon a certain high degree of intensity ; and if common electricity be reduced in that quality to a similar degree with the thermo-electricity, it can produce no effects beyond the latter.

## V. *Animal Electricity.*

351. After an examination of the experiments of Walsh †, Ingenhousz ‡, Cavendish §, Sir H. Davy‖, and Dr. Davy ¶, no doubt remains on my mind as to the identity of the electricity of the torpedo with common and voltaic electricity; and I presume that so little will remain on the minds of others as to justify my refraining from entering at length into the philosophical proofs of that identity. The doubts raised by Sir H. Davy have been removed by his brother Dr. Davy ; the results of the latter being the reverse of those of the former. At present the sum of evidence is as follows :—

* Bibliothèque Universelle, xxxvii. 15.
† Philosophical Transactions, 1773, p. 461.     ‡ Ibid. 1775, p. 1.
§ Ibid. 1776, p. 196.     ‖ Ibid. 1829, p. 15.
¶ Ibid. 1832, p. 259.

352. *Tension.*—No sensible attractions or repulsions due to tension have been observed.

353. *In motion* : i. *Evolution of Heat* ; not yet observed ; I have little or no doubt that Harris's electrometer would show it (287. 359.).

354. ii. *Magnetism.*—Perfectly distinct. According to Dr. Davy *, the current deflected the needle and made magnets under the same law, as to direction, which governs currents of ordinary and voltaic electricity.

355. iii. *Chemical decomposition.*—Also distinct; and though Dr. Davy used an apparatus of similar construction with that of Dr. Wollaston (327.), still no error in the present case is involved, for the decompositions were polar, and in their nature truly electro-chemical. By the direction of the magnet, it was found that the under surface of the fish was negative, and the upper positive; and in the chemical decompositions, silver and lead were precipitated on the wire connected with the under surface and not on the other ; and when these wires were either steel or silver, in solution of common salt, gas (hydrogen ?) rose from the negative wire, but none from the positive.

356. Another reason for the decomposition being electro-chemical is, that a Wollaston's apparatus constructed with *wires*, coated with sealing wax, would most probably not have decomposed water, even in its own peculiar way, unless the electricity had risen high enough in intensity to produce sparks in some part of the circuit ; whereas the torpedo was not able to produce sensible sparks. A third reason is, that the purer the water in Wollaston's apparatus, the more abundant is the decomposition : and I have found that a machine and wire points which succeeded perfectly well with distilled water, failed altogether when the water was rendered a good conductor by sulphate of soda, common salt, or other saline bodies. But in Dr. Davy's experiments with the torpedo, *strong* solutions of salt, nitrate of silver, and superacetate of lead were used successfully, and there is no doubt with more success than weaker ones.

357. iv. *Physiological effects.*—These are so characteristic, that by them the peculiar powers of the torpedo and gymnotus are principally recognised.

* Philosophical Transactions, 1832, p. 260.

358. v. *Spark.*—The electric spark has not yet been obtained, or at least I think not ; but perhaps I had better refer to the evidence on this point.   Humboldt, speaking of results obtained by M. Fahlberg, of Sweden, says, "This philosopher has seen an electric spark, as Walsh and Ingenhousz had done before him at London, by placing the gymnotus in the air, and interrupting the conducting chain by two gold leaves pasted upon glass, and a line distant from each other *." I cannot, however, find any record of such an observation by either Walsh or Ingenhousz, and do not know where to refer to that by M. Fahlberg.    M. Humboldt could not himself perceive any luminous effect.

Again, Sir John Leslie, in his dissertation on the progress of mathematical and physical science, prefixed to the seventh edition of the Encyclopædia Britannica, Edinb. 1830, p. 622, says, " From a healthy specimen " of the *Silurus electricus,* meaning rather the *gymnotus,* "exhibited in London, vivid sparks were drawn in a darkened room " ; but he does not say he saw them himself, nor state who did see them ; nor can I find any account of such a phenomenon ; so that the statement is doubtful †.

359. In concluding this summary of the powers of torpedinal electricity, I cannot refrain from pointing out the enormous absolute quantity of electricity which the animal must put in circulation at each effort.    It is doubtful whether any common electrical machine has as yet been able to supply electricity sufficient in a reasonable time to cause true electro-chemical decomposition of water (330. 339.), yet the current from the torpedo has done it.   The same high proportion is shown by the magnetic effects (296. 371.)    These circumstances indicate that the torpedo has power (in the way probably that Cavendish describes,) to continue the evolution for a sensible time, so that its successive discharges rather resemble those of a voltaic arrangement, intermitting in its action, than those of a Leyden apparatus, charged and discharged many times in succession.    In reality, however, there is no *philosophical difference* between these two cases.

360. The *general conclusion* which must, I think, be drawn

* Edinburgh Phil. Journal, ii. p. 249.

† Mr. Brayley, who referred me to these statements, and has extensive knowledge of recorded facts, is unacquainted with any further account relating to them.

from this collection of facts is, that *electricity, whatever may be its source, is identical in its nature.* The phenomena in the five kinds or species quoted, differ, not in their character but only in degree; and in that respect vary in proportion to the variable circumstances of *quantity* and *intensity*\* which can at pleasure be made to change in almost any one of the kinds of electricity, as much as it does between one kind and another.

Table of the experimental Effects common to the Electricities derived from different Sources †.

| | Physiological Effects. | Magnetic Deflection. | Magnets made. | Spark. | Heating Power. | True chemical Action. | Attraction and Repulsion. | Discharge by Hot Air. |
|---|---|---|---|---|---|---|---|---|
| 1. Voltaic electricity .... | × | × | × | × | × | × | × | × |
| 2. Common electricity... | × | × | × | × | × | × | × | × |
| 3. Magneto-Electricity.. | × | × | × | × | × | × | × | |
| 4. Thermo-Electricity... | × | × | + | + | + | + | | |
| 5. Animal Electricity... | × | × | × | + | + | × | | |

§ 8. *Relation by Measure of common and voltaic Electricity.*‡

361. Believing the point of identity to be satisfactorily established, I next endeavoured to obtain a common measure, or

\* The term *quantity* in electricity is perhaps sufficiently definite as to sense; the term *intensity* is more difficult to define strictly. I am using the terms in their ordinary and accepted meaning.

† Many of the spaces in this table originally left blank may now be filled. Thus with *thermo-electricity*, Botto made magnets and obtained polar chemical decomposition: Antinori produced the spark; and if it has not been done before, Mr. Watkins has recently heated a wire in Harris's thermo-electrometer. In respect to *animal electricity*, Matteucci and Linari have obtained the spark from the torpedo, and I have recently procured it from the gymnotus: Dr. Davy has observed the heating power of the current from the torpedo. I have therefore filled up these spaces with crosses, in a different position to the others originally in the table. There remain but five spaces unmarked, two under *attraction* and *repulsion*, and three under *discharge by hot air*; and though these effects have not yet been obtained, it is a necessary conclusion that they must be possible, since the *spark* corresponding to them has been procured. For when a discharge across cold air can occur, that intensity which is the only essential additional requisite for the other effects must be present.—*Dec.* 13, 1838.

‡ In further illustration of this subject see 855-873 in Series VII.—*Dec.*1838.

a known relation as to quantity, of the electricity excited by a machine, and that from a voltaic pile; for the purpose not only of confirming their identity (378.), but also of demonstrating certain general principles (366. 377, &c.), and creating an extension of the means of investigating and applying the chemical powers of this wonderful and subtile agent.

362. The first point to be determined was, whether the same absolute quantity of ordinary electricity, sent through a galvanometer, under different circumstances, would cause the same deflection of the needle. An arbitrary scale was therefore attached to the galvanometer, each division of which was equal to about 4°, and the instrument arranged as in former experiments (296.). The machine (290.), battery (291.), and other parts of the apparatus were brought into good order, and retained for the time as nearly as possible in the same condition. The experiments were alternated so as to indicate any change in the condition of the apparatus and supply the necessary corrections.

363. Seven of the battery jars were removed, and eight retained for present use. It was found that about forty turns would fully charge the eight jars. They were then charged by thirty turns of the machine, and discharged through the galvanometer, a thick wet string, about ten inches long, being included in the circuit. The needle was immediately deflected five divisions and a half, on the one side of the zero, and in vibrating passed as nearly as possible through five divisions and a half on the other side.

364. The other seven jars were then added to the eight, and the whole fifteen charged by thirty turns of the machine. The Henley's electrometer stood not quite half as high as before; but when the discharge was made through the galvanometer, previously at rest, the needle immediately vibrated, passing *exactly* to the same division as in the former instance. These experiments with eight and with fifteen jars were repeated several times alternately with the same results.

365. Other experiments were than made, in which all the battery was used, and its charge (being fifty turns of the machine,) sent through the galvanometer: but it was modified by being passed sometimes through a mere wet thread, sometimes through thirty-eight inches of thin string wetted by distilled water

and sometimes through a string of twelve times the thickness, only twelve inches in length, and soaked in dilute acid (298.). With the thick string the charge passed at once; with the thin string it occupied a sensible time, and with the thread it required two or three seconds before the electrometer fell entirely down. The current therefore must have varied extremely in intensity in these different cases, and yet the deflection of the needle was sensibly the same in all of them. If any difference occurred, it was that the thin string and thread caused greatest deflection; and if there is any lateral transmission, as M. Colladon says, through the silk in the galvanometer coil, it ought to have been so, because then the intensity is lower and the lateral transmission less.

366. Hence it would appear that *if the same absolute quantity of electricity pass through the galvanometer, whatever may be its intensity, the deflecting force upon the magnetic needle is the same.*

367. The battery of fifteen jars was then charged by sixty revolutions of the machine, and discharged, as before, through the galvanometer. The deflection of the needle was now as nearly as possible to the eleventh division, but the graduation was not accurate enough for me to assert that the arc was exactly double the former arc; to the eye it appeared to be so. The probability is, that *the deflecting force of an electric current is directly proportional to the absolute quantity of electricity passed,* at whatever intensity that electricity may be*.

368. Dr. Ritchie has shown that in a case where the intensity of the electricity remained the same, the deflection of the magnetic needle was directly as the quantity of electricity passed through the galvanometer †. Mr. Harris has shown that the *heating* power of common electricity on metallic wires is the same for the same quantity of electricity whatever its intensity might have previously been ‡.

* The great and general value of the galvanometer, as an actual measure of the electricity passing through it, either continuously or interruptedly, must be evident from a consideration of these two conclusions. As constructed by Professor Ritchie with glass threads (see Philosophical Transactions, 1830, p. 218, and Quarterly Journal of Science, New Series, vol. i. p. 29), it apparently seems to leave nothing unsupplied in its own department.

† Quarterly Journal of Science, New Series, vol. i. p. 33.

‡ Plymouth Transactions, page 22.

369. The next point was to obtain a *voltaic* arrangement producing an effect equal to that just described (367). A platina and a zinc wire were passed through the same hole of a draw-plate, being then one eighteenth of an inch in diameter; these were fastened to a support, so that their lower ends projected, were parallel, and five sixteenths of an inch apart. The upper ends were well connected with the galvanometer wires. Some acid was diluted, and, after various preliminary experiments, that adopted as a standard which consisted of one drop strong sulphuric acid in four ounces distilled water. Finally, the time was noted which the needle required in swinging either from right to left or left to right : it was equal to seventeen beats of my watch, the latter giving one hundred and fifty in a minute. The object of these preparations was to arrange a voltaic apparatus, which, by immersion in a given acid for a given time, much less than that required by the needle to swing in one direction, should give equal deflection to the instrument with the discharge of ordinary electricity from the battery (363, 364.) ; and a new part of the zinc wire having been brought into position with the platina, the comparative experiments were made.

370. On plunging the zinc and platina wires five eighths of an inch deep into the acid, and retaining them there for eight beats of the watch, (after which they were quickly withdrawn,) the needle was deflected, and continued to advance in the same direction some time after the voltaic apparatus had been removed from the acid. It attained the five-and-a-half division, and then returned, swinging an equal distance on the other side. This experiment was repeated many times, and always with the same result.

371. Hence, as an approximation, and judging from *magnetic force* only at present (376.), it would appear that two wires, one of platina and one of zinc, each one eighteenth of an inch in diameter, placed five sixteenths of an inch apart and immersed to the depth of five eighths of an inch in acid, consisting of one drop oil of vitriol and four ounces distilled water, at a temperature about 60°, and connected at the other extremities by a copper wire eighteen feet long and one eighteenth of an inch thick (being the wire of the galvanometer coils), yield as much electricity in eight beats of my watch, or in $\frac{8}{150}$ths of a minute, as the electrical battery charged by thirty turns of the

large machine, in excellent order (363. 364.). Notwithstanding
this apparently enormous disproportion, the results are perfectly in harmony with those effects which are known to be
produced by variations in the intensity and quantity of the electric fluid.

372. In order to procure a reference to *chemical action,* the
wires were now retained immersed in the acid to the depth of
five eighths of an inch, and the needle, when stationary, observed; it stood, as nearly as the unassisted eye could decide,
at $5\frac{1}{3}$ division. Hence a permanent deflection to that extent
might be considered as indicating a constant voltaic current,
which in eight beats of my watch (369.), could supply as much
electricity as the electrical battery charged by thirty turns of
the machine.

373. The following arrangements and results are selected
from many that were made and obtained relative to chemical
action. A platina wire one twelfth of an inch in diameter,
weighing two hundred and sixty grains, had the extremity rendered plain so as to offer a definite surface equal to a circle of
the same diameter as the wire; it was then connected in turn
with the conductor of the machine, or with the voltaic apparatus (369.), so as always to form the positive pole, and at the
same time retain a perpendicular position, that it might rest,
with its whole weight, upon the test paper to be employed.
The test paper itself was supported upon a platina spatula,
connected either with a discharging train (292.), or with the
negative wire of the voltaic apparatus, and it consisted of four
thicknesses, moistened at all times to an equal degree in a
standard solution of hydriodate of potassa (316.).

374. When the platina wire was connected with the prime
conductor of the machine, and the spatula with the discharging
train, ten turns of the machine had such decomposing power as
to produce a pale round spot of iodine of the diameter of the
wire; twenty turns made a much darker mark, and thirty turns
made a dark brown spot penetrating to the second thickness
of the paper. The difference in effect produced by two or
three turns, more or less, could be distinguished with facility.

375. The wire and spatula were then connected with the
voltaic apparatus (369.) the galvanometer being also included
in the arrangement; and, a stronger acid having been prepared,

consisting of nitric acid and water, the voltaic apparatus was immersed so far as to give a permanent deflection of the needle to the $5\frac{1}{3}$ division (372.), the fourfold moistened paper intervening as before.* Then by shifting the end of the wire from place to place upon the test paper, the effect of the current for five, six, seven, or any number of the beats of the watch (369.) was observed, and compared with that of the machine. After alternating and repeating the experiments of comparison many times, it was constantly found that this standard current of voltaic electricity, continued for eight beats of the watch, was equal, in chemical effect, to thirty turns of the machine ; twenty-eight revolutions of the machine were sensibly too few.

376. Hence it results that both in *magnetic deflection* (371.) and in *chemical force*, the current of electricity of the standard voltaic battery for eight beats of the watch was equal to that of the machine evolved by thirty revolutions.

377. It also follows that for this case of electro-chemical decomposition, and it is probable for all cases, that the *chemical power, like the magnetic force* (366.) *is in direct proportion to the absolute quantity of electricity* which passes.

378. Hence arises still further confirmation, if any were required, of the identity of common and voltaic electricity, and that the differences of intensity and quantity are quite sufficient to account for what were supposed to be their distinctive qualities.

379. The extension which the present investigations have enabled me to make of the facts and views constituting the theory of electro-chemical decomposition, will, with some other points of electrical doctrine, be almost immediately submitted to the Royal Society in another series of these Researches.

* Of course the heightened power of the voltaic battery was necessary to compensate for the bad conductor now interposed.

*Royal Institution,*
    15*th Dec.* 1832.

———————

NOTE.—I am anxious, and am permitted, to add to this paper a correction of an error which I have attributed to M. Ampère in the first series of these Experimental Researches. In referring to his experiment on the induction of electrical currents (78.), I have called that a disc which I should have called a

circle or a ring. M. Ampère used a ring, or a very short cylinder made of a
narrow plate of copper bent into a circle, and he tells me that by such an arrangement the motion is very readily obtained. I have not doubted that M. Ampère
obtained the motion he described; but merely mistook the kind of mobile
conductor used, and so far I described his *experiment* erroneously.

In the same paragraph I have stated that M. Ampère says the disc turned
"to take a position of equilibrium exactly as the spiral itself would have turned
had it been free to move"; and further on I have said that my results tended
to invert the sense of the proposition "stated by M. Ampère, *that a current of
electricity tends to put the electricity of conductors near which it passes in motion
in the same direction.*" M. Ampère tells me in a letter which I have just received from him, that he carefully avoided, when describing the experiment,
any reference to the direction of the induced current; and on looking at the
passages he quotes to me, I find that to be the case. I have therefore done him
injustice in the above statements, and am anxious to correct my error.

But that it may not be supposed I lightly wrote those passages, I will briefly
refer to my reasons for understanding them in the sense I did. At first the experiment failed. When re-made successfully about a year afterwards, it was
at Geneva in company with M. A. De la Rive : the latter philosopher described
the results[*], and says that the plate of copper bent into a circle which was used
as the mobile conductor "sometimes advanced between the two branches of
the (horse-shoe) magnet, and sometimes was repelled, *according* to the direction of the current in the surrounding conductors."

I have been in the habit of referring to Demonferrand's *Manuel d Electricité
Dynamique,* as a book of authority in France ; containing the general results
and laws of this branch of science, up to the time of its publication, in a well-
arranged form. At p. 173, the author when describing this experiment says,
" The mobile circle turns to take a position of equilibrium as a conductor
would do in which the current moved in the *same direction* as in the spiral; "
and in the same paragraph he adds, " it is therefore proved *that a current of electricity tends to put the electricity of conductors, near which it passes, in motion in
the same direction.*" These are the words I quoted in my paper (78.).

Le Lycée of 1st of January, 1832, No. 36, in an article written after the re-
ceipt of my first unfortunate letter to M. Hachette, and before my papers were
printed, reasons upon the direction of the induced currents, and says, that there
ought to be " an elementary current produced in the same direction as the corresponding portion of the producing current. A little further on it says,
" therefore we ought to obtain currents, moving in the *same direction*, produced
upon a metallic wire, either by a magnate or a current. M. Ampère *was so
thoroughly persuaded that such ought to be the direction of the currents by influence,* that he neglected to assure himself of it in his experiment at Geneva."

It was the precise statements in Demonferrand's Manuel, agreeing as they
did with the expression in M. De la Rive's paper, (which, however, I now understand as only meaning that when the inducing current was changed, the
motion of the mobile circle changed also) and not in discordance with anything
expressed by M. Ampère himself where he speaks of the experiment, which

made me conclude, when I wrote the paper, that what I wrote was really his avowed opinion ; and when the Number of the Lycée referred to appeared, which was before my paper was printed, it could excite no suspicion that I was in error.

Hence the mistake into which I unwittingly fell. I am proud to correct it and do full justice to the acuteness and accuracy which, as far as I can understand the subjects, M. Ampère carries into all the branches of philosophy which he investigates.

Finally, my note to (79.) says that the Lycée, No. 36, " mistakes the erroneous results of MM. Fresnel and Ampère for true ones," &c. &c. In calling M. Ampère's results erroneous, I spoke of the results described in, and referred to by the Lycée itself; but *now* that the expression of the direction of the induced current is to be separated, the term *erroneous* ought no longer to be attached to them.

April 29, 1833.

## FOURTH SERIES.

§ 9. *On a new Law of Electric Conduction.* § 10. *On Conducting Power generally.*

Received April 24,—Read May 23, 1833.

§ 9. *On a new Law of Electric Conduction\*.*

**380.** I⊤ was during the progress of investigations relating to
electro-chemical decomposition, which I still have to submit to
the Royal Society, that I encountered effects due to a very
*general law* of electric conduction not hitherto recognised; and
though they prevented me from obtaining the condition I sought
for, they afforded abundant compensation for the momentary
disappointment, by the new and important interest which they
gave to an extensive part of electrical science.

**381.** I was working with ice, and the solids resulting from
the freezing of solutions, arranged either as barriers across a
substance to be decomposed, or as the actual poles of a voltaic
battery, that I might trace and catch certain elements in their
transit, when I was suddenly stopped in my progress by finding
that ice was in such circumstances a non-conductor of electricity; and that as soon as a thin film of it was interposed, in
the circuit of a very powerful voltaic battery, the tranmission
of electricity was prevented, and all decomposition ceased.

**382.** At first the experiments were made with common ice,
during the cold freezing weather of the latter end of January
1833; but the results were fallacious, from the imperfection
of the arrangements, and the following more unexceptionable
form of experiment was adopted.

**383.** Tin vessels were formed, five inches deep, one inch and
a quarter wide in one direction, of different widths from three
eights to five eights of an inch in the other, and open at
one extremity. Into these were fixed by corks, plates of platina,

* In reference to this law see further considerations at 910. 1358. 1705.—
*Dec.* 1838.

so that the latter should not touch the tin cases ; and copper wires having previously been soldered to the plates, these were easily connected, when required, with a voltaic pile. Then distilled water, previously boiled for three hours, was poured into the vessels, and frozen by a mixture of salt and snow, so that pure transparent solid ice intervened between the platina and tin : and finally these metals were connected with the opposite extremities of the voltaic apparatus, a galvanometer being at the same time included in the circuit.

384. In the first experiment, the platina pole was three inches and a half long, and seven eights of an inch wide ; it was wholly immersed in the water or ice, and as the vessel was four eighths of an inch in width, the average thickness of the intervening ice was only a quarter of an inch, whilst the surface of contact with it at both poles was nearly fourteen square inches. After the water was frozen, the vessel was still retained in the frigorific mixture, whilst contact between the tin and platina respectively was made with the extremities of a well-charged voltaic battery, consisting of twenty pairs of four-inch plates, each with double coppers. Not the slightest deflection of the galvanometer needle occurred.

385. On taking the frozen arrangement out of the cold mixture, and applying warmth to the bottom of the tin case, so as to melt part of the ice, the connexion with the battery being in the mean time retained, the needle did not at first move; and it was only when the thawing process had extended so far as to liquefy part of the ice touching the platina pole, that conduction took place ; but then it occurred effectually, and the galvanometer needle was permanently deflected nearly 70°.

386. In another experiment, a platina spatula, five inches in length and seven eighths of an inch in width, had four inches fixed in the ice, and the latter was only three sixteenths of an inch thick between one metallic surface and the other ; yet this arrangement insulated as perfectly as the former.

387. Upon pouring a little water in at the top of this vessel on the ice, still the arrangement did not conduct; yet fluid water was evidently there. This result was the consequence of the cold metals having frozen the water where they touched it, and thus insulating the fluid part ; and it well illustrates the non-conducting power of ice, by showing how thin a film

could prevent the transmission of the battery current. Upon thawing parts of this thin film, at *both* metals, conduction occurred.

338. Upon warming the tin case and removing the piece of ice, it was found that a cork having slipped, one of the edges of the platina had been all but in contact with the inner surface of the tin vessel; yet, notwithstanding the extreme thinness of the interfering ice in this place, no sensible portion of electricity had passed.

389. These experiments were repeated many times with the same results. At last a battery of fifteen troughs, or one hundred and fifty pairs of four-inch plates, powerfully charged, was used; yet even here no sensible quantity of electricity passed the thin barrier of ice.

390. It seemed at first as if occasional departures from these effects occurred; but they could always be traced to some interfering circumstances. The water should in every instance be well frozen; for though it is not necessary that the ice should reach from pole to pole, since a barrier of it about one pole would be quite sufficient to prevent conduction, yet, if part remain fluid, the mere necessary exposure of the apparatus to the air, or the approximation of the hands, is sufficient to produce, at the *upper surface* of the water and ice, a film of fluid, extending from the platina to the tin; and then conduction occurs. Again, if the corks used to block the platina in its place are damp or wet within, it is necessary that the cold be sufficiently well applied to freeze the water in them, or else when the surfaces of their contact with the tin become slightly warm by handling, that part will conduct, and the interior being ready to conduct also, the current will pass. The water should be pure, not only that unembarrassed results may be obtained, but also that, as the freezing proceeds, a minute portion of concentrated saline solution may not be formed, which remaining fluid, and being interposed in the ice, or passing into cracks resulting from contraction, may exhibit conducting powers independent of the ice itself.

391. On one occasion I was surprised to find that after thawing much of the ice the conducting power had not been restored; but I found that a cork which held the wire just where it joined the platina, dipped so far into the ice, that with the ice itself

it protected the platina from contact with the melted part long after that contact was expected.

392. This insulating power of ice is not effective with electricity of exalted intensity. On touching a diverged gold-leaf electrometer with a wire connected with the platina, whilst the tin case was touched by the hand or another wire, the electrometer was instantly discharged (419.).

393. But though electricity of an intensity so low that it cannot diverge the electrometer, can still pass (though in very limited quantities (419.),) through ice ; the comparative relation of water and ice to the electricity of the voltaic apparatus is not less extraordinary on that account, or less important in its consequences.

394. As it did not seem likely that this *law of the assumption of conducting power during liquefaction, and loss of it during congelation,* would be peculiar to water, I immediately proceeded to ascertain its influence in other cases, and found it to be very general. For this purpose bodies were chosen which were solid at common temperatures, but readily fusible ; and of such composition as, for other reasons connected with electro-chemical action, led to the conclusion that they would be able when fused to replace water as conductors. A voltaic battery of two troughs, or twenty pairs of four-inch plates (384.), was used as the source of electricity, and a galvanometer introduced into the circuit to indicate the presence or absence of a current.

395. On fusing a little chloride of lead by a spirit-lamp on a fragment of a Florence flask, and introducing two platina wires connected with the poles of the battery, there was instantly powerful action, the galvanometer was most violently affected, and the chloride rapidly decomposed. On removing the lamp, the instant the chloride solidified all current and consequent effects ceased, though the platina wires remained inclosed in the chloride not more than the one-sixteenth of an inch from each other. On renewing the heat, as soon as the fusion had proceeded far enough to allow liquid matter to connect the poles, the electrical current instantly passed.

396. On fusing the chloride, with one wire introduced, and then touching the liquid with the other, the latter being cold, caused a little knob to concrete on its extremity, and no current

passed; it was only when the wire became so hot as to be able to admit or allow of contact with the liquid matter, that conduction took place, and then it was very powerful.

397. When chloride of silver and chlorate of potassa were experimented with, in a similar manner, exactly the same results occurred.

398. Whenever the current passed in these cases, there was decomposition of the substances; but the electro-chemical part of this subject I purpose connecting with more general views in a future paper *.

399. Other substances, which could not be melted on glass, were fused by the lamp and blowpipe on platina connected with one pole of the battery, and then a wire, connected with the other, dipped into them. In this way chloride of sodium, sulphate of soda, protoxide of lead, mixed carbonates of potash and soda, &c. &c., exhibited exactly the same phenomena as those already described: whilst liquid, they conducted and were decomposed; whilst solid, though very hot, they insulated the battery current even when four troughs were used.

400. Occasionally the substances were contained in small bent tubes of green glass, and when fused, the platina poles introduced, one on each side. In such cases the same general re-sults as those already described were procured; but a further advantage was obtained, namely, that whilst the substance was conducting and suffering decomposition, the final arrangement of the elements could be observed. Thus, iodides of potassium and lead gave iodine at the positive pole, and potassium or lead at the negative pole. Chlorides of lead and silver gave chlorine at the positive, and metals at the negative pole.

* In 1801, Sir H. Davy knew that "dry nitre, caustic potash, and soda are conductors of galvanism when rendered fluid by a high degree of heat," (Journals of the Royal Institution, 1802, p. 53,) but was not aware of the general law which I have been engaged in developing. It is remarkable, that eleven years after that, he should say, "There are no fluids known except such as contain water, which are capable of being made the medium of connexion between the metal or metals of the voltaic apparatus." Elements of Chemical Philosophy, p. 169.

Nitre and chlorate of potassa gave oxygen, &c., at the positive, and alkali, or even potassium, at the negative pole.

401. A fourth arrangement was used for substances requiring very high temperatures for their fusion. A platina wire was connected with one pole of the battery; its extremity bent into a small ring, in the manner described by Berzelius, for blow-pipe experiments; a little of the salt, glass, or other substance, was melted on this ring by the ordinary blowpipe, or even in some cases by the oxy-hydrogen blowpipe, and when the drop, retained in its place by the ring, was thoroughly hot and fluid, a platina wire from the opposite pole of the battery was made to touch it, and the effects observed.

402. The following are various substances, taken from very different classes chemically considered, which are subject to this law. The list might, no doubt, be enormously extended; but I have not had time to do more than confirm the law by a sufficient number of instances.

First, *water*.

Amongst *oxides*;—potassa, protoxide of lead, glass of antimony, protoxide of antimony, oxide of bismuth.

*Chlorides* of potassium, sodium, barium, strontium, calcium, magnesium, manganese, zinc, copper (proto-), lead, tin (proto-), antimony, silver.

*Iodides* of potassium, zinc and lead, protiodide of tin, periodide of mercury; *fluoride* of potassium; *cyanide* of potassium; *sulpho-cyanide* of potassium.

*Salts.* Chlorate of potassa; nitrates of potassa, soda, baryta, strontia, lead, copper, and silver; sulphates of soda and lead, proto-sulphate of mercury; phosphates of potassa, soda, lead, copper, phosphoric glass or acid phosphate of lime; carbonates of potassa and soda, mingled and separate; borax, borate of lead, per-borate of tin; chromate of potassa, bi-chromate of potassa, chromate of lead; acetate of potassa.

*Sulphurets.* Sulphuret of antimony, sulphuret of potassium made by reducing sulphate of potassa by hydrogen; ordinary sulphuret of potassa.

Silicated potassa; chameleon mineral.

403. It is highly interesting in the instances of those substances which soften before they liquefy, to observe at what period the conducting power is acquired, and to what degree

it is exalted by perfect fluidity. Thus, with the borate of lead, when heated by the lamp upon glass, it becomes as soft as treacle, but it did not conduct, and it was only when urged by the blowpipe and brought to a fair red heat, that it conducted. When rendered quite liquid, it conducted with extreme facility.

404. I do not mean to deny that part of the increased conducting power in these cases of softening was probably due to the elevation of temperature (432. 445.) ; but I have no doubt that by far the greater part was due to the influence of the general law already demonstrated, and which in these instances came gradually, instead of suddenly, into operation.

405. The following are bodies which acquired no conducting power upon assuming the liquid state :—

Sulphur, phosphorus ; iodide of sulphur, per-iodide of tin ; orpiment, realgar ; glacial acetic acid, mixed margaric and oleic acids, artificial camphor ; caffeine, sugar, adipocire, stearine of cocoa-nut oil, spermaceti, camphor, naphthaline, resin, gum sandarach, shell lac.

406. Perchloride of tin, chloride of arsenic, and the hydrated chloride of arsenic, being liquids, had no sensible conducting power indicated by the galvanometer, nor were they decomposed.

407. Some of the above substances are sufficiently remarkable as exceptions to the general law governing the former cases. These are orpiment, realgar, acetic acid, artificial camphor, per-iodide of tin, and the chlorides of tin and arsenic. I shall have occasion to refer to these cases in the paper on Electro-chemical Decomposition.

408. Boracic acid was raised to the highest possible temperature by an oxy-hydrogen flame (401.), yet it gained no conducting powers sufficient to affect the galvanometer, and underwent no apparent voltaic decomposition. It seemed to be quite as bad a conductor as air. Green bottle-glass, heated in the same manner, did not gain conducting power sensible to the galvanometer. Flint glass, when highly heated, did conduct a little and decompose ; and as the proportion of potash or oxide of lead was increased in the glass, the effects were more powerful. Those glasses, consisting of boracic acid on the one hand, and oxide of lead or potassa on the other, show the assumption of

conducting power upon fusion and the accompanying decomposition very well.

409. I was very anxious to try the general experiment with sulphuric acid, of about specific gravity 1·783, containing that proportion of water which gives it the power of crystallizing at 40° Fahr. ; but I found it impossible to obtain it so that I could be sure the whole would congeal even at 0° Fahr. A ten-thousandth part of water, more or less than necessary, would, upon cooling the whole, cause a portion of uncongealable liquid to separate, and that remaining in the interstices of the solid mass, and moistening the planes of division, would prevent the correct observation of the phenomena due to entire solidification and subsequent liquefaction.

410. With regard to the substances on which conducting power is thus conferred by liquidity, the degree of power so given is generally very great. Water is that body in which this acquired power is feeblest. In the various oxides, chlorides, salts, &c., &c., it is given in a much higher degree. I have not had time to measure the conducting power in these cases, but it is apparently some hundred times that of pure water. The increased conducting power known to be given to water by the addition of salts, would seem to be in a great degree dependent upon the high conducting power of these bodies when in the liquid state, that state being given them for the time, not by heat but solution in the water*.

411. Whether the conducting power of these liquefied bodies is a consequence of their decomposition or not (413.), or whether the two actions of conduction and decomposition are essentially connected or not, would introduce no difference affecting the probable accuracy of the preceding statement.

412. This *general assumption of conducting power* by bodies as soon as they pass from the solid to the liquid state, offers a new and extraordinary character, the existence of which, as far as I know, has not before been suspected; and it seems importantly connected with some properties and relations of the particles of matter which I may now briefly point out.

413. In almost all the instances, as yet observed, which are governed by this law, the substances experimented with have been those which were not only compound bodies, but such as

* See a doubt on this point at 1356.—*Dec.* 1838.

contain elements known to arrange themselves at the opposite poles; and were also such as could be *decomposed* by the electrical current.    When conduction took place, decomposition occurred; when decomposition ceased, conduction ceased also; and it becomes a fair and an important question, Whether the conduction itself may not, wherever the law holds good, be a consequence not merely of the capability, but of the act of decomposition?    And that question may be accompanied by another, namely, Whether solidification does not prevent conduction, merely by chaining the particles to their places, under the influence of aggregation, and preventing their final separation in the manner necessary for decomposition?

414. But, on the other hand, there is one substance (and others may occur), the *per-iodide of mercury*, which, being experimented with like the others (400.), was found to insulate when solid, and to acquire conducting power when fluid; yet it did not seem to undergo decomposition in the latter case.

415. Again, there are many substances which contain elements such as would be expected to arrange themselves at the opposite poles of the pile, and therefore in that respect fitted for decomposition, which yet do not conduct.    Amongst these are the iodide of sulphur, per-iodide of zinc, per-chloride of tin, chloride of arsenic, hydrated chloride of arsenic, acetic acid, orpiment, realgar, artificial camphor, &c.; and from these it might perhaps be assumed that decomposition is dependent upon conducting power, and not the latter upon the former. The true relation, however, of conduction and decomposition in those bodies governed by the general law which it is the object of this paper to establish, can only be satisfactorily made out from a far more extensive series of observations than those I have yet been able to supply*.

416. The relation, under this law, of the conducting power for electricity to that for heat, is very remarkable, and seems to imply a natural dependence of the two.    As the solid becomes a fluid, it loses almost entirely the power of conduction for heat, but gains in a high degree that for electricity; but as it reverts back to the solid state, it gains the power of conducting heat, and loses that of conducting electricity.    If, therefore, the properties are not incompatible, still they are most strongly

* See 679, &c. &c.—*Dec.* 1838.

contrasted, one being lost as the other is gained. We may hope, perhaps, hereafter to understand the physical reason of this very extraordinary relation of the two conducting powers, both of which appear to be directly connected with the corpuscular condition of the substances concerned.

417. The assumption of conducting power and a decomposable condition by liquefaction, promises new opportunities of, and great facilities in, voltaic decomposition. Thus, such bodies as the oxides, chlorides, cyanides, sulpho-cyanides, fluorides, certain vitreous mixtures, &c. &c., may be submitted to the action of the voltaic battery under new circumstances ; and indeed I have already been able, with ten pairs of plates, to decompose common salt, chloride of magnesium, borax, &c. &c., and to obtain sodium, magnesium, boron, &c., in their separate states.

§ 10. *On Conducting Power generally\*.*

418. It is not my intention here to enter into an examination of all the circumstances connected with conducting power, but to record certain facts and observations which have arisen during recent inquiries, as additions to the general stock of knowledge relating to this point of electrical science.

419. I was anxious, in the first place, to obtain some idea of the conducting power of ice and solid salts for electricity of high tension (392.), that a comparison might be made between it and the large accession of the same power gained upon liquefaction. For this purpose the large electrical machine (290.) was brought into excellent action, its conductor connected with a delicate gold-leaf electrometer, and also with the platina inclosed in the ice (383.), whilst the tin case was connected with the discharging train (292.). On working the machine moderately, the gold leaves barely separated ; on working it rapidly, they could be opened nearly two inches. In this instance the tin case was five eighths of an inch in width ; and as, after the experiment, the platina plate was found very nearly in the middle of the ice, the average thickness of the latter had been five sixteenths of an inch, and the extent of surface of contact with tin and platina fourteen square inches (384.). Yet, under

\* In reference to this § refer to 983 in series viii., and the results connected with it.—*Dec.* 1838.

these circumstances, it was but just able to conduct the small quantity of electricity which this machine could evolve (371.), even when of a tension competent to open the leaves two inches; no wonder, therefore, that it could not conduct any sensible portion of the electricity of the troughs (384.), which, though almost infinitely surpassing that of the machine in quantity, had a tension so low as not to be sensible to an electrometer.

420. In another experiment, the tin case was only four eighths of an inch in width, and it was found afterwards that the platina had been not quite one eighth of an inch distant in the ice from one side of the tin vessel. When this was introduced into the course of the electricity from the machine (419.), the gold leaves could be opened, but not more than half an inch; the thinness of the ice favouring the conduction of the electricity, and permitting the same quantity to pass in the same time, though of a much lower tension.

421. Iodide of potassium which had been fused and cooled was introduced into the course of the electricity from the machine. There were two pieces, each about a quarter of an inch in thickness, and exposing a surface on each side equal to about half a square inch; these were placed upon platina plates, one connected with the machine and electrometer (419.), and the other with the discharging train, whilst a fine platina wire connected the two pieces, resting upon them by its two points. On working the electrical machine, it was possible to open the electrometer leaves about two thirds of an inch.

422. As the platina wire touched only by points, the facts show that this salt is a far better conductor than ice; but as the leaves of the electrometer opened, it is also evident with what difficulty conduction, even of the small portion of electricity produced by the machine, is effected by this body in the solid state, when compared to the facility with which enormous quantities at very low tensions are transmitted by it when in the fluid state.

423. In order to confirm these results by others, obtained from the voltaic apparatus, a battery of one hundred and fifty plates, four inches square, was well charged: its action was good; the shock from it strong; the discharge would *continue* from copper to copper through four tenths of an inch of air,

and the gold-leaf electrometer before used could be opened nearly a quarter of an inch.

424. The ice vessel employed (420.) was half an inch in width : as the extent of contact of the ice with the tin and platina was nearly fourteen square inches, the whole was equivalent to a plate of ice having a surface of seven square inches of perfect contact at each side, and only one fourth of an inch thick. It was retained in a freezing mixture during the experiment.

425. The order of arrangement in the course of the electric current was as follows. The positive pole of the battery was connected by a wire with the platina plate in the ice; the plate was in contact with the ice, the ice with the tin jacket, the jacket with a wire, which communicated with a piece of tin foil, on which rested one end of a bent platina wire (312.), the other or decomposing end being supported on paper moistened with solution of iodide of potassium (316.) : the paper was laid flat on a platina spatula connected with the negative end of the battery. All that part of the arrangement between the ice-vessel and the decomposing wire point, including both these, was insulated, so that no electricity might pass through the latter which had not traversed the former also.

426. Under these circumstances, it was found that a pale brown spot of iodine was slowly formed under the decomposing platina point, thus indicating that ice could conduct a little of the electricity evolved by a voltaic battery charged up to the degree of intensity indicated by the electrometer. But it is quite evident that notwithstanding the enormous quantity of electricity which the battery could furnish, it was, under present circumstances, a very inferior instrument to the ordinary machine; for the latter could send as much through the ice as it could carry, being of a far higher intensity, *i. e.* able to open the electrometer leaves half an inch or more (419. 420.).

427. The decomposing wire and solution of iodide of potassium were then removed, and replaced by a very delicate galvanometer (205.); it was so nearly astatic, that it vibrated to and fro in about sixty-three beats of a watch giving one hundred and fifty beats in a minute. The same feebleness of current as before was still indicated; the galvanometer needle was deflected, but it required to break and make contact three or four times (297.), before the effect was decided.

428. The galvanometer being removed, two platina plates were connected with the extremities of the wires, and the tongue placed between them, so that the whole charge of the battery, so far as the ice would let it pass, was free to go through the tongue. Whilst standing on the stone floor, there was shock, &c., but when insulated, I could feel no sensation. I think a frog would have been scarcely, if at all, affected.

429. The ice was now removed, and experiments made with other solid bodies, for which purpose they were placed under the end of the decomposing wire instead of the solution of iodide of potassium (425.). For instance, a piece of dry iodide of potassium was placed on the spatula connected with the negative pole of the battery, and the point of the decomposing wire placed upon it, whilst the positive end of the battery communicated with the latter. A brown spot of iodine very slowly appeared, indicating the passage of a little electricity, and agreeing in that respect with the results obtained by the use of the electrical machine (421.). When the galvanometer was introduced into the circuit at the same time with the iodide, it was with difficulty that the action of the current on it could be rendered sensible.

430. A piece of common salt previously fused and solidified being introduced into the circuit was sufficient almost entirely to destroy the action on the galvanometer. Fused and cooled chloride of lead produced the same effect. The conducting power of these bodies *when fluid,* is very great (395. 402.).

431. These effects, produced by using the common machine and the voltaic battery, agree therefore with each other, and with the law laid down in this paper (394.) ; and also with the opinion I have supported, in the Third Series of these Researches, of the identity of electricity derived from different sources (360.).

432. The effect of heat in increasing the conducting power of many substances, especially for electricity of high tension, is well known. I have lately met with an extraordinary case of this kind, for electricity of low tension, or that of the voltaic pile, and which is in direct contrast with the influence of heat upon metallic bodies, as observed and described by Sir Humphry Davy *.

433. The substance presenting this effect is sulphuret of sil-

* Philosophical Transactions, 1821, p. 431.

ver. It was made by fusing a mixture of precipitated silver and sublimed sulphur, removing the film of silver by a file from the exterior of the fused mass, pulverizing the sulphuret, mingling it with more sulphur, and fusing it again in a green glass tube, so that no air should obtain access during the process. The surface of the sulphuret being again removed by a file or knife, it was considered quite free from uncombined silver.

434. When a piece of this sulphuret, half an inch in thickness, was put between surfaces of platina, terminating the poles of a voltaic battery of twenty pairs of four-inch plates, a galvanometer being also included in the circuit, the needle was slightly deflected, indicating a feeble conducting power. On pressing the platina poles and sulphuret together with the fingers, the conducting power increased as the whole became warm. On applying a lamp under the sulphuret between the poles, the conducting power rose rapidly with the heat, and at last the galvanometer needle jumped into a fixed position, and the sulphuret was found conducting in the manner of a metal. On removing the lamp and allowing the heat to fall, the effects were reversed, the needle at first began to vibrate a little, then gradually left its transverse direction, and at last returned to a position very nearly that which it would take when no current was passing through the galvanometer.

435. Occasionally, when the contact of the sulphuret with the platina poles was good, the battery freshly charged, and the commencing temperature not too low, the mere current of electricity from the battery was sufficient to raise the temperature of the sulphuret; and then, without any application of extraneous heat, it went on increasing conjointly in temperature and conducting power, until the cooling influence of the air limited the effects. In such cases it was generally necessary to cool the whole purposely, to show the returning series of phenomena.

436. Occasionally, also, the effects would sink of themselves, and could not be renewed until a fresh surface of the sulphuret had been applied to the positive pole. This was in consequence of peculiar results of decomposition, to which I shall have occasion to revert in the section on Electro-chemical Decomposition, and was conveniently avoided by inserting the ends of two pieces of platina wire into the opposite extremities of a

portion of sulphuret fused in a glass tube, and placing this arrangement between the poles of the battery.

437. The hot sulphuret of silver conducts sufficiently well to give a bright spark with charcoal, &c. &c., in the manner of a metal.

438. The native grey sulphuret of silver, and the ruby silver ore, both presented the same phenomena. The native malleable sulphuret of silver presented precisely the same appearances as the artificial sulphuret.

439. There is no other body with which I am acquainted, that, like sulphuret of silver, can compare with metals in conducting power for electricity of low tension when hot, but which, unlike them, during cooling, loses in power, whilst they, on the contrary, gain. Probably, however, many others may, when sought for, be found*.

440. The proto-sulphuret of iron, the native per-sulphuret of iron, arsenical sulphuret of iron, native yellow sulphuret of copper and iron, grey artificial sulphuret of copper, artificial sulphuret of bismuth, and artificial grey sulphuret of tin, all conduct the voltaic battery current when cold, more or less, some giving sparks like the metals, others not being sufficient for that high effect. They did not seem to conduct better when heated, than before; but I had not time to enter accurately into the investigation of this point. Almost all of them became much heated by the transmission of the current, and present some very interesting phenomena in that respect. The sulphuret of antimony does not conduct the same current sensibly either hot or cold, but is amongst those bodies acquiring conducting power when fused (402.). The sulphuret of silver and perhaps some others decompose whilst in the solid state; but the phenomena of this decomposition will be reserved for its proper place in the next series of these Researches.

441. Notwithstanding the extreme dissimilarity between sulphuret of silver and gases or vapours, I cannot help suspecting the action of heat upon them to be the same, bringing them all into the same class as conductors of electricity, although with those great differences in degree, which are found to exist under common circumstances. When gases are heated, they increase in conducting power, both for common and voltaic elec-

* See now on this subject, 1340, 1341.—*Dec.* 1838.

tricity (271.) ; and it is probable that if we could compress and condense them at the same time, we should still further increase their conducting power. Cagniard de la Tour has shown that a substance, for instance, water, may be so expanded by heat whilst in the liquid state, or condensed whilst in the vaporous state, that the two states shall coincide at one point, and the transition from one to the other be so gradual that no line of demarcation can be pointed out*; that, in fact, the two states shall become one ;—which one state presents us at different times with differences in degree as to certain properties and relations ; and which differences are, under ordinary circumstances, so great as to be equivalent to two different states.

442. I cannot but suppose at present that at that point where the liquid and the gaseous state coincide, the conducting properties are the same for both ; but that they diminish as the expansion of the matter into a rarer form takes place by the removal of the necessary pressure ; still, however, retaining, as might be expected, the capability of having what feeble conducting power remains, increased by the action of heat.

443. I venture to give the following summary of the conditions of electric conduction in bodies, not however, without fearing that I may have omitted some important points†.

444. All bodies conduct electricity in the same manner from metals to lac and gases, but in very different degrees.

445. Conducting power is in some bodies powerfully increased by heat, and in others diminished, yet without our perceiving any accompanying essential electrical difference, either in the bodies or in the changes occasioned by the electricity conducted.

446. A numerous class of bodies, insulating electricity of low intensity, when solid, conduct it very freely when fluid, and are then decomposed by it.

447. But there are many fluid bodies which do not sensibly conduct electricity of this low intensity ; there are some which conduct it and are not decomposed ; nor is fluidity essential to decomposition‡.

* Annales de Chimie, xxi. pp. 127, 178.
† See now in relation to this subject, 1320—1342.—*Dec.* 1838.
‡ See the next series of these Experimental Researches.

448. There is but one body yet discovered* which, insulating a voltaic current when solid, and conducting it when fluid, is not decomposed in the latter case (414.).

449. There is no strict electrical distinction of conduction which can, as yet, be drawn between bodies supposed to be elementary, and those known to be compounds.

\* It is just possible that this case may, by more delicate experiment, hereafter disappear. (See now, 1340, 1341, in relation to this note.—*Dec.* 1838.)

*Royal Institution,*
 *April* 15, 1833.

# FIFTH SERIES.

§ 11. *On Electro-chemical Decomposition.* ¶ i. *New conditions of Electro-chemical Decomposition.* ¶ ii. *Influence of Water in Electro-chemical Decomposition.* ¶ iii. *Theory of Electro-chemical Decomposition.*

Received June 18,—Read June 20, 1833.

§ 11. *On Electro-chemical Decomposition*\*.

450. I HAVE in a recent series of these Researches (265.) proved (to my own satisfaction, at least,) the identity of electricities derived from different sources, and have especially dwelt upon the proofs of the sameness of those obtained by the use of the common electrical machine and the voltaic battery.

451. The great distinction of the electricities obtained from these two sources is the very high tension to which the small quantity obtained by aid of the machine may be raised, and the enormous quantity (371. 376.) in which that of comparatively low tension, supplied by the voltaic battery, may be procured; but as their actions, whether magnetical, chemical, or of any other nature, are essentially the same (360.), it appeared evident that we might reason from the former as to the manner of action of the latter; and it was, to me, a probable consequence, that the use of electricity of such intensity as that afforded by the machine, would, when applied to effect and elucidate electro-chemical decomposition, show some new conditions of that action, evolve new views of the internal arrangements and changes of the substances under decomposition, and perhaps give efficient powers over matter as yet undecomposed.

452. For the purpose of rendering the bearings of the different parts of this series of researches more distinct, I shall divide it into several heads.

¶ i. *New conditions of Electro-chemical Decomposition.*

453. The tension of machine electricity causes it, however

* Refer to the note after 1047, Series viii.—*Dec.* 1838.

small in quantity, to pass through any length of water, solutions, or other substances classing with these as conductors, as fast as it can be produced, and therefore, in relation to quantity, as fast as it could have passed through much shorter portions of the same conducting substance. With the voltaic battery the case is very different, and the passing current of electricity supplied by it suffers serious diminution in any substance, by considerable extension of its length, but especially in such bodies as those mentioned above.

454. I endeavoured to apply this facility of transmitting the current of electricity through any length of a conductor, to an investigation of the transfer of the elements in a decomposing body, in contrary directions, towards the poles. The general form of apparatus used in these experiments has been already described (312. 316.) ; and also a particular experiment (319.), in which, when a piece of litmus paper and a piece of turmeric paper were combined and moistened in solution of sulphate of soda, the point of the wire from the machine (representing the positive pole) put upon the litmus paper, and the receiving point from the discharging train (292. 316.), representing the negative pole, upon the turmeric paper, a very few turns of the machine sufficed to show the evolution of acid at the former, and alkali at the latter, exactly in the manner effected by a volta-electric current.

455. The pieces of litmus and turmeric paper were *now* placed each upon a separate plate of glass, and connected by an insulated string four feet long, moistened in the same solution of sulphate of soda ; the terminal decomposing wire points were placed upon the papers as before. On working the machine, the same evolution of acid and alkali appeared as in the former instance, and with equal readiness, notwithstanding that the places of their appearance were four feet apart from each other. Finally, a piece of string, seventy feet long, was used. It was insulated in the air by suspenders of silk, so that the electricity passed through its entire length : decomposition took place exactly, as in former cases, alkali and acid appearing at the two extremities in their proper places.

456. Experiments were then made both with sulphate of soda and iodide of potassium, to ascertain if any diminution of decomposing effect was produced by such great extension as

those just described of the moist conductor or body under decomposition ; but whether the contact of the decomposing
point connected with the discharging train was made with turmeric paper touching the prime conductor, or with other turmeric paper connected with it through the seventy feet of
string, the spot of alkali for an equal number of turns of the
machine had equal intensity of colour.   The same results occurred at the other decomposing wire, whether the salt or the
iodide were used ; and it was fully proved that this great extension of the distance between the poles produced no effect
whatever on the amount of decomposition, provided the same
*quantity* of electricity were passed in both cases (377.).

457. The negative point of the discharging train, the turmeric paper, and the string were then removed ; the positive
point was left resting upon the litmus paper, and the latter
touched by a piece of moistened string held in the hand.   A
few turns of the machine evolved acid at the positive point as
freely as before.

458. The end of the moistened string, instead of being held
in the hand, was suspended by glass in the air.   On working the machine the electricity proceeded from the conductor
through the wire point to the litmus paper, and thence away
by the intervention of the string to the air, so that there was
(as in the last experiment,) but one metallic pole ; still acid
was evolved there as freely as in any former case.

459. When any of these experiments were repeated with
electricity from the negative conductor, corresponding effects
were produced whether one or two decomposing wires were
used.   The results were always constant, considered in relation to the *direction* of the electric current.

460. These experiments were varied so as to include the
action of only one metallic pole, but that not the pole connected
with the machine.   Turmeric paper was moistened in solution
of sulphate of soda, placed upon glass, and connected with the
discharging train (292.) by a decomposing wire (312.) ; a piece
of wet string was hung from it, the lower extremity of which
was brought opposite a point connected with the positive prime
conductor of the machine.   The machine was then worked for
a few turns, and alkali immediately appeared at the point of
the discharging train which rested on the turmeric paper.

Corresponding effects took place at the negative conductor of a machine.

461. These cases are abundantly sufficient to show that electro-chemical decomposition does not depend upon the simultaneous action of two metallic poles, since a single pole might be used, decomposition ensue, and one or other of the elements liberated, pass to the pole, according as it was positive or negative. In considering the course taken by, and the final arrangement of, the other element, I had little doubt that I should find it had receded towards the other extremity, and that the air itself had acted as a pole, an expectation which was fully confirmed in the following manner.

462. A piece of turmeric paper, not more than 0·4 of an inch in length and 0·5 of an inch in width, was moistened with sulphate of soda and placed upon the edge of a glass plate opposite to, and about two inches from, a point connected with the discharging train (Plate IV. fig. 47.) ; a piece of tinfoil, resting upon the same glass plate, was connected with the machine, and also with the turmeric paper, by a decomposing wire $a$ (312). The machine was then worked, the positive electricity passing into the turmeric paper at the point $p$, and out at the extremity $n$. After forty or fifty turns of the machine, the extremity $n$ was examined, and the two points or angles found deeply coloured by the presence of free alkali (fig. 48.).

463. A similar piece of litmus paper, dipped in solution of sulphate of soda $n$, fig. 49, was now supported upon the end of the discharging train $a$, and its extremity brought opposite to a point $p$, connected with the conductor of the machine. After working the machine for a short time, acid was developed at both the corners towards the point, *i. e.* at both the corners receiving the electricities from the air. Every precaution was taken to prevent this acid from being formed by sparks or brushes passing through the air (322.) ; and these, with the accompanying general facts, are sufficient to show that the acid was really the result of electro-chemical decomposition (466.).

464. Then a long piece of turmeric paper, large at one end and pointed at the other, was moistened in the saline solution, and immediately connected with the conductor of the machine, so that its pointed extremity was opposite a point upon the

discharging train.  When the machine was worked, alkali was evolved at that point; and even when the discharging train was removed, and the electricity left to be diffused and carried off altogether by the air, still alkali was evolved where the electricity left the turmeric paper.

465. Arrangements were then made in which no metallic communication with the decomposing matter was allowed, but both poles (if they might now be called by that name,) formed of air only.  A piece of turmeric paper *a* fig. 50, and a piece of litmus paper *b*, were dipped in solution of sulphate of soda, put together so as to form one moist pointed conductor, and supported on wax between two needle points, one *p* connected by a wire with the conductor of the machine, and the other, *n*, with the discharging train.  The interval in each case between the points was about half an inch : the positive point *p* was opposite the litmus paper; the negative point *n* opposite the turmeric.  The machine was then worked for a time, upon which evidence of decomposition quickly appeared, for the point of the litmus *b* became reddened from acid evolved there, and the point of the turmeric *a* red from a similar and simultaneous evolution of alkali.

466. Upon turning the paper conductor round, so that the litmus point should now give off the positive electricity, and the turmeric point receive it, and working the machine for a short time, both the red spots disappeared, and as on continuing the action of the machine no red spot was re-formed at the litmus extremity, it proved that in the first instance (463.) the effect was not due to the action of brushes or mere electric discharges causing the formation of nitric acid from the air (322.).

467. If the combined litmus and turmeric paper in this experiment be considered as constituting a conductor independent of the machine or the discharging train, and the final places of the elements evolved be considered in relation to this conductor, then it will be found that the acid collects at the *negative* or receiving end or pole of the arrangement, and the alkali at the *positive* or delivering extremity.

468. Similar litmus and turmeric paper points were now placed upon glass plates, and connected by a string six feet long, both string and paper being moistened in solution of

sulphate of soda ; a needle point connected with the machine
was brought opposite the litmus paper point, and another
needle point connected with the discharging train brought opposite the turmeric paper.   On working the machine, acid appeared on the litmus, and alkali on the turmeric paper ; but
the latter was not so abundant as in former cases, for much of
the electricity passed off from the string into the air, and
diminished the quantity discharged at the turmeric point.

469. Finally, a series of four small compound conductors,
consisting of litmus and turmeric paper (fig. 51.) moistened in
solution of sulphate of soda, were supported on glass rods, in
a line at a little distance from each other, between the points
*p* and *n* of the machine and discharging train, so that the electricity might pass in succession through them, entering in at
the litmus points *b, b,* and passing out at the turmeric points *a,
a.*  On working the machine carefully, so as to avoid sparks and
brushes (322.), I soon obtained evidence of decomposition in
each of the moist conductors, for all the litmus points exhibited
free acid; and the turmeric points equally showed free alkali.

470. On using solutions of iodide of potassium, acetate of
lead, &c., similar effects were obtained ; but as they were all
consistent with the results above described, I refrain from describing the appearances minutely.

471. These cases of electro-chemical decomposition are in
their nature exactly of the same kind as those affected under
ordinary circumstances by the voltaic battery, notwithstanding
the great differences as to the presence or absence, or at least
as to the nature of the parts usually called poles ; and also of
the final situation of the elements eliminated at the electrified
boundary surfaces (467.).   They indicate at once an internal
action of the parts suffering decomposition, and appear to show
that the power which is effectual in separating the elements is
exerted there, and not at the poles.   But I shall defer the consideration of this point for a short time (493. 518.), that I may
previously consider another supposed condition of electro-
chemical decomposition *.

* I find (since making and describing these results,) from a note to Sir
Humphry Davy's paper in the Philosophical Transactions, 1807, p. 31, that
that philosopher, in repeating Wollaston's experiment of the decomposition of
water bv common electricity (327. 330.) used an arrangement somewhat like

¶ ii. *Influence of Water in Electro-chemical Decomposition.*

472. It is the opinion of several philosophers, that the presence of water is essential in electro-chemical decomposition,
and also for the evolution of electricity in the voltaic battery
itself.   As the decomposing cell is merely one of the cells of
the battery, into which particular substances are introduced for
the purpose of experiment, it is probable that what is an essential condition in the one case is more or less so in the other.  The
opinion, therefore, that water is necessary to decomposition,
may have been founded on the statement made by Sir Humphry
Davy, that " there are no fluids known, except such as contain
water, which are capable of being made the medium of connexion between the metals or metal of the voltaic apparatus \*:" and
again, " when any substance rendered fluid by heat, consisting
of *water*, oxygen, and inflammable or metallic matter, is exposed
to those wires, similar phenomena (of decomposition) occur †."

473. This opinion has, I think, been shown by other philosophers not to be accurate, though I do not know where to
refer for a contradiction of it.   Sir Humphry Davy himself
said in 1801 ‡, that dry nitre, caustic potash and soda are conductors of galvanism when rendered fluid by a high degree of
heat ; but he must have considered them, or the nitre at least,
as not suffering decomposition, for the statements above were
made by him eleven years subsequently.   In 1826 he also
pointed out, that bodies not containing water, as *fused litharge*
and *chlorate of potassa,* were sufficient to form, with platina
and zinc, powerful electromotive circles § ; but he is here speaking of the *production* of electricity in the pile, and not of its
effects when evolved ; nor do his words at all imply that any
correction of his former distinct statements relative to *decomposition* was required.

474. I may refer to the last series of these Experimental
some of those I have described.   He immersed a guarded platina point connected with the machine in distilled water, and dissipated the electricity from
the water into the air by moistened filaments of cotton. In this way he states
that he obtained oxygen and hydrogen *separately* from each other.  This experiment, had I known of it, ought to have been quoted in an earlier series of
these Researches (342.) ; but it does not remove any of the objections I have
made to the use of Wollaston's apparatus as a test of true chemical action (331.).

\* Elements of Chemical Philosophy, p. 169, &c.        † Ibid. pp. 144, 145.
‡ Journal of the Royal Institution, 1802, p. 53.
§ Philosophical Transactions, 1826, p. 406.

Researches (380. 402.) as setting the matter at rest, by proving that there are hundreds of bodies equally influential with water in this respect; that amongst binary compounds, oxides, chlorides, iodides, and even sulphurets (402.) were effective; and that amongst more complicated compounds, cyanides and salts of equal efficacy, occurred in great numbers (402.).

475. Water, therefore, is in this respect merely one of a very numerous class of substances, instead of being the *only one* and *essential*; and it is of that class one of the *worst* as to its capability of facilitating conduction and suffering decomposition. The reasons why it obtained for a time an exclusive character which it so little deserved are evident, and consist, in the general necessity of a fluid condition (394.); in its being the *only one* of this class of bodies existing in the fluid state at common temperatures; its abundant supply as the great natural solvent; and its constant use in that character in philosophical investigations, because of its having a smaller interfering, injurious, or complicating action upon the bodies, either dissolved or evolved, than any other substance.

476. The analogy of the decomposing or experimental cell to the other cells of the voltaic battery, renders it nearly certain that any of those substances which are decomposable when fluid, as described in my last paper (402.), would, if they could be introduced between the metallic plates of the pile be equally effectual with water if not more so. Sir Humphry Davy found that litharge and chlorate of potassa were thus effectual*. I have constructed various voltaic arrangements, and found the above conclusion to hold good. When any of the following substances in a fused state were interposed between copper and platina, voltaic action more or less powerful was produced. Nitre; chlorate of potassa; carbonate of potassa; sulphate of soda; chloride of lead, of sodium, of bismuth, of calcium; iodide of lead; oxide of bismuth; oxide of lead: the electric current was in the same direction as if acids had acted upon the metals. When any of the same substances, or phosphate of soda, were made to act on platina and iron, still more powerful voltaic combinations of the same kind were produced. When either nitrate of silver or chloride of silver was the fluid substance interposed, there was voltaic action, but the electric current was in the reverse direction.

* Philosophical Transactions, 1826, p. 406.

¶ iii. *Theory of Electro-chemical Decomposition.*

477. The extreme beauty and value of electro-chemical decompositions have given to that power which the voltaic pile
possesses of causing their occurrence an interest surpassing that of any other of its properties; for the power is not
only intimately connected with the continuance, if not with the
production, of the electrical phenomena, but it has furnished
us with the most beautiful demonstrations of the nature of
many compound bodies; has in the hands of Becquerel been
employed in compounding substances; has given us several
new combinations, and sustains us with the hope that when
thoroughly understood it will produce many more.

478. What may be considered as the general facts of electro-
chemical decomposition are agreed to by nearly all who have
written on the subject. They consist in the separation of the
decomposable substance acted upon into its proximate or sometimes ultimate principles, whenever both poles of the pile are
in contact with that substance in a proper condition; in the
evolution of these principles at distant points, *i. e.* at the poles
of the pile, where they are either finally set free or enter into
union with the substance of the poles; and in the constant determination of the evolved elements or principles to particular
poles according to certain well ascertained laws.

479. But the views of men of science vary much as to the
nature of the action by which these effects are produced; and
as it is certain that we shall be better able to apply the power
when we really understand the manner in which it operates,
this difference of opinion is a strong inducement to further inquiry. I have been led to hope that the following investigations might be considered, not as an increase of that which is
doubtful, but a real addition to this branch of knowledge.

480. It will be needful that I briefly state the views of electro-chemical decomposition already put forth, that their present contradictory and unsatisfactory state may be seen before
I give that which seems to me more accurately to agree with
facts; and I have ventured to discuss them freely, trusting that
I should give no offence to their high-minded authors; for I
felt convinced that if I were right, they would be pleased that
their views should serve as stepping-stones for the advance of

science; and that if I were wrong, they would excuse the zeal which misled me, since it was exerted for the service of that great cause whose prosperity and progress they have desired.

481. Grotthuss, in the year 1805, wrote expressly on the decomposition of liquids by voltaic electricity\*. He considers the pile as an electric magnet, *i. e.* as an attractive and repulsive agent; the poles having *attractive* and *repelling* powers. The pole from whence resinous electricity issues attracts hydrogen and repels oxygen, whilst that from which vitreous electricity proceeds attracts oxygen and repels hydrogen; so that each of the elements of a particle of water, for instance, is subject to an attractive and a repulsive force, acting in contrary directions, the centres of action of which are reciprocally opposed. The action of each force in relation to a molecule of water situated in the course of the electric current is in the inverse ratio of the square of the distance at which it is exerted, thus giving (it is stated) for such a molecule a *constant force* †. He explains the appearance of the elements at a distance from each other by referring to a succession of decompositions and recompositions occurring amongst the intervening particles ‡, and he thinks it probable that those which are about to separate at the poles unite to the two electricities there, and in consequence become gases §.

482. Sir Humphry Davy's celebrated Bakerian Lecture on some chemical agencies of electricity was read in November 1806, and is almost entirely occupied in the consideration of *electro-chemical decompositions*. The facts are of the utmost value, and, with the general points established, are universally known. The *mode of action* by which the effects take place is stated very generally, so generally, indeed, that probably a dozen precise schemes of electro-chemical action might be drawn up, differing essentially from each other, yet all agreeing with the statement there given.

483. When Sir Humphry Davy uses more particular expressions, he seems to refer the decomposing effects to the attractions of the poles. This is the case in the " general ex-

* Annales de Chimie, 1806, tom. lviii. p. 64.
† Ibid. pp. 66, 67, also tom. lxiii. p. 20.
‡ Ibid. tom. lviii. p 68, tom. lxiii. p. 20.
§ Ibid. tom. lxiii. p. 34.

pression of facts " given at pp. 28 and 29 of the Philosophical
Transactions for 1807, also at p. 30.   Again at p. 161 of the
Elements of Chemical Philosophy, he speaks of the great attracting powers of the surfaces of the poles.   He mentions the probability of a succession of decompositions and recompositions
throughout the fluid,—agreeing in that respect with Grotthuss * ; and supposes that the attractive and repellent agencies
may be communicated from the metallic surfaces throughout
the whole of the menstruum †, being communicated from *one
particle to another particle of the same kind* ‡, and diminishing
in strength from the place of the poles to the middle point, which
is necessarily neutral §.   In reference to this diminution of power
at increased distances from the poles, he states that in a circuit
of ten inches of water, solution of sulphate of potassa placed
four inches from the positive pole, did not decompose; whereas
when only two inches from that pole, it did render up its
elements ‖.

484. When in 1826 Sir Humphry Davy wrote again on this
subject, he stated that he found nothing to alter in the fundamental theory laid down in the original communication ¶, and
uses the terms attraction and repulsion apparently in the same
sense as before **.

485. Messrs. Riffault and Chompré experimented on this
subject in 1807.   They came to the conclusion that the voltaic
current caused decompositions throughout its whole course in
the humid conductor, not merely as preliminary to the recompositions spoken of by Grotthuss and Davy, but producing final
separation of the elements in the *course* of the current, and
elsewhere than at the poles.   They considered the *negative*
current as collecting and carrying the acids, &c., to the *positive*
pole, and the *positive* current as doing the same duty with the
bases, and collecting them at the *negative* pole.   They likewise
consider the currents as *more powerful* the nearer they are to
their respective poles, and state that the positive current is
*superior* in power to the negative current ††.

486. M. Biot is very cautious in expressing an opinion as to

* Philosophical Transactions, 1807, pp. 29, 30.          † Ibid. p. 39.
‡ Ib'd. p. 29.                § Ibid. p. 42.               ‖ Ibid. p. 42.
¶ Ibid. 1826, p. 383.           ** Ibid. pp. 389, 407, 415.
†† Annales de Chimie, 1807, tom. lxiii. p. 83, &c.

the cause of the separation of the elements of a compound
body*.    But as far as the effects can be understood, he refers
them to the opposite electrical states of the portions of the decomposing substance in the neighbourhood of the two poles.
The fluid is most positive at the positive pole; that state gradually diminishes to the middle distance, where the fluid is
neutral or not electrical; but from thence to the negative pole
it becomes more and more negative †.    When a particle in
salt is decomposed at the negative pole, the acid particle is
considered as acquiring a negative electrical state from the pole,
stronger than that of the surrounding *undecomposed* particles,
and is therefore repelled from amongst them, and from out of
that portion of the liquid towards the positive pole, towards
which also it is drawn by the attraction of the pole itself and
the particles of positive *undecomposed* fluid around it ‡.

487. M. Biot does not appear to admit the successive decompositions and recompositions spoken of by Grotthuss, Davy,
&c. &c.; but seems to consider the substance whilst in transit
as combined with, or rather attached to, the electricity for the
time§, and though it communicates this electricity to the surrounding undecomposed matter with which it is in contact, yet
it retains during the transit a little superiority with respect to
that kind which it first received from the pole, and is, by virtue
of that difference, carried forward through the fluid to the opposite pole‖.

488. This theory implies that decomposition takes place at
both poles upon distinct portions of fluid, and not at all in the
intervening parts.    The latter serve merely as imperfect conductors, which, assuming an electric state, urge particles electrified more highly at the poles through them in opposite directions, by virtue of a series of ordinary electrical attractions and
repulsions¶.

489. M. A. de la Rive investigated this subject particularly,
and published a paper on it in 1825**.    He thinks those who
have referred the phenomena to the attractive powers of the
poles, rather express the general fact than give any explication

---

* Précis Elémentaire de Physique, 3$^{me}$ édition, 1824, tom. i. p. 641.
† Ibid. p. 637.          ‡ Ibid. pp. 641, 642.          § Ibid. p. 636.
‖ Ibid. p. 642.          ¶ Ibid. pp. 633, 642.
** Annales de Chimie, tom. xxviii. p. 190.

of it. He considers the results as due to an actual combination of the elements, or rather of half of them, with the electricities passing from the poles in consequence of a kind of play of affinities between the matter and electricity*. The current from the positive pole combining with the hydrogen, or the bases it finds there, leaves the oxygen and acids at liberty, but carries the substances it is united with across to the negative pole, where, because of the peculiar character of the metal as a conductor†, it is separated from them, entering the metal and leaving the hydrogen or bases upon its surface. In the same manner the electricity from the negative pole sets the hydrogen and bases which it finds there, free, but combines with the oxygen and acids, carries them across to the positive pole, and there deposits them‡. In this respect M. de la Rive's hypothesis accords in part with that of MM. Riffault and Chompré (485.).

490. M. de la Rive considers the portions of matter which are decomposed to be those contiguous to *both* poles§. He does not admit with others the successive decompositions and recompositions in the whole course of the electricity through the humid conductor‖, but thinks the middle parts are in themselves unaltered, or at least serve only to conduct the two contrary currents of electricity and matter which set off from the opposite poles¶. The decomposition, therefore, of a particle of water, or a particle of salt, may take place at either pole, and when once effected, it is final for the time, no recombination taking place, except the momentary union of the transferred particle with the electricity be so considered.

491. The latest communication that I am aware of on the subject is by M. Hachette : its date is October 1832**. It is incidental to the description of the decomposition of water by the magneto-electric currents (346.). One of the results of the experiment is, that "it is not necessary, as has been supposed, that for the chemical decomposition of water, the action of the two electricities, positive and negative, should be simultaneous."

492. It is more than probable that many other views of electro-chemical decomposition may have been published, and perhaps amongst them some which, differing from those above,

* Annales de Chimie, tom. xxviii. pp. 200, 202.
† Ibid. p. 202.   ‡ Ibid. p. 201.   § Ibid. pp. 197, 198.
‖ Ibid. pp. 192, 199.   ¶ Ibid. p. 200.   ** Ibid. tom. li. p. 73.

might, even in my own opinion, were I acquainted with them, obviate the necessity for the publication of my views. If such be the case, I have to regret my ignorance of them, and apologize to the authors.

493. That electro-chemical decomposition does not depend upon any direct attraction and repulsion of the poles (meaning thereby the metallic terminations either of the voltaic battery, or ordinary electrical machine arrangements (312),) upon the elements in contact with or near to them, appeared very evident from the experiments made in air (462, 465, &c.), when the substances evolved did not collect about any poles, but, in obedience to the direction of the current, were evolved, and I would say ejected, at the extremities of the decomposing substance. But notwithstanding the extreme dissimilarity in the character of air and metals, and the almost total difference existing between them as to their mode of conducting electricity, and becoming charged with it, it might perhaps still be contended, although quite hypothetically, that the bounding portions of air were now the surfaces or places of attraction, as the metals had been supposed to be before. In illustration of this and other points, I endeavoured to devise an arrangement by which I could decompose a body against a surface of water, as well as against air or metal, and succeeded in doing so unexceptionably in the following manner. As the experiment for very natural reasons requires many precautions, to be successful, and will be referred to hereafter in illustration of the views I shall venture to give, I must describe it minutely.

494. A glass basin (fig. 52.), four inches in diameter and four inches deep, had a division of mica *a*, fixed across the upper part so as to descend one inch and a half below the edge, and be perfectly water-tight at the sides : a plate of platina *b*, three inches wide, was put into the basin on one side of the division *a*, and retained there by a glass block below, so that any gas produced by it in a future stage of the experiment should not ascend beyond the mica, and cause currents in the liquid on that side. A strong solution of sulphate of magnesia was carefully poured without splashing into the basin, until it rose a little above the lower edge of the mica division *a*, great care being taken that the glass or mica on the unoccupied or *c* side of the division in the figure, should not be moistened by agita-

tion of the solution above the level to which it rose.   A thin
piece of clean cork, well wetted  in distilled water, was then
carefully and lightly  placed on  the solution at the *c* side, and
distilled water poured gently on to it until a stratum the eighth
of an inch in thickness appeared over the sulphate of magnesia ;
all was then left for  a few  minutes, that any solution  adhering
to the cork  might  sink  away from  it, or be removed  by  the
water  on which  it now floated ; and  then more distilled water
was  added in a similar  manner, until  it  reached  nearly to the
top of the glass.   In this way solution of the sulphate occupied
the lower part of the glass, and also the upper on the right hand
side  of the mica ;  but on the left  hand  side  of the division a
stratum of water from *c* to  *d*, one inch and a half in depth, re-
posed upon it, the two  presenting, when  looked  through horizontally,  a  comparatively definite plane of contact.   A second
platina pole *e*, was arranged so  as to be just under the surface
of the water, in a position nearly horizontal, a little inclination
being  given to  it, that gas evolved during decomposition might
escape :  the part immersed was three inches  and a half long by
one inch wide, and about seven eighths of  an inch of water intervened between it and the solution of sulphate of magnesia.

495. The latter  pole *e* was now connected with  the  negative
end of a voltaic battery, of  forty  pairs  of plates four inches
square, whilst  the former pole  *b*  was connected with the positive end.   There  was  action  and  gas evolved at both  poles ;
but from the intervention of  the pure water, the decomposition
was  very  feeble compared  to  what  the  battery would  have
effected  in a uniform solution.   After  a little  while (less than
a minute), magnesia also appeared at  the negative  side :  *it did
not make its  appearance at the  negative metallic pole, but in
the water*, at the  plane where the solution and the water met ;
and on looking at it horizontally, it  could  be  there perceived
lying  in  the water upon the solution, not  rising more than the
fourth of an inch above the latter, whilst the water between it
and the negative pole was  perfectly clear.   On continuing the
action, the  bubbles of hydrogen rising upwards from the negative pole impressed a circulatory movement on  the stratum
of  water,  upwards  in  the  middle,  and  downwards  at  the
side, which gradually gave an ascending form to the cloud of
magnesia in the part  just under the pole, having an appearance

as if it were there attracted to it; but this was altogether an effect of the currents, and did not occur until long after the phenomena looked for were satisfactorily ascertained.

496. After a little while the voltaic communication was broken, and the platina poles removed with as little agitation as possible from the water and solution, for the purpose of examining the liquid adhering to them. The pole *e*, when touched by turmeric paper, gave no trace of alkali, nor could anything but pure water be found upon it. The pole *b*, though drawn through a much greater depth and quantity of fluid, was found so acid as to give abundant evidence to litmus paper, the tongue, and other tests. Hence there had been no interference of alkaline salts in any way, undergoing first decomposition, and then causing the separation of the magnesia at a distance from the pole by mere chemical agencies. This experiment was repeated again and again, and always successfully.

497. As, therefore, the substances evolved in cases of electro-chemical decomposition may be made to appear against air (465. 469.),—which, according to common language, is not a conductor, nor is decomposed, or against water (495.), which is a conductor, and can be decomposed,—as well as against the metal poles, which are excellent conductors, but undecomposable, there appears but little reason to consider the phenomena generally, as due to the *attraction* or attractive powers of the latter, when used in the ordinary way, since similar attractions can hardly be imagined in the former instances.

498. It may be said that the surfaces of air or of water in these cases become the poles, and exert attractive powers; but what proof is there of that, except the fact that the matters evolved collect there, which is the point to be explained, and cannot be justly quoted as its own explanation? Or it may be said, that any section of the humid conductor, as that in the present case, where the solution and the water meet, may be considered as representing the pole. But such does not appear to me to be the view of those who have written on the subject, certainly not of some of them, and is inconsistent with the supposed laws which they have assumed, as governing the diminution of power at increased distances from the poles.

499. Grotthuss, for instance, describes the poles as centres of attractive and repulsive forces (481.), these forces varying

inversely as the squares of the distances, and says, therefore, that a particle placed anywhere between the poles will be acted upon by a constant force. But the compound force, resulting from such a combination as he supposes, would be anything but a constant force; it would evidently be a force greatest at the poles, and diminishing to the middle distance. Grotthuss is right, however, *in the fact*, according to my experiments (502. 505.), that the particles are acted upon by equal force everywhere in the circuit, when the conditions of the experiment are the simplest possible; but the fact is against his theory, and is also, I think, against all theories that place the decomposing effect in the attractive power of the poles.

500. Sir Humphry Davy, who also speaks of the *diminution* of power with increase of distance from the poles* (483.), supposes, that when both poles are acting on substances to decompose them, still the power of decomposition *diminishes* to the middle distance. In this statement of fact he is opposed to Grotthuss, and quotes an experiment in which sulphate of potassa, placed at different distances from the poles in a humid conductor of constant length, decomposed when near the pole, but not when at a distance. Such a consequence would necessarily result theoretically from considering the poles as centres of attraction and repulsion; but I have not found the statement borne out by other experiments (505.); and in the one quoted by him the effect was doubtless due to some of the many interfering causes of variation which attend such investigations.

501. A glass vessel had a platina plate fixed perpendicularly across it, so as to divide it into two cells: a head of mica was fixed over it, so as to collect the gas it might evolve during experiments; then each cell, and the space beneath the mica, was filled with dilute sulphuric acid. Two poles were provided, consisting each of a platina wire terminated by a plate of the same metal; each was fixed into a tube passing through its upper end by an air-tight joint, that it might be moveable, and yet that the gas evolved at it might be collected. The tubes were filled with the acid, and one immersed in each cell. Each platina pole was equal in surface to one side of the dividing plate in the middle glass vessel, and the whole might be con-

* Philosophical Transactions, 1807, p. 42.

sidered as an arrangement between the poles of the battery of a humid decomposable conductor divided in the middle by the interposed platina diaphragm. It was easy, when required, to draw one of the poles further up the tube, and then the platina diaphragm was no longer in the middle of the humid conductor. But whether it was thus arranged at the middle, or towards one side, it always evolved a quantity of oxygen and hydrogen equal to that evolved by the extreme plates*.

502. If the wires of a galvanometer be terminated by plates, and these be immersed in dilute acid, contained in a regularly formed rectangular glass trough, connected at each end with a voltaic battery by poles equal to the section of the fluid, a part of the electricity will pass through the instrument and cause a certain deflection. And if the plates are always retained at the *same distance from each other* and from the sides of the trough, are always parallel to each other, and uniformly placed relative to the fluid, then, whether they are immersed near the middle of the decomposing solution, or at one end, still the instrument will indicate the same deflection, and consequently the same electric influence.

503. It is very evident, that when the width of the decom— posing conductor varies, as is always the case when mere wires or plates, as poles, are dipped into or are surrounded by solu- tion, no constant expression can be given as to the action upon a single particle placed in the course of the current, nor any conclusion of use, relative to the supposed attractive or repul- sive force of the poles, be drawn. The force will vary as the distance from the pole varies; as the particle is directly between the poles, or more or less on one side; and even as it is nearer to or further from the sides of the containing vessels, or as the shape of the vessel itself varies; and, in fact by making variations in the form of the arrangement, the force upon any single particle may be made to increase, or diminish, or remain constant, whilst the distance between the particle and the pole shall remain the same; or the force may be made to increase, or diminish, or remain constant, either as the distance increases or as it diminishes.

* There are certain precautions, in this and such experiments, which can only be understood and guarded against by a knowledge of the phenomena to be described in the first part of the Sixth Series of these Researches.

504. From numerous experiments, I am led to believe the following general expression to be correct; but I purpose examining it much further, and would therefore wish not to be considered at present as pledged to its accuracy. The *sum of chemical decomposition is constant* for any section taken across a decomposing conductor, uniform in its nature, at whatever distance the poles may be from each other or from the section; or however that section may intersect the currents, whether directly across them, or so oblique as to reach almost from pole to pole, or whether it be plain, or curved, or irregular in the utmost degree; provided the current of electricity be retained constant in quantity (377.), and that the section passes through every part of the current through the decomposing conductor.

505. I have reason to believe that the statement might be made still more general, and expressed thus : That *for a constant quantity of electricity, whatever the decomposing conductor may be, whether water, saline solutions, acids, fused bodies, &c., the amount of electro-chemical action is also a constant quantity, i. e. would always be equivalent to a standard chemical effect founded upon ordinary chemical affinity.* I have this investigation in hand, with several others, and shall be prepared to give it in the next series but one of these Researches.

506. Many other arguments might be adduced against the hypotheses of the attraction of the poles being the cause of electro-chemical decomposition; but I would rather pass on to the view I have thought more consistent with facts, with this single remark; that if decomposition by the voltaic battery depended upon the attraction of the poles, or the parts about them, being stronger than the mutual attraction of the particles separated, it would follow that the weakest *electrical* attraction was stronger than, if not the strongest, yet very strong *chemical* attraction, namely, such as exists between oxygen and hydrogen, potassium and oxygen, chloride and sodium, acid and alkali, &c., a consequence which, although perhaps not impossible, seems in the present state of the subject very unlikely.

507. The view which M. De la Rive has taken (489.), and also MM. Riffault and Chompré (485.), of the manner in which electro-chemical decomposition is effected, is very different to that already considered, and is not affected by either the argu-

ments or facts urged against the latter. Considering it as stated
by the former philosopher, it appears to me to be incompetent
to account for the experiments of decomposition against surfaces
of air (462. 469.) and water (495.), which I have described; for
if the physical differences between metals and humid conductors, which M. de la Rive supposes to account for the transmission of the compound of matter and electricity in the latter,
and the transmission of the electricity only with the rejection
of the matter in the former, be allowed for a moment, still the
analogy of air to metal is, electrically considered, so small, that
instead of the former replacing the latter (462.), an effect the
very reverse might have been expected. Or if even that were
allowed, the experiment with water (495.) at once sets the matter
at rest, the decomposing pole being now of a substance which
is admitted as competent to transmit the assumed compound of
electricity and matter.

508. With regard to the views of MM. Riffault and Chompré
(485.), the occurrence of decomposition alone in the *course* of
the current is so contrary to the well-known effects obtained in
the forms of experiment adopted up to this time, that it must
be proved before the hypothesis depending on it need be considered.

509. The consideration of the various theories of electro-
chemical decomposition, whilst it has made me diffident, has
also give me confidence to add another to the number; for it is
because the one I have to propose appears, after the most atten-
tive consideration, to explain and agree with the immense collection of facts belonging to this branch of science, and to remain
uncontradicted by, or unopposed to, any of them, that I have
been encouraged to give it.

510. Electro-chemical decomposition is well-known to depend
essentially upon the *current* of electricity. I have shown that in
certain cases (375.) the decomposition is proportionate to the
quantity of electricity passing, whatever may be its intensity or
its source, and that the same is probably true for all cases (377.),
even when the utmost generality is taken on the one hand, and
great precision of expression on the other (505.).

511. In speaking of the current, I find myself obliged to be
still more particular than on a former occasion (283.), in consequence of the variety of views taken by philosophers, all agree-

ing in the effect of the current itself. Some philosophers, with Franklin, assume but one electric fluid; and such must agree together in the general uniformity and character of the electric current. Others assume two electric fluids; and here singular differences have arisen.

512. MM. Riffault and Chompré, for instance, consider the positive and negative currents each as causing decomposition, and state that the positive current is *more powerful* than the negative current\*, the nitrate of soda being, under similar circumstances, decomposed by the former, but not by the latter.

513. M. Hachette states† that "it is not necessary, as has been believed, that the action of the two electricities, positive and negative, should be simultaneous for the decomposition of water." The passage implying, if I have caught the meaning aright, that one electricity can be obtained, and can be applied in effecting decompositions, independent of the other.

514. The view of M. de la Rive to a certain extent agrees with that of M. Hachette, for he considers that the two electricities decompose separate portions of water (490.) ‡. In one passage he speaks of the two electricities as two influences, wishing perhaps to avoid offering a decided opinion upon the independent existence of electric fluids; but as these influences are considered as combining with the elements set free as by a species of chemical affinity, and for the time entirely masking their character, great vagueness of idea is thus introduced, inasmuch as such a species of combination can only be conceived to take place between things having independent existences. The two elementary electric currents, moving in opposite directions, from pole to pole, constitute the ordinary *voltaic current*.

515. M. Grotthuss is inclined to believe that the elements of water, when about to separate at the poles, combine with the electricities, and so become gases. M. de la Rive's view is the exact reverse of this: whilst passing through the fluid, they are, according to him, compounds with the electricities; when evolved at the poles, they are de-electrified.

---

516. I have sought amongst the various experiments quoted

\* Annales de Chimie, 1807, tom. lxiii. p. 84.    † Ibid. 1832, tom. li. p. 73.
‡ Ibid. 1825, tom. xxviii. pp. 197, 201.

in support of these views, or connected with electro-chemical decompositions or electric currents, for any which might be considered as sustaining the theory of two electricities rather than that of one, but have not been able to perceive a single fact which could be brought forward for such a purpose : or, admitting the hypothesis of two electricities, much less have I been able to perceive the slightest grounds for believing that one electricity in a current can be more powerful than the other, or that it can be present without the other, or that one can be varied or in the slightest degree affected, without a corresponding variation in the other*.  If, upon the supposition of two electricities, a current of one can be obtained without the other, or the current of one be exalted or diminished more than the other, we might surely expect some variation either of the chemical or magnetical effects, or of both; but no such variations have been observed.   If a current be so directed that it may act chemically in one part of its course, and magnetically in another, the two actions are always found to take place together.   A current has not, to my knowledge, been produced which could act chemically and not magnetically, nor any which can act on the magnet, and not *at the same time* chemically†.

517. *Judging from facts only,* there is not as yet the slightest reason for considering the influence which is present in what we call the electric current,—whether in metals or fused bodies or humid conductors, or even in air, flame, and rarefied elastic media, —as a compound or complicated influence.   It has never been resolved into simpler or elementary influences, and may perhaps best be conceived of as *an axis of power having contrary forces, exactly equal in amount, in contrary directions.*

---

518. Passing to the consideration of electro-chemical decomposition, it appears to me that the effect is produced by an *internal corpuscular action*, exerted according to the direction of the electric current, and that it is due to a force either *superadded to,* or *giving direction to the ordinary chemical affinity* of the bodies present.   The body under decomposition may be

---

* See now in relation to this subject, 1627—1645.—*Dec.* 1838.

† Thermo–electric currents are of course no exception, because when they fail to act chemically they also fail to be currents.

considered as a mass of acting particles, all those which are included in the course of the electric current contributing to the
final effect ; and it is because the ordinary chemical affinity is
relieved, weakened, or partly neutralized by the influence of
the electric current in one direction parallel to the course of
the latter, and strengthened or added to in the opposite direction, that the combining particles have a tendency to pass in
opposite courses.

519. In this view the effect is considered as *essentially dependent* upon the *mutual chemical affinity* of the particles of
opposite kinds.   Particles *a a*, fig. 53, could not be transferred
or travel from one pole N towards the other P, unless they
found particles of the opposite kind *b b*, ready to pass in the
contrary direction : for it is by virtue of their increased affinity
for those particles, combined with their diminished affinity for
such as are behind them in their course, that they are urged
forward : and when any one particle *a*, fig. 54, arrives at the
pole, it is excluded or set free, because the particle *b* of the
opposite kind, with which it was the moment before in combination, has, under the superinducing influence of the current,
a greater attraction for the particle *a′*, which is before it in its
course, than for the particle *a*, towards which its affinity has
been weakened.

520. As far as regards any single compound particle, the
case may be considered as analogous to one of ordinary decomposition, for in fig. 54, *a* may be conceived to be expelled from
the compound *a b* by the superior attraction of *a′* for *b*, that
superior attraction belonging to it in consequence of the relative
position of *a′ b* and *a* to the direction of the axis of electric
power (517.) superinduced by the current.  But as all the compound particles in the course of the current, except those
actually in contact with the poles, act conjointly, and consist of
elementary particles, which, whilst they are in one direction ex-
pelling, are in the other being expelled, the case becomes more
complicated, but not more difficult of comprehension.

521. It is not here assumed that the acting particles must be
in a right line between the poles.  The lines of action which
may be supposed to represent the electric currents passing
through a decomposing liquid, have in many experiments very
irregular forms ; and even in the simplest case of two wires or
points immersed as poles in a drop or larger single portion of

fluid, these lines must diverge rapidly from the poles; and the direction in which the chemical affinity between particles is most powerfully modified (519. 520.) will vary with the direction of these lines, according constantly with them. But even in reference to these lines or currents, it is not supposed that the particles which mutually affect each other must of necessity be parallel to them, but only that they shall accord generally with their direction. Two particles, placed in a line perpendicular to the electric current passing in any particular place, are not supposed to have their ordinary chemical relations towards each other affected; but as the line joining them is inclined one way to the current their mutual affinity is increased; as it is inclined in the other direction it is diminished; and the effect is a maximum, when that line is parallel to the current *.

522. That the actions, of whatever kind they may be, take place frequently in oblique directions is evident from the circumstance of those particles being included which in numerous cases are not in a line between the poles. Thus, when wires are used as poles in a glass of solution, the decompositions and recompositions occur to the right or left of the direct line between the poles, and indeed in every part to which the currents extend, as is proved by many experiments, and must therefore often occur between particles obliquely placed as respects the current itself; and when a metallic vessel containing the solution is made one pole, whilst a mere point or wire is used for the other, the decompositions and recompositions must frequently be still more oblique to the course of the currents.

523. The theory which I have ventured to put forth (almost) requires an admission, that in a compound body capable of electro-chemical decomposition the elementary particles have a mutual relation to, and influence upon each other, extending beyond those with which they are immediately combined. Thus in water, a particle of hydrogen in combination with oxygen is considered as not altogether indifferent to other particles of oxygen, although they are combined with other particles of hydrogen; but to have an affinity or attraction towards them, which, though it does not at all approach in force, under ordinary circumstances, to that by which it is combined with its own particle, can, under the electric influence, exerted in a defi-

* In reference to this subject see now electrolytic induction and discharge, Series XII. ¶ viii. 1343—1351, &c.—*Dec.* 1838.

nite direction, be made even to surpass it. This general relation of particles already in combination to other particles with
which they are not combined, is sufficiently distinct in numerous results of a purely chemical character; especially in those
where partial decompositions only take place, and in Berthollet's
experiments on the effects of quantity upon affinity: and it
probably has a direct relation to, and connexion with, attraction
of aggregation, both in solids and fluids. It is a remarkable
circumstance, that in gases and vapours, where the attraction
of aggregation ceases, there likewise the decomposing powers
of electricity apparently cease, and there also the chemical
action of quantity is no longer evident. It seems not unlikely,
that the inability to suffer decomposition in these cases may be
dependent upon the absence of that mutual attractive relation
of the particles which is the cause of aggregation.

524. I hope I have now distinctly stated, although in general
terms, the view I entertain of the cause of electro-chemical decomposition, *as far as that cause can at present be traced and
understood.* I conceive the effects to arise from forces which
are *internal,* relative to the matter under decomposition—and
not *external,* as they might be considered, if directly dependent
upon the poles. I suppose that the effects are due to a modification, by the electric current, of the chemical affinity of the
particles through or by which that current is passing, giving
them the power of acting more forcibly in one direction than in
another, and consequently making them travel by a series of
successive decompositions and recompositions in opposite directions, and finally causing their expulsion or exclusion at the
boundaries of the body under decomposition, in the direction
of the current, *and that* in larger or smaller quantities, according
as the current is more or less powerful (377.). I think, therefore, it would be more philosophical, and more directly expressive of the facts, to speak of such a body, in relation to the current passing through it, rather than to the poles, as they are
usually called, in contact with it; and say that whilst under decomposition, oxygen, chlorine, iodine, acids, &c., are rendered
at its negative extremity, and combustibles, metals, alkalies,
bases, &c., at its positive extremity (467.). I do not believe
that a substance can be transferred in the electric current beyond the point where it ceases to find particles with which it
can combine; and I may refer to the experiments made in air

(465.), and in water (495.), already quoted, for facts illustrating these views in the first instance ; to which I will now add others.

525. In order to show the dependence of the decomposition and transfer of elements upon the chemical affinity of the substances present, experiments were made upon sulphuric acid in the following manner.    Dilute sulphuric acid was prepared : its specific gravity was 1021·2.    A solution of sulphate of soda was also prepared, of such strength that a measure of it contained exactly as much sulphuric acid as an equal measure of the diluted acid just referred to.    A solution of pure soda, and another of pure ammonia, were likewise prepared, of such strengths that a measure of either should be exactly neutralized by a measure of the prepared sulphuric acid.

526. Four glass cups were then arranged, as in fig. 55 ; seventeen measures of the free sulphuric acid (525.) were put into each of the vessels $a$ and $b$, and seventeen measures of the solution of sulphate of soda into each of the vessels A and B. Asbestus, which had been well washed in acid, acted upon by the voltaic pile, well washed in water, and dried by pressure, was used to connect $a$ with $b$ and A with B, the portions being as equal as they could be made in quantity, and cut as short as was consistent with their performing the part of effectual communications.    $b$ and A were connected by two platina plates or poles soldered to the extremities of one wire, and the cups $a$ and B were by similar platina plates connected with a voltaic battery of forty pairs of plates four inches square, that in $a$ being connected with the negative, and that in B with the positive pole.    The battery, which was not powerfully charged, was retained in communication above half an hour.    In this manner it was certain that the same electric current had passed through $a\ b$ and A B, and that in each instance the same quantity and strength of acid had been submitted to its action, but in one case merely dissolved in water, and in the other dissolved and also combined with an alkali.

527. On breaking the connexion with the battery, the portions of asbestus were lifted out, and the drops hanging at the ends allowed to fall each into its respective vessel.    The acids in $a$ and $b$ were then first compared, for which purpose two evaporating dishes were balanced, and the acid from $a$ put into one, and that from $b$ into the other ; but as one was a little heavier than the other, a small drop was transferred from the

JUNE 1833.] *Transference of acid and alkali.* 153

heavier to the lighter, and the two rendered equal in weight. Being neutralized by the addition of the soda solution (525.), that from *a*, or the negative vessel, required 15 parts of the soda solution, and that from *b*, or the positive vessel, required 16·3 parts. That the sum of these is not 34 parts is principally due to the acid removed with the asbestus; but taking the mean of 15·65 parts, it would appear that a twenty-fourth part of the acid originally in the vessel *a* had passed, through the influence of the electric current, from *a* into *b*.

528. In comparing the difference of acid in A and B, the necessary equality of weight was considered as of no consequence, because the solution was at first neutral, and would not, therefore, affect the test liquids, and all the evolved acid would be in B, and the free alkali in A. The solution in A required 3·2 measures of the prepared acid (525.) to neutralize it, and the solution in B required also 3·2 measures of the soda solution (525.) to neutralize it. As the asbestus must have removed a little acid and alkali from the glasses, these quantities are by so much too small; and therefore it would appear that about a tenth of the acid originally in the vessel A had been transferred into B during the continuance of the electric action.

529. In another similar experiment, whilst a thirty-fifth part of the acid passed from *a* to *b* in the free acid vessels, between a tenth and an eleventh passed from A to B in the combined acid vessels. Other experiments of the same kind gave similar results.

530. The variation of electro-chemical decomposition, the transfer of elements and their accumulation at the poles, according as the substance submitted to action consists of particles opposed more or less in their chemical affinity, together with the consequent influence of the latter circumstances, are sufficiently obvious in these cases, where sulphuric acid is acted upon in the *same quantity* by the *same* electric current, but in one case opposed to the comparatively weak affinity of water for it, and in the other to the stronger one of soda. In the latter case the quantity transferred is from two and a half to three times what it is in the former; and it appears therefore very evident that the transfer is greatly dependent upon the mutual action of the particles of the decomposing bodies*.

* See the note to (675).—*Dec.* 1838.

531. In some of the experiments the acid from the vessels *a* and *b* was neutralized by ammonia, then evaporated to dryness, heated to redness, and the residue examined for sulphates. In these cases more sulphate was always obtained from *a* than from *b*; showing that it had been impossible to exclude saline bases (derived from the asbestus, the glass, or perhaps impurities originally in the acid,) and that they had helped in transferring the acid into *b*. But the quantity was small, and the acid was principally transferred by relation to the water present.

532. I endeavoured to arrange certain experiments by which saline solutions should be decomposed against surfaces of water; and at first worked with the electric machine upon a piece of bibulous paper, or asbestus moistened in the solution, and in contact at its two extremities with pointed pieces of paper moistened in pure water, which served to carry the electric current to and from the solution in the middle piece. But I found numerous interfering difficulties. Thus, the water and solutions in the pieces of paper could not be prevented from mingling at the point where they touched. Again, sufficient acid could be derived from the paper connected with the discharging train, or it may be even from the air itself, under the influence of electric action, to neutralize the alkali developed at the positive extremity of the decomposing solution, and so not merely prevent its appearance, but actually transfer it on to the metal termination: and, in fact, when the paper points were not allowed to touch there, and the machine was worked until alkali was evolved at the delivering or positive end of the turmeric paper, containing the sulphate of soda solution, it was merely necessary to place the opposite receiving point of the paper connected with the discharging train, which had been moistened by distilled water, upon the brown turmeric point and press them together, when the alkaline effect immediately disappeared.

533. The experiment with sulphate of magnesia already described (495.) is a case in point, however, and shows most clearly that the sulphuric acid and magnesia contributed to each other's transfer and final evolution, exactly as the same acid and soda affected each other in the results just given (527, &c.); and that so soon as the magnesia advanced beyond the reach of the acid, and found no other substance with which it could

combine, it appeared in its proper character, and was no longer able to continue its progress towards the negative pole.

534. The theory I have ventured to put forth appears to me to explain all the prominent features of electro-chemical decomposition in a satisfactory manner.

535. In the first place, it explains why, in all ordinary cases, the evolved substances *appear only at the poles*; for the poles are the limiting surfaces of the decomposing substance, and except at them, every particle finds other particles having a contrary tendency with which it can combine.

536. Then it explains why, in numerous cases, the elements or evolved substances are not *retained* by the poles ; and this is no small difficulty in those theories which refer the decomposing effect directly to the attractive power of the poles. If, in accordance with the usual theory, a piece of platina be supposed to have sufficient power to attract a particle of hydrogen from the particle of oxygen with which it was the instant before combined, there seems no sufficient reason, nor any fact, except those to be explained, which show why it should not, according to analogy with all ordinary attractive forces, as those of gravitation, magnetism, cohesion, chemical affinity, &c., *retain* that particle which it had just before taken from a distance and from previous combination. Yet it does not do so, but allows it to escape freely. Nor does this depend upon its assuming the gaseous state, for acids and alkalies, &c., are left equally at liberty to diffuse themselves through the fluid surrounding the pole, and show no particular tendency to combine with or adhere to the latter. And though there are plenty of cases where combination with the pole does take place, they do not at all explain the instances of non-combination, and do not therefore in their particular action reveal the general principle of decomposition.

537. But in the theory that I have just given, the effect appears to be a natural consequence of the action : the evolved substances are *expelled* from the decomposing mass (518. 519.), not *drawn out by an attraction* which ceases to act on one particle without any assignable reason, while it continues to act on another of the same kind : and whether the poles be metal, water, or air, still the substances are evolved, and are sometimes set free, whilst at others they unite to the matter of the poles,

according to the chemical nature of the latter, *i. e.* their chemical relation to those particles which are leaving the substance under operation.

538. The theory accounts for the *transfer of elements* in a manner which seems to me at present to leave nothing unexplained; and it was, indeed, the phenomena of transfer in the numerous cases of decomposition of bodies rendered fluid by heat (380. 402.), which, in conjunction with the experiments in air, led to its construction.    Such cases as the former where binary compounds of easy decomposability are acted upon, are perhaps the best to illustrate the theory.

539. Chloride of lead, for instance, fused in a bent tube (400.), and decomposed by platina wires, evolves lead, passing to what is usually called the negative pole, and chlorine, which being evolved at the positive pole, is in part set free, and in part combines with the platina.    The chloride of platina formed, being soluble in the chloride of lead, is subject to decomposition, and the platina itself is gradually transferred across the decomposing matter, and found with the lead at the negative pole.

540. Iodide of lead evolves abundance of lead at the negative pole, and abundance of iodine at the positive pole.

541. Chloride of silver furnishes a beautiful instance, especially when decomposed by silver wire poles.    Upon fusing a portion of it on a piece of glass, and bringing the poles into contact with it, there is abundance of silver evolved at the negative pole, and an equal abundance absorbed at the positive pole, for no chlorine is set free: and by careful management, the negative wire may be withdrawn from the fused globule as the silver is reduced there, the latter serving as the continuation of the pole, until a wire or thread of revived silver, five or six inches in length, is produced; at the same time the silver at the positive pole is as rapidly dissolved by the chlorine, which seizes upon it, so that the wire has to be continually advanced as it is melted away.    The whole experiment includes the action of only two elements, silver and chlorine, and illustrates in a beautiful manner their progress in opposite directions, parallel to the electric current, which is for the time giving a uniform general direction to their mutual affinities (524.).

542. According to my theory, an element or a substance not decomposable under the circumstances of the experiment, (as, for instance, a dilute acid or alkali,) should not be transferred,

or pass from pole to pole, unless it be in chemical relation to some other element or substance tending to pass in the opposite direction, for the effect is considered as essentially due to the mutual relation of such particles. But the theories attributing the determination of the elements to the attractions and repulsions of the poles require no such condition, *i. e.* there is no reason apparent why the attraction of the positive pole, and the repulsion of the negative pole, upon a particle of free acid, placed in water between them, should not (with equal currents of electricity) be as strong as if that particle were previously combined with alkali ; but, on the contrary, as they have not a powerful chemical affinity to overcome, there is every reason to suppose they would be stronger, and would sooner bring the acid to rest at the positive pole *. Yet such is not the case, as has been shown by the experiments on free and combined acid (526. 528.).

543. Neither does M. de la Rive's theory, as I understand it, *require* that the particles should be in combination : it does not even admit, where there are two sets of particles capable of combining with and passing by each other, that they do combine, but supposes that they travel as separate compounds of matter and electricity. Yet in fact the free substance *cannot* travel, the combined one *can.*

544. It is very difficult to find cases amongst solutions or fluids which shall illustrate this point, because of the difficulty of finding two fluids which shall conduct, shall not mingle, and in which an element evolved from one shall not find a combinable element in the other. *Solutions* of acids or alkalies will not answer, because they exist by virtue of an attraction ; and increasing the solubility of a body in one direction, and diminishing it in the opposite, is just as good a reason for transfer, as modifying the affinity between the acids and alkalies themselves †. Nevertheless the case of sulphate of magnesia is in point (494. 495.), and shows that *one element or principle only* has no power of transference or of passing towards either pole.

545. Many of the metals, however, in their solid state, offer very fair instances of the kind required. Thus, if a plate of platina be used as the positive pole in a solution of sulphuric

---

* Even Sir Humphry Davy considered the attraction of the pole as being communicated from one particle to another of the *same* kind (483).

† See the note to 675.—*Dec.* 1838.

acid, oxygen will pass towards it, and so will acid; but these
are not substances having such chemical relation to the platina
as, even under the favourable condition superinduced by the
current (518. 524.), to combine with it; the platina therefore
remains where it was first placed, and has no tendency to pass
towards the negative pole.    But if a plate of iron, zinc or copper, be substituted for the platina, then the oxygen and acid
can combine with these, and the metal immediately begins to
travel (as an oxide) to the opposite pole, and is finally deposited
there.    Or if, retaining the platina pole, a fused chloride, as
of lead, zinc, silver, &c., be substituted for the sulphuric acid,
then, as the platina finds an element it can combine with, it
enters into union, acts as other elements do in cases of voltaic
decomposition, is rapidly transferred across the melted matter,
and expelled at the negative pole.

546. I can see but little reason in the theories referring the
electro-chemical decomposition to the attractions and repulsions of the poles, and I can perceive none in M. de la Rive's
theory, why the metal of the positive pole should not be transferred across the intervening conductor, and deposited at the
negative pole, even when it cannot act chemically upon the
element of the fluid surrounding it.    It cannot be referred to
the attraction of cohesion preventing such an effect; for if the
pole be made of the lightest spongy platina, the effect is the
same.    Or if gold precipitated by sulphate of iron be diffused
through the solution, still accumulation of it at the negative
pole will not take place; and yet in it the attraction of cohesion
is almost perfectly overcome, the particles are so small as to
remain for hours in suspension, and are perfectly free to move
by the slightest impulse towards either pole; and *if in relation*
by chemical affinity to any substance present, are powerfully
determined to the negative pole*.

* In making this experiment, care must be taken that no substance be present that can act chemically on the gold.   Although I used the metal very
carefully washed, and diffused through dilute sulphuric acid, yet in the first
instance I obtained gold at the negative pole, and the effect was repeated
when the platina poles were changed.   But on examining the clear liquor in
the cell, after subsidence of the metallic gold, I found a little of that metal in
solution, and a little chlorine was also present.   I therefore well washed the
gold which had thus been subjected to voltaic action, diffused it through other
pure dilute sulphuric acid, and then found, that on subjecting it to the action
of the pile, not the slightest tendency to the negative pole could be perceived.

547. In support of these arguments, it may be observed, that as yet no determination of a substance to a pole, or tendency to obey the electric current, has been observed (that I am aware of,) in cases of mere mixture; *i. e.* a substance diffused through a fluid, but having no sensible chemical affinity with it, or with substances that may be evolved from it during the action, does not in any case seem to be affected by the electric current. Pulverised charcoal was diffused through dilute sulphuric acid, and subjected with the solution to the action of a voltaic battery, terminated by platina poles; but not the slightest tendency of the charcoal to the negative pole could be observed. Sublimed sulphur was diffused through similar acid, and submitted to the same action, a silver plate being used as the negative pole; but the sulphur had no tendency to pass to that pole, the silver was not tarnished, nor did any sulphuretted hydrogen appear. The case of magnesia and water (495. 533.), with those of comminuted metals in certain solutions (546.), are also of this kind; and, in fact, substances which have the instant before been powerfully determined towards the pole, as magnesia from sulphate of magnesia, become entirely *indifferent to it* the moment they assume their independent state, and pass away, diffusing themselves through the surrounding fluid.

548. There are, it is true, many instances of insoluble bodies being acted upon, as glass, sulphate of baryta, marble, slate, basalt, &c., but they form no exception; for the substances they give up are in direct and strong relation as to chemical affinity with those which they find in the surrounding solution, so that these decompositions enter into the class of ordinary effects.

------------

549. It may be expressed as a general consequence, that the more directly bodies are opposed to each other in chemical affinity, the more *ready* is their separation from each other in cases of electro-chemical decomposition, *i. e.* provided other circumstances, as insolubility, deficient conducting power, proportions, &c., do not interfere. This is well known to be the case with water and saline solutions; and I have found it to be equally true with *dry* chlorides, iodides, salts, &c., rendered subject to electro-chemical decomposition by fusion (402.). So that in applying the voltaic battery for the purpose of decom-

posing bodies not yet resolved into forms of matter simpler than their own, it must be remembered, that success may depend not upon the weakness, or failure upon the strength, of the affinity by which the elements sought for are held together, but contrariwise; and then modes of application may be devised, by which, in *association* with ordinary chemical powers, and the assistance of fusion (394. 417.), we may be able to penetrate much further than at present into the constitution of our chemical elements.

550. Some of the most beautiful and surprising cases of electro-chemical decomposition and *transfer* which Sir Humphry Davy described in his celebrated paper [*], were those in which acids were passed hrough alkalies, and alkalies or earths through acids [†]; and the way in which substances having the most powerful attractions for each other were thus prevented from combining, or, as it is said, had their natural affinity destroyed or suspended throughout the whole of the circuit, excited the utmost astonishment. But if I be right in the view I have taken of the effects, it will appear, that that which made the *wonder*, is in fact the *essential condition* of transfer and decomposition, and that the more alkali there is in the course of an acid, the more will the transfer of that acid be facilitated from pole to pole; and perhaps a better illustration of the difference between the theory I have ventured, and those previously existing, cannot be offered than the views they respectively give of such facts as these.

551. The instances in which sulphuric acid could not be passed through baryta, or baryta through sulphuric acid [‡], because of the precipitation of sulphate of baryta, enter within the pale of the law already described (380. 412.), by which liquidity is so generally required for conduction and decomposition. In assuming the solid state of sulphate of baryta, these bodies became virtually non-conductors to electricity of so low a tension as that of the voltaic battery, and the power of the latter over them was almost infinitely diminished.

552. The theory I have advanced accords in a most satisfactory manner with the fact of an element or substance finding its place of rest, or rather of evolution, sometimes at one

[*] Philosophical Transactions, 1807, p. 1.          [†] Ibid. p. 24, &c.
[‡] Ibid. p. 25, &c.

pole and sometimes at the other.    Sulphur illustrates this
effect very well*.    When sulphuric acid is decomposed by the
pile, sulphur is evolved at the negative pole; but when sulphuret of silver is decomposed in a similar way (436.), then the
sulphur appears at the positive pole; and if a hot platina pole
be used so as to vaporize the sulphur evolved in the latter case,
then the relation of that pole to the sulphur is exactly the same
as the relation of the same pole to oxygen upon its immersion
in water.    In both cases the element evolved is liberated at the
pole, but not retained by it; but by virtue of its elastic, un-
combinable, and immiscible condition passes away into the surrounding medium.    The sulphur is evidently determined in
these opposite directions by its opposite chemical relations to
oxygen and silver; and it is to such relations generally that I
have referred all electro-chemical phenomena.    Where they
do not exist, no electro-chemical action can take place.    Where
they are strongest, it is most powerful; where they are reversed, the direction of transfer of the substance is reversed
with them.

553. *Water* may be considered as one of those substances
which can be made to pass to *either* pole.    When the poles
are immersed in dilute sulphuric acid (527.), acid passes towards the positive pole, and water towards the negative pole; but
when they are immersed in dilute alkali, the alkali passes towards
the negative pole, and water towards the positive pole.

554. Nitrogen is another substance which is considered as
determinable to either pole; but in consequence of the numerous compounds which it forms, some of which pass to one
pole, and some to the other, I have not always found it easy to
determine the true circumstances of its appearance.    A pure
strong solution of ammonia is so bad a conductor of electricity
that it is scarcely more decomposable than pure water; but if
sulphate of ammonia be dissolved in it, then decomposition
takes place very well; nitrogen almost pure, and in some cases
quite, is evolved at the positive pole, and hydrogen at the negative pole.

* At 681 and 757 of Series VII. will be found corrections of the statement
here made respecting sulphur and sulphuric acid.    At present there is no well-
ascertained fact which proves that the same body can go directly to *either* of
the two poles at pleasure.—*Dec.* 1838.

555. On the other hand, if a strong solution of nitrate of ammonia be decomposed, oxygen appears at the positive pole, and hydrogen, with sometimes nitrogen, at the negative pole. If fused nitrate of ammonia be employed, hydrogen appears at the negative pole, mingled with a little nitrogen. Strong nitric acid yields plenty of oxygen at the positive pole, but no gas (only nitrous acid,) at the negative pole. Weak nitric acid yields the oxygen and hydrogen of the water present, the acid apparently remaining unchanged. Strong nitric acid with nitrate of ammonia dissolved in it, yields a gas at the negative pole, of which the greater part is hydrogen, but apparently a little nitrogen is present. I believe that in some of these cases a little nitrogen appeared at the negative pole. I suspect, however, that in all these, and in all former cases, the appearance of the nitrogen at the positive or negative pole is entirely a secondary effect, and not an immediate consequence of the decomposing power of the electric current*.

556. A few observations on what are called the *poles* of the voltaic battery now seem necessary. The poles are merely the surfaces or doors by which the electricity enters into or passes out of the substance suffering decomposition. They limit the extent of that substance in the course of the electric current, being its *terminations* in that direction : hence the elements evolved pass so far and no further.

557. Metals make admirable poles, in consequence of their high conducting power, their immiscibilility with the substances generally acted upon, their solid form, and the opportunity afforded of selecting such as are not chemically acted upon by ordinary substances.

558. Water makes a pole of difficult application, except in a few cases (494.), because of its small conducting power, its miscibility with most of the substances acted upon, and its general relation to them in respect to chemical affinity. It consists of elements, which in their electrical and chemical relations are directly and powerfully opposed, yet combining to produce a body more neutral in its character than any other. So that there are but few substances which do not come into relation, by chemical affinity, with water or one of its elements ;

* Refer for proof of the truth of this supposition to 748, 752, &c.—*Dec.* 1838.

and therefore either the water or its elements are transferred and assist in transferring the infinite variety of bodies which, in association with it, can be placed in the course of the electric current. Hence the reason why it so rarely happens that the evolved substances rest at the first surface of the water, and why it therefore does not exhibit the ordinary action of a pole.

559. Air, however, and some gases are free from the latter objection, and may be used as poles in many cases (461, &c.); but, in consequence of the extremely low degree of conducting power belonging to them, they cannot be employed with the voltaic apparatus. This limits their use; for the voltaic apparatus is the only one as yet discovered which supplies sufficient quantity of electricity (371. 376.) to effect electro-chemical decomposition with facility.

560. When the poles are liable to the chemical action of the substances evolved, either simply in consequence of their natural relation to them, or of that relation aided by the influence of the current (518.), then they suffer corrosion, and the parts dissolved are subject to transference, in the same manner as the particles of the body originally under decomposition. An immense series of phenomena of this kind might be quoted in support of the view I have taken of the cause of electro-chemical decomposition, and the transfer and evolution of the elements. Thus platina being made the positive and negative poles in a solution of sulphate of soda, has no affinity or attraction for the oxygen, hydrogen, acid, or alkali evolved, and refuses to combine with or retain them. Zinc can combine with the oxygen and acid; at the positive pole it does combine, and immediately begins to travel as oxide towards the negative pole. Charcoal, which cannot combine with the metals, if made the negative pole in a metallic solution, refuses to unite to the bodies which are ejected from the solution upon its surface; but if made the positive pole in a dilute solution of sulphuric acid, it is capable of combining with the oxygen evolved there, and consequently unites with it, producing both carbonic acid and carbonic oxide in abundance.

561. A great advantage is frequently supplied, by the opportunity afforded amongst the metals of selecting a substance for the pole, which shall or shall not be acted upon by the elements

to be evolved.   The consequent use of platina is notorious.   In the decomposition of sulphuret of silver and other sulphurets, a positive silver pole is superior to a platina one, because in the former case the sulphur evolved there combines with the silver, and the decomposition of the original sulphuret is rendered evident; whereas in the latter case it is dissipated, and the assurance of its separation at the pole not easily obtained.

562. The effects which take place when a succession of conducting decomposable and undecomposable substances are placed in the electric circuit, as, for instance, of wires and solutions, or of air and solutions (465. 469.), are explained in the simplest possible manner by the theoretical view I have given.   In consequence of the reaction of the constituents of each portion of decomposable matter, affected as they are by the supervention of the electric current (524.), portions of the proximate or ultimate elements proceed in the direction of the current as far as they find matter of a contrary kind capable of effecting their transfer, and being equally affected by them; and where they cease to find such matter, they are evolved in their free state, *i. e.* upon the surfaces of metal or air bounding the extent of decomposable matter in the direction of the current.

563. Having thus given my theory of the mode in which electro-chemical decomposition is effected, I will refrain for the present from entering upon the numerous general considerations which it suggests, wishing first to submit it to the test of publication and discussion.

*Royal Institution,*
   *June* 1833.

## SIXTH SERIES.

§ 12. *On the power of Metals and other Solids to induce the Combination of Gaseous Bodies.*

Received November 30, 1833,—Read January 11, 1834.

564. THE conclusion at which I have arrived in the present communication may seem to render the whole of it unfit to form part of a series of researches in electricity; since, remarkable as the phenomena are, the power which produces them is not to be considered as of an electric origin, otherwise than as all attraction of particles may have this subtile agent for their common cause. But as the effects investigated arose out of electrical researches, as they are directly connected with other effects which are of an electric nature, and must of necessity be understood and guarded against in a very extensive series of electro-chemical decompositions (707.), I have felt myself fully justified in describing them in this place.

365. Believing that I had proved (by experiments hereafter to be described (705.),) the constant and definite chemical action of a certain quantity of electricity, whatever its intensity might be, or however the circumstances of its tranmission through either the body under decomposition or the more perfect conductors were varied, I endeavoured upon that result to construct a new measuring instrument, which from its use might be called, at least provisionally, a *Volta-electrometer* (739.)*.

566. During the course of the experiments made to render the instrument efficient, I was occasionally surprised at observing a deficiency of the gases resulting from the decompositions of water, and at last an actual disappearance of portions which had been evolved, collected, and measured. The circumstances of the disappearance were these. A glass tube, about twelve inches in length and ¾ths of an inch in diameter, had two platina poles fixed into its upper, hermetically sealed,

* Or Voltameter.—*Dec.* 1838.

extremity: the poles, where they passed through the glass, were of wire; but terminated below in plates, which were soldered to the wires with gold (Plate V. fig. 56.). The tube was filled with dilute sulphuric acid, and inverted in a cup of the same fluid; a voltaic battery was connected with the two wires, and sufficient oxygen and hydrogen evolved to occupy $\frac{4}{5}$ths of the tube, or by the graduation, 116 parts. On separating the tube from the voltaic battery the volume of gas immediately began to diminish, and in about five hours only $13\frac{1}{2}$ parts remained, and these ultimately disappeared.

567. It was found by various experiments, that this effect was not due to the escape or solution of the gas, nor to recombination of the oxygen or hydrogen in consequence of any peculiar condition *they* might be supposed to possess under the circumstances; but to be occasioned by the action of one or both of the poles within the tube upon the gas around them. On disuniting the poles from the pile after they had acted upon dilute sulphuric acid, and introducing them into separate tubes containing mixed oxygen and hydrogen, it was found that the *positive* pole effected the union of the gases, but the negative pole apparently not (588.). It was ascertained also that no action of a sensible kind took place between the positive pole with oxygen or hydrogen alone.

568. These experiments reduced the phenomena to the consequence of a power possessed by the platina, after it had been the positive pole of a voltaic pile, of causing the combination of oxygen and hydrogen at common, or even at low, temperatures. This effect is, as far as I am aware, altogether new, and was immediately followed out to ascertain whether it was really of an electric nature, and how far it would interfere with the determination of the quantities evolved in the cases of electro-chemical decomposition required in the fourteenth section of these Researches.

569. Several platina plates were prepared (fig. 57.). They were nearly half an inch wide, and two inches and a half long: some were $\frac{1}{200}$dth of an inch, others not more than $\frac{1}{800}$dth, whilst some were as much as $\frac{1}{70}$th of an inch in thickness. Each had a piece of platina wire, about seven inches long, soldered to it by pure gold. Then a number of glass tubes were prepared: they were about nine or ten inches in length, $\frac{5}{8}$ths

of an inch in internal diameter, were sealed hermetically at one
extremity, and were graduated.    Into these tubes was put a
mixture of two volumes of hydrogen and one of oxygen, at the
water pneumatic trough, and when one of the plates described
had been connected with the positive or negative pole of the
voltaic battery for a given time, or had been otherwise prepared, it was introduced through the water into the gas within
the tube ; the whole set aside in a test-glass (fig. 58.), and left
for a longer or shorter period, that the action might be observed.

570. The following result may be given as an illustration of
the phenomenon to be investigated.    Diluted sulphuric acid,
of the specific gravity 1·336, was put into a glass jar, in which
was placed also a large platina plate, connected with the negative end of a voltaic battery of forty pairs of four-inch plates,
with double coppers, and moderately charged.    One of the
plates above described (569.) was then connected with the
positive extremity, and immersed in the same jar of acid for
five minutes, after which it was separated from the battery,
washed in distilled water and introduced through the water
of the pneumatic trough into a tube containing the mixture of
oxygen and hydrogen (569.).    The volume of gases immediately began to lessen, the diminution proceeding more and
more rapidly until about $\frac{3}{4}$ths of the mixture had disappeared.
The upper end of the tube became quite warm, the plate itself
so hot that the water boiled as it rose over it ; and in less
than a minute a cubical inch and a half of the gases were gone,
having been combined by the power of the platina, and converted into water.

571. This extraordinary influence acquired by the platina at
the positive pole of the pile, is exerted far more readily and
effectively on oxygen and hydrogen than on any other mixture
of gases that I have tried.    One volume of nitrous gas was
mixed with a volume of hydrogen, and introduced into a tube
with a plate which had been made positive in the dilute sulphuric acid for four minutes (570.).    There was no sensible action
in an hour; being left for thirty-six hours, there was a diminution
of about one eighth of the whole volume.    Action had taken
place, but it had been very feeble.

572. A mixture of two volumes of nitrous oxide with one

volume of hydrogen was put with a plate similarly prepared into a tube (569. 570.). This also showed no action immediately; but in thirty-six hours nearly a fourth of the whole had disappeared, *i.e.* about half of a cubic inch. By comparison with another tube containing the same mixture without a plate, it appeared that a part of the diminution was due to solution, and the other part to the power of the platina; but the action had been very slow and feeble.

573. A mixture of one volume olefiant gas and three volumes oxygen was not affected by such a platina plate, even though left together for several days (640. 641.).

574. A mixture of two volumes carbonic oxide and one volume oxygen was also unaffected by the prepared platina plate in several days (645. &c.).

575. A mixture of equal volumes of chlorine and hydrogen was used in several experiments, with plates prepared in a similar manner (570.). Diminution of bulk soon took place; but when after thirty-six hours the experiments were examined, it was found that nearly all the chlorine had disappeared, having been absorbed, principally by the water, and that the original volume of hydrogen remained unchanged. No combination of the gases, therefore, had here taken place.

576. Reverting to the action of the prepared plates on mixtures of oxygen and hydrogen (570.), I found that the power, though gradually diminishing in all cases, could still be retained for a period, varying in its length with circumstances. When tubes containing plates (569.) were supplied with fresh portions of mixed oxygen and hydrogen as the previous portions were condensed, the action was found to continue for above thirty hours, and in some cases slow combination could be observed even after eighty hours; but the continuance of the action greatly depended upon the purity of the gases used (638.).

577. Some plates (569.) were made positive for four minutes in dilute sulphuric acid of specific gravity 1·336: they were rinsed in distilled water, after which two were put into a small bottle and closed up, whilst others were left exposed to the air. The plates preserved in the limited portion of air were found to retain their power after eight days, but those exposed to the atmosphere had lost their force almost entirely in twelve hours

and in some situations, where currents existed, in a much shorter time.

578. Plates were made positive for five minutes in sulphuric acid, specific gravity 1·336. One of these was retained in similar acid for eight minutes after separation from the battery ; it then acted on mixed oxygen and hydrogen with apparently undiminished vigour. Others were left in similar acid for forty hours, and some even for eight days, after the electrization, and then acted as well in combining oxygen and hydrogen gas as those which were used immediately after electrization.

579. The effect of a solution of caustic potassa in preserving the platina plates was tried in a similar manner. After being retained in such a solution for forty hours, they acted exceedingly well on oxygen and hydrogen, and one caused such rapid condensation of the gases, that the plate became much heated, and I expected the temperature would have risen to ignition.

580. When similarly prepared plates (569.) had been put into distilled water for forty hours, and then introduced into mixed oxygen and hydrogen, they were found to act but very slowly and feebly as compared with those which had been preserved in acid or alkali. When, however, the quantity of water was but small, the power was very little impaired after three or four days. As the water had been retained in a wooden vessel, portions of it were redistilled in glass, and this was found to preserve prepared plates for a great length of time. Prepared plates were put into tubes with this water and closed up ; some of them, taken out at the end of twenty-four days, were found very active on mixed oxygen and hydrogen ; others, which were left in the water for fifty-three days, were still found to cause the combination of the gases. The tubes had been closed only by corks.

581. The act of combination always seemed to diminish, or apparently exhaust, the power of the platina plate. It is true, that in most, if not all instances, the combination of the gases, at first insensible, gradually increased in rapidity, and sometimes reached to explosion ; but when the latter did not happen, the rapidity of combination diminished ; and although fresh portions of gas were introduced into the tubes, the combination went on more and more slowly, and at last ceased altogether. The first effect of an increase in the rapidity of combination dependent

in part upon the water flowing off from the platina plate, and
allowing a better contact with the gas, and in part upon the
heat evolved during the progress of the combination (630.).
But notwithstanding the effect of these causes, diminution, and
at last cessation of the power, always occurred. It must not,
however, be unnoticed, that the purer the gases subjected to
the action of the plate, the longer was its combining power retained. With the mixture evolved at the poles of the voltaic
pile, in pure dilute sulphuric acid, it continued longest; and
with oxygen and hydrogen, of perfect purity, it probably would
not be diminished at all.

582. Different modes of treatment applied to the platina plate,
after it had ceased to be the positive pole of the pile, affected
its power very curiously. A plate which had been a positive
pole in diluted sulphuric acid of specific gravity 1·336 for four
or five minutes, if rinsed in water and put into mixed oxygen
and hydrogen, would act very well, and condense perhaps one
cubic inch and a half of gas in six or seven minutes; but if that
same plate, instead of being merely rinsed, had been left in
distilled water for twelve or fifteen minutes, or more, it would
rarely fail, when put into the oxygen and hydrogen, of becoming,
in the course of a minute or two, ignited, and would generally
explode the gases. Occasionally the time occupied in bringing
on the action extended to eight or nine minutes, and sometimes
even to forty minutes, and yet ignition and explosion would
result. This effect is due to the removal of a portion of acid
which otherwise adheres firmly to the plate *.

583. Occasionally the platina plates (569.), after being made
the positive pole of the battery, were washed, wiped with filter-
ing-paper or a cloth, and washed and wiped again. Being then
introduced into mixed oxygen and hydrogen, they acted apparently as if they had been unaffected by the treatment. Sometimes the tubes containing the gas were opened in the air for
an instant, and the plates put in dry; but no sensible difference
in action was perceived, except that it commenced sooner.

584. The power of heat in altering the action of the prepared
platina plates was also tried (595.). Plates which had been
rendered positive in dilute sulphuric acid for four minutes
were well washed in water, and heated to redness in the flame

* In proof that this is the case, refer to 1038.—*Dec.* 1838.

of a spirit-lamp : after this they acted very well on mixed oxygen and hydrogen.   Others, which had been heated more power-fully by the blowpipe, acted afterwards on the gases, though not so powerfully as the former.   Hence it appears that heat does not take away the power acquired by the platina at the positive pole of the pile : the occasional diminution of force seemed always referable to other causes than the mere heat. If, for instance, the plate had not been well washed from the acid, or if the flame used was carbonaceous, or was that of an alcohol lamp trimmed with spirit containing a little acid, or having a wick on which salt, or other extraneous matter, had been placed, then the power of the plate was quickly and greatly diminished (634. 636.).

585. This remarkable property was conferred upon platina when it was made the positive pole in sulphuric acid of specific gravity 1·336, or when it was considerably weaker, or when stronger, even up to the strength of oil of vitriol.   Strong and dilute nitric acid, dilute acetic acid, solutions of tartaric, citric, and oxalic acids, were used with equal success.   When muri-atic acid was used, the plates acquired the power of condensing the oxygen and hydrogen, but in a much inferior degree.

586. Plates which were made positive in solution of caustic potassa did not show any sensible action upon the mixed oxygen and hydrogen.   Other plates made positive in solutions of carbonates of potassa and soda exhibited the action, but only in a feeble degree.

587. When a neutral solution of sulphate of soda, or of nitre, or of chlorate of potassa, or of phosphate of potassa, or acetate of potassa, or sulphate of copper, was used, the plates, rendered positive in them for four minutes, and then washed in water, acted very readily and powerfully on the mixed oxygen and hydrogen.

588. It became a very important point, in reference to the *cause* of this action of the platina, to determine whether the *positive* pole *only* could confer it (567.), or whether, notwith-standing the numerous contrary cases, the *negative* pole might not have the power when such circumstances as could interfere with or prevent the action were avoided.   Three plates were therefore rendered negative, for four minutes in diluted sul-phuric acid of specific gravity 1·336, washed in distilled water,

and put into mixed oxygen and hydrogen. *All* of them *acted,* though not so strongly as they would have done if they had been rendered positive. Each combined about a cubical inch and a quarter of the gases in twenty-five minutes. On every repetition of the experiment the same result was obtained ; and when the plates were retained in distilled water for ten or twelve minutes, before being introduced into the gas (582.), the action was very much quickened.

589. But when there was any metallic or other substance present in the acid, which could be precipitated on the negative plate, then that plate ceased to act upon the mixed oxygen and hydrogen.

590. These experiments led to the expectation that the power of causing oxygen and hydrogen to combine, which could be conferred upon any piece of platina by making it the positive pole of a voltaic pile, was not essentially dependent upon the action of the pile, or upon any structure or arrangement of parts it might receive whilst in association with it, but belonged to the platina *at all times,* and was *always effective* when the surface was *perfectly clean.* And though, when made the *positive* pole of the pile in acids, the circumstances might well be considered as those which would cleanse the surface of the platina in the most effectual manner, it did not seem impossible that ordinary operations should produce the same result, although in a less eminent degree.

591. Accordingly, a platina plate (569.) was cleaned by being rubbed with a cork, a little water, and some coal-fire ashes upon a glass plate : being washed, it was put into mixed oxygen and hydrogen, and was found to act at first slowly, and then more rapidly. In an hour, a cubical inch and a half had disappeared.

592. Other plates were cleaned with ordinary sand-paper and water ; others with chalk and water ; others with emery and water ; others, again, with black oxide of manganese and water ; and others with a piece of charcoal and water. All of these acted in tubes of oxygen and hydrogen, causing combination of the gases. The action was by no means so powerful as that produced by plates having been in communication with the battery ; but from one to two cubical inches of the gases disappeared, in periods extending from twenty-five to eighty or ninety minutes.

593. Upon cleaning the plates with a cork, ground emery, and dilute sulphuric acid, they were found to act still better. In order to simplify the conditions, the cork was dismissed, and a piece of platina foil used instead ; still the effect took place. Then the acid was dismissed, and a solution of *potassa* used, but the effect occurred as before.

594. These results are abundantly sufficient to show that the mere mechanical cleansing of the surface of the platina is sufficient to enable it to exert its combining power over oxygen and hydrogen at common temperatures.

595. I now tried the effect of heat in conferring this property upon platina (584.). Plates which had no action on the mixture of oxygen and hydrogen were heated by the flame of a freshly trimmed spirit-lamp, urged by a mouth blowpipe, and when cold were put into tubes of the mixed gases : they acted slowly at first, but after two or three hours condensed nearly all the gases.

596. A plate of platina, which was about one inch wide and two and three quarters in length, and which had not been used in any of the preceding experiments, was curved a little so as to enter a tube, and left in a mixture of oxygen and hydrogen for thirteen hours : not the slightest action or combination of the gases occurred. It was withdrawn at the pneumatic trough from the gas through the water, heated red hot by the spirit-lamp and blowpipe, and then returned when cold into the *same* portion of gas. In the course of a few minutes diminution of the gases could be observed, and in forty-five minutes about one cubical inch and a quarter had disappeared. In many other experiments platina plates when heated were found to acquire the power of combining oxygen and hydrogen.

597. But it happened not unfrequently that plates, after being heated, showed no power of combining oxygen and hydrogen gases, though left undisturbed in them for two hours. Sometimes also it would happen that a plate which, having been heated to dull redness, acted feebly, upon being heated to whiteness ceased to act ; and at other times a plate which, having been slightly heated, did not act, was rendered active by a more powerful ignition.

598. Though thus uncertain in its action, and though often diminishing the power given to the plates at the positive pole

of the pile (584.), still it is evident that heat can render platina active, which before was inert (595.)   The cause of its occasional failure appears to be due to the surface of the metal becoming soiled, either from something previously adhering to it, which is made to adhere more closely by the action of the heat, or from matter communicated from the flame of the lamp, or from the air itself.   It often happens that a polished plate of platina, when heated by the spirit-lamp and a blowpipe, becomes dulled and clouded on its surface by something either formed or deposited there ; and this, and much less than this, is sufficient to prevent it from exhibiting the curious power now under consideration (634. 636.).   Platina also has been said to combine with carbon ; and it is not at all unlikely that in processes of heating, where carbon or its compounds are present, a film of such a compound may be thus formed, and thus prevent the exhibition of the properties belonging to *pure* platina\*.

599. The action of alkalies and acids in giving platina this property was now experimentally examined.   Platina plates (569.) having no action on mixed oxygen and hydrogen, being boiled in a solution of caustic potassa, washed, and then put into the gases, were found occasionally to act pretty well, but at other times to fail.   In the latter case I concluded that the impurity upon the surface of the platina was of a nature not to be removed by the mere solvent action of the alkali, for when the plates were rubbed with a little emery, and the same solution of alkali (592.), they became active.

600. The action of acids was far more constant and satisfactory.   A platina plate was boiled in dilute nitric acid : being washed and put into mixed oxygen and hydrogen gases, it acted well.   Other plates were boiled in strong nitric acid for periods extending from half a minute to four minutes, and then being washed in distilled water, were found to act very well, condensing one cubic inch and a half of gas in the space of eight or nine minutes, and rendering the tube warm (570.).

601. Strong sulphuric acid was very effectual in rendering the platina active.   A plate (569.) was heated in it for a minute,

* When heat does confer the property it is only by the destruction or dissipation of organic or other matter which had previously soiled the plate (632. 633. 634.).—*Dec.* 1838.

then washed and put into the mixed oxygen and hydrogen, upon which it acted as well as if it had been made the positive pole of a voltaic pile (570.).

602. Plates which, after being heated or electrized in alkali, or after other treatment, were found inert, immediately received power by being dipped for a minute or two, or even only for an instant, into hot oil of vitriol, and then into water.

603. When the plate was dipped into the oil of vitriol, taken out, and then heated so as to drive off the acid, it did not act, in consequence of the impurity left by the acid upon its surface.

604. Vegetable acids, as acetic and tartaric, sometimes rendered inert platina active, at other times not. This, I believe, depended upon the character of the matter previously soiling the plates, and which may easily be supposed to be sometimes of such a nature as to be removed by these acids, and at other times not. Weak sulphuric acid showed the same difference, but strong sulphuric acid (601.) never failed in its action.

605. The most favourable treatment, except that of making the plate a positive pole in strong acid, was as follows. The plate was held over a spirit-lamp flame, and when hot, rubbed with a piece of potassa fusa (caustic potash), which melting, covered the metal with a coat of very strong alkali, and this was retained fused upon the surface for a second or two*: it was then put into water for four or five minutes to wash off the alkali, shaken, and immersed for about a minute in hot strong oil of vitriol; from this it was removed into distilled water, where it was allowed to remain ten or fifteen minutes to remove the last traces of acid (582.). Being then put into a mixture of oxygen and hydrogen, combination immediately began, and proceeded rapidly; the tube became warm, the platina became red hot, and the residue of the gases was inflamed. This effect could be repeated at pleasure, and thus the maximum phenomenon could be produced without the aid of the voltaic battery.

606. When a solution of tartaric or acetic acid was substituted, in this mode of preparation, for the sulphuric acid, still the plate was found to acquire the same power, and would

---

* The heat need not be raised so much as to make the alkali tarnish the platina, although if that effect does take place it does not prevent the ultimate action.

often produce explosion in the mixed gases ; but the strong
sulphuric acid was most certain and powerful.

607. If borax, or a mixture of the carbonates of potash and
soda, be fused on the surface of a platina plate, and that plate
be well washed in water, it will be found to have acquired the
power of combining oxygen and hydrogen, but only in a moderate degree ; but if, after the fusion and washing, it be dipped in the hot sulphuric acid (601.), it will become very active.

608. Other metals than platina were then experimented with.
Gold and palladium exhibited the power either when made the
positive pole of the voltaic battery (570.), or when acted on by
hot oil of vitriol (601.). When palladium is used, the action
of the battery or acid should be moderated, as that metal is
soon acted upon under such circumstances. Silver and copper could not be made to show any effect at common temperatures.

---

609. There can remain no doubt that the property of inducing combination, which can thus be conferred upon masses of
platina and other metals by connecting them with the poles of
the battery, or by cleansing processes either of a mechanical
or chemical nature, is the same as that which was discovered
by Dobereiner*, in 1823, to belong in so eminent a degree to
spongy platina, and which was afterwards so well experimented
upon and illustrated by MM. Dulong and Thenard†, in 1823.
The latter philosophers even quote experiments in which a
very fine platina wire, which had been coiled up and digested
in nitric, sulphuric, or muriatic acid, became ignited when put
into a jet of hydrogen gas‡. This effect I can now produce at
pleasure with either wires or plates by the processes described
(570. 601. 605.) ; and by using a smaller plate cut so that it
shall rest against the glass by a few points, and yet allow the
water to flow off (fig. 59.), the loss of heat is less, the metal is
assimilated somewhat to the spongy state, and the probability
of failure almost entirely removed.

610. M. Dobereiner refers the effect entirely to an electric
action. He considers the platina and hydrogen as forming a
voltaic element of the ordinary kind, in which the hydrogen,

* Annales de Chimie, tom. xxiv. p. 93.
† Ibid. tom. xxiii. p. 440 ; tom. xxiv. p. 380.    ‡ Ibid. tom. xxiv. p. 383.

being very highly positive, represents the zinc of the usual arrangement, and like it, therefore, attracts oxygen and combines with it *.

611. In the two excellent experimental papers by MM. Dulong and Thenard †, those philosophers show that elevation of temperature favours the action, but does not alter its character; Sir Humphry Davy's incandescent platina wire being the same phenomenon with Dobereiner's spongy platina. They show that *all* metals have this power in a greater or smaller degree, and that it is even possessed by such bodies as charcoal, pumice, porcelain, glass, rock crystal, &c., when their temperatures are raised; and that another of Davy's effects, in which oxygen and hydrogen had combined slowly together at a heat below ignition, was really dependent upon the property of the heated glass, which it has in common with the bodies named above.  They state that liquids do not show this effect, at least that mercury, at or below the boiling point, has not the power; that it is not due to porosity; that the same body varies very much in its action, according to its state; and that many other gaseous mixtures besides oxygen and hydrogen are affected, and made to act chemically, when the temperature is raised.  They think it probable that spongy platina acquires its power from contact with the acid evolved during its reduction, or from the heat itself to which it is then submitted.

612. MM. Dulong and Thenard express themselves with great caution on the theory of this action; but, referring to the decomposing power of metals on ammonia when heated to temperatures not sufficient alone to affect the alkali, they remark that those metals which in this case are most efficacious, are the least so in causing the combination of oxygen and hydrogen; whilst platina, gold, &c., which have least power of decomposing ammonia, have most power of combining the elements of water:—from which they are led to believe, that amongst gases, some tend to *unite* under the influence of metals, whilst others tend to *separate,* and that this property varies in opposite directions with the different metals.  At the

* Annales de Chimie, tom. xxiv. pp. 94, 95.  Also Bibliothque Universelle, tom. xxiv. p. 54.

† Ibid. tom. xxiii. p. 440; tom. xxiv. p. 380.

close of their second paper they observe, that the action is of a kind that cannot be connected with any known theory ; and though it is very remarkable that the effects are transient, like those of most electrical actions, yet they state that the greater number of the results observed by them are inexplicable, by supposing them to be of a purely electric origin.

613. Dr. Fusinieri has also written on this subject, and given a theory which he considers as sufficient to account for the phenomena *. He expresses the immediate cause thus : " The platina determines upon its surface a continual renovation of *concrete laminæ* of the combustible substance of the gases or vapours, which flowing over it are burnt, pass away, and are renewed : this combustion at the surface raises and sustains the temperature of the metal." The combustible substance, thus reduced into imperceptible laminæ, of which the concrete parts are in contact with the oxygen, is presumed to be in a state combinable with the oxygen at a much lower temperature than when it is in the gaseous state, and more in analogy with what is called the nascent condition. That combustible gases should lose their elastic state, and become concrete, assuming the form of exceedingly attenuated but solid strata, is considered as proved by facts, some of which are quoted in the Giornale di Fisica for 1824 † ; and though the theory requires that they should assume this state at high temperatures, and though the *similar* films of aqueous and other matter are dissipated by the action of heat, still the facts are considered as justifying the conclusion against all opposition of reasoning.

614. The power or force which makes combustible gas or vapour abandon its elastic state in contact with a solid, that it may cover the latter with a thin stratum of its own proper substance, is considered as being neither attraction nor affinity. It is able also to extend liquids and solids in concrete laminæ over the surface of the acting solid body, and consists in a *repulsion,* which is developed from the parts of the solid body by the simple fact of attenuation, and is highest when the attenuation is most complete. The force has a progressive development, and acts most powerfully, or at first, in the direction in which the dimensions of the attenuated mass decrease, and then in the direction of the angles or corners which from

* Giornale di Fisica, &c., 1825, tom. viii. p. 259. † pp. 138, 371.

any cause may exist on the surface.   This force not only causes spontaneous diffusion of gases and other substances over the surface, but is considered as very elementary in its nature, and competent to account for all the phenomena of capillarity, chemical affinity, attraction of aggregation, rarefaction, ebullition, volatilization, explosion, and other thermometric effects, as well as inflammation, detonation, &c. &c.   It is considered as a form of heat to which the term *native caloric* is given, and is still further viewed as the principle of the two electricities and the two magnetisms.

615. I have been the more anxious to give a correct abstract of Dr. Fusinieri's view, both because I cannot form a distinct idea of the power to which he refers the phenomena, and because of my imperfect knowledge of the language in which the memoir is written.   I would therefore beg to refer those who pursue the subject to the memoir itself.

616. Not feeling, however, that the problem has yet been solved, I venture to give the view which seems to me sufficient, upon *known principles,* to account for the effect.

617. It may be observed of this action, that, with regard to platina, it cannot be due to any peculiar, temporary condition, either of an electric or of any other nature : the activity of plates rendered either positive or negative by the pole, or cleaned with such different substances as acids, alkalies, or water; charcoal, emery, ashes, or glass ; or merely heated, is sufficient to negative such an opinion.   Neither does it depend upon the spongy and porous, or upon the compact and burnished, or upon the massive or the attenuated state of the metal, for in any of these states it may be rendered effective, or its action may be taken away.   The only essential condition appears to be a *perfectly clean* and *metallic surface,* for whenever that is present the platina acts, whatever its form and condition in other respects may be ; and though variations in the latter points will very much affect the rapidity, and therefore the visible appearances and secondary effects, of the action, *i. e.* the ignition of the metal and the inflammation of the gases, they, even in their most favourable state, cannot produce any effect unless the condition of a clean, pure, metallic surface be also fulfilled.

618. The effect is evidently produced by most, if not all,

solid bodies, weakly perhaps by many of them, but rising to a high degree in platina.  Dulong and Thenard have very philosophically extended our knowledge of the property to its possession by all the metals, and by earths, glass, stones, &c. (611.) ; and every idea of its being a known and recognised electric action is in this way removed.

619. All the phenomena connected with this subject press upon my mind the conviction that the effects in question are entirely incidental and of a secondary nature ; that they are dependent upon the *natural conditions* of gaseous elasticity, combined with the exertion of that attractive force possessed by many bodies, especially those which are solid, in an eminent degree, and probably belonging to all ; by which they are drawn into association more or less close, without at the same time undergoing chemical combination, though often assuming the condition of adhesion ; and which occasionally leads, under very favourable circumstances, as in the present instance, to the combination of bodies simultaneously subjected to this attraction.  I am prepared myself to admit (and probably many others are of the same opinion), both with respect to the attraction of aggregation and of chemical affinity, that the sphere of action of particles extends beyond those other particles with which they are immediately and evidently in union (523.), and in many cases produces effects rising into considerable importance : and I think that this kind of attraction is a determining cause of Dobereiner's effect, and of the many others of a similar nature.

620. Bodies which become wetted by fluids with which they do not combine chemically, or in which they do not dissolve, are simple and well known instances of this kind of attraction.

621. All those cases of bodies which being insoluble in water and not combining with it are hygrometric, and condense its vapour around or upon their surface, are stronger instances of the same power, and approach a little nearer to the cases under investigation.  If pulverised clay, protoxide or peroxide of iron, oxide of manganese, charcoal, or even metals, as spongy platina or precipitated silver, be put into an atmosphere containing vapour of water, they soon become moist by virtue of an attraction which is able to condense the vapour upon,

although not to combine it with, the substances; and if, as is well known, these bodies so damped be put into a dry atmosphere, as, for instance, one confined over sulphuric acid, or if they be heated, then they yield up this water again almost entirely, it not being in direct or permanent combination*.

622. Still better instances of the power I refer to, because they are more analogous to the cases to be explained, are furnished by the attraction existing between glass and air, so well known to barometer and thermometer makers, for here the adhesion or attraction is exerted between a solid and gases, bodies having very different physical conditions, having no power of combination with each other, and each retaining, during the time of action, its physical state unchanged†. When mercury is poured into a barometer tube, a film of air will remain between the metal and glass for months, or, as far as is known, for years, for it has never been displaced except by the action of means especially fitted for the purpose. These consist in boiling the mercury, or in other words, of forming an abundance of vapour, which coming in contact with every part of the glass and every portion of surface of the mercury, gradually mingles with, dilutes, and carries off the air attracted by, and adhering to, those surfaces, replacing it by other vapour, subject to an equal or perhaps greater attraction, but which when cooled condenses into the same liquid as that with which the tube is filled.

623. Extraneous bodies, which, acting as nuclei in crystallizing or depositing solutions, cause deposition of substances on them, when it does not occur elsewhere in the liquid, seem to produce their effects by a power of the same kind, *i. e.* a power of attraction extending to neighbouring particles, and causing them to become attached to the nuclei, although it is not strong enough to make them combine chemically with their substance.

* I met at Edinburgh with a case, remarkable as to its extent, of hygrometric action, assisted a little perhaps by very slight solvent power. Some turf had been well dried by long exposure in a covered place to the atmosphere, but being then submitted to the action of a hydrostatic press, it yielded, *by the mere influence of the pressure,* 54 per cent. of water.

† Fusinieri and Bellani consider the air as forming solid concrete films these cases.—Giornale di Fisica, tom. viii. p. 262. 1825.

624. It would appear from many cases of nuclei in solutions, and from the effects of bodies put into atmospheres containing the vapours of water, or camphor, or iodine, &c., as if this attraction were in part elective, partaking in its characters both of the attraction of aggregation and chemical affinity ; nor is this inconsistent with, but agreeable to, the idea entertained, that it is the power of particles acting, not upon others with which they can immediately and intimately combine, but upon such as are either more distantly situated with respect to them, or which, from previous condition, physical constitution, or feeble relation, are unable to enter into decided union with them.

625. Then, of all bodies, the gases are those which might be expected to show some *mutual* action whilst *jointly* under the attractive influence of the platina or other solid acting substance. Liquids, such as water, alcohol, &c., are in so dense and comparatively incompressible a state, as to favour no expectation that their particles should approach much closer to each other by the attraction of the body to which they adhere, and yet that attraction must (according to its effects) place their particles as near to those of the solid wetted body as they are to each other, and in many cases it is evident that the former attraction is the stronger. But gases and vapours are bodies competent to suffer very great changes in the relative distances of their particles by external agencies ; and where they are in immediate contact with the platina, the approximation of the particles to those of the metal may be very great. In the case of the hygrometric bodies referred to (621.), it is sufficient to reduce the vapour to the fluid state, frequently from atmospheres so rare that without this influence it would be needful to compress them by mechanical force into a bulk not more than $\frac{1}{10}$ or even $\frac{1}{20}$ of their original volume before the vapours would become liquids.

626. Another most important consideration in relation to this action of bodies, and which, as far as I am aware, has not hitherto been noticed, is the condition of elasticity under which the gases are placed against the acting surface. We have but very imperfect notions of the real and intimate conditions of the particles of a body existing in the solid, the liquid, and the gaseous state ; but when we speak of the gaseous state

as being due to the mutual repulsions of the particles or of
their atmospheres, although we may err in imagining each particle to be a little nucleus to an atmosphere of heat, or electricity, or any other agent, we are still not likely to be in error in
considering the elasticity as dependent on *mutuality* of action.
Now this mutual relation fails altogether on the side of the
gaseous particles next to the platina, and we might be led to
expect *à priori* a deficiency of elastic force there to at least
one half; for if, as Dalton has shown, the elastic force of the
particles of one gas cannot act against the elastic force of the
particles of another, the two being as vacua to each other, so
is it far less likely that the particles of the platina can exert
any influence on those of the gas against it, such as would be
exerted by gaseous particles of its own kind.

627. But the diminution of power to one half on the side of
the gaseous body towards the metal is only a slight result of
what seems to me to flow as a necessary consequence of the
known constitution of gases.  An atmosphere of one gas or
vapour, however dense or compressed, is in effect as a vacuum
to another ; thus, if a little water were put into a vessel containing a dry gas, as air, of the pressure of one hundred atmospheres, as much vapour of the water would *rise* as if it were
in a perfect vacuum.  Here the particles of watery vapour appear to have no difficulty in approaching within any distance of
the particles of air, being influenced solely by relation to particles of their own kind ; and if it be so with respect to a body
having the same elastic powers as itself, how much more surely
must it be so with particles, like those of the platina, or other
limiting body, which at the same time that they have not these
elastic powers, are also unlike it in nature.  Hence it would
seem to result that the particles of hydrogen or any other gas
or vapour which are next to the platina, &c., must be in such
contact with it as if they were in the liquid state, and therefore almost infinitely closer to it than they are to each other,
even though the metal be supposed to exert no attractive influence over them.

628. A third and very important consideration in favour of
the mutual action of gases under these circumstances is their
perfect miscibility.  If fluid bodies capable of combining together are also capable of mixture, *they do combine* when they

are mingled, not waiting for any other determining circumstance; but if two such gases as oxygen and hydrogen are put
together, though they are elements having such powerful affinity as to unite naturally under a thousand different circumstances, they do not combine by mere mixture.   Still it is evident that, from their perfect association, the particles are in the
most favourable state possible for combination, upon the supervention of any determining cause, such either as the negative
action of the platina in suppressing or annihilating, as it were,
their elasticity on its side; or the positive action of the metal
in condensing them against its surface by an attractive force;
or the influence of both together.

629. Although there are not many distinct cases of combination under the influence of forces external to the combining
particles, yet there are sufficient to remove any difficulty which
might arise on that ground.   Sir James Hall found carbonic
acid and lime to remain combined under pressure at temperatures at which they would not have remained combined if the
pressure had been removed; and I have had occasion to observe
a case of direct combination in chlorine*, which being compressed at common temperatures will combine with water, and
form a definite crystalline hydrate, incapable either of being
formed or of existing if that pressure be removed.

630. The course of events when platina acts upon, and combines oxygen and hydrogen, may be stated, according to these
principles, as follows.   From the influence of the circumstances
mentioned (619. &c.), *i. e.* the deficiency of elastic power and
the attraction of the metal for the gases, the latter, when they
are in association with the former, are so far condensed as to be
brought within the action of their mutual affinities at the existing temperature; the deficiency of elastic power, not merely
subjecting them more closely to the attractive influence of the
metal, but also bringing them into a more favourable state for
union, by abstracting a part of that power (upon which depends
their elasticity,) which elsewhere in the mass of gases is opposing their combination.   The consequence of their combination is the production of the vapour of water and an elevation
of temperature.   But as the attraction of the platina for the
water formed is not greater than for the gases, if so great,

* Philosophical Transactions, 1823, p. 161.

(for the metal is scarcely hygrometric,) the vapour is quickly diffused through the remaining gases; fresh portions of the latter, therefore, come into juxtaposition with the metal, combine, and the fresh vapour formed is also diffused, allowing new portions of gas to be acted upon. In this way the process advances, but is accelerated by the evolution of heat, which is known by experiment to facilitate the combination in proportion to its intensity, and the temperature is thus gradually exalted until ignition results.

631. The dissipation of the vapour produced at the surface of the platina, and the contact of fresh oxygen and hydrogen with the metal, form no difficulty in this explication. The platina is not considered as causing the combination of any particles with itself, but only associating them closely around it; and the compressed particles are as free to move from the platina, being replaced by other particles, as a portion of dense air upon the surface of the globe, or at the bottom of a deep mine, is free to move by the slightest impulse, into the upper and rarer parts of the atmosphere.

632. It can hardly be necessary to give any reasons why platina does not show this effect under ordinary circumstances. It is then not sufficiently clean (617.), and the gases are prevented from touching it, and suffering that degree of effect which is needful to commence their combination at common temperatures, and which they can only experience at its surface. In fact, the very power which causes the combination of oxygen and hydrogen, is competent, under the usual casual exposure of platina, to condense extraneous matters upon its surface, which soiling it, take away for the time its power of combining oxygen and hydrogen, by preventing their contact with it (598.).

633. Clean platina, by which I mean such as has been made the positive pole of a pile (570.), or has been treated with acid (605.), and has then been put into distilled water for twelve or fifteen minutes, has a *peculiar friction* when one piece is rubbed against another. It wets freely with pure water, even after it has been shaken and dried by the heat of a spirit lamp; and if made the pole of a voltaic pile in a dilute acid, it evolves minute bubbles from every part of its surface. But platina in its common state wants that peculiar friction : it will not wet

freely with water as the clean platina does; and when made
the positive pole of a pile, it for a time gives off large bubbles,
which seem to cling or adhere to the metal, and are evolved
at distinct and separate points of the surface.    These appearances and effects, as well as its want of power on oxygen and
hydrogen, are the consequences, and the indications, of a soiled
surface.

634.  I found also that platina plates which had been cleaned
perfectly soon became soiled by mere exposure to the air; for
after twenty-four hours they no longer moistened freely with
water, but the fluid run up into portions, leaving part of the
surface bare, whilst other plates which had been retained in water
for the same time, when they were dried (580.) did moisten, and
gave the other indications of a clean surface.

635.  Nor was this the case with platina or metals only, but
also with earthy bodies.    Rock crystal and obsidian would not
wet freely upon the surface, but being moistened with strong
oil of vitriol, then washed, and left in distilled water to remove
all the acid, they did freely become moistened, whether they
were previously dry or whether they were left wet; but being
dried and left exposed to the air for twenty-four hours, their
surface became so soiled that water would not then adhere
freely to it, but ran up into partial portions.    Wiping with a
cloth (even the cleanest) was still worse than exposure to air;
the surface either of the minerals or metals immediately became
as if it were slightly greasy.    The floating upon water of small
particles of metals under ordinary circumstances is a consequence of this kind of soiled surface.    The extreme difficulty of
cleaning the surface of mercury when it has once been soiled
or greased, is due to the same cause.

636.  The same reasons explain why the power of the platina
plates in some circumstances soon disappear, and especially
upon use : MM. Dulong and Thenard have observed the same
effect with the spongy metal*, as indeed have all those who
have used Dobereiner's instantaneous light machines.    If left
in the air, if put into ordinary distilled water, if made to act
upon ordinary oxygen and hydrogen, they can still find in all
these cases *that* minute portion of impurity which, when once
in contact with the surface of the platina, is retained there, and

* Annales de Chimie, tom. xxiv. p. 386.

is sufficient to prevent its full action upon oxygen and hydrogen at common temperatures : a slight elevation of temperature is again sufficient to compensate this effect, and cause combination.

637. No state of a solid body can be conceived more favourable for the production of the effect than that which is possessed by platina obtained from the ammonio-muriate by heat. Its surface is most extensive and pure, yet very accessible to the gases brought in contact with it : if placed in impurity, the interior, as Thenard and Dulong have observed, is preserved clean by the exterior ; and as regards temperature, it is so bad a conductor of heat, because of its divided condition, that almost all which is evolved by the combination of the first portions of gas is retained within the mass, exalting the tendency of the succeeding portions to combine.

638. I have now to notice some very extraordinary interferences with this phenomenon, dependent, not upon the nature or condition of the metal or other acting solid, but upon the presence of certain substances mingled with the gases acted upon ; and as I shall have occasion to speak frequently of a mixture of oxygen and hydrogen, I wish it always to be understood that I mean a mixture composed of one volume oxygen to two volumes of hydrogen, being the proportions that form water. Unless otherwise expressed, the hydrogen was always that obtained by the action of dilute sulphuric acid on pure zinc, and the oxygen that obtained by the action of heat from the chlorate of potassa.

639. Mixtures of oxygen and hydrogen with *air*, containing one fourth, one half, and even two thirds of the latter, being introduced with prepared platina plates (570. 605.), into tubes, were acted upon almost as well as if no air were present : the retardation was far less than might have been expected from the mere dilution and consequent obstruction to the contact of the gases with the plates. In two hours and a half nearly all the oxygen and hydrogen introduced as mixture was gone.

640. But when similar experiments were made with *olefiant gas* (the platina plates having been made the positive poles of a voltaic pile (570.) in acid), very different results occurred. A mixture was made of 29·2 volumes hydrogen and 14·6 volumes

oxygen, being the proportions for water; and to this was added another mixture of 3 volumes oxygen and one volume olefiant gas, so that the olefiant gas formed but $\frac{1}{48}$th part of the whole ; yet in this mixture the platina plate would not act in forty-five hours. The failure was not for want of any power in the plate, for when after that time it was taken out of this mixture and put into one of oxygen and hydrogen, it immediately acted, and in seven minutes caused explosion of the gas. This result was obtained several times, and when larger proportions of olefiant gas were used, the action seemed still more hopeless.

641. A mixture of forty-nine volumes oxygen and hydrogen (638.) with one volume of olefiant gas had a well-prepared platina plate introduced. The diminution of gas was scarcely sensible at the end of two hours, during which it was watched ; but on examination twenty-four hours afterwards, the tube was found blown to pieces. The action, therefore, though it had been very much retarded, had occurred at last, and risen to a maximum.

642. With a mixture of ninety-nine volumes of oxygen and hydrogen (638.) with one of olefiant gas, a feeble action was evident at the end of fifty minutes; it went on accelerating (630.) until the eighty-fifth minute, and then became so intense that the gas exploded. Here also the retarding effect of the olefiant gas was very beautifully illustrated.

643. Plates prepared by alkali and acid (605.) produced effects corresponding to those just described.

644. It is perfectly clear from these experiments, that *olefiant gas,* even in small quantities, has a very remarkable influence in preventing the combination of oxygen and hydrogen under these circumstances, and yet without at all injuring or affecting the power of the platina.

645. Another striking illustration of similar interference may be shown in *carbonic oxide* ; especially if contrasted with *carbonic acid*. A mixture of one volume oxygen and hydrogen (638.) with four volumes of carbonic acid was affected at once by a platina plate prepared with acid, &c. (605.), and in one hour and a quarter nearly all the oxygen and hydrogen was gone. Mixtures containing less carbonic acid were still more readily affected.

646. But when carbonic oxide was substituted for the car-

bonic acid, not the slightest effect of combination was produced ; and when the carbonic oxide was only one eighth of
the whole volume, no action occurred in forty and fifty hours.
Yet the plates had not lost their power ; for being taken out
and put into pure oxygen and hydrogen, they acted well and
at once.

647. Two volumes of carbonic oxide and one of oxygen were
mingled with nine volumes of oxygen and hydrogen (638).
This mixture was not affected by a plate which had been made
positive in acid, though it remained in it fifteen hours.    But
when to the same volumes of carbonic oxide and oxygen were
added thirty-three volumes of oxygen and hydrogen, the carbonic oxide being then only $\frac{1}{18}$th part of the whole, the plate
acted, slowly at first, and at the end of forty-two minutes the
gases exploded.

648. These experiments were extended to various gases and
vapours, the general results of which may be given as follow.
Oxygen, hydrogen, nitrogen, and nitrous oxide, when used to
dilute the mixture of oxygen and hydrogen, did not prevent
the action of the plates even when they made four-fifths of
the whole volume of gas acted upon.    Nor was the retardation so great in any case as might have been expected from
the mere dilution of the oxygen and hydrogen, and the consequent mechanical obstruction to its contact with the platina.
The order in which carbonic acid and these substances seemed
to stand was as follows, the first interfering least with the
action ; *nitrous oxide, hydrogen, carbonic acid, nitrogen, oxygen*:
but it is possible the plates were not equally well prepared in
all the cases, and that other circumstances also were unequal ;
consequently more numerous experiments would be required
to establish the order accurately.

649. As to cases of *retardation*, the powers of olefiant gas
and carbonic oxide have been already described.    Mixtures of
oxygen and hydrogen, containing from $\frac{1}{16}$th to $\frac{1}{20}$th of sulphuretted hydrogen or phosphuretted hydrogen, seemed to show
a little action at first, but were not further affected by the prepared plates, though in contact with them for seventy hours.
When the plates were removed they had lost all power over
pure oxygen and hydrogen, and the interference of these gases
was therefore of a different nature from that of the two former,
having permanently affected the plate.

650. A small piece of cork was dipped in sulphuret of car_bon and passed up through water into a tube containing oxygen and hydrogen (638.), so as to diffuse a portion of its vapour through the gases. A plate being introduced appeared at first to act a little, but after sixty-one hours the diminution was very small. Upon putting the same plate into a pure mixture of oxygen and hydrogen, it acted at once and powerfully, having apparently suffered no diminution of its force.

651. A little vapour of ether being mixed with the oxygen and hydrogen retarded the action of the plate, but did not prevent it altogether. A little of the vapour of the condensed oil-gas liquor * retarded the action still more, but not nearly so much as an equal volume of olefiant gas would have done. In both these cases it was the original oxygen and hydrogen which combined together, the ether and the oil-gas vapour remaining unaffected, and in both cases the plates retained the power of acting on fresh oxygen and hydrogen.

652. Spongy platina was then used in place of the plates, and jets of hydrogen mingled with the different gases thrown against it in air. The results were exactly of the same kind, although presented occasionally in a more imposing form. Thus, mixtures of one volume of olefiant gas or carbonic oxide with three of hydrogen could not heat the spongy platina when the experiments were commenced at common temperatures; but a mixture of equal volumes of nitrogen and hydrogen acted very well, causing ignition. With carbonic acid the results were still more striking. A mixture of three volumes of that gas with one of hydrogen caused *ignition* of the platina, yet that mixture would not continue to burn from the jet when attempts were made to light it by a taper. A mixture even of *seven* volumes of carbonic acid and *one* of hydrogen will thus cause the ignition of cold spongy platina, and yet, as if to supply a contrast, than which none can be greater, *it cannot burn at a taper*, but causes the extinction of the latter. On the other hand, the mixtures of carbonic oxide or olefiant gas, which can do nothing with the platina, are *inflamed* by the taper, burning well.

653. Hydrogen mingled with the vapour of ether or oil-gas liquor causes the ignition of the spongy platina. The mixture with oil-gas burns with a flame far brighter than that of the

* Philosophical Transactions, 1825, p. 440.

mixture of hydrogen and olefiant gas already referred to, so that it would appear that the retarding action of the hydro-carbons is not at all in proportion merely to the quantity of carbon present.

654. In connexion with these interferences, I must state, that hydrogen itself, prepared from steam passed over ignited iron, was found when mingled with oxygen to resist the action of platina. It had stood over water seven days, and had lost all fetid smell; but a jet of it would not cause the ignition of spongy platina, commencing at common temperatures; nor would it combine with oxygen in a tube either under the influ-ence of a prepared plate or of spongy platina. A mixture of one volume of this gas with three of pure hydrogen, and the due proportion of oxygen, was not affected by plates after fifty hours. I am inclined to refer the effect to carbonic oxide pre-sent in the gas, but have not had time to verify the suspicion. The power of the plates was not destroyed (640. 646.).

655. Such are the general facts of these remarkable inter-ferences. Whether the effect produced by such small quan-tities of certain gases depends upon any direct action which they may exert upon the particles of oxygen and hydrogen, by which the latter are rendered less inclined to combine, or whether it depends upon their modifying the action of the plate temporarily (for they produce no real change on it), by invest-ing it through the agency of a stronger attraction than that of the hydrogen, or otherwise, remains to be decided by more ex-tended experiments.

-------------------

656. The theory of action which I have given for the original phenomena appears to me quite sufficient to account for all the effects by reference to known properties, and dispenses with the assumption of any new power of matter. I have pursued this subject at some length, as one of great consequence, be-cause I am convinced that the superficial actions of matter, whether between two bodies, or of one piece of the same body, and the actions of particles not directly or strongly in combi-nation, are becoming daily more and more important to our theories of chemical as well as mechanical philosophy *. In

* As a curious illustration of the influence of mechanical forces over chemi-cal affinity, I will quote the refusal of certain substances to effloresce when

all ordinary cases of combustion it is evident that an action of the kind considered, occurring upon the surface of the carbon in the fire, and also in the bright part of a flame, must have great influence over the combinations there taking place.

657. The condition of elasticity upon the exterior of the gaseous or vaporous mass already referred to (626. 627.), must be connected directly with the action of solid bodies, as nuclei, on vapours, causing condensation upon them in preference to any condensation in the vapours themselves; and in the well-known effect of nuclei on solutions a similar condition may have existence (623.), for an analogy in condition exists between the parts of a body in solution, and those of a body in the vaporous or gaseous state. This thought leads us to the consideration of what are the respective conditions at the surfaces of contact of two portions of the same substance at the same temperature, one in the solid or liquid, and the other in the vaporous state; as, for instance, steam and water. It would seem that the particles of vapour next to the particles of liquid are in a different relation to the latter to what they would be with respect to any other liquid or solid substance; as, for instance, mercury or platina, if they were made to replace the water, *i. e.* if the view of independent action which I have taken (626. 627.) as a consequence of Dalton's principles, be correct. It would also seem that the mutual relation of similar particles, and the indifference of dissimilar particles which Dalton has established as a matter of fact amongst gases and vapours, extends to a certain degree amongst solids and fluids, that is, when they are in relation by contact with vapours, either of their own substance or of other bodies. But though I view these points as of great importance with respect to the relations existing between different substances and their physical constitution in the solid,

their surfaces are perfect, which yield immediately upon the surface being broken. If crystals of carbonate of soda, or phosphate of soda, or sulphate of soda, having no part of their surfaces broken, be preserved from external violence, they will not effloresce. I have thus retained crystals of carbonate of soda perfectly transparent and unchanged from September 1827 to January 1833; and crystals of sulphate of soda from May 1832 to the present time, November 1833. If any part of the surface were scratched or broken, then efflorescence began at that part, and covered the whole. The crystals were merely placed in evaporating basins and covered with paper.

liquid, or gaseous state, I have not sufficiently considered them to venture any strong opinions or statements here *.

658. There are numerous well-known cases, in which substances, such as oxygen and hydrogen, act readily in their *nascent* state, and produce chemical changes which they are not able to effect if once they have assumed the gaseous condition. Such instances are very common at the poles of the voltaic pile, and are, I think, easily accounted for, if it be considered that at the moment of separation of any such particle it is entirely surrounded by other particles of a *different* kind with which it is in close contact, and has not yet assumed those relations and conditions which it has in its fully developed state, and which it can only assume by association with other particles of its own kind. For, at the moment, its elasticity is absent, and it is in the same relation to particles with which it is in contact, and for which it has an affinity, as the particles of oxygen and hydrogen are to each other on the surface of clean platina (626. 627.).

659. The singular effects of retardation produced by very small quantities of some gases, and not by large quantities of others (640. 645. 652.), if dependent upon any relation of the added gas to the surface of the solid, will then probably be found immediately connected with the curious phenomena which are presented by different gases when passing through narrow tubes at low pressures, which I observed many years ago † ; and this action of surfaces must, I think, influence the highly interesting phenomena of the diffusion of gases, at least in the form in which it has been experimented upon by Mr. Graham in 1829 and 1831 ‡, and also by Dr. Mitchell of Philadelphia § in 1830. It seems very probable that if such a substance as spongy platina were used, another law for the diffusion of gases under the circumstances would come out than that obtained by the use of plaster of Paris.

* In reference to this paragraph and also 626, see a correction by Dr. C. Henry, in his valuable paper on this curious subject. Philosophical Magazine, 1835, vol. vi. p. 365.—*Dec.* 1838.

† Quarterly Journal of Science, 1819, vol. vii. p. 106.

‡ Quarterly Journal of Science, vol. xxviii. p. 74., and Edinburgh Transactions, 1831.

§ Journal of the Royal Institution for 1831, p. 101.

660. I intended to have followed this section by one on the secondary piles of Ritter, and the peculiar properties of the poles of the pile, or of metals through which electricity has passed, which have been observed by Ritter, Van Marum, Yelin, De la Rive, Marianini, Berzelius, and others. It appears to me that all these phenomena bear a satisfactory explanation on known principles, connected with the investigation just terminated, and do not require the assumption of any new state or new property. But as the experiments advanced, especially those of Marianini, require very careful repetition and examination, the necessity of pursuing the subject of electro-chemical decomposition obliges me for a time to defer the researches to which I have just referred.

*Royal Institution,*
  *November* 30, 1833.

SEVENTH SERIES.

§ 11. *On Electro-chemical Decomposition, continued\**. ¶ iv. *On some general conditions of Electro-decomposition.* ¶ v. *On a new Measurer of Volta-electricity.* ¶ vi. *On the primary or secondary character of bodies evolved in Electro-decomposition.* ¶ vii. *On the definite nature and extent of Electro-chemical Decompositions.* § 13. *On the absolute quantity of Electricity associated with the particles or atoms of Matter.*

Received January 9.—Read January 23, February 6 and 13, 1834.

*Preliminary.*

661. THE theory which I believe to be a true expression of the facts of electro-chemical decomposition, and which I have therefore detailed in a former series of these Researches, is so much at variance with those previously advanced, that I find the greatest difficulty in stating results, as I think, correctly, whilst limited to the use of terms which are current with a certain accepted meaning. Of this kind is the term *pole,* with its prefixes of positive and negative, and the attached ideas of attraction and repulsion. The general phraseology is that the positive pole *attracts* oxygen, acids, &c., or more cautiously, that it *determines* their evolution upon its surface ; and that the negative pole acts in an equal manner upon hydrogen, combustibles, metals, and bases. According to my view, the determining force is *not* at the poles, but *within* the body under decomposition ; and the oxygen and acids are rendered at the *negative* extremity of that body, whilst hydrogen, metals, &c., are evolved at the *positive* extremity (518. 524.).

662. To avoid, therefore, confusion and circumlocution, and for the sake of greater precision of expression than I can otherwise obtain, I have deliberately considered the subject with two friends, and with their assistance and concurrence in framing

\* Refer to the note after 1047, Series VIII.—*Dec.* 1838.

them, I purpose henceforward using certain other terms, which I will now define. The *poles*, as they are usually called, are only the doors or ways by which the electric current passes into and out of the decomposing body (556.) ; and they of course, when in contact with that body, are the limits of its extent in the direction of the current. The term has been generally applied to the metal surfaces in contact with the decomposing substance; but whether philosophers generally would also apply it to the surfaces of air (465. 471.) and water (493.), against which I have effected electro-chemical decomposition, is subject to doubt. In place of the term pole, I propose using that of *Electrode* *, and I mean thereby that substance, or rather surface, whether of air, water, metal, or any other body, which bounds the extent of the decomposing matter in the direction of the electric current.

663. The surfaces at which, according to common phraseology, the electric current enters and leaves a decomposing body, are most important places of action, and require to be distinguished apart from the poles, with which they are mostly, and the electrodes, with which they are always, in contact. Wishing for a natural standard of electric direction to which I might refer these, expressive of their difference and at the same time free from all theory, I have thought it might be found in the earth. If the magnetism of the earth be due to electric currents passing round it, the latter must be in a constant direction, which, according to present usage of speech, would be from east to west, or, which will strengthen this help to the memory, that in which the sun appears to move. If in any case of electro-decomposition we consider the decomposing body as placed so that the current passing through it shall be in the same direction, and parallel to that supposed to exist in the earth, then the surfaces at which the electricity is passing into and out of the substance would have an invariable reference, and exhibit constantly the same relations of powers. Upon this notion we purpose calling that towards the east the *anode* †, and that towards the west the *cathode* ‡ ; and whatever changes may take place in our views of the nature of electricity and electrical

* ἤλεκτρον, and ὁδὸς *a way.*
† ἄνω *upwards,* and ὁδὸς *a way* ; the way which the sun rises.
‡ κατὰ *downwards,* and ὁδὸς *a way* ; the way which the sun sets.

action, as they must affect the *natural standard* referred to, in
the same direction, and to an equal amount with any decomposing substances to which these terms may at any time be
applied, there seems no reason to expect that they will lead to
confusion, or tend in any way to support false views.   The
*anode* is therefore that surface at which the electric current according to our present expression, enters : it is the *negative*
extremity of the decomposing body ; is where oxygen, chlorine,
acids, &c., are evolved; and is against or opposite the positive
electrode.   The *cathode* is that surface at which the current
leaves the decomposing body ; and is its *positive* extremity ; the
combustible bodies, metals, alkalies, and bases, are evolved there,
and it is in contact with the negative electrode.

664. I shall have occasion in these Researches, also, to class
bodies together according to certain relations derived from their
electrical actions (822.) ; and wishing to express those relations
without at the same time involving the expression of any hypothetical views, I intend using the following names and terms.
Many bodies are decomposed directly by the electric current,
their elements being set free : these I propose to call *electrolytes*\*.   Water, therefore, is an electrolyte.   The bodies which,
like nitric or sulphuric acids, are decomposed in a secondary
manner (752. 757.), are not included under this term.   Then
for *electro-chemically decomposed*, I shall often use the term
*electrolyzed*, derived in the same way, and implying that the
body spoken of is separated into its components under the influence of electricity : it is analogous in its sense and sound to
*analyze*, which is derived in a similar manner. · The term *electrolytical* will be understood at once : muriatic acid is electrolytical, boracic acid is not.

665. Finally, I require a term to express those bodies which
can pass to the *electrodes*, or, as they are usually called, the
poles.   Substances are frequently spoken of as being *electro-
negative*, or *electro-positive*, according as they go under the
supposed influence of a direct attraction to the positive or negative pole.   But these terms are much too significant for the use
to which I should have to put them; for though the meanings are
perhaps right, they are only hypothetical, and may be wrong ;
and then, through a very imperceptible, but still very dangerous,

\* ἤλεκτρον, and λύω, *solvo*.   N. Electrolyte, V. Electrolyze.

because continual, influence, they do great injury to science, by contracting and limiting the habitual views of those engaged in pursuing it. I propose to distinguish such bodies by calling those *anions** which go to the *anode* of the decomposing body; and those passing to the *cathode, cations*†; and when I have occasion to speak of these together, I shall call them *ions.* Thus, the chloride of lead is an *electrolyte,* and when *electrolyzed* evolves the two *ions,* chlorine and lead, the former being an *anion,* and the latter a *cation.*

666. These terms being once well defined, will, I hope, in their use enable me to avoid much periphrasis and ambiguity of expression. I do not mean to press them into service more frequently than will be required, for I am fully aware that names are one thing and science another‡.

667. It will be well underssood that I am giving no opinion respecting the nature of the electric current now, beyond what I have done on former occasions (283. 517.); and that though I speak of the current as proceeding from the parts which are positive to those which are negative (663.), it is merely in accordance with the conventional, though in some degree tacit, agreement entered into by scientific men, that they may have a constant, certain, and definite means of referring to the direction of the forces of that current.

¶ iv. *On some general conditions of electro-chemical Decomposition.*

669. From the period when electro-chemical decomposition was first effected to the present time, it has been a remark, that those elements which in the ordinary phenomena of chemical affinity, were the most directly opposed to each other, and combined with the greatest attractive force, were those which were the most readily evolved at the opposite extremities of the decomposing bodies (549.).

670. If this result was evident when water was supposed to be essential to, and was present, in almost every case of such

* ἀνιὼν *that which goes up.* (Neuter participle.)

† κατιὼν *that which goes down*

‡ Since this paper was read, I have changed some of the terms which were first proposed, that I might employ only such as were at the same time simple in their nature, clear in their reference, and from hypothesis.

decomposition (472.), it is far more evident now that it has been shown and proved that water is not necessarily concerned in the phenomena (474.), and that other bodies much surpass it in some of the effects supposed to be peculiar to that substance.

671. Water, from its constitution and the nature of its elements, and from its frequent presence in cases of electrolytic action, has hitherto stood foremost in this respect. Though a compound formed by very powerful affinity, it yields up its elements under the influence of a very feeble electric current; and it is doubtful whether a case of electrolyzation can occur, where, being present, it is not resolved into its first principles.

672. The various oxides, chlorides, iodides, and salts, which I have shown are decomposable by the electric current when in the liquid state, under the same general law with water (402.), illustrate in an equally striking manner the activity, in such decompositions, of elements directly and powerfully opposed to each other by their chemical relations.

673. On the other hand, bodies dependent on weak affinities very rarely give way. Take, for instance, glasses : many of those formed of silica, lime, alkali, and oxide of lead, may be considered as little more than solutions of substances one in another*. If bottle-glass be fused, and subjected to the voltaic pile, it does not appear to be at all decomposed (408.) If flint glass, which contains substances more directly opposed, be operated upon, it suffers some decomposition ; and if borate of lead glass, which is a definite chemical compound, be experimented with, it readily yields up its elements (408.).

674. But the result which is found to be so striking in the instances quoted is not at all borne out by reference to other cases where a similar consequence might have been expected. It may be said, that my own theory of electro-chemical decomposition would lead to the expectation that all compound bodies should give way under the influence of the electric current with a facility proportionate to the strength of the affinity by which their elements, either proximate or ultimate, are combined. I am not sure that that follows as a consequence of the theory ; but if the objection is supposed to be one presented by the facts, I have no doubt it will be removed when we obtain a more inti-

* Philosophical Transactions, 1830, p. 49.

mate acquaintance with, and precise idea of, the nature of chemical affinity and the mode of action of an electric current over it (518. 524.) : besides which it is just as directly opposed to any other theory of electro-chemical decomposition as the one I have propounded ; for if it be admitted, as is generally the case, that the more directly bodies are opposed to each other in their attractive forces, the more powerfully do they combine, then the objection applies with equal force to any of the theories of electrolyzation which have been considered, and is an addition to those which I have taken against them.

675. Amongst powerful compounds which are not decomposed, boracic acid stands prominent (408.). Then again, the iodide of sulphur, and the chlorides of sulphur, phosphorus, and carbon, are not decomposable under common circumstances, though their elements are of a nature which would lead to a contrary expectation.    Chloride of antimony (402. 690.), the hydrocarbons, acetic acid, ammonia, and many other bodies undecomposable by the voltaic pile, would seem to be formed by an affinity sufficiently strong to indicate that the elements were so far contrasted in their nature as to sanction the expectation that the pile would separate them, especially as in some cases of mere solution (530. 544.), where the affinity must by comparison be very weak, separation takes place*.

676. It must not be forgotten, however, that much of this difficulty, and perhaps the whole, may depend upon the absence of conducting power, which, preventing the transmission of the current, prevents of course the effects due to it. All known compounds being non-conductors when solid, but conductors when liquid, are decomposed, with *perhaps* the single exception at present known of periodide of mercury (679. 691.) †; and even water itself, which so easily yields up its elements when the current passes, if rendered quite pure, scarcely suffers change, because it then becomes a very bad conductor.

677. If it should hereafter be proved that the want of decomposition in those cases where, from chemical considerations, it might be so strongly expected (669. 672. 674.), is due to the

---

* With regard to solution, I have met with some reasons for supposing that it will probably disappear as a cause of transference, and intend resuming the consideration at a convenient opportunity.

† See now, 1340, 1341.—*Dec.* 1838.

absence or deficiency of conducting power, it would also at the same time be proved that decomposition *depends* upon conduction, and not the latter upon the former (413.) ; and in water this seems to be very nearly decided. On the other hand, the conclusion is almost irresistible, that in electrolytes the power of transmitting the electricity across the substance is *dependent* upon their capability of suffering decomposition ; taking place only whilst they are decomposing, and being proportionate to the quantity of elements separated (821.). I may not, however, stop to discuss this point experimentally at present.

678. When a compound contains such elements as are known to pass towards the opposite extremities of the voltaic pile, still the proportions in which they are present appear to be intimately connected with capability in the compound of suffering or resisting decomposition. Thus, the protochloride of tin readily conducts, and is decomposed (402.), but the perchloride neither conducts nor is decomposed (406.). The protiodide of tin is decomposed when fluid (402.) ; the periodide is not (405.). The periodide of mercury when fused is not decomposed (691.), even though it does conduct. I was unable to contrast it with the protiodide, the latter being converted into mercury and periodide by heat.

679. These important differences induced me to look more closely to certain binary compounds, with a view of ascertaining whether a *law* regulating the *decomposability* according to some *relation of the proportionals or equivalents* of the elements, could be discovered. The proto compounds only, amongst those just referred to, were decomposable ; and on referring to the substances quoted to illustrate the force and generality of the law of conduction and decomposition which I discovered (402.), it will be found that all the oxides, chlorides, and iodides subject to it, except the chloride of antimony and the periodide of mercury, (to which may now perhaps be added corrosive sublimate,) are also decomposable, whilst many per compounds of the same elements, not subject to the law, were not so (405. 406.).

680. The substances which appeared to form the strongest exceptions to this general result were such bodies as the sulphuric, phosphoric, nitric, arsenic, and other acids.

681. On experimenting with sulphuric acid, I found no rea-

son to believe that it was by itself a conductor of, or decomposable by, electricity, although I had previously been of that opinion (552.). When very strong it is a much worse conductor than if diluted*. If then subjected to the action of a powerful battery, oxygen appears at the *anode,* or positive electrode, although much is absorbed (728.), and hydrogen and sulphur appear at the *cathode,* or negative electrode. Now the hydrogen has with me always been pure, not sulphuretted, and has been deficient in proportion to the sulphur present, so that it is evident that when decomposition occurred water must have been decomposed. I endeavoured to make the experiment with anhydrous sulphuric acid; and it appeared to me that, when fused, such acid was not a conductor, nor decomposed; but I had not enough of the dry acid in my possession to allow me to decide the point satisfactorily. My belief is, that when sulphur appears during the action of the pile on sulphuric acid, it is the result of a secondary action, and that the acid itself is not electrolyzable (757.).

682. Phosphoric acid is, I believe, also in the same condition; but I have found it impossible to decide the point, because of the difficulty of operating on fused anhydrous phosphoric acid. Phosphoric acid which has once obtained water cannot be deprived of it by heat alone. When heated, the hydrated acid volatilizes. Upon subjecting phosphoric acid, fused upon the ring end of a wire (401.), to the action of the voltaic apparatus, it conducted, and was decomposed; but gas, which I believe to be hydrogen, was always evolved at the negative electrode, and the wire was not affected as would have happened had phosphorus been separated. Gas was also evolved at the positive electrode. From all the facts, I conclude it was the water and not the acid which was decomposed.

683. *Arsenic acid.* This substance conducted, and was decomposed; but it contained water, and I was unable at the time to press the investigation so as to ascertain whether a fusible anhydrous arsenic acid could be obtained. It forms, therefore, at present no exception to the general result.

684. Nitrous acid, obtained by distilling nitrate of lead, and keeping it in contact with strong sulphuric acid, was found to conduct and decompose slowly. But on examination there were

* De la Rive.

strong reasons for believing that water was present, and that the decomposition and conduction depended upon it. I endeavoured to prepare a perfectly anhydrous portion, but could not spare the time required to procure an unexceptionable result.

685. Nitric acid is a substance which I believe is not decomposed directly by the electric current. As I want the facts in illustration of the distinction existing between primary and secondary decomposition, I will merely refer to them in this place (752.).

686. That these mineral acids should confer facility of conduction and decomposition on water, is no proof that they are competent to favour and suffer these actions in themselves. Boracic acid does the same thing, though not decomposable. M. de la Rive has pointed out that chlorine has this power also ; but being to us an elementary substance, it cannot be due to its capability of suffering decomposition.

687. *Chloride of sulphur* does not conduct, nor is it decomposed. It consists of single proportionals of its elements, but is not on that account an exception to the rule (679.), which does not affirm that *all* compounds of single proportionals of elements are decomposable, but that such as are decomposable are so constituted.

688. *Protochloride of phosphorus* does not conduct nor become decomposed.

689. *Protochloride of carbon* does not conduct nor suffer decomposition. In association with this substance, I submitted the *hydro-chloride of carbon* from olefiant gas and chlorine to the action of the electric current ; but it also refused to conduct or yield up its elements.

690. With regard to the exceptions (679.), upon closer examination, some of them disappear. Chloride of antimony (a compound of one proportional of antimony and one and a half of chlorine) of recent preparation was put into a tube (fig. 68.) (789.), and submitted when fused to the action of the current, the positive electrode being of plumbago. No electricity passed, and no appearance of decomposition was visible at first; but when the positive and negative electrodes were brought very near each other in the chloride, then a feeble action occurred and a feeble current passed. The effect altogether was so

small (although quite amenable to the law before given (394.) ), and so unlike the decomposition and conduction occurring in all the other cases, that I attribute it to the presence of a minute quantity of water, (for which this and many other chlorides have strong attractions, producing hydrated chlorides,) or perhaps of a true protochloride consisting of single proportionals (695. 796.).

691. *Periodide of mercury* being examined in the same manner, was found most distinctly to insulate whilst solid, but conduct when fluid, according to the law of *liquido-conduction* (402.) ; but there was no appearance of decomposition. No iodine appeared at the *anode*, nor mercury or other substance at the *cathode*. The case is, therefore, no exception to the rule, that only compounds of single proportionals are decomposable ; but it is an exception, and I think the only one, to the statement, that all bodies subject to the law of liquido-conduction are decomposable. I incline, however, to believe, that a portion of protiodide of mercury is retained dissolved in the periodide, and that to its slow decomposition the feeble conducting power is due. Periodide would be formed, as a secondary result, at the *anode* ; and the mercury at the *cathode* would also form, as a secondary result, protiodide. Both these bodies would mingle with the fluid mass, and thus no final separation appear, notwithstanding the continued decomposition.

692. When *perchloride of mercury* was subjected to the voltaic current, it did not conduct in the solid state, but it did conduct when fluid. I think, also, that in the latter case it was decomposed ; but there are many interfering circumstances which require examination before a positive conclusion can be drawn*.

693. When the ordinary protoxide of antimony is subjected to the voltaic current in a fused state, it also is decomposed, although the effect from other causes soon ceases (402. 801.). This oxide consists of one proportional of antimony and one and a half of oxygen, and is therefore an exception to the general law assumed. But in working with this oxide and the chloride, I observed facts which lead me to doubt whether the compounds usually called the protoxide and the protochloride do not often contain other compounds, consisting of single pro-

* With regard to perchloride and periodide of mercury, see now 1340, 1341.*D ec.* 1838.

portions, which are the true proto compounds, and which, in the case of the oxide, might give rise to the decomposition above described.

694. The ordinary sulphuret of antimony is considered as being the compound with the smallest quantity of sulphur, and analogous in its proportions to the ordinary protoxide. But I find that if it be fused with metallic antimony, a new sulphuret is formed, containing much more of the metal than the former, and separating distinctly, when fused, both from the pure metal on the one hand, and the ordinary gray sulphuret on the other. In some rough experiments, the metal thus taken up by the ordinary sulphuret of antimony was equal to half the proportion of that previously in the sulphuret, in which case the new sulphuret would consist of *single* proportionals.

695. When this new sulphuret was dissolved in muriatic acid, although a little antimony separated, yet it appeared to me that a true protochloride, consisting of *single* proportionals, was formed, and from that, by alkalies, &c., a true protoxide, consisting also of *single* proportionals, was obtainable. But I could not stop to ascertain this matter strictly by analysis.

696. I believe, however, that there is such an oxide; that it is often present in variable proportions in what is commonly called protoxide, throwing uncertainty upon the results of its analysis, and causing the electrolytic decomposition above described *.

697. Upon the whole, it appears probable that all those binary compounds of elementary bodies which are capable of being electrolyzed when fluid, but not whilst solid, according to the law of liquido-conduction (394.), consist of single proportionals of their elementary principles ; and it may be because of their departure from this simplicity of composition, that boracic acid, ammonia, perchlorides, periodides, and many other direct compounds of elements, are indecomposable.

698. With regard to salts and combinations of compound bodies, the same simple relation does not appear to hold good. I could not decide this by bisulphates of the alkalies, for as long

* In relation to this and the three preceding paragraphs, and also 801, see Berzelius's correction of the nature of the supposed new sulphuret and oxide, Phil. Mag. 1836, vol. viii. 476: and for the probable explanation of the effects obtained with the protoxide, refer to 1340, 1341.—*Dec.* 1838.

as the second proportion of acid remained, water was retained with it. The fused salts conducted, and were decomposed ; but hydrogen always appeared at the negative electrode.

699. A biphosphate of soda was prepared by heating, and ultimately fusing, the ammonia-phosphate of soda. In this case the fused bisalt conducted, and was decomposed ; but a little gas appeared at the negative electrode ; and though I believe the salt itself was electrolyzed, I am not quite satisfied that water was entirely absent.

700. Then a biborate of soda was prepared ; and this, I think, is an unobjectionable case. The salt, when fused, conducted, and was decomposed, and gas appeared at both electrodes : even when the boracic acid was increased to three proportionals, the same effect took place.

701. Hence this class of compound combinations does not seem to be subject to the same simple law as the former class of binary combinations. Whether we may find reason to consider them as mere solutions of the compound of single proportionals in the excess of acid, is a matter which, with some apparent exceptions occurring amongst the sulphurets, must be left for decision by future examination.

702. In any investigation of these points, great care must be taken to exclude water ; for if present, secondary effects are so frequently produced as often seemingly to indicate an electro-decomposition of substances, when no true result of the kind has occurred (742, &c.).

703. It is evident that all the cases in which decomposition *does not occur, may* depend upon the want of conduction (677. 413.) ; but that does not at all lessen the interest excited by seeing the great difference of effect due to a change, not in the nature of the elements, but merely in their proportions ; especially in any attempt which may be made to elucidate and expound the beautiful theory put forth by Sir Humphry Davy*, and illustrated by Berzelius and other eminent philosophers, that ordinary chemical affinity is a mere result of the electrical attractions of the particles of matter.

¶ v. *On a new Measurer of Volta-electricity.*

704. I have already said, when engaged in reducing common

---

* Philosophical Transactions, 1807, pp. 32, 39; also 1826, pp. 387, 389.

and voltaic electricity to one standard of measurement (377.),
and again when introducing my theory of electro-chemical decomposition (504. 505. 510.), that the chemical decomposing
action of a current *is constant for a constant quantity of electricity*, notwithstanding the greatest variations in its sources,
in its intensity, in the size of the *electrodes* used, in the nature
of the conductors (or non conductors (307.) ) through which it
is passed, or in other circumstances.   The conclusive proofs of
the truth of these statements shall be given almost immediately
(783, &c.).

705. I endeavoured upon this law to construct an instrument
which should measure out the electricity passing through it,
and which, being interposed in the course of the current used
in any particular experiment, should serve at pleasure, either as
a *comparative standard* of effect, or as a *positive measurer* of
this subtile agent.

706. There is no substance better fitted, under ordinary circumstances, to be the indicating body in such an instrument
than water; for it is decomposed with facility when rendered
a better conductor by the addition of acids or salts; its elements may in numerous cases be obtained and collected without any embarrassment from secondary action, and, being
gaseous, they are in the best physical condition for separation
and measurement.   Water, therefore, acidulated by sulphuric
acid, is the substance I shall generally refer to, although it
may become expedient in peculiar cases or forms of experiment
to use other bodies (843.).

707. The first precaution needful in the construction of the
instrument was to avoid the recombination of the evolved gases,
an effect which the positive electrode has been found so capable of producing (571.).   For this purpose various forms of
decomposing apparatus were used.   The first consisted of
straight tubes, each containing a plate and wire of platina
soldered together by gold, and fixed hermetically in the glass
at the closed extremity of the tube (Plate V. fig. 60.).   The
tubes were about eight inches long, 0·7 of an inch in diameter,
and graduated.   The platina plates were about an inch long,
as wide as the tubes would permit, and adjusted as near to the
mouths of the tubes as was consistent with the safe collection
of the gases evolved.   In certain cases, where it was required

to evolve the elements upon as small a surface as possible, the
metallic extremity, instead of being a plate, consisted of the
wire bent into the form of a ring (fig. 61.).   When these tubes
were used as measures, they were filled with the dilute sulphuric acid, inverted in a basin of the same liquid (fig. 62.),
and placed in an inclined position, with their mouths near to
each other, that as little decomposing matter should intervene
as possible ; and also, in such a direction that the platina plates
should be in vertical planes (720.).

708. Another form of apparatus is that delineated (fig. 63.).
The tube is bent in the middle ; one end is closed ; in that end
is fixed a wire and plate, *a*, proceeding so far downwards, that,
when in the position figured, it shall be as near to the angle as
possible, consistently with the collection, at the closed extremity of the tube, of all the gas evolved against it.   The
plane of this plate is also perpendicular (720.).   The other
metallic termination, *b*, is introduced at the time decomposition
is to be effected, being brought as near the angle as possible,
without causing any gas to pass from it towards the closed end
of the instrument.   The gas evolved against it is allowed to
escape.

709. The third form of apparatus contains both electrodes
in the same tube ; the transmission, therefore, of the electricity,
and the consequent decomposition, is far more rapid than in the
separate tubes.   The resulting gas is the sum of the portions
evolved at the two electrodes, and the instrument is better
adapted than either of the former as a measurer of the quantity of voltaic electricity transmitted in ordinary cases.   It consists of a straight tube (fig. 64.) closed at the upper extremity,
and graduated, through the sides of which pass platina wires
(being fused into the glass), which are connected with two
plates within.   The tube is fitted by grinding into one mouth
of a double-necked bottle.   If the latter be one half or two thirds
full of the dilute sulphuric acid (706.), it will, upon inclination
of the whole, flow into the tube and fill it.   When an electric
current is passed through the instrument, the gases evolved
against the plates collect in the upper portion of the tube, and
are not subject to the recombining power of the platina.

710. Another form of the instrument is given at fig. 65.

711. A fifth form is delineated (fig. 66.).   This I have found

exceedingly useful in experiments continued in succession for days together, and where large quantities of indicating gas were to be collected. It is fixed on a weighted foot, and has the form of a small retort containing the two electrodes : the neck is narrow, and sufficiently long to deliver gas issuing from it into a jar placed in a small pneumatic trough. The electrode chamber, sealed hermetically at the part held in the stand, is five inches in length, and 0·6 of an inch in diameter ; the neck about nine inches in length, and 0·4 of an inch in diameter internally. The figure will fully indicate the construction.

712. It can hardly be requisite to remark, that in the arrangement of any of these forms of apparatus, they, and the wires connecting them with the substance, which is collaterally subjected to the action of the same electric current, should be so far insulated as to ensure a certainty that all the electricity which passes through the one shall also be transmitted through the other.

---

713. Next to the precaution of collecting the gases, if mingled, out of contact with the platinum, was the necessity of testing the law of a *definite electrolytic* action, upon water at least, under all varieties of condition ; that, with a conviction of its certainty, might also be obtained a knowledge of those interfering circumstances which would require to be practically guarded against.

714. The first point investigated was the influence or indifference of extensive variations in the size of the electrodes, for which purpose instruments like those last described (709. 710. 711.) were used. One of these had plates 0·7 of an inch wide, and nearly four inches long ; another had plates only 0·5 of an inch wide, and 0·8 of an inch long ; a third had wires 0·02 of an inch in diameter, and three inches long ; and a fourth, similar wires only half an inch in length. Yet when these were filled with dilute sulphuric acid, and, being placed in succession, had one common current of electricity passed through them, very nearly the same quantity of gas was evolved in all. The difference was sometimes in favour of one, and sometimes on the side of another ; but the general result was that the largest quantity of gases was evolved at the smallest electrodes, namely, those consisting merely of platina wires.

715. Experiments of a similar kind were made with the single-plate, straight tubes (707.), and also with the curved tubes (708.), with similar consequences ; and when these, with the former tubes, were arranged together in various ways, the result, as to the equality of action of large and small metallic surfaces when delivering and receiving the same current of electricity, was constantly the same. As an illustration, the following numbers are given. An instrument with two wires evolved 74·3 volumes of mixed gases ; another with plates 73·25 volumes; whilst the sum of the oxygen and hydrogen in two separate tubes amounted to 73·65 volumes. In another experiment the volumes were 55·3, 55·3, and 54·4.

716. But it was observed in these experiments, that in single-plate tubes (707.) more hydrogen was evolved at the negative electrode than was proportionate to the oxygen at the positive electrode ; and generally, also, more than was proportionate to the oxygen and hydrogen in a double plate-tube. Upon more minutely examining these effects, I was led to refer them, and also the differences between wires and plates (714.), to the solubility of the gases evolved, especially at the positive electrode.

717. When the positive and negative electrodes are equal in surface, the bubbles which rise from them in dilute sulphuric acid are always different in character. Those from the positive plate are exceedingly small, and separate instantly from every part of the surface of the metal, in consequence of its perfect cleanliness (633.) ; whilst in the liquid they give it a hazy appearance, from their number and minuteness ; are easily carried down by currents ; and therefore not only present far greater surface of contact with the liquid than larger bubbles would do, but are retained a much longer time in mixture with it. But the bubbles at the negative surface, though they constitute twice the volume of the gas at the positive electrode, are nevertheless very inferior in number. They do not rise so universally from every part of the surface, but seemed to be evolved at different points ; and though so much larger, they appear to cling to the metal, separating with difficulty from it, and when separated, instantly rising to the top of the liquid. If, therefore, oxygen and hydrogen had equal solubility in, or powers of combining with, water under similar circumstances, still under the present conditions the oxygen would be far the most liable to solution;

but when to these is added its well-known power of forming a compound with water, it is no longer surprising that such a compound should be produced in small quantities at the positive electrode; and indeed the bleaching power which some philosophers have observed in a solution at this electrode, when chlorine and similar bodies have been carefully excluded, is probably due to the formation there, in this manner, of oxy-water.

718. That more gas was collected from the wires than from the plates, I attribute to the circumstance, that as equal quantities were evolved in equal times, the bubbles at the wires having been more rapidly produced, in relation to any part of the surface, must have been much larger; have been therefore in contact with the fluid by a much smaller surface, and for a much shorter time than those at the plates; hence less solution and a greater amount collected.

719. There was also another effect produced, especially by the use of large electrodes, which was both a consequence and a proof of the solution of part of the gas evolved there. The collected gas, when examined, was found to contain small portions of nitrogen. This I attribute to the presence of air dissolved in the acid used for decomposition. It is a well-known fact, that when bubbles of a gas but slightly soluble in water or solutions pass through them, the portion of this gas which is dissolved displaces a portion of that previously in union with the liquid : and so, in the decompositions under consideration, as the oxygen dissolves, it displaces a part of the air, or at least of the nitrogen, previously united to the acid ; and this effect takes place *most extensively* with large plates, because the gas evolved at them is in the most favourable condition for solution.

720. With the intention of avoiding this solubility of the gases as much as possible, I arranged the decomposing plates in a vertical position (707. 708.), that the bubbles might quickly escape upwards, and that the downward currents in the fluid should not meet ascending currents of gas. This precaution I found to assist greatly in producing constant results, and especially in experiments to be hereafter referred to, in which other liquids than dilute sulphuric acid, as for instance solution of potash, were used.

721. The irregularities in the indications of the measurer proposed, arising from the solubility just referred to, are but small, and may be very nearly corrected by comparing the results of two or three experiments. They may also be almost entirely avoided by selecting that solution which is found to favour them in the least degree (728.) ; and still further by collecting the hydrogen only, and using that as the indicating gas ; for being much less soluble than oxygen, being evolved with twice the rapidity and in larger bubbles (717.), it can be collected more perfectly and in greater purity.

722. From the foregoing and many other experiments, it re- sults that *variation in the size of the electrodes causes no varia- tion in the chemical action of a given quantity of electricity upon water.*

---

723. The next point in regard to which the principle of con- stant electro-chemical action was tested, was *variation of inten- sity.* In the first place, the preceding experiments were re- peated, using batteries of an *equal* number of plates, *strongly* and *weakly* charged ; but the results were alike. They were then repeated, using batteries sometimes containing forty, and at other times only five pairs of plates ; but the results were still the same. *Variations therefore in the intensity,* caused by difference in the strength of charge, or in the number of alter- nations used, *produced no difference as to the equal action of large and small electrodes.*

724. Still these results did not prove that variation in the intensity of the current was not accompanied by a corresponding variation in the electro-chemical effects, since the actions at *all* the surfaces might have increased or diminished together. The deficiency in the evidence is, however, completely supplied by the former experiments on different-sized electrodes ; for with variation in the size of these, a variation in the intensity must have occurred. The intensity of an electric current traversing conductors alike in their nature, quality, and length, is probably as the quantity of electricity passing through a given sectional area perpendicular to the current, divided by the time (360. *note*) ; and therefore when large plates were contrasted with wires separated by an equal length of the same decomposing conductor (714.), whilst one current of electricity passed through

both arrangements, that electricity must have been in a very different state, as to *tension*, between the plates and between the wires ; yet the chemical results were the same.

725. The difference in intensity, under the circumstances described, may be easily shown practically, by arranging two decomposing apparatus as in fig. 67, where the same fluid is subjected to the decomposing power of the same current of electricity, passing in the vessel A. between large platina plates, and in the vessel B. between small wires.  If a third decomposing apparatus, such as that delineated fig. 66. (711.), be connected with the wires at *a, b,* fig. 67, it will serve sufficiently well, by the degree of decomposition occurring in it, to indicate the relative state of the two plates as to intensity ; and if it then be applied in the same way, as a test of the state of the wires at $a'$ $b'$, it will, by the increase of decomposition within, show how much greater the intensity is there than at the former points.   The connexions of P and N with the voltaic battery are of course to be continued during the whole time.

726. A third form of experiment in which difference of intensity was obtained, for the purpose of testing the principle of equal chemical action, was to arrange three volta-electrometers, so that after the electric current had passed through one, it should divide into two parts, each of which should traverse one of the remaining instruments, and should then reunite.   The sum of the decomposition in the two latter vessels was always equal to the decomposition in the former vessel.   But the *intensity* of the divided current could not be the same as that it had in its original state ; and therefore *variation of intensity has no influence on the results if the quantity of electricity remain the same.* The experiment, in fact, resolves itself simply into an increase in the size of the electrodes (725.).

727. The *third point,* in respect to which the principle of equal electro-chemical action on water was tested, was *variation of the strength of the solution used.*   In order to render the water a conductor, sulphuric acid had been added to it (707.) ; and it did not seem unlikely that this substance, with many others, might render the water more subject to decomposition, the electricity remaining the same in quantity.   But such did not

prove to be the case.   Diluted sulphuric acid, of different
strengths, was introduced into different decomposing apparatus,
and submitted simultaneously to the action of the same electric
current (714.).   Slight differences occurred, as before, sometimes
in one direction, sometimes in another ; but the final result was,
that *exactly the same quantity of water was decomposed in all
the solutions by the same quantity of electricity*, though the
sulphuric acid in some was seventy-fold what it was in others.
The strengths used were of specific gravity 1·495, and downwards.

728. When an acid having a specific gravity of about 1·336
was employed, the results were most uniform, and the oxygen
and hydrogen (716.) most constantly in the right proportion to
each other.   Such an acid gave more gas than one much weaker
acted upon by the same current, apparently because it had less
solvent power.   If the acid were very strong, then a remarkable disappearance of oxygen took place ; thus, one made by
mixing two measures of strong oil of vitriol with one of water,
gave forty-two volumes of hydrogen, but only twelve of oxygen.
The hydrogen was very nearly the same with that evolved from
acid of the specific gravity 1·232.   I have not yet had time to
examine minutely the circumstances attending the disappearance of the oxygen in this case, but imagine it is due to the
formation of oxywater, which Thénard has shown is favoured
by the presence of acid.

------

729. Although not necessary for the practical use of the
instrument I am describing, yet as connected with the important point of constant electro-chemical action upon water, I now
investigated the effects produced by an electric current passing
through aqueous solutions of acids, salts, and compounds, exceedingly different from each other in their nature, and found
them to yield astonishingly uniform results.   But many of them
which are connected with a secondary action will be more use-
fully described hereafter (778.).

730. When solutions of caustic potassa or soda, or sulphate
of magnesia, or sulphate of soda, were acted upon by the electric current, just as much oxygen and hydrogen was evolved
from them as from the diluted sulphuric acid, with which they
were compared.   When a solution of ammonia, rendered a better

conductor by sulphate of ammonia (554.), or a solution of sub-carbonate of potassa was experimented with, the *hydrogen* evolved was in the same quantity as that set free from the diluted sulphuric acid with which they were compared.  Hence *changes in the nature of the solution do not alter the constancy of electrolytic action upon water.*

731. I have already said, respecting large and small electrodes, that change of order caused no change in the general effect (715.).  The same was the case with different solutions, or with different intensities; and however the circumstances of an experiment might be varied, the results came forth exceedingly consistent, and proved that the electro-chemical action was still the same.

_____

732. I consider the foregoing investigation as sufficient to prove the very extraordinary and important principle with respect to WATER, *that when subjected to the influence of the electric current, a quantity of it is decomposed exactly proportionate to the quantity of electricity which has passed,* notwithstanding the thousand variations in the conditions and circumstances under which it may at the time be placed ; and further, that when the interference of certain secondary effects (742. &c.), together with the solution or recombination of the gas and the evolution of air, are guarded against, *the products of the decomposition may be collected with such accuracy, as to afford a very excellent and valuable measurer of the electricity concerned in their evolution.*

733. The forms of instrument which I have given, figg. 64, 65, 66 (709. 710. 711.), are probably those which will be found most useful, as they indicate the quantity of electricity by the largest volume of gases, and cause the least obstruction to the passage of the current.  The fluid which my present experience leads me to prefer, is a solution of sulphuric acid of specific gravity about 1·336, or from that to 1·25 ; but it is very essential that there should be no organic substance, nor any vegetable acid, nor other body, which, by being liable to the action of the oxygen or hydrogen evolved at the electrodes (773. &c.), shall diminish their quantity, or add other gases to them.

734. In many cases when the instrument is used as a *com-*

*parative standard,* or even as a *measurer,* it may be desirable
to collect the hydrogen only, as being less liable to absorption
or disappearance in other ways than the oxygen; whilst at the
same time its volume is so large, as to render it a good and
sensible indicator. In such cases the first and second form of
apparatus have been used, figg. 62, 63 (707. 708.). The indications obtained were very constant, the variations being
much smaller than in those forms of apparatus collecting both
gases; and they can also be procured when solutions are used
in comparative experiments, which, yielding no oxygen or only
secondary results of its action, can give no indications if the
educts at both electrodes be collected. Such is the case when
solutions of ammonia, muriatic acid, chlorides, iodides, acetates
or other vegetable salts, &c., are employed.

735. In a few cases, as where solutions of metallic salts liable
to reduction at the negative electrode are acted upon, the
oxygen may be advantageously used as the measuring substance. This is the case, for instance, with sulphate of
copper.

736. There are therefore two general forms of the instrument which I submit as a measurer of electricity; one, in
which both the gases of the water decomposed are collected
(709. 710. 711.); and the other, in which a single gas, as the
hydrogen only, is used (707. 708.). When referred to as a
*comparative instrument,* (a use I shall now make of it very extensively,) it will not often require particular precaution in the
observation; but when used as an *absolute measurer,* it will be
needful that the barometric pressure and the temperature be
taken into account, and that the graduation of the instruments
should be to one scale : the hundredths and smaller divisions
of a cubical inch are quite fit for this purpose, and the hundredth may be very conveniently taken as indicating a DEGREE
of electricity.

737. It can scarcely be needful to point out further than has
been done how this instrument is to be used. It is to be introduced into the course of the electric current, the action of
which is to be exerted anywhere else, and if 60° or 70° of electricity are to be measured out, either in one or several portions,
the current, whether strong or weak, is to be continued
until the gas in the tube occupies that number of divisions or

hundredths of a cubical inch.   Or if a quantity competent to produce a certain effect is to be measured, the effect is to be obtained, and then the indication read off.   In exact experiments it is necessary to correct the volume of gas for changes in temperature and pressure, and especially for moisture*. For the latter object the volta-electrometer (fig. 66.) is most accurate, as its gas can be measured over water, whilst the others retain it over acid or saline solutions.

738. I have not hesitated to apply the term *degree* (736), in analogy with the use made of it with respect to another most important imponderable agent, namely, heat; and as the definite expansion of air, water, mercury, &c., is there made use of to measure heat, so the equally definite evolution of gases is here turned to a similar use for electricity.

739. The instrument offers the only *actual measurer* of voltaic electricity which we at present possess.   For without being at all affected by variations in time or intensity, or alterations in the current itself, of any kind, or from any cause, or even of intermissions of action, it takes note with accuracy of the quantity of electricity which has passed through it, and reveals that quantity by inspection; I have therefore named it a VOLTA-ELECTROMETER.

740. Another mode of measuring volta-electricity may be adopted with advantage in many cases, dependent on the quantities of metals or other substances evolved either as primary or as secondary results; but I refrain from enlarging on this use of the products, until the principles on which their constancy depends have been fully established (791. 843.).

741. By the aid of this instrument I have been able to establish the definite character of electro-chemical action in its most general sense; and I am persuaded it will become of the utmost use in the extensions of the science which these views afford.   I do not pretend to have made its detail perfect, but to have demonstrated the truth of the principle, and the utility of the application†.

* For a simple table of correction for moisture, I may take the liberty of referring to my Chemical Manipulation, edition of 1830, p. 376.

† As early as the year 1811, Messrs. Gay Lussac, and Thénard, employed chemical decomposition as a measure of the electricity of the voltaic pile. See *Recherches Physico-chymiques*, p. 12. The principles and precautions by which it becomes an exact measure were of course not then known.—*Dec.* 1838.

¶ vi. *On the primary or secondary character of the bodies evolved at the Electrodes.*

742. Before the *volta-electrometer* could be employed in determining, as a *general law*, the constancy of electro-decomposition, it became necessary to examine a distinction, already recognised among scientific men, relative to the products of that action, namely, their primary or secondary character; and, if possible, by some general rule or principle, to decide when they were of the one or the other kind. It will appear hereafter that great mistakes respecting electro-chemical action and its consequences have arisen from confounding these two classes of results together.

743. When a substance under decomposition yields at the electrodes those bodies uncombined and unaltered which the electric current has separated, then they may be considered as primary results, even though themselves compounds. Thus the oxygen and hydrogen from water are primary results; and so also are the acid and alkali (themselves compound bodies) evolved from sulphate of soda. But when the substances separated by the current are changed at the electrodes before their appearance, then they give rise to secondary results, although in many cases the bodies evolved are elementary.

744. These secondary results occur in two ways, being sometimes due to the mutual action of the evolved substance and the matter of the electrode, and sometimes to its action upon the substances contained in the body itself under decomposition. Thus, when carbon is made the positive electrode in dilute sulphuric acid, carbonic oxide and carbonic acid occasionally appear there instead of oxygen; for the latter, acting upon the matter of the electrode, produces these secondary results. Or if the positive electrode, in a solution of nitrate or acetate of lead, be platina, then peroxide of lead appears there, equally a secondary result with the former, but now depending upon an action of the oxygen on a substance in the solution. Again, when ammonia is decomposed by platina electrodes, nitrogen appears at the *anode** ; but though an *elementary* body, it is a *secondary* result in this case, being derived from the chemical action of the oxygen electrically evolved there, upon the am-

* Annales de Chimie, 1804, tom. li. p. 167.

monia in the surrounding solution (554.). In the same manner
when aqueous solutions of metallic salts are decomposed by the
current, the metals evolved at the *cathode,* though elements,
are *always* secondary results, and not immediate consequences
of the decomposing power of the electric current.

745. Many of these secondary results are extremely valuable; for instance, all the interesting compounds which M. Becquerel has obtained by feeble electric currents are of this
nature; but they are essentially chemical, and must, in the
theory of electrolytic action, be carefully distinguished from
those which are directly due to the action of the electric current.

746. The nature of the substances evolved will often lead to a
correct judgment of their primary or secondary character, but
is not sufficient alone to establish that point. Thus, nitrogen
is said to be attracted sometimes by the positive and sometimes
by the negative electrode, according to the bodies with which
it may be combined (554. 555.), and it is on such occasions
evidently viewed as a primary result*; but I think I shall show,
that, when it appears at the positive electrode, or rather at the
*anode,* it is a secondary result (748.). Thus, also, Sir Humphry Davy†, and with him the great body of chemical philosophers, (including myself,) have given the appearance of copper, lead, tin, silver, gold, &c., at the negative electrode, when
their aqueous solutions were acted upon by the voltaic current,
as proofs that the metals, as a class, were attracted to that
surface; thus assuming the metal, in each case, to be a primary result. These, however, I expect to prove, are all
secondary results; the mere consequence of chemical action,
and no proofs either of the attraction of the law announced
respecting their places‡.

747. But when we take to our assistance the law of *constant
electro-chemical action* already proved with regard to water
(732.), and which I hope to extend satisfactorily to all bodies

---

* Annales de Chimie, 1804, tom. li. p. 172.

† Elements of Chemical Philosophy, pp. 144, 161.

‡ It is remarkable that up to 1804 it was the received opinion that the
metals were reduced by the nascent hydrogen. At that date the general opinion was reversed by Hisinger and Berzelius (Annales de Chimie, 1804, tom.
li. p. 174.), who stated that the metals were evolved directly by the electricity :
in which opinion it appears, from that time, Davy coincided (Philosophical
Transactions, 1826, p. 388.).

(821.), and consider the *quantities* as well as the *nature* of the substances set free, a generally accurate judgment of the primary or secondary character of the results may be formed : and this important point, so essential to the theory of electrolyzation, since it decides what are the particles directly under the influence of the current, (distinguishing them from such as are not affected), and what are the results to be expected, may be established with such degree of certainty as to remove innumerable ambiguities and doubtful considerations from this branch of the science.

748. Let us apply these principles to the case of ammonia, and the supposed determination of nitrogen to one or the other *electrode* (554. 555.). A pure strong solution of ammonia is as bad a conductor, and therefore as little liable to electrolyzation, as pure water ; but when sulphate of ammonia is dissolved in it, the whole becomes a conductor ; nitrogen *almost* and occasionally *quite* pure is evolved at the *anode*, and hydrogen at the *cathode* ; the ratio of the volume of the former to that of the latter varying, but being as 1 to about 3 or 4. This result would seem at first to imply that the electric current had decomposed ammonia, and that the nitrogen had been determined towards the positive electrode. But when the electricity used was measured out by the volta-electrometer (707. 736.), it was found that the hydrogen obtained was exactly in the proportion which would have been supplied by decomposed water, whilst the nitrogen had no certain or constant relation whatever. When, upon multiplying experiments, it was found that, by using a stronger or weaker solution, or a more or less powerful battery, the gas evolved at the *anode* was a mixture of oxygen and nitrogen, varying both in proportion and absolute quantity, whilst the hydrogen at the *cathode* remained constant, no doubt could be entertained that the nitrogen at the *anode* was a secondary result, depending upon the chemical action of the nascent oxygen, determined to that surface by the electric current, upon the ammonia in solution. It was the water, therefore, which was electrolyzed, not the ammonia. Further, the experiment gives no real indication of the tendency of the element nitrogen to either one electrode or the other ; nor do I know of any experiment with nitric acid, or other compounds of nitrogen, which shows the tendency of this element, under the influence

of the electric current, to pass in either direction along its course.

749. As another illustration of secondary results, the effects on a solution of acetate of potassa may be quoted. When a very strong solution was used, more gas was evolved at the *anode* than at the *cathode*, in the proportion of 4 to 3 nearly : that from the *anode* was a mixture of carbonic oxide and carbonic acid ; that from the *cathode* pure hydrogen. When a much weaker solution was used, less gas was evolved at the *anode* than at the *cathode* ; and it now contained carburetted hydrogen, as well as carbonic oxide and carbonic acid. This result of carburetted hydrogen at the positive electrode has a very anomalous appearance, if considered as an immediate consequence of the decomposing power of the current. It, however, as well as the carbonic oxide and acid, is only a *secondary result* ; for it is the water alone which suffers electro-decomposition, and it is the oxygen eliminated at the *anode* which, reacting on the acetic acid, in the midst of which it is evolved, produces those substances that finally appear there. This is fully proved by experiments with the volta-electrometer (707.) ; for then the hydrogen evolved from the acetate at the *cathode* is always found to be definite, being exactly proportionate to the electricity which has passed through the solution, and, in quantity, the same as the hydrogen evolved in the volta-electrometer itself. The appearance of the carbon in combination with the hydrogen at the positive electrode, and its non-appearance at the negative electrode, are in curious contrast with the results which might have been expected from the law usually accepted respecting the final places of the elements.

750. If the salt in solution be an acetate of lead, then the results at both electrodes are secondary, and cannot be used to estimate or express the amount of electro-chemical action, except by a circuitous process (843.). In place of oxygen or even the gases already described (749.), peroxide of lead now appears at the positive, and lead itself at the negative electrode. When other metallic solutions are used, containing, for instance, peroxides, as that of copper, combined with this or any other decomposable acid, still more complicated results will be obtained ; which, viewed as direct results of the electro-chemical

action, will, in their proportions, present nothing but confusion, but will appear perfectly harmonious and simple if they be considered as secondary results, and will accord in their proportions with the oxygen and hydrogen evolved from water by the action of a definite quantity of electricity.

751. I have experimented upon many bodies, with a view to determine whether the results were primary or secondary. I have been surprised to find how many of them, in ordinary cases, are of the latter class, and how frequently water is the only body electrolyzed in instances where other substances have been supposed to give way. Some of these results I will give in as few words as possible.

752. *Nitric acid.*—When very strong, it conducted well, and yielded oxygen at the positive electrode. No gas appeared at the negative electrode; but nitrous acid, and apparently nitric oxide, were formed there, which, dissolving, rendered the acid yellow or red, and at last even effervescent, from the spontaneous separation of nitric oxide. Upon diluting the acid with its bulk or more of water, gas appeared at the negative electrode. Its quantity could be varied by variations, either in the strength of the acid or of the voltaic current: for that acid from which no gas separated at the *cathode*, with a weak voltaic battery, did evolve gas there with a stronger; and that battery which evolved no gas there with a strong acid, did cause its evolution with an acid more dilute. The gas at the *anode* was always oxygen; that at the *cathode* hydrogen. When the quantity of products was examined by the volta-electrometer (707.), the oxygen, whether from strong or weak acid, proved to be in the same proportion as from water. When the acid was diluted to specific gravity 1·24, or less, the hydrogen also proved to be the same in quantity as from water. Hence I conclude that the nitric acid does not undergo electrolyzation, but the water only; that the oxygen at the *anode* is always a primary result, but that the products at the *cathode* are often secondary, and due to the reaction of the hydrogen upon the nitric acid.

753. *Nitre.*—A solution of this salt yields very variable results, according as one or other form of tube is used, or as the electrodes are large or small. Sometimes the whole of the hydrogen of the water decomposed may be obtained at the nega-

tive electrode; at other times, only a part of it, because of the ready formation of secondary results.    The solution is a very excellent conductor of electricity.

754. *Nitrate of ammonia,* in aqueous solution, gives rise to secondary results very varied and uncertain in their proportions.

755. *Sulphurous acid.*—Pure liquid sulphurous acid does not conduct nor suffer decomposition by the voltaic current*, but, when dissolved in water, the solution acquires conducting power, and is decomposed, yielding oxygen at the *anode,* and hydrogen and sulphur at the *cathode.*

756. A solution containing sulphuric acid in addition to the sulphurous acid, was a better conductor.    It gave very little gas at either electrode : that at the *anode* was oxygen, that at the *cathode* pure hydrogen.    From the *cathode* also rose a white turbid stream, consisting of diffused sulphur, which soon rendered the whole solution milky.    The volumes of gases were in no regular proportion to the quantities evolved from water in the voltameter.    I conclude that the sulphurous acid was not at all affected by the electric current in any of these cases, and that the water present was the only body electro-chemically decomposed; that, at the *anode,* the oxygen from the water converted the sulphurous acid into sulphuric acid, and, at the *cathode,* the hydrogen electrically evolved decomposed the sulphurous acid, combining with its oxygen, and setting its sulphur free.    I conclude that the sulphur at the negative electrode was only a secondary result; and, in fact, no part of it was found combined with the small portion of hydrogen which escaped when weak solutions of sulphurous acid were used.

757. *Sulphuric acid.*—I have already given my reasons for concluding that sulphuric acid is not electrolyzable, *i. e.* not decomposable directly by the electric current, but occasionally suffering by a secondary action at the *cathode* from the hydrogen evolved there (681.).    In the year 1800, Davy considered the sulphur from sulphuric acid as the result of the action of the nascent hydrogen†.    In 1804, Hisinger and Berzelius stated

---

* See also De la Rive, Bibliothèque Universelle, tcm. xl. p. 205; or Quarterly Journal of Science, vol. xxvii. p. 407.

† Nicholson's Quarterly Journal, vol. iv. pp. 280, 281.

that it was the direct result of the action of the voltaic pile*, an opinion which from that time Davy seems to have adopted, and which has since been commonly received by all. The change of my own opinion requires that I should correct what I have already said of the decomposition of sulphuric acid in a former series of these Researches (552.) : I do not now think that the appearance of the sulphur at the negative electrode is an immediate consequence of electrolytic action.

758. *Muriatic acid.*—A strong solution gave hydrogen at the negative electrode, and chlorine only at the positive electrode; of the latter, a part acted on the platina and a part was dissolved. A minute bubble of gas remained ; it was not oxygen, but probably air previously held in solution.

759. It was an important matter to determine whether the chlorine was a primary result, or only a secondary product, due to the action of the oxygen evolved from water at the *anode* upon the muriatic acid ; *i. e.* whether the muriatic acid was electrolyzable, and if so, whether the decomposition was *definite*.

760. The muriatic acid was gradually diluted. One part with six of water gave only chlorine at the *anode*. One part with eight of water gave only chlorine ; with nine of water, a little oxygen appeared with the chlorine : but the occurrence or non-occurrence of oxygen at these strengths depended, in part, on the strength of the voltaic battery used. With fifteen parts of water, a little oxygen, with much chlorine, was evolved at the *anode*. As the solution was now becoming a bad conductor of electricity, sulphuric acid was added to it : this caused more ready decomposition, but did not sensibly alter the proportion of chlorine and oxygen.

761. The muriatic acid was now diluted with 100 times its volume of dilute sulphuric acid. It still gave a large proportion of chlorine at the *anode,* mingled with oxygen ; and the result was the same, whether a voltaic battery of 40 pairs of plates or one containing only 5 pairs were used. With acid of this strength, the oxygen evolved at the *anode* was to the hydrogen at the *cathode,* in volume, as 17 is to 64 ; and therefore the chlorine would have been 30 volumes, had it not been dissolved by the fluid.

* Annales de Chimie, 1804, tom. li. p. 173.

762. Next with respect to the quantity of elements evolved. On using the volta-electrometer, it was found that, whether the strongest or the weakest muriatic acid were used, whether chlorine alone or chlorine mingled with oxygen appeared at the *anode*, still the hydrogen evolved at the *cathode* was a constant quantity, *i. e.* exactly the same as the hydrogen which the *same quantity of electricity* could evolve from water.

763. This constancy does not decide whether the muriatic acid is electrolyzed or not, although it proves that if so, it must be in definite proportions to the quantity of electricity used. Other considerations may, however, be allowed to decide the point. The analogy between chlorine and oxygen, in their relations to hydrogen, is so strong, as to lead almost to the certainty, that, when combined with that element, they would perform similar parts in the process of electro-decomposition. They both unite with it in single proportional or equivalent quantities; and the number of proportionals appearing to have an intimate and important relation to the decomposability of a body (697.), those in muriatic acid, as well as in water are the most favourable, or those perhaps even necessary, to decomposition. In other binary compounds of chlorine also, where nothing equivocal depending on the simultaneous presence of it and oxygen is involved, the chlorine is directly eliminated at the *anode* by the electric current. Such is the case with the chloride of lead (395.), which may be justly compared with protoxide of lead (402.), and stands in the same relation to it as muriatic acid to water. The chlorides of potassium, sodium, barium, &c., are in the same relation to the protoxides of the same metals and present the same results under the influence of the electric current (402.).

764. From all the experiments, combined with these considerations, I conclude that muriatic acid is decomposed by the direct influence of the electric current, and that the quantities evolved are, and therefore the chemical action is, *definite for a definite quantity of electricity*. For though I have not collected and measured the chlorine, in its separate state, at the *anode*, there can exist no doubt as to its being proportional to the hydrogen at the *cathode*: and the results are therefore sufficient to establish the general law of *constant electro-chemical action* in the case of muriatic acid.

765. In the dilute acid (761.), I conclude that a part of the water is electro-chemically decomposed, giving origin to the oxygen, which appears mingled with the chlorine at the *anode*. The oxygen *may* be viewed as a secondary result; but I incline to believe that it is not so: for, if it were, it might be expected in largest proportion from the stronger acid, whereas the reverse is the fact. This consideration, with others, also leads me to conclude that muriatic acid is more easily decomposed by the electric current than water; since, even when diluted with eight or nine times its quantity of the latter fluid, it alone gives way, the water remaining unaffected.

766. *Chlorides.*—On using solutions of chlorides in water,— for instance, the chlorides of sodium or calcium,—there was evolution of chlorine only at the positive electrode, and of hydrogen, with the oxide of the base, as soda or lime, at the negative electrode. The process of decomposition may be viewed as proceeding in two or three ways, all terminating in the same results. Perhaps the simplest is to consider the chloride as the substance electrolyzed, its chlorine being determined to and evolved at the *anode*, and its metal passing to the *cathode*, where, finding no more chlorine, it acts upon the water, producing hydrogen and an oxide as secondary results. As the discussion would detain me from more important matter, and is not of immediate consequence, I shall defer it for the present. It is, however, of *great consequence* to state, that, on using the volta-electrometer, the hydrogen in both cases was definite; and if the results do not prove the definite decomposition of chlorides, (which shall be proved elsewhere,—789. 794. 814.,) they are not in the slightest degree opposed to such a conclusion, and do support the *general law*.

767. *Hydriodic acid.*—A solution of hydriodic acid was affected exactly in the same manner as muriatic acid. When strong, hydrogen was evolved at the negative electrode, in definite proportion to the quantity of electricity which had passed, *i. e.* in the same proportion as was evolved by the same current from water; and iodine without any oxygen was evolved at the positive electrode. But when diluted, small quantities of oxygen appeared with the iodine at the *anode*, the proportion of hydrogen at the *cathode* remaining undisturbed.

768. I believe the decomposition of the hydriodic acid in this

case to be direct, for the reasons already given respecting muriatic acid (763. 764.).

769. *Iodides.*—A solution of iodide of potassium being subjected to the voltaic current, iodine appeared at the positive electrode (without any oxygen), and hydrogen with free alkali at the negative electrode. The same observations as to the mode of decomposition are applicable here as were made in relation to the chlorides when in solution (766.).

770. *Hydro-fluoric acid and fluorides.*—Solution of hydrofluoric acid did not appear to be decomposed under the influence of the electric current : it was the water which gave way apparently. The fused fluorides were electrolyzed (417.) ; but having during these actions obtained *fluorine* in the separate state, I think it better to refer to a future series of these Researches, in which I purpose giving a fuller account of the results than would be consistent with propriety here *.

771. *Hydro-cyanic acid* in solution conducts very badly. The definite proportion of hydrogen (equal to that from water) was set free at the *cathode*, whilst at the *anode* a small quantity of oxygen was evolved and apparently a solution of cyanogen formed. The action altogether corresponded with that on a dilute muriatic or hydriodic acid. When the hydrocyanic acid was made a better conductor by sulphuric acid, the same results occurred.

*Cyanides.*—With a solution of the cyanide of potassium, the result was precisely the same as with a chloride or iodide. No oxygen was evolved at the positive electrode, but a brown solution formed there. For the reasons given when speaking of the chlorides (766.), and because a fused cyanide of potassium evolves cyanogen at the positive electrode †, I incline to believe that the cyanide in solution is *directly* decomposed.

772. *Ferro-cyanic acid* and the *ferro-cyanides*, as also *sulpho-cyanic acid* and the *sulpho-cyanides*, presented results corresponding with those just described (771.).

---

* I have not obtained fluorine : my expectations, amounting to conviction, passed away one by one when subjected to rigorous examination; some very singular results were obtained ; and to one of these I refer at 1340.—(*Dec.* 1838).

† It is a very remarkable thing to see carbon and nitrogen in this case determined powerfully towards the positive surface of the voltaic battery ; but it is perfectly in harmony with the theory of electro-chemical decomposition which I have advanced.

773. *Acetic acid.*—Glacial acetic acid, when fused (405.), is not decomposed by, nor does it conduct, electricity. On adding a little water to it, still there were no signs of action; on adding more water, it acted slowly and about as pure water would do. Dilute sulphuric acid was added to it in order to make it a better conductor; then the definite proportion of hydrogen was evolved at the *cathode*, and a mixture of oxygen in very deficient quantity, with carbonic acic, and a little carbonic oxide, at the *anode*. Hence it appears that acetic acid is not electrolyzable, but that a portion of it is decomposed by the oxygen evolved at the *anode*, producing secondary results, varying with the strength of the acid, the intensity of the current, and other circumstances.

774. *Acetates.*—One of these has been referred to already, as affording only secondary results relative to the acetic acid (749.). With many of the metallic acetates the results at both electrodes are secondary (746. 750.).

Acetate of soda fused and anhydrous is directly decomposed, being, as I believe, a true electrolyte, and evolving soda and acetic acid at the *cathode* and *anode*. These however have no sensible duration, but are immediately resolved into other substances; charcoal, sodiuretted hydrogen, &c. being set free at the former, and, as far as I could judge under the circumstances, acetic acid mingled with carbonic oxide, carbonic acid, &c. at the latter.

775. *Tartaric acid.*—Pure solution of tartaric acid is almost as bad a conductor as pure water. On adding sulphuric acid, it conducted well, the results at the positive electrode being primary or secondary in different proportions, according to variations in the strength of the acid and the power of the electric current (752.). Alkaline tartrates gave a large proportion of secondary results at the positive electrode. The hydrogen at the negative electrode remained constant unless certain triple metallic salts were used.

776. Solutions, of salts containing other vegetable acids, as the benzoates; of sugar, gum, &c., dissolved in dilute sulphuric acid; of resin, albumen, &c., dissolved in alkalies, were in turn submitted to the electrolytic power of the voltaic current. In all these cases, secondary results to a greater or smaller extent were produced at the positive electrode.

777. In concluding this division of these Researches, it can-

not but occur to the mind that the final result of the action of
the electric current upon substances placed between the electrodes, instead of being simple may be very complicated.
There are two modes by which these substances may be decomposed, either by the direct force of the electric current, or
by the action of bodies which that current may evolve.   There
are also two modes by which new compounds may be formed,
*i. e.* by combination of the evolving substances whilst in their
nascent state (658.), directly with the matter of the electrode ;
or else their combination with those bodies, which being contained in, or associated with, the body suffering decomposition,
are necessarily present at the *anode* and *cathode*.   The complexity is rendered still greater by the circumstance that two
or more of these actions may occur simultaneously, and also in
variable proportions to each other.   But it may in a great
measure be resolved by attention to the principles already laid
down (747.).

778. When *aqueous* solutions of bodies are used, secondary
results are exceedingly frequent.   Even when the water is not
present in large quantity, but is merely that of combination,
still secondary results often ensue : for instance, it is very possible that in Sir Humphry Davy's decomposition of the hydrates
of potassa and soda, a part of the potassium produced was the
result of a secondary action.   Hence, also, a frequent cause for
the disappearance of the oxygen and hydrogen which would
otherwise be evolved : and when hydrogen does *not* appear at
the *cathode* in an *aqueous solution*, it perhaps always indicates
that a secondary action has taken place there.   No exception
to this rule has as yet occurred to my observation.

779. Secondary actions are *not confined to aqueous solutions*,
or cases where water is present.   For instance, various chlorides acted upon, when fused (402.), by platina electrodes,
have the chlorine determined electrically to the *anode*.   In
many cases, as with the chlorides of lead, potassium, barium,
&c., the chlorine acts on the platina and forms a compound
with it, which dissolves ; but when protochloride of tin is used,
the chlorine at the *anode* does not act upon the platina, but
upon the chloride already there, forming a perchloride which
rises in vapour (790. 804.).   These are, therefore, instances of

secondary actions of both kinds, produced in bodies containing no water.

780. The production of boron from fused borax (402, 417.) is also a case of secondary action; for boracic acid is not decomposable by electricity (408.), and it was the sodium evolved at the *cathode* which, re-acting on the boracic acid around it, took oxygen from it, and set boron free in the experiments formerly described.

781. Secondary actions have already in the hands of M. Becquerel, produced many interesting results in the formation of compounds; some of them new, others imitations of those occurring naturally *. It is probable they may prove equally interesting in an opposite direction, *i. e.* as affording cases of analytic decomposition. Much information regarding the composition, and perhaps even the arrangement, of the particles of such bodies as the vegetable acids and alkalies, and organic compounds generally, will probably be obtained by submitting them to the action of nascent oxygen, hydrogen, chlorine, &c. at the electrodes; and the action seems the more promising, because of the thorough command which we possess over attendant circumstances, such as the strength of the current, the size of the electrodes, the nature of the decomposing conductor, its strength, &c., all of which may be expected to have their corresponding influence upon the final result.

782. It is to me a great satisfaction that the extreme variety of secondary results has presented nothing opposed to the doctrine of a constant and definite electro-chemical action, to the particular consideration of which I shall now proceed.

¶ vii. *On the definite nature and extent of Electro-Chemical Decomposition.*

783. In the third series of these Researches, after proving the identity of electricities derived from different sources, and showing, by actual measurement, the extraordinary quantity of electricity evolved by a very feeble voltaic arrangement (371. 376.), I announced a law, derived from experiment, which seemed to me of the utmost importance to the science of elec-

* Annales de Chimie, tom. xxxv. p. 113.

tricity in general, and that branch of it denominated electro-chemistry in particular. The law was expressed thus : *The chemical power of a current of electricity is in direct proportion to the absolute quantity of electricity which passes* (377.).

784. In the further progress of the successive investigations, I have had frequent occasion to refer to the same law, sometimes in circumstances offering powerful corroboration of its truth (456. 504. 505.) ; and the present series already supplies numerous new cases in which it holds good (704. 722. 726. 732.). It is now my object to consider this great principle more closely, and to develope some of the consequences to which it leads. That the evidence for it may be the more distinct and applicable, I shall quote cases of decomposition subject to as few interferences from secondary results as possible, effected upon bodies very simple, yet very definite in their nature.

785. In the first place, I consider the law as so fully established with respect to the decomposition of *water,* and under so many circumstances which might be supposed, if anything could, to exert an influence over it, that I may be excused entering into further detail respecting that substance, or even summing up the results here (732.). I refer, therefore, to the whole of the subdivision of this series of Researches which contains the account of the *volta-electrometer* (704. &c.).

786. In the next place, I also consider the law as established with respect to *muriatic acid* by the experiments and reasoning already advanced, when speaking of that substance, in the subdivision respecting primary and secondary results (758. &c.).

787. I consider the law as established also with regard to *hydriodic acid* by the experiments and considerations already advanced in the preceding division of this series of Researches (767. 768.).

788. Without speaking with the same confidence, yet from the experiments described, and many others not described, relating to hydro-fluoric, hydro-cyanic, ferro-cyanic, and sulpho-cyanic acids (770. 771. 772.), and from the close analogy which holds between these bodies and the hydracids of chlorine, iodine, bromine, &c., I consider these also as coming under subjection to the law, and assisting to prove its truth.

789. In the preceding cases, except the first, the water is believed to be inactive; but to avoid any ambiguity arising

from its presence, I sought for substances from which it should
be absent altogether ; and, taking advantage of the law of conduction already developed (380. &c.), I soon found abundance,
amongst which *protochloride of tin* was first subjected to decomposition in the following manner. A piece of platina wire
had one extremity coiled up into a small knob, and, having been
carefully weighed, was sealed hermetically into a piece of bottle-
glass tube, so that the knob should be at the bottom of the
tube within (fig. 68.). The tube was suspended by a piece of
platina wire, so that the heat of a spirit-lamp could be applied
to it. Recently fused protochloride of tin was introduced in
sufficient quantity to occupy, when melted, about one half of
the tube ; the wire of the tube was connected with a volta-electrometer (711.), which was itself connected with the negative
end of a voltaic battery ; and a platina wire connected with the
positive end of the same battery was dipped into the fused
chloride in the tube ; being however so bent, that it could not
by any shake of the hand or apparatus touch the negative electrode at the bottom of the vessel. The whole arrangement is
delineated in fig. 69.

790. Under these circumstances the chloride of tin was decomposed : the chlorine evolved at the positive electrode
formed bichloride of tin (779.), which passed away in fumes,
and the tin evolved at the negative electrode combined with the
platina, forming an alloy, fusible at the temperature to which
the tube was subjected, and therefore never occasioning metallic
communication through the decomposing chloride. When the
experiment had been continued so long as to yield a reasonable
quantity of gas in the volta-electrometer, the battery connexion
was broken, the positive electrode removed, and the tube and
remaining chloride allowed to cool. When cold, the tube was
broken open, the rest of the chloride and the glass being easily
separable from the platina wire and its button of alloy. The
latter when washed was then reweighed, and the increase gave
the weight of the tin reduced.

791. I will give the particular results of one experiment, in
illustration of the mode adopted in this and others, the results
of which I shall have occasion to quote. The negative electrode weighed at first 20 grains ; after the experiment, it, with
its button of alloy, weighed 23·2 grains. The tin evolved by

the electric current at the *cathode* weighed therefore 3·2 grains. The quantity of oxygen and hydrogen collected in the volta-electrometer = 3·85 cubic inches. As 100 cubic inches of oxygen and hydrogen, in the proportions to form water, may be considered as weighing 12·92 grains, the 3·85 cubic inches would weigh 0·49742 of a grain ; that being, therefore, the weight of water decomposed by the same electric current as was able to decompose such weight of protochloride of tin as could yield 3·2 grains of metal. Now 0·49742 : 3·2 : : 9 the equivalent of water is to 57·9, which should therefore be the equivalent of tin, if the experiment had been made without error, and if the electro-chemical decomposition *is in this case also definite.* In some chemical works 58 is given as the chemical equivalent of tin, in others 57·9. Both are so near to the result of the experiment, and the experiment itself is so subject to slight causes of variation (as from the absorption of gas in the volta-electrometer (716.), &c.), that the numbers leave little doubt of the applicability of the *law of definite action* in this and all similar cases of electro-decomposition.

792. It is not often I have obtained an accordance in numbers so near as that I have just quoted. Four experiments were made on the protochloride of tin, the quantities of gas evolved in the volta-electrometer being from 2·05 to 10·29 cubic inches. The average of the four experiments gave 58·53 as the electro-chemical equivalent for tin.

793. The chloride remaining after the experiment was pure protochloride of tin ; and no one can doubt for a moment that the equivalent of chlorine had been evolved at the *anode*, and, having formed bichloride of tin as a secondary result, had passed away.

794. *Chloride of lead* was experimented upon in a manner exactly similar, except that a change was made in the nature of the positive electrode ; for as the chlorine evolved at the *anode* forms no perchloride of lead, but acts directly upon the platina, it produces, if that metal be used, a solution of chloride of platina in the chloride of lead ; in consequence of which a portion of platina can pass to the *cathode*, and would then produce a vitiated result. I therefore sought for, and found in plumbago, another substance, which could be used safely as the positive electrode in such bodies as chlorides, iodides, &c.

The chlorine or iodine does not act upon it, but is evolved in the free state; and the plumbago has no re-action, under the circumstances, upon the fused chloride or iodide in which it is plunged. Even if a few particles of plumbago should separate by the heat or the mechanical action of the evolved gas, they can do no harm in the chloride.

795. The mean of three experiments gave the number of 100·85 as the equivalent for lead. The chemical equivalent is 103·5. The deficiency in my experiments I attribute to the solution of part of the gas (716.) in the volta-electrometer; but the results leave no doubt on my mind that both the lead and the chlorine are, in this case, evolved in *definite quantities* by the action of a given quantity of electricity (814. &c.).

796. *Chloride of antimony.*—It was in endeavouring to obtain the electro-chemical equivalent of antimony from the chloride, that I found reasons for the statement I have made respecting the presence of water in it in an earlier part of these Researches (690. 693. &c.).

797. I endeavoured to experiment upon the *oxide of lead* obtained by fusion and ignition of the nitrate in a platina crucible, but found great difficulty, from the high temperature required for perfect fusion, and the powerful fluxing qualities of the substance. Green-glass tubes repeatedly failed. I at last fused the oxide in a small porcelain crucible, heated fully in a charcoal fire; and, as it was essential that the evolution of the lead at the *cathode* should take place beneath the surface, the negative electrode was guarded by a green-glass tube, fused around it in such a manner as to expose only the knob of platina at the lower end (fig. 70.), so that it could be plunged beneath the surface, and thus exclude contact of air or oxygen with the lead reduced there. A platina wire was employed for the positive electrode, that metal not being subject to any action from the oxygen evolved against it. The arrangement is given in fig. 71.

798. In an experiment of this kind the equivalent for the lead came out 93·17, which is very much too small. This, I believe, was because of the small interval between the positive and negative electrodes in the oxide of lead; so that it was not unlikely that some of the froth and bubbles formed by the oxygen at the *anode* should occasionally even touch the lead

reduced at the *cathode*, and re-oxidize it.   When I endeavoured to correct this by having more litharge, the greater
heat required to keep it all fluid caused a quicker action on the
crucible, which was soon eaten through, and the experiment
stopped.

799. In one experiment of this kind I used borate of lead
(408. 673.).   It evolves lead, under the influence of the electric current, at the *anode*, and oxygen at the *cathode*; and as
the boracic acid is not either directly (408.) or incidentally
decomposed during the operation, I expected a result dependent on the oxide of lead.   The borate is not so violent a flux
as the oxide, but it requires a higher temperature to make it
quite liquid; and if not very hot, the bubbles of oxygen cling
to the positive electrode, and retard the transfer of electricity.
The number for lead came out 101·29, which is so near to 103·5
as to show that the action of the current had been definite.

800. *Oxide of bismuth.*—I found this substance required
too high a temperature, and acted too powerfully as a flux,
to allow of any experiment being made on it, without the
application of more time and care than I could give at
present.

801. The ordinary *protoxide of antimony*, which consists of
one proportional of metal and one and a half of oxygen, was
subjected to the action of the electric current in a green-glass
tube (789.), surrounded by a jacket of platina foil, and heated
in a charcoal fire.   The decomposition began and proceeded
very well at first, apparently indicating, according to the general law (679.697.), that this substance was one containing such
elements and in such proportions as made it amenable to the
power of the electric current.   This effect I have already given
reasons for supposing may be due to the presence of a true
protoxide, consisting of single proportionals (696. 693.).   The
action soon diminished, and finally ceased, because of the formation of a higher oxide of the metal at the positive electrode.
This compound, which was probably the peroxide, being infusible and insoluble in the protoxide, formed a crystalline crust
around the positive electrode; and thus insulating it, prevented
the transmission of the electricity.   Whether, if it had been
fusible and still immiscible, it would have decomposed, is doubtful, because of its departure from the required composition

(697.).  It was a very natural secondary product at the positive electrode (779.).  On opening the tube it was found that a little antimony had been separated at the negative electrode; but the quantity was too small to allow of any quantitative result being obtained*.

802. *Iodide of lead.*—This substance can be experimented with in tubes heated by a spirit-lamp (789.) ; but I obtained no good results from it, whether I used positive electrodes of platina or plumbago.  In two experiments the numbers for the lead came out only 75·46 and 73·45, instead of 103·5.  This I attribute to the formation of a periodide at the positive electrode, which, dissolving in the mass of liquid iodide, came in contact with the lead evolved at the negative electrode, and dissolved part of it, becoming itself again protiodide. Such a periodide does exist; and it is very rarely that the iodide of lead formed by precipitation, and well washed, can be fused without evolving much iodine, from the presence of this percompound; nor does crystallization from its hot aqueous solution free it from this substance.  Even when a little of the protiodide and iodine are merely rubbed together in a mortar, a portion of the periodide is formed.  And though it is decomposed by being fused and heated to dull redness for a few minutes, and the whole reduced to protiodide, yet that is not at all opposed to the possibility, that a little of that which is formed in great excess of iodine at the *anode*, should be carried by the rapid currents in the liquid into contact with the *cathode*.

803. This view of the result was strengthened by a third experiment, where the space between the electrodes was increased to one third of an inch; for now the interfering effects were much diminished, and the number of the lead came out 89·04; and it was fully confirmed by the results obtained in the cases of *transfer* to be immediately described (818.).

The experiments on iodide of lead therefore offer no exception to the *general law* under consideration, but on the contrary may, from general considerations, be admitted as included in it.

804. *Protiodide of tin.*—This substance, when fused (402.),

* This paragraph is subject to the corrective note now appended to paragraph 696.—*Dec.* 1838.

conducts and is decomposed by the electric current, tin is evolved at the *anode*, and periodide of tin as a secondary result (779. 790.) at the *cathode*. The temperature required for its fusion is too high to allow of the production of any results fit for weighing.

805. *Iodide of potassium* was subjected to electrolytic action in a tube, like that in fig. 68. (789.). The negative electrode was a globule of lead, and I hoped in this way to retain the potassium, and obtain results that could be weighed and compared with the volta-electrometer indication ; but the difficulties dependent upon the high temperature required, the action upon the glass, the fusibility of the platina induced by the presence of the lead, and other circumstances, prevented me from procuring such results. The iodide was decomposed with the evolution of iodine at the *anode*, and of potassium at the *cathode*, as in former cases.

806. In some of these experiments several substances were placed in succession, and decomposed simultaneously by the same electric current : thus, protochloride of tin, chloride of lead, and water, were thus acted on at once. It is needless to say that the results were comparable, the tin, lead, chlorine, oxygen, and hydrogen evolved being *definite in quantity* and electro-chemical equivalents to each other.

807. Let us turn to another kind of proof of the *definite chemical action of electricity*. If any circumstances could be supposed to exert an influence over the quantity of the matters evolved during electrolytic action, one would expect them to be present when electrodes of different substances, and possessing very different chemical affinities for such matters, were used. Platina has no power in dilute sulphuric acid of combining with the oxygen at the *anode*, though the latter be evolved in the nascent state against it. Copper, on the other hand, immediately unites with the oxygen, as the electric current sets it free from the hydrogen ; and zinc is not only able to combine with it, but can, without any help from the electricity, abstract it directly from the water, at the same time setting torrents of hydrogen free. Yet in cases where these three substances were used as the positive electrodes in three similar portions of the same dilute sulphuric acid, specific gravity 1·336 pre-

cisely the same quantity of water was decomposed by the electric current, and precisely the same quantity of hydrogen set
free at the *cathodes* of the three solutions.

808. The experiment was made thus. Portions of the dilute sulphuric acid were put into three basins. Three volta-
electrometer tubes, of the form figg. 60. 62. were filled with
the same acid, and one inverted in each basin (707.). A zinc
plate, connected with the positive end of a voltaic battery, was
dipped into the first basin, forming the positive electrode there,
the hydrogen, which was abundantly evolved from it by the direct action of the acid, being allowed to escape. A copper
plate, which dipped into the acid of the second basin, was connected with the negative electrode of the *first* basin; and a
platina plate, which dipped into the acid of the third basin,
was connected with the negative electrode of the *second* basin.
The negative electrode of the third basin was connected with a
volta-electrometer (711.), and that with the negative end of the
voltaic battery.

809. Immediately that the circuit was complete, the *electro-
chemical action* commenced in all the vessels. The hydrogen
still rose in, apparently, undiminished quantities from the positive zinc electrode in the first basin. No oxygen was evolved
at the positive copper electrode in the second basin, but a sulphate of copper was formed there; whilst in the third basin
the positive platina electrode evolved pure oxygen gas, and was
itself unaffected. But in *all* the basins the hydrogen liberated
at the *negative* platina electrodes was the *same in quantity,* and
the same with the volume of hydrogen evolved in the volta-
electrometer, showing that in all the vessels the current had
decomposed an equal quantity of water. In this trying case,
therefore, the *chemical action of electricity* proved to be *perfectly definite.*

810. A similar experiment was made with muriatic acid diluted with its bulk of water. The three positive electrodes were
zinc, silver, and platina; the first being able to separate and
combine with the chlorine *without* the aid of the current; the
second combining with the chlorine only after the current had
set it free; and the third rejecting almost the whole of it. The
three negative electrodes were, as before, platina plates fixed
within glass tubes. In this experiment, as in the former, the

quantity of hydrogen evolved at the *cathodes* was the same for all, and the same as the hydrogen evolved in the volta-electrometer.   I have already given my reasons for believing that in these experiments it is the muriatic acid which is directly decomposed by the electricity (764.) ; and the results prove that the quantities so decomposed are *perfectly definite* and proportionate to the quantity of electricity which has passed.

811. In this experiment the chloride of silver formed in the second basin retarded the passage of the current of electricity, by virtue of the law of conduction before described (394.), so that it had to be cleaned off four or five times during the course of the experiment; but this caused no difference between the results of that vessel and the others.

812. Charcoal was used as the positive electrode in both sulphuric and muriatic acids (808. 810.) ; but this change produced no variation of the results.   A zinc positive electrode, in sulphate of soda or solution of common salt, gave the same constancy of operation.

813. Experiments of a similar kind were then made with bodies altogether in a different state, *i. e.* with *fused* chlorides, iodides, &c.   I have already described an experiment with fused chloride of silver, in which the electrodes were of metallic silver, the one rendered negative becoming increased and lengthened by the addition of metal, whilst the other was dissolved and eaten away by its abstraction.   This experiment was repeated, two weighed pieces of silver wire being used as the electrodes, and a volta-electrometer included in the circuit. Great care was taken to withdraw the negative electrode so regularly and steadily that the crystals of reduced silver should not form a *metallic* communication beneath the surface of the fused chloride.  On concluding the experiment the positive electrode was re-weighed, and its loss ascertained.   The mixture of chloride of silver, and metal, withdrawn in successive portions at the negative electrode, was digested in solution of ammonia, to remove the chloride, and the metallic silver remaining also weighed : it was the reduction at the *cathode*, and exactly equalled the solution at the *anode* ; and each portion was as nearly as possible the equivalent to the water decomposed in the volta-electrometer.

814. The infusible condition of the silver at the temperature

used, and the length and ramifying character of its crystals, render the above experiment difficult to perform, and uncertain in its results. I therefore wrought with chloride of lead, using a green-glass tube, formed as in fig. 72. A weighed platina wire was fused into the bottom of a small tube, as before described (789.). The tube was then bent to an angle, at about half an inch distance from the closed end; and the part between the angle and the extremity being softened, was forced upward, as in the figure, so as to form a bridge, or rather separation, producing two little depressions or basins *a*, *b*, within the tube. This arrangement was suspended by a platina wire, as before, so that the heat of a spirit-lamp could be applied to it, such inclination being given to it as would allow all air to escape during the fusion of the chloride of lead. A positive electrode was then provided, by bending up the end of a platina wire into a knot, and fusing about twenty grains of metallic lead on to it, in a small closed tube of glass, which was afterwards broken away. Being so furnished, the wire with its lead was weighed, and the weight recorded.

815. Chloride of lead was now introduced into the tube, and carefully fused. The leaded electrode was also introduced; after which the metal, at its extremity, soon melted. In this state of things the tube was filled up to *c* with melted chloride of lead; the end of the electrode to be rendered negative was in the basin *b*, and, the electrode of melted lead was retained in the basin *a*, and, by connexion with the proper conducting wire of a voltaic battery, was rendered positive. A volta-electrometer was included in the circuit.

816. Immediately upon the completion of the communication with the voltaic battery, the current passed, and decomposition proceeded. No chlorine was evolved at the positive electrode; but as the fused chloride was transparent, a button of alloy could be observed gradually forming and increasing in size at *b*, whilst the lead at *a* could also be seen gradually to diminish. After a time, the experiment was stopped; the tube allowed to cool, and broken open; the wires, with their buttons, cleaned and weighed; and their change in weight compared with the indication of the volta-electrometer.

817. In this experiment the positive electrode had lost just as much lead as the negative one had gained (795.), and the

loss and gain were very nearly the equivalents of the water de-composed in the volta-electrometer, giving for lead the number 101·5.   It is therefore evident, in this instance, that causing a *strong affinity*, or *no affinity*, for the substance evolved at the *anode*, to be active during the experiment (807.), produces no variation in the definite action of the electric current.

818. A similar experiment was then made with iodide of lead, and in this manner all confusion from the formation of a perio-dide avoided (803.).   No iodine was evolved during the whole action, and finally the loss of lead at the *anode* was the same as the gain at the *cathode*, the equivalent number, by comparison with the result in the volta-electrometer, being 103·5.

819. Then protochloride of tin was subjected to the electric current in the same manner, using of course, a tin positive elec-trode.   No bichloride of tin was now formed (779. 790.).   On examining the two electrodes, the positive had lost precisely as much as the negative had gained ; and by comparison with the volta-electrometer, the number for tin came out 59.

820. It is quite necessary in these and similar experiments to examine the interior of the bulbs of alloy at the ends of the conducting wires ; for occasionally, and especially with those which have been positive, they are cavernous, and contain por-tions of the chloride or iodide used, which must be removed before the final weight is ascertained.   This is more usually the case with lead than tin.

821. All these facts combine into, I think, an irresistible mass of evidence, proving the truth of the important proposi-tion which I at first laid down, namely, *that the chemical power of a current of electricity is in direct proportion to the abso-lute quantity of electricity which passes* (377. 783.).   They prove, too, that this is not merely true with one substance, as water, but generally with all electrolytic bodies ; and, further, that the results obtained with any *one substance* do not merely agree amongst themselves, but also with those obtained from *other substances*, the whole combining together into *one series of definite electro-chemical actions* (505.).   I do not mean to say that no exceptions will appear : perhaps some may arise, especially amongst substances existing only by weak affinity ; but I do not expect that any will seriously disturb the result announced.   If, in the well considered, well examined, and, I

may surely say, well ascertained doctrines of the definite nature of ordinary chemical affinity, such exceptions occur, as they do in abundance, yet, without being allowed to disturb our minds as to the general conclusion, they ought also to be allowed if they should present themselves at this, the opening of a new view of electro-chemical action; not being held up as obstructions to those who may be engaged in rendering that view more and more perfect, but laid aside for a while, in hopes that their perfect and consistent explanation will ultimately appear.

822. The doctrine of *definite electro-chemical action* just laid down, and, I believe, established, leads to some new views of the relations and classifications of bodies associated with or subject to this action. Some of these I shall proceed to consider.

823. In the first place, compound bodies may be separated into two great classes, namely, those which are decomposable by the electric current, and those which are not: of the latter, some are conductors, others non-conductors, of voltaic electricity*. The former do not depend for their decomposability upon the nature of their elements only; for, of the same two elements, bodies may be formed, of which one shall belong to one class and another to the other class; but probably on the proportions also (697.). It is further remarkable, that with very few, if any, exceptions (414. 691.), these decomposable bodies are exactly those governed by the remarkable law of conduction I have before described (394.); for that law does not extend to the many compound fusible substances that are excluded from this class. I propose to call bodies of this, the decomposable class, *Electrolytes* (664.).

824. Then, again, the substances into which these divide, under the influence of the electric current, form an exceedingly important general class. They are combining bodies; are directly associated with the fundamental parts of the doctrine of chemical affinity; and have each a definite proportion, in which they are always evolved during electrolytic action. I have proposed to call these bodies generally *ions*, or particularly *anions* and

---

* I mean here by voltaic electricity, merely electricity from a most abundant source, but having very small intensity.

*cations,* according as they appear at the *anode* or *cathode* (665.) ; and the numbers representing the proportions in which they are evolved *electro-chemical equivalents.* Thus hydrogen, oxygen, chlorine, iodine, lead, tin are *ions*; the three former are *anions,* the two metals are *cations,* and 1, 8, 36, 125, 104, 58, are their *electro-chemical equivalents* nearly.

825. A summary of certain points already ascertained respecting *electrolytes, ions,* and *electro-chemical equivalents,* may be given in the following general form of propositions, without, I hope, including any serious error.

826. i. A single *ion, i. e.* one not in combination with another, will have no tendency to pass to either of the electrodes, and will be perfectly indifferent to the passing current, unless it be itself a compound of more elementary *ions,* and so subject to actual decomposition. Upon this fact is founded much of the proof adduced in favour of the new theory of electro-chemical decomposition, which I put forth in a former series of these Researches (518. &c.).

827. ii. If one *ion* be combined in right proportions (697.) with another strongly opposed to it in its ordinary chemical relations, *i. e.* if an *anion* be combined with a *cation,* then both will travel, the one to the *anode,* the other to the *cathode,* of the decomposing body (530. 542. 547.).

828. iii. If, therefore, an *ion* pass towards one of the electrodes, another *ion* must also be passing simultaneously to the other electrode, although, from secondary action, it may not make its appearance (743.).

829. iv. A body decomposable directly by the electric current, *i. e.* an *electrolyte,* must consist of two *ions,* and must also render them up during the act of decomposition.

830. v. There is but one *electrolyte* composed of the same two elementary *ions*; at least such appears to be the fact (697.), dependent upon a law, that *only single electro-chemical equivalents of elementary ions can go to the electrodes, and not multiples.*

831. vi. A body not decomposable when alone, as boracic acid, is not directly decomposable by the electric current when in combination (780.). It may act as an *ion* going wholly to the *anode* or *cathode,* but does not yield up its elements, except occasionally by a secondary action. Perhaps it superfluous for me to point out that this proposition has *no relation* to such

cases as that of water, which, by the presence of other bodies, is rendered a better conductor of electricity, and *therefore* is more freely decomposed.

832. vii. The nature of the substance of which the electrode is formed, provided it be a conductor, causes no difference in the electro-decomposition, either in kind or degree (807. 813.) : but it seriously influences, by secondary action (744.), the state in which the *ions* finally appear.   Advantage may be taken of this principle in combining and collecting such *ions* as, if evolved in their free state, would be unmanageable*.

833. viii. A substance which, being used as the electrode, can combine with the *ion* evolved against it, is also, I believe, an *ion,* and combines, in such cases, in the quantity represented by its *electro-chemical equivalent*.   All the experiments I have made agree with this view; and it seems to me, at present, to result as a necessary consequence.   Whether, in the secondary actions that take place, where the *ion* acts, not upon the matter of the electrode, but on that which is around it in the liquid (744.), the same consequence follows, will require more extended investigation to determine.

834. ix. Compound *ions* are not necessarily composed of electro-chemical equivalents of simple *ions*.   For instance, sulphuric acid, boracic acid, phosphoric acid, are *ions,* but not *electrolytes, i. e.* not composed of electro-chemical equivalents of simple *ions*.

835. x. Electro-chemical equivalents are always consistent; *i. e.* the same number which represents the equivalent of a substance A when it is separating from a substance B, will also represent A when separating from a third substance C.   Thus, 8 is the electro-chemical equivalent of oxygen, whether separating from hydrogen, or tin, or lead ; and 103·5 is the electro-chemical equivalent of lead, whether separating from oxygen, or chlorine, or iodine.

* It will often happen that the electrodes used may be of such a nature as, with the fluid in which they are immersed, to produce an electric current, either according with or opposing that of the voltaic arrangement used, and in this way, or by direct chemical action, may sadly disturb the results.   Still, in the midst of all these confusing effects, the electric current, which actually passes in any direction through the body suffering decomposition, will produce its own definite electrolytic action.

836. xi. Electro-chemical equivalents coincide, and are the same, with ordinary chemical equivalents.

837. By means of experiment and the preceding propositions, a knowledge of *ions* and their electro-chemical equivalents may be obtained in various ways.

838. In the first place, they may be determined directly, as has been done with hydrogen, oxygen, lead, and tin, in the numerous experiments already quoted.

839. In the next place, from propositions ii. and iii., may be deduced the knowledge of many other *ions,* and also their equivalents. When chloride of lead was decomposed, platina being used for both electrodes (395.), there could remain no more doubt that chlorine was passing to the *anode,* although it combined with the platina there, than when the positive electrode, being of plumbago (794.), allowed its evolution in the free state; neither could there, in either case, remain any doubt that for every 103·5 parts of lead evolved at the *cathode,* 36 parts of chlorine were evolved at the *anode,* for the remaining chloride of lead was unchanged. So also, when in a metallic solution one volume of oxygen, or a secondary compound containing that proportion, appeared at the *anode,* no doubt could arise that hydrogen, equivalent to two volumes, had been determined to the *cathode,* although, by a secondary action, it had been employed in reducing oxides of lead, copper, or other metals, to the metallic state. In this manner, then, we learn from the experiments already described in these Researches, that chlorine, iodine, bromine, fluorine, calcium, potassium, strontium, magnesium, manganese, &c., are *ions,* and that their *electro-chemical equivalents* are the same as their *ordinary chemical equivalents.*

840. Propositions iv. and v. extend our means of gaining information. For if a body of known chemical composition is found to be decomposable, and the nature of the substance evolved as a primary or even a secondary result (743. 777.) at one of the electrodes, be ascertained, the electro-chemical equivalent of that body may be deduced from the known constant composition of the substance evolved. Thus, when fused protiodide of tin is decomposed by the voltaic current (804.), the conclusion may be drawn, that both the iodine and tin are *ions,* and that the proportions in which they com ine in the

fused compound express their electro-chemical equivalents. Again, with respect to the fused iodide of potassium (805.), it is an electrolyte; and the chemical equivalents will also be the electro-chemical equivalents.

841. If proposition viii. sustain extensive experimental investigation, then it will not only help to confirm the results obtained by the use of the other propositions, but will give abundant original information of its own.

842. In many instances, the *secondary results* obtained by the action of the evolved *ion* on the substances present in the surrounding liquid or solution, will give the electro-chemical equivalent. Thus, in the solution of acetate of lead, and, as far as I have gone, in other proto-salts subjected to the reducing action of the nascent hydrogen at the *cathode,* the metal precipitated has been in the same quantity as if it had been a primary product, (provided no free hydrogen escaped there,) and therefore gave accurately the number representing its electro-chemical equivalent.

843. Upon this principle it is that secondary results may occasionally be used as measurers of the volta-electric current (706. 740.); but there are not many metallic solutions that answer this purpose well: for unless the metal is easily precipitated, hydrogen will be evolved at the *cathode* and vitiate the result. If a soluble peroxide is formed at the *anode,* or if the precipitated metal crystallize across the solution and touch the positive electrode, similar vitiated results are obtained. I expect to find in some salts, as the acetates of mercury and zinc, solutions favourable for this use.

844. After the first experimental investigations to establish the definite chemical action of electricity, I have not hesitated to apply the more strict results of chemical analysis to correct the numbers obtained as electrolytic results. This, it is evident, may be done in a great number of cases, without using too much liberty towards the due severity of scientific research. The series of numbers representing electro-chemical equivalents must, like those expressing the ordinary equivalents of chemically acting bodies, remain subject to the continual correction of experiment and sound reasoning.

845. I give the following brief Table of *ions* and their electro-chemical equivalents, rather as a specimen of a first attempt

than as anything that can supply the want which must very
quickly be felt, of a full and complete tabular account of this
class of bodies. Looking forward to such a table as of extreme
utility (if well constructed) in developing the intimate relation
of ordinary chemical affinity to electrical actions, and identifying the two, not to the imagination merely, but to the conviction
of the senses and a sound judgement, I may be allowed to express a hope, that the endeavour will always be to make it a
table of *real*, and not *hypothetical*, electro-chemical equivalents; for we shall else overrun the facts, and lose all sight and
consciousness of the knowledge lying directly in our path.

846. The equivalent numbers do not profess to be exact,
and are taken almost entirely from the chemical results of other
philosophers in whom I could repose more confidence, as to
these points, than in myself.

### 847. Table of Ions.

#### Anions.

| | | | | | |
|---|---|---|---|---|---|
| Oxygen | 8 | Selenic acid | 64 | Tartaric acid | 66 |
| Chlorine | 35·5 | Nitric acid | 54 | Citric acid | 53 |
| Iodine | 126 | Chloric acid | 75·5 | Oxalic acid | 36 |
| Bromine | 78·3 | Phosphoric acid | 35·7 | Sulphur (?) | 16 |
| Fluorine | 18·7 | Carbonic acid | 22 | Selenium (?) | |
| Cyanogen | 26 | Boracic acid | 24 | Sulpho-cyanogen | |
| Sulphuric acid | 40 | Acetic acid | 51 | | |

#### Cations.

| | | | | | |
|---|---|---|---|---|---|
| Hydrogen | 1 | Cadmium | 55·8 | Soda | 31·3 |
| Potassium | 39·2 | Cerium | 46 | Lithia | 18 |
| Sodium | 23·3 | Cobalt | 29·5 | Baryta | 76·7 |
| Lithium | 10 | Nickel | 29·5 | Strontia | 51·8 |
| Barium | 68·7 | Antimony | 64·6? | Lime | 28· |
| Strontium | 43·8 | Bismuth | 71 | Magnesia | 20·7 |
| Calcium | 20·5 | Mercury | 200 | Alumina | (?) |
| Magnesium | 12·7 | Silver | 108 | Protoxides generally. | |
| Manganese | 27·7 | Platina | 98·6? | Quinia | 171·6 |
| Zinc | 32·5 | Gold | (?) | Cinchona | 160 |
| Tin | 57·9 | | | Morphia | 290 |
| Lead | 103·5 | Ammonia | 17 | Vegeto-alkalies gene- | |
| Iron | 28 | Potassa | 47·2 | rally. | |
| Copper | 31·6 | | | | |

848. This Table might be further arranged into groups of
such substances as either act with, or replace, each other.
Thus, for instance, acids and bases act in relation to each

other; but they do not act in association with oxygen, hydrogen, or elementary substances. There is indeed little or no doubt that, when the electrical relations of the particles of matter come to be closely examined, this division must be made. The simple substances, with cyanogen, sulpho-cyanogen, and one or two other compound bodies, will probably form the first group; and the acids and bases, with such analogous compounds as may prove to be *ions*, the second group. Whether these will include all *ions*, or whether a third class of more complicated results will be required, must be decided by future experiments.

849. It is *probable* that all our present elementary bodies are *ions*, but that is not as yet certain. There are some, such as carbon, phosphorus, nitrogen, silicon, boron, alumium, the right of which to the title of *ion* it is desirable to decide as soon as possible. There are also many compound bodies, and amongst them alumina and silica, which it is desirable to class immediately by unexceptionable experiments. It is also *possible*, that all combinable bodies, compound as well as simple, may enter into the class of *ions*; but at present it does not seem to me probable. Still the experimental evidence I have is so small in proportion to what must gradually accumulate around, and bear upon, this point, that I am afraid to give a strong opinion upon it.

850. I think I cannot deceive myself in considering the doctrine of definite electro-chemical action as of the utmost importance. It touches by its facts more directly and closely than any former fact, or set of facts, have done, upon the beautiful idea, that ordinary chemical affinity is a mere consequence of the electrical attractions of the particles of different kinds of matter; and it will probably lead us to the means by which we may enlighten that which is at present so obscure, and either fully demonstrate the truth of the idea, or develope that which ought to replace it.

851. A very valuable use of electro-chemical equivalents will be to decide, in cases of doubt, what is the true chemical equivalent, or definite proportional, or atomic number of a body; for I have such conviction that the power which governs electro-decomposition and ordinary chemical attractions is the same; and such confidence in the overruling influence of those natu-

ral laws which render the former definite, as to feel no hesita-
tion in believing that the latter must submit to them also. Such
being the case, I can have no doubt that, assuming hydrogen
as 1, and dismissing small fractions for the simplicity of expression, the equivalent number or atomic weight of oxygen is 8,
of chlorine 36, of bromine 78·4, of lead 103·5, of tin 59, &c.,
notwithstanding that a very high authority doubles several of
these numbers.

§ 13. *On the absolute quantity of Electricity associated with*
*the particles or atoms of Matter.*

852. The theory of definite electrolytical or electro-chemical
action appears to me to touch immediately upon the *absolute*
*quantity* of electricity or electric power belonging to different
bodies.   It is impossible, perhaps, to speak on this point without committing oneself beyond what present facts will sustain ;
and yet it is equally impossible, and perhaps would be impoli-
tic, not to reason upon the subject.   Although we know nothing of what an atom is, yet we cannot resist forming some
idea of a small particle, which represents it to the mind ; and
though we are in equal, if not greater, ignorance of electricity,
so as to be unable to say whether it is a particular matter or
matters, or mere motion of ordinary matter, or some third kind
of power or agent, yet there is an immensity of facts which justify us in believing that the atoms of matter are in some way
endowed or associated with electrical powers, to which they
owe their most striking qualities, and amongst them their
mutual chemical affinity.   As soon as we perceive, through the
teaching of Dalton, that chemical powers are, however, varied
the circumstances in which they are exerted, definite for each
body, we learn to estimate the relative degree of force which
resides in such bodies : and when upon that knowledge comes
the fact, that the electricity, which we appear to be capable of
loosening from its habitation for a while, and conveying from
place to place, *whilst it retains its chemical force,* can be measured out, and being so measured is found to be *as definite in*
*its action* as any of *those portions* which, remaining associated
with the particles of matter, give them their *chemical rela-*
*tion* ; we seem to have found the link which connects the pro-

portion of that we have evolved to the proportion of that belonging to the particles in their natural state.

853. Now it is wonderful to observe how small a quantity
of a compound body is decomposed by a certain portion of electricity. Let us, for instance, consider this and a few other
points in relation to water. *One grain* of water, acidulated to
facilitate conduction, will require an electric current to be continued for three minutes and three quarters of time to effect
its decomposition, which current must be powerful enough to
retain a platina wire $\frac{1}{104}$ of an inch in thickness*, red hot, in
the air during the whole time; and if interrupted anywhere by
charcoal points, will produce a very brilliant and constant star
of light. If attention be paid to the instantaneous discharge of
electricity of tension, as illustrated in the beautiful experiments
of Mr. Wheatstone†, and to what I have said elsewhere on the
relation of common and voltaic electricity (371. 375.), it will not
be too much to say that this necessary quantity of electricity is
equal to a very powerful flash of lightning. Yet we have it
under perfect command; can evolve, direct, and employ it at
pleasure; and when it has performed its full work of electrolyzation, it has only separated the elements of *a single grain
of water*.

854. On the other hand, the relation between the conduction
of the electricity and the decomposition of the water is so close,
that one cannot take place without the other. If the water is
altered only in that small degree which consists in its having

* I have not stated the length of wire used, because I find by experiment,
as would be expected in theory, that it is indifferent. The same quantity of
electricity which, passed in a given time, can heat an inch of platina wire of a
certain diameter red hot, can also heat a hundred, a thousand, or any length
of the same wire to the same degree, provided the cooling circumstances are
the same for every part in all cases. This I have proved by the volta-electrometer. I found that whether half an inch or eight inches were retained at one
constant temperature of dull redness, equal quantities of water were decomposed in equal times. When the half-inch was used, only the centre portion of
wire was ignited. A fine wire may even be used as a rough but ready regula-
tor of a voltaic current; for if it be made part of the circuit, and the larger
wires communicating with it be shifted nearer to or further apart, so as to keep
the portion of wire in the circuit sensibly at the same temperature, the current
passing through it will be nearly uniform.

† Literary Gazette, 1833, March 1 and 8. Philosophical Magazine, 1833,
p. 204. L'Institute, 1833, p. 261.

the solid instead of the fluid state, the conduction is stopped, and the decomposition is stopped with it. Whether the conduction be considered as depending upon the decomposition, or not (413. 703.), still the relation of the two functions is equally intimate and inseparable.

855. Considering this close and twofold relation, namely, that without decomposition transmission of electricity does not occur; and, that for a given definite quantity of electricity passed, an equally definite and constant quantity of water or other matter is decomposed; considering also that the agent, which is electricity, is simply employed in overcoming electrical powers in the body subjected to its action; it seems a probable, and almost a natural consequence, that the quantity which passes is the *equivalent* of, and therefore equal to, that of the particles separated; *i. e.* that if the electrical power which holds the elements of a grain of water in combination, or which makes a grain of oxygen and hydrogen in the right proportions unite into water when they are made to combine, could be thrown into the condition of *a current,* it would exactly equal the current required for the separation of that grain of water into its elements again.

856. This view of the subject gives an almost overwhelming idea of the extraordinary quantity or degree of electric power which naturally belongs to the particles of matter; but it is not inconsistent in the slightest degree with the facts which can be brought to bear on this point. To illustrate this I must say a few words on the voltaic pile*.

857. Intending hereafter to apply the results given in this and the preceding series of Researches to a close investigation of the source of electricity in the voltaic instrument, I have refrained from forming any decided opinion on the subject; and without at all meaning to dismiss metallic contact, or the contact of dissimilar substances, being conductors, but not metallic, as if they had nothing to do with the origin of the current,

* By the term voltaic pile, I mean such apparatus or arrangement of metals as up to this time have been called so, and which contain water, brine, acids, or other aqueous solutions or decomposable substances (476.), between their plates. Other kinds of electric apparatus may be hereafter invented, and I hope to construct some not belonging to the class of instruments discovered by Volta.

I still am fully of opinion with Davy, that it is at least continued by chemical action, and that the supply constituting the current is almost entirely from that source.

858. Those bodies which, being interposed between the metals of the voltaic pile, render it active, *are all of them electrolytes* (476.) ; and it cannot but press upon the attention of every one engaged in considering this subject, that in those bodies (so essential to the pile) decomposition and the transmission of a current are so intimately connected, that one cannot happen without the other. This I have shown abundantly in water, and numerous other cases (402. 476.). If, then, a voltaic trough have its extremities connected by a body capable of being decomposed, as water, we shall have a continuous current through the apparatus ; and whilst it remains in this state we may look at the part where the acid is acting upon the plates, and that where the current is acting upon the water, as the reciprocals of each other. In both parts we have the two conditions *inseparable in such bodies as these,* namely, the passing of the current, and decomposition ; and this is as true of the cells in the battery as of the water cell ; for no voltaic battery has as yet been constructed in which the chemical action is only that of combination : *decomposition is always included,* and is, I believe, an essential chemical part.

859. But the difference in the two parts of the connected battery, that is, the decomposition or experimental cell, and the acting cells, is simply this. In the former we urge the current through, but it, apparently of necessity, is accompanied by decomposition : in the latter we cause decompositions by ordinary chemical actions, (which are, however, themselves electrical,) and, as a consequence, have the electrical current ; and as the decomposition dependent upon the current is definite in the former case, so is the current associated with the decomposition also definite in the latter (862. &c.).

860. Let us apply this in support of what I have surmised respecting the enormous electric power of each particle or atom of matter (856.). I showed in a former series of these Researches on the relation by measure of common and voltaic electricity, that two wires, one of platina and one of zinc, each one eighteenth of an inch in diameter, placed five sixteenths of an inch apart, and immersed to the depth of five

eighths of an inch in acid, consisting of one drop of oil of vitriol and four ounces of distilled water at a temperature of about 60° Fahr., and connected at the other extremities by a copper wire eighteen feet long, and one eighteenth of an inch in thickness, yielded as much electricity in little more than three seconds of time as a Leyden battery charged by thirty turns of a very large and powerful plate electric machine in full action (371.). This quantity, though sufficient if passed at once through the head of a rat or cat to have killed it, as by a flash of lightning, was evolved by the mutual action of so small a portion of the zinc wire and water in contact with it, that the loss of weight sustained by either would be inappreciable by our most delicate instruments ; and as to the water which could be decomposed by that current, it must have been insensible in quantity, for no trace of hydrogen appeared upon the surface of the platina during those three seconds.

861. What an enormous quantity of electricity, therefore, is required for the decomposition of a single grain of water ! We have already seen that it must be in quantity sufficient to sustain a platina wire $\frac{1}{104}$ of an inch in thickness, red hot, in contact with the air, for three minutes and three quarters (853.), a quantity which is almost infinitely greater than that which could be evolved by the little standard voltaic arrangement to which I have just referred (860. 371.). I have endeavoured to make a comparison by the loss of weight of such a wire in a given time in such an acid, according to a principle and experiment to be almost immediately described (862.) ; but the proportion is so high that I am almost afraid to mention it. It would appear that 800,000 such charges of the Leyden battery as I have referred to above, would be necessary to supply electricity sufficient to decompose a single grain of water ; or, if I am right, to equal the quantity of electricity which is naturally associated with the elements of that grain of water, endowing them with their mutual chemical affinity.

862. In further proof of this high electric condition of the particles of matter, and the *identity as to quantity of that belonging to them with that necessary for their separation,* I will describe an experiment of great simplicity but extreme beauty, when viewed in relation to the evolution of an electric current and its decomposing powers.

863. A dilute sulphuric acid, made by adding about one part by measure of oil of vitriol to thirty parts of water, will act energetically upon a piece of zinc plate in its ordinary and simple state : but, as Mr. Sturgeon as shewn\*, not at all, or scarcely so, if the surface of the metal has in the first instance been amalgamated ; yet the amalgamated zinc will act powerfully with platina as an electromoter, hydrogen being evolved on the surface of the latter metal, as the zinc is oxidized and dissolved. The amalgamation is best effected by sprinkling a few drops of mercury upon the surface of the zinc, the latter being moistened with the dilute acid, and rubbing with the fingers or tow so as to extend the liquid metal over the whole of the surface. Any mercury in excess, forming liquid drops upon the zinc, should be wiped off †.

864. Two plates of zinc thus amalgamated were dried and accurately weighed; one, which we will call A, weighed 163·1 grains ; the other to be called B, weighed 148·3 grains. They were about five inches long, and 0·4 of an inch wide. An earthenware pneumatic trough was filled with dilute sulphuric acid, of the strength just described (863.), and a gas jar, also filled with the acid, inverted in it‡. A plate of platina of nearly the same length, but about three times as wide as the zinc plates, was put up into this jar. The zinc plate A was also introduced into the jar, and brought in contact with the platina, and at the same moment the plate B was put into the acid of the trough, but out of contact with other metallic matter.

865. Strong action immediately occurred in the jar upon the contact of the zinc and platina plates. Hydrogen gas rose from the platina, and was collected in the jar, but no hydrogen or other gas rose from *either* zinc plate. In about ten or twelve minutes, sufficient hydrogen having been collected, the experiment was stopped ; during its progress a few small bubbles had appeared upon plate B, but none upon plate A. The plates

---

\* Recent Experimental Researches, &c., 1830, p. 74, &c.

† The experiment may be made with pure zinc, which, as chemists well know, is but slightly acted upon by dilute sulphuric acid in comparison with ordinary zinc, which during the action is subject to an infinity of voltaic actions. See De la Rive on this subject, Bibliothèque Universelle, 1830, p. 391.

‡ The acid was left during a night with a small piece of unamalgamated zinc in it, for the purpose of evolving such air as might be inclined to separate, and bringing the whole into a constant state.

were washed in distilled water, dried, and reweighed. Plate B weighed 148·3 grains, as before, having lost nothing by the direct chemical action of the acid. Plate A weighed 154·65 grains, 8·45 grains of it having been oxidized and dissolved during the experiment.

866. The hydrogen gas was next transferred to a water-trough and measured ; it amounted to 12·5 cubic inches, the temperature being 52°, and the barometer 29·2 inches. This quantity, corrected for temperature, pressure, and moisture, becomes 12·15453 cubic inches of dry hydrogen at mean temperature and pressure ; which, increased by one half for the oxygen that must have gone to the *anode, i.e.* to the zinc, gives 18·232 cubic inches as the quantity of oxygen and hydrogen evolved from the water decomposed by the electric current. According to the estimate of the weight of the mixed gas before adopted (791.), this volume is equal to 2·3535544 grains, which therefore is the weight of water decomposed ; and this quantity is to 8·45, the quantity of zinc oxidized, as 9 is to 32·31. Now taking 9 as the equivalent number of water, the number 32·5 is given as the equivalent number of zinc ; a coincidence sufficiently near to show, what indeed could not but happen, that for an equivalent of zinc oxidized an equivalent of water must be decomposed*.

867. But let us observe *how* the water is decomposed. It is electrolyzed, *i.e* is decomposed voltaically, and not in the ordinary manner (as to appearance) of chemical decompositions; for the oxygen appears at the *anode* and the hydrogen at the *cathode* of the body under decomposition, and these were in many parts of the experiment above an inch asunder. Again, the ordinary chemical affinity was not enough under the circumstances to effect the decomposition of the water, as was abundantly proved by the inaction on plate B; the voltaic current was essential. And to prevent any idea that the chemical affinity was almost sufficient to decompose the water, and that a smaller current of electricity might under the circumstances, cause the hydrogen to pass to the *cathode,* I need only refer to the results which I have given (807. 813.) to show that the chemical action at the electrodes has not the slightest influence over the *quantities* of water or other substances decomposed between them, but

* The experiment was repeated several times with the same results.

that they are entirely dependent upon the quantity of electricity which passes.

868. What, then, follows as a necessary consequence of the whole experiment ? Why, this : that the chemical action upon 32·31 parts, or one equivalent of zinc, in this simple voltaic circle, was able to evolve such quantity of electricity in the form of a current, as passing through water, should decompose 9 parts, or one equivalent of that substance : and considering the definite relations of electricity as developed in the preceding parts of the present paper, the results prove that the quantity of electricity which, being naturally associated with the particles of matter, gives them their combining power, is able, when thrown into a current, to separate those particles from their state of combination ; or, in other words, that *the electricity which decomposes, and that which is evolved by the decomposition of, a certain quantity of matter, are alike.*

869. The harmony which this theory of the definite evolution and the equivalent definite action of electricity introduces into the associated theories of definite proportions and electro-chemical affinity, is very great. According to it, the equivalent weights of bodies are simply those quantities of them which contain equal quantities of electricity, or have naturally equal electric powers ; it being the ELECTRICITY which *determines* the equivalent number, *because* it determines the combining force. Or, if we adopt the atomic theory or phraseology, then the atoms of bodies which are equivalents to each other in their ordinary chemical action, have equal quantities of electricity naturally associated with them. But I must confess I am jealous of the term *atom*; for though it is very easy to talk of atoms, it is very difficult to form a clear idea of their nature, especially when compound bodies are under consideration.

870. I cannot refrain from recalling here the beautiful idea put forth, I believe, by Berzelius (703.). in his development of his views of the electro-chemical theory of affinity, that the heat and light evolved during cases of powerful combination are the consequence of the electric discharge which is at the moment taking place. The idea is in perfect accordance with the view I have taken of the *quantity* of electricity associated with the particles of matter.

871. In this exposition of the law of the definite action of

electricity, and its corresponding definite proportion in the particles of bodies, I do not pretend to have brought, as yet, every case of chemical or electro-chemical action under its dominion. There are numerous considerations of a theoretical nature, especially respecting the compound particles of matter and the resulting electrical forces which they ought to possess, which I hope will gradually receive their development; and there are numerous experimental cases, as, for instance, those of compounds formed by weak affinities, the simultaneous decomposition of water and salts, &c., which still require investigation. But whatever the results on these and numerous other points may be, I do not believe that the facts which I have advanced, or even the general laws deduced from them, will suffer any serious change; and they are of sufficient importance to justify their publication, though much may yet remain imperfect or undone. Indeed, it is the great beauty of our science, CHEMISTRY, that advancement in it, whether in a degree great or small, instead of exhausting the subjects of research, opens the doors to further and more abundant knowledge, overflowing with beauty and utility, to those who will be at the easy personal pains of undertaking its experimental investigation.

872. The definite production of electricity (868.) in association with its definite action proves, I think, that the current of electricity in the voltaic pile is sustained by chemical decomposition, or rather by chemical action, and not by contact only. But here, as elsewhere (857.), I beg to reserve my opinion as to the real action of contact, not having yet been able to make up my mind as to whether it is an exciting cause of the current, or merely necessary to allow of the conduction of electricity, otherwise generated, from one metal to the other.

873. But admitting that chemical action is the source of electricity, what an infinitely small fraction of that which is active do we obtain and employ in our voltaic batteries! Zinc and platina wires, one eighteenth of an inch in diameter and about half an inch long, dipped into dilute sulphuric acid, so weak that it is not sensibly sour to the tongue, or scarcely to our most delicate test papers, will evolve more electricity in one twentieth of a minute (860.) than any man would willingly allow to pass through his body at once. The chemical action of a grain of water upon four grains of zinc can evolve electricity

equal in quantity to that of a powerful thunder-storm (868. 861.).   Nor is it merely true that the quantity is active ; it can be directed and made to perform its full equivalent duty (867. &c.).   Is there not, then, great reason to hope and believe that, by a closer *experimental* investigation of the principles which govern the development and action of this subtile agent, we shall be able to increase the power of our batteries, or invent new instruments which shall a thousandfold surpass in energy those which we at present possess ?

874. Here for a while I must leave the consideration of the *definite chemical action of electricity.*   But before I dismiss this series of experimental Researches, I would call to mind that, in a former series, I showed the current of electricity was also *definite in its magnetic action* (216. 366. 367. 376. 377.) ; and, though this result was not pursued to any extent, I have no doubt that the success which has attended the development of the chemical effects is not more than would accompany an investigation of the magnetic phenomena.

*Royal Institution,*
*December* 31*st*, 1833.

## EIGHTH SERIES.

§ 14. *On the Electricity of the Voltaic Pile ; its source, quantity, intensity, and general characters.* ¶ i. *On simple Voltaic Circles.* ¶ ii. *On the intensity necessary for Electrolyzation.* ¶ iii. *On associated Voltaic Circles, or the Voltaic Battery.* ¶ iv. *On the resistance of an Electrolyte to Electrolytic action.* ¶ v. *General remarks on the active Voltaic Battery.*

Received April 7.—Read June 5, 1834.

¶ i. *On simple Voltaic Circles.*

875. THE great question of the source of electricity in the voltaic pile has engaged the attention of so many eminent philosophers, that a man of liberal mind and able to appreciate their powers would probably conclude, although he might not have studied the question, that the truth was somewhere revealed. But if in pursuance of this impression he were induced to enter upon the work of collating results and conclusions, he would find such contradictory evidence, such equilibrium of opinion, such variation and combination of theory, as would leave him in complete doubt respecting what he should accept as the true interpretation of nature : he would be forced to take upon himself the labour of repeating and examining the facts, and then use his own judgement on them in preference to that of others.

876. This state of the subject must, to those who have made up their minds on the matter, be my apology for entering upon its investigation. The views I have taken of the definite action of electricity in decomposing bodies (783.), and the identity of the power so used with the power to be overcome (855.), founded not on a mere opinion or general notion, but on facts which, being altogether new, were to my mind precise and conclusive, gave me, as I conceived, the power of examining the question with advantages not before possessed by any, and which might compensate, on my part, for the superior clearness and extent

of intellect on theirs.   Such are the considerations which have
induced me to suppose I might help in deciding the question,
and be able to render assistance in that great service of removing *doubtful knowledge.*   Such knowledge is the early morning
light of every advancing science, and is essential to its development; but the man who is engaged in dispelling that which
is deceptive in it, and revealing more clearly that which
is true, is as useful in his place, and as necessary to the general
progress of the science, as he who first broke through the intellectual darkness, and opened a path into knowledge before
unknown to man.

877. The identity of the force constituting the voltaic current
or electrolytic agent, with that which holds the elements of electrolytes together (855.), or in other words with chemical affinity,
seemed to indicate that the electricity of the pile itself was
merely a mode of exertion, or exhibition, or existence of *true
chemical action,* or rather of its cause; and I have consequently
already said that I agree with those who believe that the *supply*
of electricity is due to chemical powers (857.).

878. But the great question of whether it is originally due
to metallic contact or to chemical action, *i. e.* whether it is the
first or the second which *originates* and determines the current,
was to me still doubtful; and the beautiful and simple experiment with amalgamated zinc and platina, which I have described minutely as to its results (863, &c.), did not decide the
point; for in that experiment the chemical action does not take
place without the contact of the metals, and the metallic contact is inefficient without the chemical action.   Hence either
might be looked upon as the *determining* cause of the current.

879. I thought it essential to decide this question by the
simplest possible forms of apparatus and experiment, that no
fallacy might be inadvertently admitted.   The well known difficulty of effecting decomposition by a single pair of plates, except in the fluid exciting them into action (863.), seemed to
throw insurmountable obstruction in the way of such experiments; but I remembered the easy decomposability of the solution of iodide of potassium (316.) and seeing no theoretical
reason, if metallic contact was not *essential,* why true electro-
decomposition should not be obtained without it, even in a single
circuit, I persevered and succeeded.

880. A plate of zinc, about eight inches long and half an inch wide, was cleaned and bent in the middle to a right angle, fig. 73 *a*. Plate VI. A plate of platina, about three inches long and half an inch wide, was fastened to a platina wire, and the latter bent as in the figure, *b*. These two pieces of metal were arranged together as delineated, but as yet without the vessel *c*, and its contents, which consisted of dilute sulphuric acid mingled with a little nitric acid. At *x* a piece of folded bibulous paper, moistened in a solution of iodide of potassium, was placed on the zinc, and was pressed upon by the end of the platina wire. When under these circumstances the plates were dipped into the acid of the vessel *c*, there was an immediate effect at *x*, the iodide being decomposed, and iodine appearing at the *anode* (663.), *i. e.* against the end of the platina wire.

881. As long as the lower ends of the plates remained in the acid the electric current continued, and the decomposition proceeded at *x*. On removing the end of the wire from place to place on the paper, the effect was evidently very powerful; and on placing a piece of turmeric paper between the white paper and zinc, both papers being moistened with the solution of iodide of potassium, alkali was evolved at the *cathode* (663.) against the zinc, in proportion to the evolution of iodine at the *anode*. Hence the decomposition was perfectly polar, and decidedly dependent upon a current of electricity passing from the zinc through the acid to the platina in the vessel *c*, and back from the platina through the solution to the zinc at the paper *x*.

882. That the decomposition at *x* was a true electrolytic action, due to a current determined by the state of things in the vessel *c*, and not dependent upon any mere direct chemical action of the zinc and platina on the iodide, or even upon any *current* which the solution of iodide might by its action on those metals tend to form at *x*, was shown, in the first place, by removing the vessel *c* and its acid from the plates, when all decomposition at *x* ceased, and in the next by connecting the metals, either in or out of the acid, together, when decomposition of the iodide at *x* occurred, but in a *reverse order*; for now alkali appeared against the end of the platina wire, and the iodine passed to the zinc, the current being the contrary of what it was in the former instance, and produced directly by

the difference of action of the solution in the paper on the two metals. The iodine of course *combined* with the zinc.

883. When this experiment was made with pieces of zinc amalgamated over the whole surface (863.), the results were obtained with equal facility and in the same direction, even when only dilute sulphuric acid was contained in the vessel *c* (fig. 73.). Whichsoever end of the zinc was immersed in the acid, still the effects were the same: so that if, for a moment, the mercury might be supposed to supply the metallic contact, the inversion of the amalgamated piece destroys that objection. The use of *unamalgamated zinc* (880.) removes all possibility of doubt*.

884. When, in pursuance of other views (930.), the vessel *c* was made to contain a solution of caustic potash in place of acid, still the same results occurred. Decomposition of the iodide was effected freely, though there was no metallic contact of dissimilar metals, and the current of electricity was in the *same direction* as when acid was used at the place of excitement.

885. Even a solution of common salt in the glass *c* could produce all these effects.

886. Having made a galvanometer with platina wires, and introduced it into the course of the current between the platina plate and the place of decomposition *x*, it was affected, giving indications of currents in the same direction as those shown to exist by the chemical action.

887. If we consider these results generally, they lead to very important conclusions. In the first place, they prove, in the

---

* The following is a more striking mode of making the above elementary experiment. Prepare a plate of zinc, ten or twelve inches long and two inches wide, and clean it thoroughly : provide also two discs of clean platina, about one inch and a half in diameter :—dip three or four folds of bibulous paper into a strong solution of iodide of potassium, place them on the clean zinc at one end of the plate, and put on them one of the platina discs : finally dip similar folds of paper or a piece of linen cloth into a mixture of equal parts nitric acid and water, and place it at the other end of the zinc plate with the second platina disc upon it. In this state of things no change at the solution of the iodide will be perceptible ; but if the two discs be connected by a platina (or any other) wire for a second or two, and then that over the iodide be raised, it will be found that the *whole* of the surface beneath is deeply stained with *evolved iodine.*—*Dec.* 1838.

most decisive manner, that *metallic contact is not necessary for the production of the voltaic current.* In the next place, they show a most extraordinary mutual relation of the chemical affinities of the fluid which *excites* the current, and the fluid which is *decomposed* by it.

888. For the purpose of simplifying the consideration, let us take the experiment with amalgamated zinc. The metal so prepared exhibits no effect until the current can pass : it at the same time introduces no new action, but merely removes an influence which is extraneous to those belonging either to the production or the effect of the electric current under investigation (1000.) ; an influence also which, when present, tends only to confuse the results.

889. Let two plates, one of amalgamated zinc and the other of platina, be placed parallel to each other (fig. 74.), and introduce a drop of dilute sulphuric acid, *y*, between them at one end ; there will be no sensible chemical action at that spot unless the two plates are connected somewhere else, as at P Z, by a body capable of conducting electricity. If that body be a metal or certain forms of carbon, then the current passes, and, as it circulates through the fluid at *y*, decomposition ensues.

890. Then remove the acid from *y*, and introduce a drop of the solution of iodide of potassium at *x* (fig. 75.). Exactly the same set of effects occur, except that when the metallic communication is made at P Z, the electric current is in the opposite direction to what it was before, as is indicated by the arrows, which show the courses of the currents (667.).

891. Now *both* the solutions used are conductors, but the conduction in them is essentially connected with decomposition (858.) in a certain constant order, and therefore the appearance of the elements in certain places *shows* in what direction a current has passed when the solutions are thus employed. Moreover, we find that when they are used at opposite ends of the plates, as in the last two experiments (889. 890.), metallic contact being allowed at the other extremities, the currents are in opposite directions. We have evidently, therefore, the power of opposing the actions of the two fluids simultaneously to each other at the opposite ends of the plates, using each one as a conductor for the discharge of the current of electricity, which

the other tends to generate; in fact, substituting them for metallic contact, and combining both experiments into one (fig.
76.). Under these circumstances, there is an opposition of
forces : the fluid, which brings into play the stronger set of
chemical affinities for the zinc, (being the dilute acid,) over-
comes the force of the other, and determines the formation and
direction of the electric current; not merely making that current pass through the weaker liquid, but actually reversing the
tendency which the elements of the latter have in relation to
the zinc and platina if not thus counteracted, and forcing them
in the contrary direction to that they are inclined to follow,
that its own current may have free course. If the dominant
action at $y$ be removed by making metallic contact there, then
the liquid at $x$ resumes its power; or if the metals be not
brought into contact at $y$, but the affinities of the solution there
weakened, whilst those active at $x$ are strengthened, then the
latter gains the ascendency, and the decompositions are produced in a contrary order.

892. Before drawing a *final* conclusion from this mutual dependence and state of the chemical affinities of two distant
portions of acting fluids (916.), I will proceed to examine more
minutely the various circumstances under which the re-action of
the body suffering decomposition is rendered evident upon the
action of the body, also undergoing decomposition, which produces the voltaic current.

893. The use of *metallic contact* in a single pair of plates, and
the cause of its great superiority above contact made by other
kinds of matter, become now very evident. When an amalgamated zinc plate is dipped into dilute sulphuric acid, the force
of chemical affinity exerted between the metal and the fluid is
not sufficiently powerful to cause sensible action at the surfaces
of contact, and occasion the decomposition of water by the oxidation of the metal, although it *is* sufficient to produce such a
condition of the electricity (or the power upon which chemical
affinity depends) as would produce a current if there were a
path open for it (916. 956.) ; and that current would complete
the conditions necessary, under the circumstances, for the decomposition of the water.

894. Now the presence of a piece of platina touching both
the zinc and the fluid to be decomposed, opens the path re-

quired for the electricity. Its *direct communication* with the zinc is effectual, far beyond any communication made between it and that metal, (*i. e.* between the platina and zinc,) by means of decomposable conducting bodies, or, in other words, *electrolytes,* as in the experiment already described (891.) ; because, when *they* are used, the chemical affinities between them and the zinc produce a contrary and opposing action to that which is influential in the dilute sulphuric acid ; or if that action be but small, still the affinity of their component parts for each other has to be overcome, for they cannot conduct without suffering decomposition ; and this decomposition is found *experimentally* to re-act back upon the forces which in the acid tend to produce the current (904. 910. &c.), and in numerous cases entirely to neutralize them. Where direct contact of the zinc and platina occurs, these obstructing forces are not brought into action, and therefore the production and the circulation of the electric current and the concomitant action of decomposition are then highly favoured.

895. It is evident, however, that one of these opposing actions may be dismissed, and yet an electrolyte be used for the purpose of completing the circuit between the zinc and platina immersed separately into the dilute acid ; for if, in fig. 73, the platina wire be retained in metallic contact with the zinc plate *a*, at *x*, and a division of the platina be made elsewhere, as at *s*, then the solution of iodide placed there, being in contact with platina at both surfaces, exerts no chemical affinities for that metal ; or if it does, they are equal on both sides. Its power, therefore, of forming a current in opposition to that dependent upon the action of the acid in the vessel *c*, is removed, and only its resistance to decomposition remains as the obstacle to be overcome by the affinities exerted in the dilute sulphuric acid.

896. This becomes the condition of a single pair of active plates where *metallic contact* is allowed. In such cases, only one set of opposing affinities are to be overcome by those which are dominant in the vessel *c* ; whereas, when metallic contact is not allowed, two sets of opposing affinities must be conquered (894.).

897. It has been considered a difficult, and by some an impossible thing, to decompose bodies by the current from a

single pair of plates, even when it was so powerful as to heat bars of metal red hot, as in the case of Hare's calorimeter, arranged as a single voltaic circuit, or of Wollaston's powerful single pair of metals. This difficulty has arisen altogether from the antagonism of the chemical affinity engaged in producing the current with the chemical affinity to be overcome, and depends entirely upon the relative intensity; for when the sum of forces in one has a certain degree of superiority over the sum of forces in the other, the former gain the ascendency, determine the current, and overcome the latter so as to make the substance exerting them yield up its elements in perfect accordance, both as to direction and quantity, with the course of those which are exerting the most intense and dominant action.

898. Water has generally been the substance, the decomposition of which has been sought for as a chemical test of the passage of an electric current. But I now began to perceive a reason for its failure, and for a fact which I had observed long before (315. 316.) with regard to the iodide of potassium, namely, that bodies would differ in facility of decomposition by a given electric current, according to the condition and intensity of their ordinary chemical affinities. This reason appeared in their *re-action upon the affinities* tending to cause the current; and it appeared probable, that many substances might be found which could be decomposed by the current of a single pair of zinc and platina plates immersed in dilute sulphuric acid, although water resisted its action. I soon found this to be the case, and as the experiments offer new and beautiful proofs of the direct relation and opposition of the chemical affinities concerned in producing and in resisting the stream of electricity, I shall briefly describe them.

899. The arrangement of the apparatus was as in fig. 77. The vessel *v* contained dilute sulphuric acid; Z and P are the zinc and platina plates; *a, b,* and *c* are platina wires; the decompositions were effected at *x,* and occasionally, indeed generally, a galvanometer was introduced into the circuit at *g* : its place only is here given, the circle at *g* having no reference to the size of the instrument. Various arrangements were made at *x,* according to the kind of decomposition to be effected. If a drop of liquid was to be acted upon, the two ends were merely dipped into it; if a solution contained in the pores of

paper was to be decomposed, one of the extremities was connected with a platina plate supporting the paper, whilst the other extremity rested on the paper, *e,* fig. 84 : or sometimes, as with sulphate of soda, a plate of platina sustained two portions of paper, one of the ends of the wires resting upon each piece, *c,* fig. 86. The darts represent the direction of the electric current (667.).

900. Solution of *iodide of potassium,* in moistened paper, being placed at the interruption of the circuit at *x,* was readily decomposed. Iodine was evolved at the *anode,* and alkali at the *cathode,* of the decomposing body.

901. *Protochloride of tin,* when fused and placed at *x,* was also readily decomposed, yielding perchloride of tin at the *anode* (779.), and tin at the *cathode.*

902. Fused chloride of silver, placed at *x,* was also easily decomposed; chlorine was evolved at the *anode,* and brilliant metallic silver, either in films upon the surface of the liquid, or in crystals beneath, evolved at the *cathode.*

903. Water acidulated with sulphuric acid, solution of muriatic acid, solution of sulphate of soda, fused nitre, and the fused chloride and iodide of lead were not decomposed by this single pair of plates, excited only by dilute sulphuric acid.

904. These experiments give abundant proofs that a single pair of plates can electrolyze bodies and separate their elements. They also show in a beautiful manner the direct relation and opposition of the chemical affinities concerned at the two points of action. In those cases where the sum of the opposing affinities at *x,* was sufficiently beneath the sum of the acting affinities in *v* decomposition took place; but in those cases where they rose higher, decomposition was effectually resisted and the current ceased to pass (891.).

905. It is however, evident, that the sum of acting affinities in *v* may be increased by using other fluids than dilute sulphuric acid, in which latter case, as I believe, it is merely the affinity of the zinc for the oxygen already combined with hydrogen in the water that is exerted in producing the electric current (919.) : and when the affinities are so increased, the view I am supporting leads to the conclusion, that bodies which resisted in the preceding experiments would then be decomposed, because of the increased difference between their affinities and

the acting affinities thus exalted. This expectation was fully confirmed in the following manner.

906. A little nitric acid was added to the liquid in the vessel *v*, so as to make a mixture which I shall call diluted nitro-sulphuric acid. On repeating the experiments with this mixture, all the substances before decomposed again gave way, and much more readily. But, besides that, many which before resisted electrolyzation now yielded up their elements. Thus, solution of sulphate of soda, acted upon in the interstices of litmus and turmeric paper, yielded acid at the *anode* and alkali at the *cathode*; solution of muriatic acid tinged by indigo yielded chlorine at the *anode* and hydrogen at the *cathode*; solution of nitrate of silver yielded silver at the *cathode*. Again, fused nitre and the fused iodide and chloride of lead were decomposable by the current of this single pair of plates, though they were not by the former (903.).

907. A solution of acetate of lead was apparently not decomposed by this pair, nor did water acidulated by sulphuric acid seem at first to give way (973.).

908. The increase of intensity or power of the current produced by a simple voltaic circle, with the increase of the force of the chemical action at the exciting place, is here sufficiently evident. But in order to place it in a clearer point of view, and to show that the decomposing effect was not at all dependent, in the latter cases, upon the mere capability of evolving *more* electricity, experiments were made in which the quantity evolved could be increased without variation in the intensity of the exciting cause. Thus the experiments in which dilute sulphuric acid was used (899.) were repeated, using large plates of zinc and platina in the acid; but still those bodies which resisted decomposition before, resisted it also under these new circumstances. Then again, where nitro-sulphuric acid was used (906.), mere wires of platina and zinc were immersed in the exciting acid; yet, notwithstanding this change, those bodies were now decomposed which resisted any current tending to be formed by the dilute sulphuric acid. For instance, muriatic acid could not be decomposed by a single pair of plates when immersed in dilute sulphuric acid; nor did making the solution of sulphuric acid strong, nor enlarging the size of the zinc and platina plates immersed in it, increase the power; but

if to a weak sulphuric acid a very little nitric acid was added, then the electricity evolved had power to decompose the muriatic acid, evolving chlorine at the *anode* and hydrogen at the *cathode*, even when mere wires of metals were used. This mode of increasing the intensity of the electric current, as it excludes the effect dependent upon many pairs of plates, or even the effect of making any one acid stronger or weaker, is at once referable to the condition and force of the chemical affinities which are brought into action, and may, both in principle and practice, be considered as perfectly distinct from any other mode.

909. The direct reference which is thus experimentally made in the simple voltaic circle of the *intensity* of the electric current to the *intensity* of the chemical action going on at the place where the existence and direction of the current is determined, leads to the conclusion that by using selected bodies, as fused chlorides, salts, solutions of acids, &c., which may act upon the metals employed with different degrees of chemical force ; and using also metals in association with platina, or with each other, which shall differ in the degree of chemical action exerted between them and the exciting fluid or electrolyte, we shall be able to obtain a series of comparatively constant effects due to electric currents of different intensities, which will serve to assist in the construction of a scale competent to supply the means of determining relative degrees of intensity with accuracy in future researches *.

910. I have already expressed the view which I take of the decomposition in the experimental place, as being the direct consequence of the superior exertion at some other spot of the same kind of power as that to be overcome, and therefore as the result of an antagonism of forces of the *same* nature (891. 904.). Those at the place of decomposition have a re-action upon, and a power over, the exerting or determining set proportionate to what is needful to overcome their own power ; and hence a curious result of *resistance* offered by decompositions to the original determining force, and consequently to the current. This is well shown in the cases where such bodies

---

* In relation to this difference and its probable cause, see considerations on inductive polarization, 1354, &c.—*Dec.* 1838.

as chloride of lead, iodide of lead, and water would not decompose with the current produced by a single pair of zinc and platina plates in sulphuric acid (903.), although they would with a current of higher intensity produced by stronger chemical powers. In such cases no sensible portion of the current passes (967.); the action is stopped; and I am now of opinion that in the case of the law of conduction which I described in the Fourth Series of these Researches (413.), the bodies which are electrolytes in the fluid state cease to be such in the solid form, because the attractions of the particles by which they are retained in combination and in their relative position, are then too powerful for the electric current *. The particles retain their places; and as decomposition is prevented, the transmission of the electricity is prevented also; and although a battery of many plates may be used, yet if it be of that perfect kind which allows of no extraneous or indirect action (1000.), the whole of the affinities concerned in the activity of that battery are at the same time also suspended and counteracted.

911. But referring to the *resistance* of each single case of decomposition, it would appear that as these differ in force according to the affinities by which the elements in the substance tend to retain their places, they also would supply cases constituting a series of degrees by which to measure the initial intensities of simple voltaic or other currents of electricity, and which, combined with the scale of intensities determined by different degrees of *acting force* (909.), would probably include a sufficient set of differences to meet almost every important case where a reference to intensity would be required.

912. According to the experiments I have already had occasion to make, I find that the following bodies are electrolytic in the order in which I have placed them, those which are first being decomposed by the current of lowest intensity. These currents were always from a single pair of plates, and may be considered as elementary *voltaic forces*.

> Iodide of potassium (solution).
> Chloride of silver (fused).
> Protochloride of tin (fused).
> Chloride of lead (fused).
> Iodide of lead (fused).

* Refer onwards to 1705.—*Dec.* 1838.

Muriatic acid (solution).

Water, acidulated with sulphuric acid.

913. It is essential that, in all endeavours to obtain the relative electrolytic intensity necessary for the decomposition of different bodies, attention should be paid to the nature of the electrodes and the other bodies present which may favour secondary actions (986.).   If in electro-decomposition one of the elements separated has an affinity for the electrode, or for bodies present in the surrounding fluid, then the affinity resisting decomposition is in part balanced by such power, and the true place of the electrolyte in a table of the above kind is not obtained : thus, chlorine combines with a positive platina electrode freely, but iodine scarcely at all, and therefore I believe it is that the fused chlorides stand first in the preceding Table.   Again, if in the decomposition of water not merely sulphuric but also a little nitric acid be present, then the water is more freely decomposed, for the hydrogen at the *cathode* is not ultimately expelled, but finds oxygen in the nitric acid, with which it can combine to produce a secondary result; the affinities opposing decomposition are in this way diminished, and the elements of the water can then be separated by a current of lower intensity.

914. Advantage may be taken of this principle to interpolate more minute degrees into the scale of initial intensities already referred to (909. 911.) than is there spoken of ; for by combining the force of a current *constant* in its intensity, with the use of electrodes consisting of matter, having more or less affinity for the elements evolved from the decomposing electrolyte, various intermediate degrees may be obtained.

----

915. Returning to the consideration of the source of electricity (878. &c.), there is another proof of the most perfect kind that metallic contact has nothing to do with the *production* of electricity in the voltaic circuit, and further, that electricity is only another mode of the exertion of chemical forces.   It is, the production of the *electric spark* before any contact of metals is made, and by the exertion of *pure and unmixed chemical forces*.   The experiment, which will be described further on (956.), consists in obtaining the spark upon making contact between a plate of zinc and a plate of copper plunged into di-

lute sulphuric acid.    In order to make the arrangement as elementary as possible, mercurial surfaces were dismissed, and the contact made by a copper wire connected with the copper plate, and then brought to touch a clean part of the zinc plate.    The electric spark appeared, and it must of necessity have existed and passed *before the zinc and the copper were in contact.*

———————

916. In order to render more distinct the principles which I have been endeavouring to establish, I will restate them in their simplest form, according to my present belief.    The electricity of the voltaic pile (856. note) is not dependent either in its origin or its continuance upon the contact of the metals with each other (880. 915.).    It is entirely due to chemical action (882.), and is proportionate in its intensity to the intensity of the affinities concerned in its production (908.) ; and in its quantity to the quantity of matter which has been chemically active during its evolution (869.).    This definite production is again one of the strongest proofs that the electricity is of chemical origin.

917. As *volta-electro-generation* is a case of mere chemical action, so *volta-electro-decomposition* is simply a case of the preponderance of one set of chemical affinities more powerful in their nature, over another set which are less powerful : and if the instance of two opposing sets of such forces (891.) be considered, and their mutual relation and dependence borne in mind, there appears no necessity for using, in respect to such cases, any other term than chemical affinity, (though that of electricity may be very convenient,) or supposing any new agent to be concerned in producing the results ; for we may consider that the powers at the two places of action are in direct communion and balanced against each other through the medium of the metals (891.), fig. 76, in a manner analogous to that in which mechanical forces are balanced against each other by the intervention of the lever (1031.).

918. All the facts show us that that power commonly called chemical affinity, can be communicated to a distance through the metals and certain forms of carbon ; that the electric current is only another form of the forces of chemical affinity ; that its power is in proportion to the chemical affinities producing it ; that when it is deficient in force it may be helped by calling in

chemical aid, the want in the former being made up by an equivalent of the latter; that, in other words, *the forces termed chemical affinity and electricity are one and the same.*

919. When the circumstances connected with the production of electricity in the ordinary voltaic circuit are examined and compared, it appears that the source of that agent, always meaning the electricity which circulates and completes the current in the voltaic apparatus, and gives that apparatus power and character (947. 996.), exists in the chemical action which takes place directly between the metal and the body with which it combines, and not at all in the subsequent action of the substance so produced with the acid present *. Thus, when zinc, platina, and dilute sulphuric acid are used, it is the union of the zinc with the oxygen of the water which determines the current; and though the acid is essential to the removal of the oxide so formed, in order that another portion of zinc may act on another portion of water, it does not, by combination with that oxide, produce any sensible portion of the current of electricity which circulates; for the quantity of electricity is dependent upon the quantity of zinc oxidized, and in definite proportion to it : its intensity is in proportion to the intensity of the chemical affinity of the zinc for the oxygen under the circumstances, and is scarcely, if at all, affected by the use of either strong or weak acid (908.).

920. Again, if zinc, platina, and muriatic acid are used, the electricity appears to be dependent upon the affinity of the zinc for the chlorine, and to be circulated in exact proportion to the number of particles of zinc and chlorine which unite, being in fact an equivalent to them.

921. But in considering this oxidation, or other direct action upon the METAL itself, as the cause and source of the electric current, it is of the utmost importance to observe that the oxygen or other body must be in a peculiar condition, namely, in the state of *combination* ; and not only so, but limited still further to such a state of combination and in such proportions as will constitute an *electrolyte* (823.). A pair of zinc and platina plates cannot be so arranged in oxygen gas as to produce a

* Wollaston, Philosophical Transactions, 1801, p. 427.

current of electricity, or act as a voltaic circle, even though the temperature may be raised so high as to cause oxidation of the zinc far more rapidly than if the pair of plates were plunged into dilute sulphuric acid; for the oxygen is not part of an electrolyte, and cannot therefore conduct the forces onwards by decomposition, or even as metals do by itself. Or if its gaseous state embarrass the minds of some, then liquid chlorine may be taken. It does not excite a current of electricity through the two plates by combining with the zinc, for its particles cannot transfer the electricity active at the point of combination across to the platina. It is not a conductor of itself, like the metals; nor is it an electrolyte, so as to be capable of conduction during decomposition, and hence there is simple chemical action at the spot, and no electric current*.

922. It might at first be supposed that a conducting body, not electrolytic, might answer as the third substance between the zinc and the platina; and it is true that we have some such capable of exerting chemical action upon the metals. They must, however, be chosen from the metals themselves, for there are no bodies of this kind except those substances and charcoal. To decide the matter by experiment, I made the following arrangement. Melted tin was put into a glass tube bent into the form of the letter V, fig. 78, so as to fill the half of each limb, and two pieces of thick platina wire, *p*, *w*, inserted, so as to have their ends immersed some depth in the tin: the whole was then allowed to cool, and the ends *p* and *w* connected with a delicate galvanometer. The part of the tube at *x* was now reheated, whilst the portion *y* was retained cool. The galvanometer was immediately influenced by the thermo-electric current produced. The heat was steadily increased at *x*, until at last the tin and platina combined there; an effect which is known to take place with strong chemical action and high ignition; but not the slightest additional effect occurred at the galvanometer. No other deflection than that due to the ther-

---

* I do not mean to affirm that no traces of electricity ever appear in such cases. What I mean is, that no electricity is evolved in any way, due or related to the causes which excite voltaic electricity, or proportionate to them. That which does appear occasionally is the smallest possible fraction of that which the acting matter could produce if arranged so as to act voltaically, probably not the one hundred thousandth, or even the millionth part, and is very probably altogether different in its source.

mo-electric current was observable the whole time. Hence, though a conductor, and one capable of exerting chemical action on the tin, was used, yet, not being an *electrolyte,* not the slightest effect of an electrical current could be observed (947.).

923. From this it seems apparent that the peculiar character and condition of an electrolyte is *essential* in one part of the voltaic circuit; and its nature being considered, good reasons appear why it and it alone should be effectual. An electrolyte is always a compound body: it can conduct, but only whilst decomposing. Its conduction depends upon its decomposition and the *transmission of its particles* in directions parallel to the current; and so intimate is this connexion, that if their transition be stopped, the current is stopped also; if their course be changed, its course and direction changes with them; if they proceed in one direction, it has no power to proceed in any other than a direction invariably dependent on them. The particles of an electrolytic body are all so mutually connected, are in such relation with each other through their whole extent in the direction of the current, that if the last is not disposed of, the first is not at liberty to take up its place in the new combination which the powerful affinity of the most active metal tends to produce; and then the current itself is stopped; for the dependencies of the current and the decomposition are so mutual, that whichsoever be originally determined, *i. e.* the motion of the particles or the motion of the current, the other is invariable in its concomitant production and its relation to it.

924. Consider, then, water as an electrolyte and also as an oxidizing body. The attraction of the zinc for the oxygen is greater, under the circumstances, than that of the oxygen for the hydrogen; but in combining with it, it tends to throw into circulation a current of electricity in a certain direction. This direction is consistent (as is found by innumerable experiments) with the transfer of the hydrogen from the zinc towards the platina, and the transfer in the opposite direction of fresh oxygen from the platina towards the zinc; so that the current *can pass* in that one line, and, whilst it passes, can consist with and favour the renewal of the conditions upon the surface of the zinc, which at first determined both the combination and circulation. Hence the continuance of the action there, and

the continuation of the current. It therefore appears quite as essential that there should be an electrolyte in the circuit, in order that the action may be transferred forward, in a *certain constant direction*, as that there should be an oxidizing or other body capable of acting directly on the metal; and it also appears to be essential that these two should merge into one, or that the principle directly active on the metal by chemical action should be one of the *ions* of the electrolyte used. Whether the voltaic arrangement be excited by solution of acids, or alkalies, or sulphurets, or by fused substances (476.), this principal has always hitherto, as far as I am aware, been an *anion* (943.) ; and I anticipate, from a consideration of the principles of electric action, that it must of necessity be one of that class of bodies.

925. If the action of the sulphuric acid used in the voltaic circuit be considered, it will be found incompetent to produce any sensible portion of the electricity of the current by its combination with the oxide formed, for this simple reason, it is deficient in a most essential condition : it forms no part of an electrolyte, nor is it in relation with any other body present in the solution which will permit of the mutual transfer of the particles and the consequent transfer of the electricity. It is true, that as the plane at which the acid is dissolving the oxide of zinc formed by the action of the water, is in contact with the metal zinc, there seems no difficulty in considering how the oxide there could communicate an electrical state, proportionate to its own chemical action on the acid, to the metal, which is a conductor without decomposition. But on the side of the acid there is no substance to complete the circuit : the water, as water, cannot conduct it, or at least only so small a proportion that it is merely an incidental and almost inappreciable effect (970.) ; and it cannot conduct it as an electrolyte, because an electrolyte conducts in consequence of the *mutual* relation and action of its particles ; and neither of the elements of the water, nor even the water itself, as far as we can perceive, are *ions* with respect to the sulphuric acid (848.)*.

926. This view of the secondary character of the sulphuric

* It will be seen that I here agree with Sir Humphry Davy, who has experimentally supported the opinion that acids and alkalies in combining do not produce any current of electricity. Philosophical Transactions, 1826, p. 398.

acid as an agent in the production of the voltaic current, is further confirmed by the fact, that the current generated and transmitted is directly and exactly proportional to the quantity of water decomposed and the quantity of zinc oxidized (868. 991.), and is the same as that required to decompose the same quantity of water. As, therefore, the decomposition of the water shows that the electricity has passed by its means, there remains no other electricity to be accounted for or to be referred to any action other than that of the zinc and the water on each other.

927. The general case (for it includes the former one (924),) of acids and bases, may theoretically be stated in the following manner. Let *a*, fig. 79, be supposed to be a dry oxacid, and *b* a dry base, in contact at *c*, and in electric communication at their extremities by plates of platina *p p*, and a platina wire *w*. If this acid and base were fluid, and combination took place at *c*, with an affinity ever so vigorous, and capable of originating an electric current, the current could not circulate in any important degree; because, according to the experimental results, neither *a* nor *b* could conduct without being decomposed, for they are either electrolytes or else insulators, under all circumstances, except to very feeble and unimportant currents (970. 986.). Now the affinities at *c* are not such as tend to cause the *elements* either of *a* or *b* to separate, but only such as would make the two bodies combine together as a whole; the point of action is, therefore, insulated, the action itself local (921. 947.), and no current can be formed.

928. If the acid and base be dissolved in water, then it is possible that a small portion of the electricity due to chemical action may be conducted by the water without decomposition (966. 984.); but the quantity will be so small as to be utterly disproportionate to that due to the equivalents of chemical force; will be merely incidental; and, as it does not involve the essential principles of the voltaic pile, it forms no part of the phenomena at present under investigation *.

* It will I trust be fully understood, that in these investigations I am not professing to take an account of every small, incidental, or barely possible effect, dependent upon slight disturbances of the electric fluid during chemical action, but am seeking to distinguish and identify those actions on which the power of the voltaic battery essentially depends.

929. If for the oxacid a hydracid be substituted (927.),—as one analagous to the muriatic, for instance,—then the state of things changes altogether, and a current due to the chemical action of the acid on the base is possible. But now both the bodies act as electrolytes, for it is only one principle of each which combine mutually,—as, for instance, the chlorine with the metal,—and the hydrogen of the acid and the oxygen of the base are ready to traverse with the chlorine of the acid and the metal of the base in conformity with the current and according to the general principles already so fully laid down.

---

930. This view of the oxidation of the metal, or other *direct* chemical action upon it, being the sole cause of the production of the electric current in the ordinary voltaic pile, is supported by the effects which take place when alkaline or sulphuretted solutions (931. 943.) are used for the electrolytic conductor instead of dilute sulphuric acid. It was in elucidation of this point that the experiments without metallic contact, and with solution of alkali as the exciting fluid, already referred to (884.), were made.

931. Advantage was then taken of the more favourable condition offered, when metallic contact is allowed (895.), and the experiments upon the decomposition of bodies by a single pair of plates (899.) were repeated, solution of caustic potassa being employed in the vessel *v*, fig. 77. in place of dilute sulphuric acid. All the effects occurred as before : the galvanometer was deflected ; the decompositions of the solutions of iodide of potassium, nitrate of silver, muriatic acid, and sulphate of soda ensued at *x*; and the places where the evolved principles appeared, as well as the deflection of the galvanometer, indicated a current in the *same direction* as when acid was in the vessel *v*; *i. e.* from the zinc through the solution to the platina, and back by the galvanometer and substance suffering decomposition to the zinc.

932. The similarity in the action of either dilute sulphuric acid or potassa goes indeed far beyond this, even to the proof of identity in *quantity* as well as in *direction* of the electricity produced. If a plate of amalgamated zinc be put into a solution of potassa, it is not sensibly acted upon ; but if touched in the solution by a plate of platina, hydrogen is evolved on the

surface of the latter metal, and the zinc is oxidized exactly as when immersed in dilute sulphuric acid (863.). I accordingly repeated the experiment before described with weighed plates of zinc (864. &c.), using however solution of potassa instead of dilute sulphuric acid. Although the time required was much longer than when acid was used, amounting to three hours for the oxidizement of 7·55 grains of zinc, still I found that the hydrogen evolved at the platina plate was the equivalent of the metal oxidized at the surface of the zinc. Hence the whole of the reasoning which was applicable in the former instance applies also here, the current being in the same direction, and its decomposing effect in the same degree, as if acid instead of alkali had been used (868.).

933. The proof, therefore, appears to me complete, that the combination of the acid with the oxide, in the former experiment, had nothing to do with the production of the electric current; for the same current is here produced when the action of the acid is absent, and the reverse action of an alkali is present. I think it cannot be supposed for a moment, that the alkali acted chemically as an acid to the oxide formed; on the contrary, our general chemical knowledge leads to the conclusion, that the ordinary metallic oxides act rather as acids to the alkalies; yet that kind of action would tend to give a reverse current in the present case, if any were due to the union of the oxide of the exciting metal with the body which combines with it. But instead of any variation of this sort, the direction of the electricity was constant, and its quantity also directly proportional to the water decomposed, or the zinc oxidized. There are reasons for believing that acids and alkalies, when in contact with metals upon which they cannot act directly, still have a power of influencing their attractions for oxygen (941.); but all the effects in these experiments prove, I think, that it is the oxidation of the metal necessarily dependent upon, and associated as it is with, the electrolyzation of the water (921. 923.) that produces the current; and that the acid or alkali merely act as solvents, and by removing the oxidized zinc, allow other portions to decompose fresh water, and so continue the evolution or determination of the current.

934. The experiments were then varied by using solution of ammonia instead of solution of potassa; and as it, when pure,

is like water, a bad conductor (554.), it was occasionally improved in that power by adding sulphate of ammonia to it. But in all the cases the results were the same as before ; decompositions of the same kind were effected, and the electric current producing these was in the same direction as in the experiments just described.

935. In order to put the equal and similar action of acid and alkali to stronger proof, arrangements were made as in fig. 80. : the glass vessel A contained dilute sulphuric acid, the corresponding glass vessel B solution of potassa, P P was a plate of platina dipping into both solutions, and Z Z two plates of amalgamated zinc connected with a delicate galvanometer. When these were plunged at the same time into the two vessels, there was generally a first feeble effect, and that in favour of the alkali, *i. e.* the electric current tended to pass through the vessels in the direction of the arrow, being the reverse direction of that which the acid in A would have produced alone ; but the effect instantly ceased, and the action of the plates in the vessels was so equal, that, being contrary because of the contrary position of the plates, no permanent current resulted.

936. Occasionally a zinc plate was substituted for the plate P P, and platina plates for the plates Z Z ; but this caused no difference in the results : nor did a further change of the middle plate to copper produce any alteration.

937. As the opposition of electric-motive pairs of plates produces results other than those due to the mere difference of their independent actions (1011. 1045.), I devised another form of apparatus, in which the action of acid and alkali might be more directly compared. A cylindrical glass cup, about two inches deep within, an inch in internal diameter, and at least a quarter of an inch in thickness, was cut down the middle into halves, fig. 81. A broad brass ring, larger in diameter than the cup, was supplied with a screw at one side ; so that when the two halves of the cup were within the ring, and the screw was made to press tightly against the glass, the cup held any fluid put into it. Bibulous paper of different degrees of permeability was then cut into pieces of such a size as to be easily introduced between the loosened halves of the cup, and served when the latter were tightened again to form a porous division down the middle of the cup, sufficient to keep any two fluids

on opposite sides of the paper from mingling, except very slowly, and yet allowing them to act freely as one *electrolyte*. The two spaces thus produced I will call the cells A and B, fig. 82. This instrument I have found of most general application in the investigation of the relation of fluids and metals amongst themselves and to each other. By combining its use with that of the galvanometer, it is easy to ascertain the relation of one metal with two fluids, or of two metals with one fluid, or of two metals and two fluids upon each other.

938. Dilute sulphuric acid, sp. gr. 1·25. was put into the cell A, and a strong solution of caustic potassa into the cell B; they mingled slowly through the paper, and at last a thick crust of sulphate of potassa formed on the side of the paper next to the alkali. A plate of clean platina was put into each cell and connected with a delicate galvanometer, but no electric current could be observed. Hence the *contact* of acid with one platina plate, and alkali with the other, was unable to produce a current; nor was the combination of the acid with the alkali more effectual (925.).

939. When one of the platina plates was removed and a zinc plate substituted, either amalgamated or not, a strong electric current was produced. But, whether the zinc were in the acid whilst the platina was in the alkali, or whether the reverse order were chosen, the electric current was always from the zinc through the electrolyte to the platina, and back through the galvanometer to the zinc, the current seeming to be strongest when the zinc was in the alkali and the platina in the acid.

940. In these experiments, therefore, the acid seems to have no power over the alkali, but to be rather inferior to it in force. Hence there is no reason to suppose that the combination of the oxide formed with the acid around it has any direct influence in producing the electricity evolved, the whole of which appears to be due to the oxidation of the metal (919.).

941. The alkali, in fact, is superior to the acid in bringing a metal into what is called the positive state; for if plates of the same metal, as zinc, tin, lead, or copper, be used both in the acid or alkali, the electric current is from the alkali across the cell to the acid, and back through the galvanometer to the alkali, as Sir Humphry Davy formerly stated*. This current is

* Elements of Chemical Philosophy, p. 149; or Philosophical Transactions, 1826, p. 403.

so powerful, that if amalgamated zinc, or tin, or lead be used, the metal in the acid evolves hydrogen the moment it is placed in communication with that in the alkali, not from any direct action of the acid upon it, for if the contact be broken, the action ceases, but because it is powerfully negative with regard to the metal in the alkali.

942. The superiority of alkali is further proved by this, that if zinc and tin be used, or tin and lead, whichsoever metal is put into the alkali becomes positive, that in the acid being negative. Whichsoever is in the alkali is oxidized, whilst that in the acid remains in the metallic state, as far as the electric current is concerned.

943. When sulphuretted solutions are used (930.) in illustration of the assertion, that it is the chemical action of the metal and one of the *ions* of the associated electrolyte that produces all the electricity of the voltaic circuit, the proofs are still the same. Thus, as Sir Humphry Davy* has shown, if iron and copper be plunged into dilute acid, the current is from the iron through the liquid to the copper; in solution of potassa it is in the same direction, but in solution of sulphuret of potassa it is reversed. In the two first cases it is oxygen which combines with the iron, in the latter sulphur which combines with the copper, that produces the electric current; but both of these are *ions*, existing as such in the electrolyte, which is at the same moment suffering decomposition; and, what is more, both of these are *anions*, for they leave the electrolytes at their *anodes*, and act just as chlorine, iodine, or any other *anion* would act which might have been previously chosen as that which should be used to throw the voltaic circle into activity.

---

944. The following experiments complete the series of proofs of the origin of the electricity in the voltaic pile. A fluid amalgam of potassium, containing not more than a hundredth of that metal, was put into pure water, and connected through the galvanometer with a plate of platina in the same water. There was immediately an electric current from the amalgam through the electrolyte to the platina. This must have been due to the oxidation only of the metal, for there was neither

* Elements of Chemical Philosophy, p. 148.

acid nor alkali to combine with, or in any way act on, the body produced.

945. Again, a plate of clean lead and a plate of platina were put into *pure* water. There was immediately a powerful current produced from the lead through the fluid to the platina : it was even intense enough to decompose solution of the iodide of potassium when introduced into the circuit in the form of apparatus already described (880.), fig. 73. Here no action of acid or alkali on the oxide formed from the lead could supply the electricity : it was due solely to the oxidation of the metal.

---

946. There is no point in electrical science which seems to me of more importance than the state of the metals and the electrolytic conductor in a simple voltaic circuit *before and at* the moment when metallic contact is first completed. If clearly understood, I feel no doubt it would supply us with a direct key to the laws under which the great variety of voltaic excitements, direct and incidental, occur, and open out new fields of research for our investigation*.

947. We seem to have the power of deciding to a certain extent in numerous cases of chemical affinity, (as of zinc with the oxygen of water, &c. &c.) which of *two modes of action of the attractive power* shall be exerted (996.). In the one mode we can transfer the power onwards, and makes it produce elsewhere its equivalent of action (867. 917.) ; in the other it is not transferred, but exerted wholly at the spot. The first is the case of volta-electric excitation, the other ordinary chemical affinity : but both are chemical actions and due to one force or principle.

948. The general circumstances of the former mode occur in all instances of voltaic currents, but may be considered as in their perfect condition, and then free from those of the second mode, in some only of the cases ; as in those of plates of zinc and platina in solution of potassa, or of amalgamated zinc and platina in dilute sulphuric acid.

949. Assuming it sufficiently proved, by the preceding experiments and considerations, that the electro-motive action de-

* In connexion with this part of the subject refer now to Series XI. 1164, Series XII. 1343—1358, and Series XIII. 1621 &c.—*Dec.* 1838.

pends, when zinc, platina, and dilute sulphuric acid are used,
upon the mutual affinity of the metal zinc and the oxygen of
the water (921. 924.), it would appear that the metal, when
alone, has not power enough, under the circumstances, to take
the oxygen and expel the hydrogen from the water ; for, in
fact, no such action takes place.   But it would also appear that
it has power so far to act, by its attraction for the oxygen of the
particles in contact with it, as to place the similar forces already
active between these and  the other particles of oxygen and the
particles of hydrogen in the water, in a peculiar state of tension
or polarity, and probably also at the same time to throw those
of its own particles which are in contact with the water into a
similar but opposed state.   Whilst this state is retained, no
further change occurs ; but when it is relieved, by completion
of the circuit, in which case the forces determined in opposite
directions, with respect to the zinc and the electrolyte, are
found exactly competent to neutralize each other, then a series
of decompositions and recompositions takes place amongst the
particles of oxygen and hydrogen constituting the water, between the place of contact with the platina and the place where
the zinc is active ; these intervening particles being evidently
in close dependence upon and relation to each other.   The
zinc forms a direct compound with those particles of oxygen
which were, previously, in divided relation to both it and the
hydrogen : the oxide is removed by the acid, and a fresh surface of zinc is presented to the water, to renew and repeat the
action.

950. Practically, the state of tension is best relieved by dipping a metal which has less attraction for oxygen than the zinc,
into the dilute acid, and making it also touch the zinc.   The
force of chemical affinity, which has been influenced or polarized in the particles of the water by the dominant attraction of
the zinc for the oxygen, is then transferred, in a most extraordinary manner, through the two metals, so as to re-enter upon
the circuit in the electrolytic conductor, which, unlike the metals
in that respect, cannot convey or transfer it without suffering
decomposition ; or rather, probably, it is exactly balanced and
neutralized by the force which at the same moment completes
the combination of the zinc with the oxygen of the water.   The
forces, in fact, of the two particles which are acting towards

each other, and which are therefore in opposite directions, are the origin of the two opposite forces, or directions of force, in the current. They are of necessity equivalent to each other. Being transferred forward in contrary directions, they produce what is called the voltaic current : and it seems to me impossible to resist the idea that it must be preceded by a *state of tension* in the fluid, and between the fluid and the zinc ; the *first consequence* of the affinity of the zinc for the oxygen of the water.

951. I have sought carefully for indications of a state of tension in the electrolytic conductor ; and conceiving that it might produce something like structure, either before or during its discharge, I endeavoured to make this evident by polarized light. A glass cell, seven inches long, one inch and a half wide, and six inches deep, had two sets of platina electrodes adapted to it, one set for the ends, and the other for the sides. Those for the *sides* were seven inches long by three inches high, and when in the cell were separated by a little frame of wood covered with calico ; so that when made active by connexion with a battery upon any solution in the cell, the bubbles of gas rising from them did not obscure the central parts of the liquid.

952. A saturated solution of sulphate of soda was put into the cell, and the electrodes connected with a battery of 150 pairs of 4-inch plates : the current of electricity was conducted across the cell so freely, that the discharge was as good as if a wire had been used. A ray of polarised light was then transmitted through the solution, directly across the course of the electric current, and examined by an analyzing plate ; but though it penetrated seven inches of solution thus subject to the action of the electricity, and though contact was sometimes made, sometimes broken, and occasionally reversed during the observations, not the slightest trace of action on the ray could be perceived.

953. The large electrodes were then removed, and others introduced which fitted the *ends* of the cell. In each a slit was cut, so as to allow the light to pass. The course of the polarized ray was now parallel to the current, or in the direction of its axis (517.) ; but still no effect, under any circumstances of contact or disunion, could be perceived upon it.

954. A strong solution of nitrate of lead was employed instead of the sulphate of soda, but no effects could be detected.

955. Thinking it possible that the discharge of the electric forces by the successive decompositions and recompositions of the particles of the electrolyte might neutralize and therefore destroy any effect which the first state of tension could by possibility produce, I took a substance which, being an excellent electrolyte when fluid, was a perfect insulator when solid, namely, borate of lead, in the form of a glass plate, and connecting the sides and the edges of this mass with the metallic plates, sometimes in contact with the poles of a voltaic battery, and sometimes even with the electric machine, for the advantage of the much higher intensity then obtained, I passed a polarized ray across it in various directions, as before, but could not obtain the slightest appearance of action upon the light.   Hence I conclude, that notwithstanding the new and extraordinary state which must be assumed by an electrolyte, either during decomposition (when a most enormous quantity of electricity must be traversing it), or in the state of tension which is assumed as preceding decomposition, and which might be supposed to be retained in the solid form of the electrolyte, still it has no power of affecting a polarized ray of light ; for no kind of structure or tension can in this way be rendered evident.

956. There is, however, one beautiful experimental proof of a state of tension acquired by the metals and the electrolyte before the electric current is produced, and *before contact* of the different metals is made (915.) ; in fact, at that moment when chemical forces only are efficient as a cause of action.  I took a voltaic apparatus, consisting of a single pair of large plates, namely, a cylinder of amalgamated zinc, and a double cylinder of copper.  These were put into a jar containing dilute sulphuric acid*, and could at pleasure be placed in metallic communication by a copper wire adjusted so as to dip at the extremities into two cups of mercury connected with the two plates.

957. Being thus arranged, there was no chemical action whilst the plates were not connected.  On *making* the con-

* When nitro-sulphuric acid is used, the spark is more powerful, but local chemical action can then commence, and proceed without requiring metallic contact.

nexion, a spark was obtained *, and the solution was immediately decomposed. On breaking it, the usual spark was obtained, and the decomposition ceased. In this case it is evident that the first spark must have occurred before metallic contact was made, for it passed through an interval of air; and also that it must have tended to pass before the electrolytic action began; for the latter could not take place until the current passed, and the current could not pass before the spark appeared. Hence I think there is sufficient proof, that as it is the zinc and water which by their mutual action produce the electricity of this apparatus, so these by their first contact with each other, were placed in a state of powerful tension (951.), which, though it could not produce the actual decomposition of the water, was able to make a spark of electricity pass between the zinc and a fit discharger as soon as the interval was rendered sufficiently small. The experiment demonstrates the direct production of the electric spark from pure chemical forces.

958. There are a few circumstances connected with the production of this spark by a single pair of plates, which should be known, to ensure success to the experiment†. When the amalgamated surfaces of contact are quite clean and dry, the spark, on making contact, is quite as brilliant as on breaking it, if not even more so. When a film of oxide or dirt was present at either mercurial surface, then the first spark was often feeble, and often failed, the breaking spark, however, continuing very constant and bright. When a little water was put over the mercury, the spark was greatly diminished in brilliancy, but very regular both on making and breaking contact. When the contact was made between clean platina, the spark was also very small, but regular both ways. The true electric spark is, in fact, very small, and when surfaces of mercury are used, it is the combustion of the metal which produces the greater part of the light. The circumstances connected with the burning of the mercury are most favourable on breaking contact; for

* It has been universally supposed that no spark is produced on making the contact between a single pair of plates. I was led to expect one from the considerations already advanced in this paper. The wire of communication should be short; for with a long wire, circumstances strongly affecting the spark are introduced.

† See in relation to precautions respecting a spark, 1074.—*Dec.* 1838.

the act of separation exposes clean surfaces of metal, whereas, on making contact a thin film of oxide, or soiling matter, often interferes. Hence the origin of the general opinion that it is only when the contact is broken that the spark passes.

---

959. With reference to the other set of cases, namely, those of local action (947.) in which chemical affinity being exerted causes no transference of the power to a distance where no electric current is produced, it is evident that forces of the most intense kind must be active, and in some way balanced in their activity, during such combinations; these forces being directed so immediately and exclusively towards each other, that no signs of the powerful electric current they can produce become apparent, although the same final state of things is obtained as if that current had passed. It was Berzelius, I believe, who considered the heat and light evolved in cases of combustion as the consequences of this mode of exertion of the electric powers of the combining particles. But it will require a much more exact and extensive knowledge of the nature of electricity, and the manner in which it is associated with the atoms of matter, before we can understand accurately the action of this power in thus causing their union, or comprehend the nature of the great difference which it presents in the two modes of action just distinguished. We may imagine, but such imaginations must for the time be classed with the great mass of *doubtful knowledge* (876.) which we ought rather to strive to diminish than to increase; for the very extensive contradictions of this knowledge by itself shows that but a small portion of it can ultimately prove true*.

960. Of the two modes of action in which chemical affinity is exerted, it is important to remark, that that which produces the electric current is as *definite* as that which causes ordinary chemical combination; so that in examining the *production* or *evolution* of electricity in cases of combination or decomposition, it will be necessary, not merely to observe certain defects dependent upon a current of electricity, but also their *quantity*; and though it may often happen that the forces concerned in any particular case of chemical action may be partly exerted in

* Refer to 1738, etc. Series XIV.—*Dec.* 1838.

one mode and partly in the other, it is only those which are efficient in producing the current that have any relation to voltaic action. Thus, in the combination of oxygen and hydrogen to produce water, electric powers to a most enormous amount are for the time active (861. 873.) ; but any mode of examining the flame which they form during energetic combination, which has as yet been devised, has given but the feeblest traces. These therefore may not, cannot, be taken as evidences of the nature of the action ; but are merely incidental results, incomparably small in relation to the forces concerned, and supplying no information of the way in which the particles are active on each other, or in which their forces are finally arranged.

961. That such cases of chemical action produce no *current of electricity*, is perfectly consistent with what we know of the voltaic apparatus, in which it is essential that one of the combining elements shall form part of, or be in direct relation with, an electrolytic conductor (921. 923.). That such cases produce no *free electricity of tension*, and that when they are converted into cases of voltaic action they produce a current in which the opposite forces are so equal as to neutralize each other, prove the equality of the forces in the opposed acting particles of matter, and therefore the equality of electric power in those quantities of matter which are called *electro-chemical equivalents* (824.). Hence another proof of the definite nature of electro-chemical action (783. &c.), and that chemical affinity and electricity are forms of the same power (917. &c.).

962. The direct reference of the effects produced by the voltaic pile at the place of experimental decomposition to the chemical affinities active at the place of excitation (891. 917.), gives a very simple and natural view of the cause why the bodies (or *ions*) evolved pass in certain directions ; for it is only when they pass in those directions that their forces can consist with and compensate (in direction at least) the superior forces which are dominant at the place where the action of the whole is determined. If, for instance, in a voltaic circuit, the activity of which is determined by the attraction of zinc for the oxygen of water, the zinc move from right to left, then any other *cation* included in the circuit, being part of an electrolyte, or forming part of it at the moment, will also move from right to left : and as the oxygen of the water, by its natural affinity for the zinc,

moves from left to right, so any other body of the same class with it (*i. e.* any other *anion*), under its government for the time, will move from left to right.

963. This I may illustrate by reference to fig. 83, the double circle of which may represent a complete voltaic circuit, the direction of its forces being determined by supposing for a moment the zinc *b* and the platina *c* as representing plates of those metals acting upon water, *d, e,* and other substances, but having their energy exalted so as to effect several decompositions by the use of a battery at *a* (989.). This supposition may be allowed, because the action in the battery will only consist of repetitions of what would take place between *b* and *c*, if they really constituted but a single pair. The zinc *b,* and the oxygen *d,* by their mutual affinity, tend to unite; but as the oxygen is already in association with the hydrogen *e,* and has its inherent chemical or electric powers neutralized for the time by those of the latter, the hydrogen *e* must leave the oxygen *d,* and advance in the direction of the arrow head, or else the zinc *b* cannot move in the same direction to unite to the oxygen *d,* nor the oxygen *d* move in the contrary direction to unite to the zinc *b,* the relation of the *similar* forces of *b* and *e,* in contrary directions, to the *opposite* forces of *d* being the preventive. As the hydrogen *e* advances, it, on coming against the platina *c, f,* which forms a part of the circuit, communicates its electric or chemical forces through it to the next electrolyte in the circuit, fused chloride of lead, *g, h,* where the chlorine must move in conformity with the direction of the oxygen at *d,* for it has to compensate the forces disturbed in its part of the circuit by the superior influence of those between the oxygen and zinc at *d, b,* aided as they are by those of the battery *a*; and for a similar reason the lead must move in the direction pointed out by the arrow head, that it may be in right relation to the first moving body of its own class, namely, the zinc *b.* If copper intervene in the circuit from *i* to *k,* it acts as the platina did before; and if another electrolyte, as the iodide of tin, occur at *l, m,* then the iodine *l,* being an *anion,* must move in conformity with the exciting *anion,* namely, the oxygen *d,* and the *cation* tin *m* move in correspondence with the other *cations, b, e,* and *h,* that the chemical forces may be in equilibrium as to their direction and quantity throughout the circuit. Should it

so happen that the anions in their circulation can combine with the metals at the *anodes* of the respective electrolytes, as would be the case at the platina $f$ and the copper $k$, then those bodies becoming parts of electrolytes, under the influence of the current, immediately travel; but considering their relation to the zinc $b$, it is evidently impossible that they can travel in any other direction than what will accord with its course, and therefore can never tend to pass otherwise than *from* the anode and *to* the cathode.

964. In such a circle as that delineated, therefore, all the known *anions* may be grouped within, and all the *cations* without. If any number of them enter as *ions* into the constitution of *electrolytes*, and, forming one circuit, are simultaneously subject to one common current, the anions must move in accordance with each other in one direction, and the cations in the other. Nay, more than that, equivalent portions of these bodies must so advance in opposite directions: for the advance of every 32·5 parts of the zinc $b$ must be accompanied by a motion in the opposite direction of 8 parts of oxygen at $d$, of 36 parts of chlorine at $g$, of 126 parts of iodine at $l$; and in the same direction by electro-chemical equivalents of hydrogen, lead, copper and tin, at $e$, $h$, $k$, and $m$.

---

965. If the present paper be accepted as a correct expression of facts, it will still only prove a confirmation of certain general views put forth by Sir Humphry Davy in his Bakerian Lecture for 1806\*, and revised and re-stated by him in another Bakerian Lecture, on electrical and chemical changes, for the year 1826†. His general statement is, that *" chemical and electrical attractions were produced by the same cause, acting in one case on particles, in the other on masses, of matter; and that the same property, under different modifications, was the cause of all the phenomena exhibited by different voltaic combinations‡."* This statement I believe to be true; but in admitting and supporting it, I must guard myself from being supposed to assent to all that is associated with it in the two papers referred to, or as admitting the experiments which are

* Philosophical Transactions, 1807.　　　　† Ibid, 1826, p. 383.
‡ Ibid. 1826, p. 389.

there quoted as decided proofs of the truth of the principle. Had I thought them so, there would have been no occasion for this investigation. It may be supposed by some that I ought to go through these papers, distinguishing what I admit from what I reject, and giving good experimental or philosophical reasons for the judgment in both cases. But then I should be equally bound to review, for the same purpose, all that has been written both for and against the necessity of metallic contact,—for and against the origin of voltaic electricity in chemical action,—a duty which I may not undertake in the present paper*.

### ¶ ii. *On the Intensity necessary for Electrolyzation.*

966. It became requisite, for the comprehension of many of the conditions attending voltaic action, to determine positively, if possible, whether electrolytes could resist the action of an electric current when beneath a certain intensity? whether the intensity at which the current ceased to act would be the same for all bodies? and also whether the electrolytes thus resisting decomposition would conduct the electric current as a metal does, after they ceased to conduct as electrolytes, or would act as perfect insulators?

967. It was evident from the experiments described (904. 906.) that different bodies were decomposed with very different facilities, and apparently that they required for their decomposition currents of different intensities, resisting some, but giving way to others. But it was needful, by very careful and express experiments, to determine whether a current could really pass through, and yet not decompose an electrolyte (910.).

968. An arrangement (fig. 84.) was made, in which two glass vessels contained the same dilute sulphuric acid, sp. gr. 1·25. The plate $z$ was amalgamated zinc, in connexion, by a platina wire $a$, with the platina plate $e$; $b$ was a platina wire connecting

---

* I at one time intended to introduce here, in the form of a note, a table of reference to the papers of the different philosophers who have referred the origin of the electricity in the voltaic pile to contact, or to chemical action, or to both; but on the publication of the first volume of M. Becquerel's highly important and valuable Traité de l'Electricité et du Magnétism, I thought it far better to refer to that work for these references, and the views held by the authors quoted. See pages 86, 91, 104, 110, 112, 117, 118, 120, 151, 152, 224, 227, 228, 232, 233, 252, 255, 257, 258, 290, &c.—July 3rd, 1834.

the two platina plates P P'; *c* was a platina wire connected with
the platina plate P''.   On the plate *e* was placed a piece of paper
moistened in solution of iodide of potassium : the wire *c* was
so curved that its end could be made to rest at pleasure on this
paper, and show, by the evolution of iodine there, whether a
current was passing ; or, being placed in the dotted position,
it formed a direct communication with the platina plate *e*, and
the electricity could pass without causing decomposition.   The
object was to produce a current by the action of the acid on
the amalgamated zinc in the first vessel A ; to pass it through
the acid in the second vessel B by platina electrodes, that its
power of decomposing water might, if existing, be observed ;
and to verify the existence of the current at pleasure, by decomposition at *e*, without involving the continual obstruction to the
current which would arise from making the decomposition there
constant.   The experiment, being arranged, was examined and
the existence of a current ascertained by the decomposition at *e* ;
the whole was then left with the end of the wire *c* resting on the
plate *e*, so as to form a constant metallic communication there.

969. After several hours, the end of the wire *c* was replaced
on the test paper at *e* : decomposition occurred, and *the proof*
of a passing current was therefore complete.   The current was
very feeble compared to what it had been at the beginning of the
experiment, because of a peculiar state acquired by the metal
surfaces in the second vessel, which caused them to oppose the
passing current by a force which they possess under these circumstances (1040.).   Still it was proved, by the decomposition,
that this state of the plates in the second vessel was not able
entirely to stop the current determined in the first, and that was
all that was needful to be ascertained in the present inquiry.

970. This apparatus was examined from time to time, and
an electric current always found circulating through it, until
twelve days had elapsed, during which the water in the second
vessel had been constantly subject to its action.   Notwithstanding this lengthened period, not the slightest appearance
of a bubble upon either of the plates in that vessel occurred.
From the results of the experiment, I conclude that a current
*had* passed, but of so low an intensity as to fall beneath that
degree at which the elements of water, unaided by any secondary force resulting from the capability of combination with the

matter of the electrodes, or of the liquid surrounding them, separated from each other.

971. It may be supposed, that the oxygen and hydrogen had been evolved in such small quantities as to have entirely dissolved in the water, and finally to have escaped at the surface, or to have reunited into water.    That the hydrogen can be so dissolved was shown in the first vessel; for after several days minute bubbles of gas gradually appeared upon a glass rod, inserted to retain the zinc and platina apart, and also upon the platina plate itself, and these were hydrogen.    They resulted principally in this way :—notwithstanding the amalgamation of the zinc, the acid exerted a little direct action upon it, so that a small stream of hydrogen bubbles was continually rising from its surface ; a little of this hydrogen gradually dissolved in the dilute acid, and was in part set free against the surfaces of the rod and the plate, according to the well-known action of such solid bodies in solutions of gases (623. &c.).

972. But if the gases had been evolved in the second vessel by the decomposition of water, and had tended to dissolve, still there would have been every reason to expect that a few bubbles should have appeared on the electrodes, especially on the negative one, if it were only because of its action as a nucleus on the solution supposed to be formed; but none appeared even after twelve days.

973. When a few drops only of nitric acid were added to the vessel A, fig. 84., then the results were altogether different.    In less than five minutes bubbles of gas appeared on the plates P′ and P″ in the second vessel.    To prove that this was the effect of the electric current (which by trial at *e* was found at the same time to be passing,) the connexion at *e* was broken, the plates P′ P″ cleared from bubbles and left in the acid of the vessel B, for fifteen minutes : during that time no bubbles appeared upon them ; but on restoring the communication at *e*, a minute did not elapse before gas appeared in bubbles upon the plates.    The proof, therefore, is most full and complete, that the current excited by dilute sulphuric acid with a little nitric acid in vessel A, has intensity enough to overcome the chemical affinity exerted between the oxygen and hydrogen of the water in the vessel B, whilst that excited by dilute sulphuric acid alone has *not* sufficient intensity.

974. On using a strong solution of caustic potassa in the vessel A, to excite the current, it was found by the decomposing effects at *e*, that the current passed.    But it had not intensity enough to decompose the water in the vessel B; for though left for fourteen days, during the whole of which time the current was found to be passing, still not the slightest appearance of gas appeared on the plates P′ P″, nor any other signs of the water having suffered decomposition.

975. Sulphate of soda in solution was then experimented with, for the purpose of ascertaining with respect to it, whether a certain electrolytic intensity was also required for its decomposition in this state, in analogy with the result established with regard to water (974.).    The apparatus was arranged as in fig. 85; P and Z are the platina and zinc plates dipping into a solution of common salt; *a* and *b* are platina plates connected by wires of platina (except in the galvanometer *g*) with P and Z; *c* is a connecting wire of platina, the ends of which can be made to rest either on the plates *a*, *b*, or on the papers moistened in solutions which are placed upon them; so that the passage of the current without decomposition, or with one or two decompositions, was under ready command, as far as arrangement was concerned.    In order to change the *anodes* and *cathodes* at the places of decomposition, the form of apparatus, fig. 86, was occasionally adopted.    Here only one platina plate, *c*, was used; both pieces of paper on which decomposition was to be effected were placed upon it, the wires from P and Z resting upon these pieces of paper, or upon the plate *c*, according as the current with or without decomposition of the solutions was required.

976. On placing solution of iodide of potassium in paper at one of the decomposing localities, and solution of sulphate of soda at the other, so that the electric current should pass through both at once, the solution of iodide was slowly decomposed, yielding iodine at the *anode* and alkali at the *cathode*; but the solution of sulphate of soda exhibited no signs of decomposition, neither acid nor alkali being evolved from it.    On placing the wires so that the iodide alone was subject to the action of the current (900.), it was quickly and powerfully decomposed; but on arranging them so that the sulphate of soda alone was subject to action, it still refused to yield up its elements.    Finally, the apparatus was so arranged under a wet

bell-glass, that it could be left for twelve hours, the current passing during the whole time through a solution of sulphate of soda, retained in its place by only two thicknesses of bibulous litmus and turmeric paper. At the end of that time it was ascertained by the decomposition of iodide of potassium at the second place of action, that the current was passing and had passed for the twelve hours, and yet no trace of acid or alkali from the sulphate of soda appeared.

977. From these experiments it may, I think, be concluded, that a solution of sulphate of soda can conduct a current of electricity, which is unable to decompose the neutral salt present ; that this salt in the state of solution, like water, requires a certain electrolytic intensity for its decomposition ; and that the necessary intensity is much higher for this substance than for the iodide of potassium in a similar state of solution.

978. I then experimented on bodies rendered decomposable by fusion, and first on *chloride of lead.* The current was excited by dilute sulphuric acid without any nitric acid between zinc and platina plates, fig. 87., and was then made to traverse a little chloride of lead fused upon glass at *a*, a paper moistened in solution of iodide of potassium at *b*, and a galvanometer at *g*. The metallic terminations at *a* and *b* were of platina. Being thus arranged, the decomposition at *b* and the deflection at *g* showed that an electric current was passing, but there was no appearance of decomposition at *a*, not even after a *metallic* communication at *b* was established. The experiment was repeated several times, and I am led to conclude that in this case the current has not intensity sufficient to cause the decomposition of the chloride of lead; and further, that, like water (974.), fused chloride of lead can conduct an electric current having an intensity below that required to effect decomposition.

979. *Chloride of silver* was then placed at *a*, fig. 87., instead of chloride of lead. There was a very ready decomposition of the solution of iodide of potassium at *b*, and when metallic contact was made there, very considerable deflection of the galvanometer needle at *g*. Platina also appeared to be dissolved at the anode of the fused chloride at *a*, and there was every appearance of a decomposition having been effected there.

980. A further proof of decomposition was obtained in the following manner. The platina wires in the fused chloride at

*a* were brought very near together (metallic contact having been established at *b*), and left so ; the deflection at the galvanometer indicated the passage of a current, feeble in its force, but constant.   After a minute or two, however, the needle would suddenly be violently affected, and indicate a current as strong as if metallic contact had taken place at *a*.   This I actually found to be the case, for the silver reduced by the action of the current crystallized in long delicate spiculæ, and these at last completed the metallic communication ; and at the same time that they transmitted a more powerful current than the fused chloride, they proved that electro-chemical decomposition of that chloride had been going on.   Hence it appears, that the current excited by dilute sulphuric acid between zinc and platina, has an intensity above that required to electrolyze the fused chloride of silver when placed between platina electrodes, although it has not intensity enough to decompose chloride of lead under the same circumstances.

981. A drop of *water* placed at *a* instead of the fused chlorides, showed as in the former case (970.), that it could conduct a current unable to decompose it, for decomposition of the solution of iodide at *b* occurred after some time.   But its conducting power was much below that of the fused chloride of lead (978.).

982. Fused *nitre* at *a* conducted much better than water : I was unable to decide with certainty whether it was electrolyzed, but I incline to think not, for there was no discoloration against the platina at the *cathode*.   If sulpho-nitric acid had been used in the exciting vessel, both the nitre and the chloride of lead would have suffered decomposition like the water (906.).

983. The results thus obtained of conduction without decomposition, and the necessity of a certain electrolytic intensity for the separation of the *ions* of different electrolytes, are immediately connected with the experiments and results given in § 10. of the Fourth Series of these Researches (418. 423. 444. 449.).   But it will require a more exact knowledge of the nature of intensity, both as regards the first origin of the electric current, and also the manner in which it may be reduced, or lowered by the intervention of longer or shorter portions of bad conductors, whether decomposable or not, before their relation can be minutely and fully understood.

984. In the case of water, the experiments I have as yet

made, appear to show, that, when the electric current is reduced in intensity below the point required for decomposition,
then the degree of conduction is the same whether sulphuric
acid, or any other of the many bodies which can affect its transferring power as an electrolyte, are present or not.  Or, in other
words, that the necessary electrolytic intensity for water is the
same whether it be pure, or rendered a better conductor by the
addition of these substances ; and that for currents of less intensity than this, the water, whether pure or acidulated, has
equal conducting power.   An apparatus, fig. 84, was arranged
with dilute sulphuric acid in the vessel A, and pure distilled
water in the vessel B.   By the decomposition at *e*, it appeared
as if water was a *better* conductor than dilute sulphuric acid
for a current of such low intensity as to cause no decomposition.
I am inclined, however, to attribute this apparent superiority of
water to variations in that peculiar condition of the platina electrodes which is referred to further on in this Series (1040.),
and which is assumed, as far as I can judge, to a greater degree
in dilute sulphuric acid than in pure water.   The power therefore, of acids, alkalies, salts, and other bodies in solution, to
increase conducting power, appears to hold good only in those
cases where the electrolyte subject to the current suffers decomposition, and loses all influence when the current transmitted
has too low an intensity to affect chemical change.  It is probable that the ordinary conducting power of an electrolyte in the
solid state (419.) is the same as that which it possesses in the
fluid state for currents the tension of which is beneath the due
electrolytic intensity.

985. Currents of electricity, produced by less than eight or
ten series of voltaic elements, can be reduced to that intensity
at which water can conduct them without suffering decomposition, by causing them to pass through three or four vessels in
which water shall be successively interposed between platina
surfaces.   The principles of interference upon which this effect
depends, will be described hereafter (1009. 1018.), but the effect may be useful in obtaining currents of standard intensity,
and is probably applicable to batteries of any number of pairs
of plates.

986. As there appears every reason to expect that all
electrolytes will be found subject to the law which requires an
electric current of a certain intensity for their decomposition,

but that they will differ from each other in the degree of intensity required, it will be desirable hereafter to arrange them in a table, in the order of their electrolytic intensities. Investigations on this point must, however, be very much extended, and include many more bodies than have been here mentioned before such a table can be constructed. It will be especially needful in such experiments, to describe the nature of the electrodes used, or, if possible, to select such as, like platina or plumbago in certain cases, shall have no power of assisting the separation of the *ions* to be evolved (913.).

987. Of the two modes in which bodies can transmit the electric forces, namely, that which is so characteristically exhibited by the metals, and usually called conduction, and that in which it is accompanied by decomposition, the first appears common to all bodies, although it occurs with almost infinite degrees of difference ; the second is at present distinctive of the electrolytes. It is, however, just possible that it may hereafter be extended to the metals; for their power of conducting without decomposition may, perhaps justly, be ascribed to their requiring a very high electrolytic intensity for their decomposition.

987$\frac{1}{2}$. The establishment of the principle that a certain electrolytic intensity is necessary before decomposition can be effected, is of great importance to all those considerations which arise regarding the probable effects of weak currents, such for instance as those produced by natural thermo-electricity, or natural voltaic arrangements in the earth. For to produce an effect of decomposition or of combination, a current must not only exist, but have a certain intensity before it can overcome the quiescent affinities opposed to it, otherwise it will be conducted, producing no permanent chemical effects. On the other hand, the principles are also now evident by which an opposing action can be so weakened by the juxtaposition of bodies not having quite affinity enough to cause direct action between them (913.), that a very weak current shall be able to raise the sum of actions sufficiently high, and cause chemical changes to occur.

988. In concluding this division *on the intensity necessary for electrolyzation,* I cannot resist pointing out the following remarkable conclusion in relation to intensity generally. It would appear that when a voltaic current is produced, having

a certain intensity, dependent upon the strength of the
chemical affinities by which that current is excited (916.), it
can decompose a particular electrolyte without relation to the
quantity of electricity passed, the *intensity* deciding whether
the electrolyte shall give way or not. If that conclusion be confirmed, then we may arrange circumstances so that the *same
quantity* of electricity may pass in the *same time*, in at the *same
surface*, into the *same decomposing body in the same state*, and
yet, differing in intensity, will *decompose in one case and in the
other not* :—for taking a source of too low an intensity to decompose, and ascertaining the quantity passed in a given time, it is
easy to take another source having a sufficient intensity, and reducing the quantity of electricity from it by the intervention
of bad conductors to the same proportion as the former current, and then all the conditions will be fulfilled which are required to produce the result described.

¶ iii. *On associated Voltaic circles, or the Voltaic battery.*

989. Passing from the consideration of single circles (875.
&c.) to their association in the voltaic battery, it is a very evident consequence, that if matters are so arranged that two sets
of affinities, in place of being opposed to each other as in figg.
73. 76. (880. 891.), are made to act in conformity, then, instead
of either interfering with the other, it will rather assist it. This
is simply the case of two voltaic pairs of metals arranged so as
to form one circuit. In such arrangements the activity of the
whole is known to be increased, and when ten, or a hundred,
or any larger number of such alterations are placed in conformable association with each other, the power of the whole
becomes proportionably exalted, and we obtain that magnificent
instrument of philosophic research, the *voltaic battery*.

990. But it is evident from the principles of definite action
already laid down, that the *quantity* of electricity in the current cannot be increased with the increase of the *quantity of
metal* oxidized and dissolved at each new place of chemical
action. A single pair of zinc and platina plates throws as
much electricity into the form of a current, by the oxidation
of 32·5 grains of the zinc (868.) as would be circulated by the
same alteration of a thousand times that quantity, or nearly
five pounds of metal oxidized at the surface of the zinc plates

of a thousand pairs placed in regular battery order. For it is evident, that the electricity which passes across the acid from the zinc to the platina in the first cell, and which has been associated with, or even evolved by, the decomposition of a definite portion of water in that cell, cannot pass from the zinc to the platina across the acid in the second cell, without the decomposition of the same quantity of water there, and the oxidation of the same quantity of zinc by it (924. 949.). The same result recurs in every other cell; the electro-chemical equivalent of water must be decomposed in each, before the current can pass through it; for the quantity of electricity passed and the quantity of electrolyte decomposed, *must* be the equivalents of each other. The action in each cell, therefore, is not to increase the quantity set in motion in any one cell, but to aid in urging forward that quantity, the passing of which is consistent with the oxidation of its own zinc; and in this way it exalts that peculiar property of the current which we endeavour to express by the term *intensity,* without increasing the *quantity* beyond that which is proportionate to the quantity of zinc oxidized in any single cell of the series.

991. To prove this, I arranged ten pairs of amalgamated zinc and platina plates with dilute sulphuric acid in the form of a battery. On completing the circuit, all the pairs acted and evolved gas at the surfaces of the platina. This was collected and found to be alike in quantity for each plate; and the quantity of hydrogen evolved at any one platina plate was in the same proportion to the quantity of metal dissolved from any one zinc plate, as was given in the experiment with a single pair (864. &c.). It was therefore certain, that, just as much electricity and no more had passed through the series of ten pair of plates as had passed through, or would have been put into motion by, any single pair, notwithstanding that ten times the quantity of zinc had been consumed.

992. This truth has been proved also long ago in another way, by the action of the evolved current on a magnetic needle; the deflecting power of one pair of plates in a battery being equal to the deflecting power of the whole, provided the wires used be sufficiently large to carry the current of the single pair freely; but the *cause* of this equality of action could not be

understood whilst the definite action and evolution of electricity (783. 869.) remained unknown.

993. The superior decomposing power of a battery over a single pair of plates is rendered evident in two ways. Electrolytes held together by an affinity so strong as to resist the action of the current from a single pair, yield up their elements to the current excited by many pairs ; and that body which is decomposed by the action of one or of few pairs of metals, &c., is resolved into its *ions* the more readily as it is acted upon by electricity urged forward by many alternations.

994. Both these effects are, I think, easily understood. Whatever *intensity* may be, (and that must of course depend upon the nature of electricity, whether it consist of a fluid or fluids, or of vibrations of an ether, or any other kind or condition of matter,) there seems to be no difficulty in comprehending that the *degree* of intensity at which a current of electricity is evolved by a first voltaic element, shall be increased when that current is subjected to the action of a second voltaic element, acting in conformity and possessing equal powers with the first : and as the decompositions are merely opposed actions, but exactly of the same kind as those which generate the current (917.), it seems to be a natural consequence, that the affinity which can resist the force of a single decomposing action may be unable to oppose the energies of many decomposing actions, operating conjointly, as in the voltaic battery.

995. That a body which can give way to a current of feeble intensity, should give way more freely to one of stronger force, and yet involve no contradiction to the law of definite electrolytic action, is perfectly consistent. All the facts and also the theory I have ventured to put forth, tend to show that the act of decomposition opposes a certain force to the passage of the electric current ; and, that this obstruction should be overcome more or less readily, in proportion to the greater or less intensity of the decomposing current, is in perfect consistency with all our notions of the electric agent.

996. I have elsewhere (947.) distinguished the chemical action of zinc and dilute sulphuric acid into two portions ; that which, acting effectually on the zinc, evolves hydrogen at once

upon its surface, and that which, producing an arrangement of the chemical forces throughout the electrolyte present, (in this case water,) tends to take oxygen from it, but cannot do so unless the electric current consequent thereon can have free passage, and the hydrogen be delivered elsewhere than against the zinc.    The electric current depends altogether upon the second of these ; but when the current can pass, by favouring the electrolytic action it tends to diminish the former and increase the latter portion.

997. It is evident, therefore, that when ordinary zinc is used in a voltaic arrangement, there is an enormous waste of that power which it is the object to throw into the form of an electric current ; a consequence which is put in its strongest point of view when it is considered that three ounces and a half of zinc, properly oxydized, can circulate enough electricity to decompose nearly one ounce of water, and cause the evolution of about 2400 cubic inches of hydrogen gas.    This loss of power not only takes place during the time the electrodes of the battery are in communication, being then proportionate to the quantity of hydrogen evolved against the surface of any one of the zinc plates, but includes also *all* the chemical action which goes on when the extremities of the pile are not in communication.

998. This loss is far greater with ordinary zinc than with the pure metal, as M. De la Rive has shown [*].    The cause is, that when ordinary zinc is acted upon by dilute sulphuric acid, portions of copper, lead, cadmium, or other metals which it may contain, are set free upon its surface ; and these, being in contact with the zinc, form small but very active voltaic circles, which cause great destruction of the zinc and evolution of hydrogen, apparently upon the zinc surface, but really upon the surface of these incidental metals.    In the same proportion as they serve to discharge or convey the electricity back to the zinc, do they diminish its power of producing an electric current which shall extend to a greater distance across the acid, and be discharged only through the copper or platina plate which is associated with it for the purpose of forming a voltaic apparatus.

[*] Quarterly Journal of Science, 1831, p. 388 ; or Bibliothèque Universelle, 1830, p. 391.

999. All these evils are removed by the employment of an amalgam of zinc in the manner recommended by Mr. Kemp*, or the use of the amalgamated zinc plates of Mr. Sturgeon (863.), who has himself suggested and objected to their application in galvanic batteries; for he says, "Were it not on account of the brittleness and other inconveniences occasioned by the incorporation of the mercury with the zinc, amalgamation of the zinc surfaces in galvanic batteries would become an important improvement; for the metal would last much longer, and remain bright for a considerable time, even for several successive hours; essential considerations in the employment of this apparatus." †

1000. Zinc so prepared, even though impure, does not sensibly decompose the water of dilute sulphuric acid, but still has such affinity for the oxygen, that the moment a metal which, like copper or platina, has little or no affinity, touches it in the acid, action ensues, and a powerful and abundant electric current is produced. It is probable that the mercury acts by bringing the surface, in consequence of its fluidity, into one uniform condition, and preventing those differences in character between one spot and another which are necessary for the formation of the minute voltaic circuits referred to (998.). If any difference does exist at the first moment, with regard to the proportion of zinc and mercury, at one spot on the *surface*, as compared with another, that spot having the least mercury is first acted on, and, by solution of the zinc, is soon placed in the same condition as the other parts, and the whole plate rendered superficially uniform. One part cannot, therefore, act as a discharger to another; and hence *all* the chemical power upon the water at its surface is in that equable condition (949.), which, though it tends to produce an electric current through the liquid to another plate of metal which can act as a discharger (950.), present no irregularities by which any one part, having weaker affinities for oxygen, can act as a discharger to another. Two excellent and important consequences follow

* Jameson's Edinburgh Journal, October 1828.

† Recent Experimental Researches, p. 42, &c. Mr. Sturgeon is of course unaware of the definite production of electricity by chemical action, and is in fact quoting the experiment as the strongest argument *against* the chemical theory of galvanism.

upon this state of the metal. The first is, that the *full equi-valent* of electricity is obtained for the oxidation of a certain quantity of zinc; the second, that a battery constructed with the zinc so prepared, and charged with dilute sulphuric acid, is active only whilst the electrodes are connected, and ceases to act or be acted upon by the acid the instant the communi-cation is broken.

1001. I have had a small battery of ten pairs of plates thus constructed, and am convinced that arrangements of this kind will be very important, especially in the development and illus-tration of the philosophical principles of the instrument. The metals I have used are amalgamated zinc and platina, con-nected together by being soldered to platina wires, the whole apparatus having the form of the couronne des tasses. The liquid used was dilute sulphuric acid of sp. gr. 1·25. No action took place upon the metals except when the electrodes were in communication, and then the action upon the zinc was only in proportion to the decomposition in the experimental cell; for when the current was retarded there, it was retarded also in the battery, and no waste of the powers of the metal was incurred.

1002. In consequence of this circumstance, the acid in the cells remained active for a very much longer time than usual. In fact, time did not tend to lower it in any sensible degree: for whilst the metal was preserved to be acted upon at the proper moment, the acid also was preserved almost at its first strength. Hence a constancy of action far beyond what can be obtained by the use of common zinc.

1003. Another excellent consequence was the renewal, during the interval of rest, between two experiments of the first and most efficient state. When an amalgamated zinc and a platina plate, immersed in dilute sulphuric acid, are first connected, the current is very powerful, but instantly sinks very much in force, and in some cases actually falls to only an eighth or a tenth of that first produced (1036.). This is due to the acid which is in contact with the zinc becoming neutral-ized by the oxide formed; the continued quick oxidation of the metal being thus prevented. With ordinary zinc, the evolu-tion of gas at its surface tends to mingle all the liquid together, and thus bring fresh acid against the metal, by which the oxide formed there can be removed. With the amalgamated zinc battery, at every cessation of the current, the saline solution against the zinc is gradually diffused amongst the rest of the liquid ; and upon the renewal of contact at the electrodes, the zinc plates are found most favourably circumstanced for the production of a ready and powerful current.

1004. It might at first be imagined that amalgamated zinc would be much inferior in force to common zinc, because of the lowering of its energy, which the mercury might be supposed to occasion over the whole of its surface; but this is not the case. When the electric currents of two pairs of platina and zinc plates were opposed, the difference being that one of the zincs was amalgamated and the other not, the current from the amalgamated zinc was most powerful, although no gas was evolved against it, and much was evolved at the surface of the unamalgamated metal. Again, as Davy has shown *, if amalgamated and unamalgamated zinc be put in contact, and dipped into dilute sulphuric acid, or other exciting fluids, the former is positive to the latter, *i. e.* the current passes from the amalgamated zinc, through the fluid, to the unprepared zinc. This he accounts for by supposing that "there is not any inherent and specific property in each metal which gives it the electrical character, but that it depends upon its peculiar state—on that form of aggregation which fits it for chemical change."

1005. The superiority of the amalgamated zinc is not, however, due to any such cause, but is a very simple consequence of the state of the fluid in contact with it ; for as the unprepared zinc acts directly and alone upon the fluid, whilst that which is amalgamated does not, the former (by the oxide it produces) quickly neutralizes the acid in contact with its surface, so that the progress of oxidation is retarded, whilst at the surface of the amalgamated zinc, any oxide formed is instantly removed by the free acid present, and the clean metallic surface is always ready to act with full energy upon the water. Hence its superiority (1037.).

1006. The progress of improvement in the voltaic battery and its applications, is evidently in the contrary direction at present to what it was a few years ago; for in place of increasing

* Philosophical Transactions, 1826, p. 405.

the number of plates, the strength of acid, and the extent alto-gether of the instrument, the change is rather towards its first state of simplicity, but with a far more intimate knowledge and application of the principles which govern its force and action. Effects of decomposition can now be obtained with ten pairs of plates (417.), which required five hundred or a thousand pairs for their production in the first instance. The capability of decomposing fused chlorides, iodides, and other compounds, according to the law before established (380. &c.), and the op-portunity of collecting certain of the products, without any loss, by the use of apparatus of the nature of those already described (789. 814. &c.), render it probable that the voltaic battery may become a useful and even economical manufacturing instrument; for theory evidently indicates that an equivalent of a rare sub-stance may be obtained at the expense of three or four equiva-lents of a very common body, namely, zinc : and practice seems thus far to justify the expectation. In this point of view I think it very likely that plates of platina or silver may be used instead of plates of copper with advantage, and that then the evil arising occasionally from solution of the copper, and its precipitation on the zinc, (by which the electro-motive power of the zinc is so much injured,) will be avoided (1047.).

¶ iv. *On the resistance of an Electrolyte to Electrolytic Action and on Interpositions.*

1007. I have already illustrated, in the simplest possible form of experiment (891. 910.), the resistance established at the place of decomposition to the force active at the exciting place. I purpose examining the effects of this resistance more generally ; but it is rather with reference to their practical in-terference with the action and phenomena of the voltaic battery, than with any intention at this time to offer a strict and philo-sophical account of their nature. Their general and principal cause is the resistance of the chemical affinities to be overcome ; but there are numerous other circumstances which have a joint influence with these forces (1034. 1040. &c.), each of which would require a minute examination before a correct account of the whole could be given.

1008. As it will be convenient to describe the experiments

in a form different to that in which they were made, both forms
shall first be explained.   Plates of platina, copper, zinc, and
other metals, about three quarters of an inch wide and three
inches long, were associated together in pairs by means
of platina wires to which they were soldered, fig. 88, the
plates of one pair being either alike or different, as might
be required.   These were arranged in glasses, fig. 89, so as to
form Volta's crown of cups.   The acid or fluid in the cups
never covered the whole of any plate ; and occasionally small
glass rods were put into the cups, between the plates, to prevent their contact.   Single plates were used to terminate
the series and complete the connection with a galvanometer,
or with a decomposing apparatus (899. 968. &c.), or both.
Now if fig. 90 be examined and compared with fig. 91, the
latter may be admitted as representing the former in its
simplest condition ; for the cups i, ii, and iii of the former,
with their contents, are represented by the cells i, ii, and iii, of
the latter, and the metal plates Z and P of the former by the
similar plates represented Z and P in the latter.   The only
difference, in fact, between the apparatus, fig. 90, and the
trough represented fig. 91, is that twice the quantity of surface
of contact between the metal and acid is allowed in the first to
what would occur in the second.

1009. When the extreme plates of the arrangement just described, fig. 90, are connected metallically through the galvanometer $g$, then the whole represents a battery consisting of two
pairs of zinc and platina plates urging a current forward, which
has, however, to decompose water unassisted by any direct
chemical affinity before it can be transmitted across the cell iii,
and therefore before it can circulate.   This decomposition of
water, which is opposed to the passage of the current, may, as
a matter of convenience, be considered as taking place either
against the surfaces of the two platina plates which constitute
the electrodes in the cell iii, or against the two surfaces of that
platina plate which separates the cells ii and iii, fig. 91, from
each other.   It is evident that if that plate were away, the battery would consist of two pairs of plates and two cells, arranged
in the most favourable position for the production of a current.
The platina plate therefore, which being introduced as at $x$,
has oxygen evolved at one surface and hydrogen at the other

(that is, if the decomposing current passes), may be considered as the cause of any obstruction arising from the decomposition of water by the electrolytic action of the current; and I have usually called it the interposed plate.

1010. In order to simplify the conditions, dilute sulphuric acid was first used in all the cells, and platina for the interposed plates; for then the initial intensity of the current which tends to be formed is constant, being due to the power which zinc has of decomposing water; and the opposing force of decomposition is also constant, the elements of the water being unassisted in their separation at the interposed plates by any affinity or secondary action at the electrodes (744.), arising either from the nature of the plate itself or the surrounding fluid.

1011. When only one voltaic pair of zinc and platina plates was used, the current of electricity was entirely stopped to all practical purposes by interposing one platina plate, fig. 92, *i. e.* by requiring of the current that it should decompose water, and evolve both its elements, before it should pass. This consequence is in perfect accordance with the views before given (910. 917. 973.). For as the whole result depends upon the opposition of forces at the places of electric excitement and electro-decomposition, and as water is the substance to be decomposed at both before the current can move, it is not to be expected that the zinc should have such powerful attraction for the oxygen, as not only to be able to take it from its associated hydrogen, but leave such a surplus of force as, passing to the second place of decomposition, should be there able to effect a second separation of the elements of water. Such an effect would require that the force of attraction between zinc and oxygen should under the circumstances be *at least* twice as great as the force of attraction between the oxygen and hydrogen.

1012. When two pairs of zinc and platina exciting plates were used, the current was also practically stopped by one interposed platina plate, fig. 93. There was a very feeble effect of a current at first, but it ceased almost immediately. It will be referred to, with many other similar effects, hereafter (1017.).

1013. Three pairs of zinc and platina plates, fig. 94, were able to produce a current which could pass an interposed platina plate, and effect the electrolyzation of water in cell iv. The current was evident, both by the continued deflexion of the galvanometer, and the production of bubbles of oxygen and hydrogen at the electrodes in cell iv. Hence the accumulated surplus force of three plates of zinc, which are active in decomposing water, is more than equal, when added together, to the force with which oxygen and hydrogen are combined in water, and is sufficient to cause the separation of these elements from each other.

1014. The three pairs of zinc and platina plates were now opposed by two intervening platina plates, fig. 95. In this case the current was stopped.

1015. Four pairs of zinc and platina plates were also neutralized by two interposed platina plates, fig. 96.

1016. Five pairs of zinc and platina, with two interposed platina plates, fig. 97, gave a feeble current; there was permanent deflexion at the galvanometer, and decomposition in the cells vi and vii. But the current was very feeble; very much less than when all the intermediate plates were removed and the two extreme ones only retained : for when they were placed six inches asunder in one cell, they gave a powerful current. Hence five exciting pairs, with two interposed obstructing plates, do not give a current at all comparable to that of a single unobstructed pair.

1017. I have already said that a *very feeble current* passed when the series included one interposed platina and two pairs of zinc and platina plates (1012.). A similarly feeble current passed in every case, and even when only one exciting pair and four intervening platina plates were used, fig. 98, a current passed which could be detected at $x$, both by chemical action on the solution of iodide of potassium, and by the galvanometer. This current I believe to be due to electricity reduced in intensity below the point requisite for the decomposition of water (970. 984.); for water can conduct electricity of such low intensity by the same kind of power which it possesses in common with metals and charcoal, though it cannot conduct electricity of higher intensity without suffering decomposition, and then opposing a new force consequent thereon. With an electric current of, or under this intensity, it is probable that increasing the number of interposed platina plates would not involve an increased difficulty of conduction.

1018. In order to obtain an idea of the additional interfering power of each added platina plate, six voltaic pairs and four intervening platinas were arranged as in fig. 99 ; a very feeble current then passed (985. 1017.). When one of the platinas was removed so that three intervened, a current somewhat stronger passed. With two intervening platinas a still stronger current passed ; and with only one intervening platina a very fair current was obtained. But the effect of the successive plates, taken in the order of their interposition, was very different, as might be expected ; for the first retarded the current more powerfully than the second, and the second more than the third.

1019. In these experiments both amalgamated and unamalgamated zinc were used, but the results generally were the same.

1020. The effects of retardation just described were altered altogether when changes were made in the *nature of the liquid* used between the plates, either in what may be called the *exciting* or the *retarding* cells. Thus, retaining the exciting force the same, by still using pure dilute sulphuric acid for that purpose, if a little nitric acid were added to the liquid in the *retarding* cells, then the transmission of the current was very much facilitated. For instance, in the experiment with one pair of exciting plates and one intervening plate (1011.) fig. 92, when a few drops of nitric acid were added to the contents of cell ii, then the current of electricity passed with considerable strength (though it soon fell from other causes (1036. 1040.),) and the same increased effect was produced by the nitric acid when many interposed plates were used.

1021. This seems to be a consequence of the diminution of the difficulty of decomposing water when its hydrogen, instead of being absolutely expelled, as in the former cases, is transferred to the oxygen of the nitric acid, producing a secondary result at the *cathode* (752.) ; for in accordance with the chemical views of the electric current and its action already advanced (913.), the water, instead of opposing a resistance to decomposition equal to the full amount of the force of mutual at-

traction between its oxygen and hydrogen, has that force counteracted in part, and therefore diminished by the attraction of
the hydrogen at the *cathode* for the oxygen of the nitric acid
which surrounds it, and with which it ultimately combines instead of being evolved in its free state.

1022. When a little nitric acid was put into the exciting
cells, then again the circumstances favouring the transmission
of the current were strengthened, for the *intensity* of the current itself was increased by the addition (906.). When therefore a little nitric acid was added to both the *exciting* and the
*retarding* cells, the current of electricity passed with very considerable freedom.

1023. When dilute muriatic acid was used, it produced and
transmitted a current more easily than pure dilute sulphuric
acid, but not so readily as dilute nitric acid. As muriatic acid
appears to be decomposed more freely than water (765.), and as
the affinity of zinc for chlorine is very powerful, it might be
expected to produce a current more intense than that from the
use of dilute sulphuric acid; and also to transmit it more freely
by undergoing decomposition at a lower intensity (912.).

1024. In relation to the effect of these interpositions, it is
necessary to state that they do not appear to be at all dependent
upon the size of the electrodes, or their distance from each
other in the acid, except that when a current *can pass*, changes
in these facilitate or retard its passage. For on repeating the
experiment with one intervening and one pair of exciting plates
(1011.), fig. 92, and in place of the interposed plate P using
sometimes a mere wire, and sometimes very large plates (1008.),
and also changing the terminal exciting plates Z and P, so that
they were sometimes wires only and at others of great size,
still the results were the same as those already obtained.

1025. In illustration of the effect of distance, an experiment
like that described with two exciting pairs and one intervening
plate (1012), fig. 93, was arranged so that the distance between the plates in the third cell could be increased to six or
eight inches, or diminished to the thickness of a piece of intervening bibulous paper. Still the result was the same in both
cases, the effect not being sensibly greater, when the plates
were merely separated by the paper, than when a great way
apart; so that the principal opposition to the current in this

case does not depend upon the *quantity* of intervening electrolytic conductor, but on the *relation of its elements to the intensity of the current,* or to the chemical nature of the electrodes and the surrounding fluids.

1026. When the acid was sulphuric acid, *increasing its strength* in any of the cells, caused no change in the effects; it did not produce a more intense current in the exciting cells (908.), or cause the current produced to traverse the decomposing cells more freely. But if to very weak sulphuric acid a few drops of nitric acid were added, then either one or other of those effects could be produced; and, as might be expected in a case like this, where the exciting or conducting action bore a *direct* reference to the acid itself, increasing the strength of this (the nitric acid), also increased its powers.

1027. The *nature of the interposed plate* was now varied to show its relation to the phenomena either of excitation or retardation, and amalgamated zinc was first substituted for platina. On employing one voltaic pair and one interposed zinc plate, fig. 100, there was as powerful a current, apparently, as if the interposed zinc plate was away. Hydrogen was evolved against P in cell ii, and against the side of the second zinc in cell i; but no gas appeared against the side of the zinc in cell ii, nor against the zinc in cell i.

1028. On interposing two amalgamated zinc plates, fig. 101, instead of one, there was still a powerful current, but interference had taken place. On using three intermediate zinc plates, fig. 102, there was still further retardation, though a good current of electricity passed.

1029. Considering the retardation as due to the inaction of the amalgamated zinc upon the dilute acid, in consequence of the slight though general effect of diminished chemical power produced by the mercury on the surface, and viewing this inaction as the circumstance which rendered it necessary that each plate should have its tendency to decompose water assisted slightly by the electric current, it was expected that plates of the metal in the unamalgamated state would probably not require such assistance, and would offer no sensible impediment to the passing of the current. This expectation was fully realized in the use of two and three interposed unamalgamated plates. The electric current passed through them as freely as if there had been no such plates in the way. They offered no obstacle, because they could decompose water without the current; and the latter had only to give direction to a part of the forces, which would have been active whether it had passed or not.

1030. Interposed plates of copper were then employed. These seemed at first to occasion no obstruction, but after a few minutes the current almost entirely ceased. This effect appears due to the surfaces taking up that peculiar condition (1040.) by which they tend to produce a reverse current; for when one or more of the plates were turned round, which could easily be effected with the couronne des tasses form of experiment, fig. 90, then the current was powerfully renewed for a few moments, and then again ceased. Plates of platina and copper, arranged as a voltaic pile with dilute sulphuric acid, could not form a voltaic trough competent to act for more than a few minutes, because of this peculiar counteracting effect.

1031. All these effects of retardation, exhibited by decomposition against surfaces for which the evolved elements have more or less affinity, or are altogether deficient in attraction, show generally, though beautifully, the chemical relations and source of the current, and also the balanced state of the affinities at the places of excitation and decomposition. In this way they add to the mass of evidence in favour of the identity of the two; for they demonstrate, as it were, the antagonism of the *chemical powers* at the electromotive part with the *chemical powers* at the interposed parts; they show that the first are *producing* electric effects, and the second *opposing* them; they bring the two into direct relation; they prove that either can determine the other, thus making what appears to be cause and effect convertible, and thereby demonstrating that both chemical and electrical action are merely two exhibitions of one single agent or power (916. &c.).

1032. It is quite evident, that as water and other electrolytes can conduct electricity without suffering decomposition (986.), when the electricity is of sufficiently low intensity, it may not be asserted as absolutely true in all cases, that whenever electricity passes through an electrolyte, it produces a definite effect of decomposition. But the quantity of electricity which can pass in a given time through an electrolyte without causing decomposition, is so small as to bear no comparison to that required in a case of very moderate decomposition, and with electricity above the intensity required for electrolyzation, I have found no sensible departure as yet from the law of *definite electrolytic action* developed in the preceding series of these Researches (783. &c.).

1033. I cannot dismiss this division of the present Paper without making a reference to the important experiments of M. Aug. De la Rive on the effects of interposed plates\*. As I have had occasion to consider such plates merely as giving rise to new decompositions, and in that way only causing obstruction to the passage of the electric current, I was freed from the necessity of considering the peculiar effects described by that philosopher. I was the more willing to avoid for the present touching upon these, as I must at the same time have entered into the views of Sir Humphry Davy upon the same subject†, and also those of Marianini‡ and Ritter§, which are connected with it.

¶ v. *General Remarks on the active Voltaic Battery.*

1034. When the ordinary voltaic battery is brought into action, its very activity produces certain effects, which re-act upon it, and cause serious deterioration of its power. These render it an exceedingly inconstant instrument as to the *quantity* of effect which it is capable of producing. They are already, in part, known and understood ; but as their importance, and that of certain other coincident results, will be more evident by reference to the principles and experiments already stated and described, I have thought it would be useful, in this investigation of the voltaic pile, to notice them briefly here.

1035. When the battery is in action, it causes such substances to be formed and arranged in contact with the plates as very much weaken its power, or even tend to produce a counter current. They are considered by Sir Humphry Davy as sufficient to account for the phenomena of Ritter's secondary

---

\* Annales de Chimie, tom. xxviii. p. 190 ; and Mémoires de Génève.
† Philosophical Transactions, 1826, p. 413.
‡ Annales de Chimie, tom. xxxiii. pp. 117, 119, &c.
§ Journal de Physique, tom. lvii. pp. 349, 350.

piles, and also for the effects observed by M. A. De la Rive with interposed platina plates*.

1036. I have already referred to this consequence (1003.), as capable, in some cases, of lowering the force of the current to one eighth or one tenth of what it was at the first moment, and have met with instances in which its interference was very great.    In an experiment in which one voltaic pair and one interposed platina plate were used with dilute sulphuric acid in the cells fig. 103., the wires of communication were so arranged, that the end of that marked 3 could be placed at pleasure upon paper moistened in the solution of iodide of potassium at $x$, or directly upon the platina plate there.    If, after an interval during which the circuit had not been complete, the wire 3 were placed upon the paper, there was evidence of a current, decomposition ensued, and the galvanometer was affected.    If the wire 3 were made to touch the metal of $p$, a comparatively strong sudden current was produced, affecting the galvanometer, but lasting only for a moment; the effect at the galvanometer ceased, and if the wire 3 were placed on the paper at $x$, no signs of decomposition occurred.    On raising the wire 3, and breaking the circuit altogether for a while, the apparatus resumed its first power, requiring, however, from five to ten minutes for this purpose; and then, as before, on making contact between 3 and $p$, there was again a momentary current, and immediately all the effects apparently ceased.

1037. This effect I was ultimately able to refer to the state of the film of fluid in contact with the zinc plate in cell i. The acid of that film is instantly neutralized by the oxide formed; the oxidation of the zinc cannot, of course, go on with the same facility as before; and the chemical action being thus interrupted, the voltaic action diminishes with it.    The time of the rest was required for the diffusion of the liquid, and its replacement by other acid.    From the serious influence of this cause in experiments with single pairs of plates of different metals, in which I was at one time engaged, and the extreme care required to avoid it, I cannot help feeling a strong suspicion that it interferes more frequently and extensively than

* Philosophical Transactions, 1826, p. 413.

experimenters are aware of, and therefore direct their attention to it.

1038. In considering the effect in  delicate experiments of this source of irregularity of action in the voltaic apparatus, it must be remembered that it is only that very small portion of matter which is directly in contact with the oxidizable metal which has to be considered with reference to the change of its nature; and this portion is not very readily displaced from its position upon the surface of the metal (582. 605.), especially if that metal be rough and irregular. In illustration of this effect, I will quote a remarkable experiment.  A burnished platina plate (569.) was put into hot strong sulphuric acid for an instant only : it was then put into distilled water, moved about in it, taken out, and wiped dry : it was put into a second portion of distilled water, moved about in it, and again wiped : it was put into a third portion of distilled water, in which it was moved about for nearly eight seconds ; it was then, without wiping, put into a fourth portion of distilled water, where it was allowed to remain five minutes.   The two latter portions of water were then tested for sulphuric acid ; the third gave no sensible appearance of that substance, but the fourth gave indications which were not merely evident, but abundant for the circumstances under which it had been introduced.   The result sufficiently shows with what difficulty that portion of the substance which is in *contact* with the metal leaves it ; and as the contact of the fluid formed against the plate in the voltaic circuit must be as intimate and as perfect as possible, it is easy to see how quickly and greatly it must vary from the general fluid in the cells, and how influential in diminishing the force of the battery this effect must be.

1039. In the ordinary voltaic pile, the influence of this effect will occur in all variety of degrees.   The extremities of a trough of twenty pairs of plates of Wollaston's construction were connected with the volta-electrometer, fig. 66. (711.), of the Seventh Series of these Researches, and after five minutes the number of bubbles of gas issuing from the extremity of the tube, in consequence of the decomposition of the water, noted.   Without moving the plates, the acid between the copper and zinc was agitated by the introduction of  a feather.   The bubbles were immediately evolved more rapidly, above twice the num-

ber being produced in the same portion of time as before.    In
this instance it is very evident that agitation by a feather must
have been a very imperfect mode of restoring the acid in the
cells against the plates towards its first equal condition ; and
yet imperfect as the means were, they more than doubled the
power of the battery.    The *first effect* of a battery which is
known to be so superior to the degree of action which the battery can sustain, is almost entirely due to the favourable condition of the acid in contact with the plates.

1040. A *second* cause of diminution in the force of the voltaic battery, consequent upon its own action, is that extraordinary state of the surfaces of the metals (969.) which was first
described, I believe, by Ritter*, to which he refers the powers
of his secondary piles, and which has been so well experimented upon by Marianini, and also by A. De la Rive.   If the apparatus, fig. 103. (1036.), be left in action for an hour or two,
with the wire 3 in contact with the plate *p*, so as to allow a free
passage for the current, then, though the contact be broken for
ten or twelve minutes, still, upon its renewal, only a feeble current will pass, not at all equal in force to what might be expected.   Further, if $P^1$ and $P^2$ be connected by a metal wire,
a powerful momentary current will pass from $P^2$ to $P^1$ through
the acid, and therefore in the reverse direction to that produced
by the action of the zinc in the arrangement ; and after this has
happened, the general current can pass through the whole of
the system as at first, but by its passage again restores the
plates $P^2$ and $P^1$ into the former opposing condition.    This,
generally, is the fact described by Ritter, Marianini, and De la
Rive.   It has great opposing influence on the action of a pile,
especially if the latter consist of but a small number of alternations, and has to pass its current through many interpositions.
It varies with the solution in which the interposed plates are
immersed, with the intensity of the current, the strength of the
pile, the time of action, and especially with accidental discharges of the plates by inadvertent contacts or reversions of
the plates during experiments, and must be carefully watched
in every endeavour to trace the source, strength, and variations
of the voltaic current.   Its effect was avoided in the experiments already described (1036. &c.), by making contact be-

* Journal de Physique, lvii. p. 349.

tween the plates $P^1$ and $P^2$ before the effect dependent upon
the state of the solution in contact with the zinc plate was observed, and by other precautions.

1041. When an apparatus like fig. 98. (1017.) with several
platina plates was used, being connected with a battery able to
force a current through them, the power which they acquired,
of producing a reverse current, was very considerable.

1042. *Weak and exhausted charges* should never be used at
the same time with *strong and fresh ones* in the different cells
of a trough, or the different troughs of a battery : the fluid in
all the cells should be alike, else the plates in the weaker cells,
in place of assisting, retard the passage of the electricity generated in, and transmitted across, the stronger cells.   Each zinc
plate so circumstanced has to be assisted in decomposing power
before the whole current can pass between it and the liquid.
So, that, if in a battery of fifty pairs of plates, ten of the cells
contain a weaker charge than the others, it is as if ten decomposing plates were opposed to the transit of the current of forty
pairs of generating plates (1031.).   Hence a serious loss of
force, and hence the reason why, if the ten pairs of plates were
removed, the remaining forty pairs would be much more powerful than the whole fifty.

1043. Five similar troughs, of ten pairs of plates each, were
prepared, four of them with a good uniform charge of acid, and
the fifth with the partially neutralized acid of a used battery.
Being arranged in right order, and connected with a volta-electrometer (711.), the whole fifty pairs of plates yielded $1\cdot1$ cubic
inch of oxygen and hydrogen in one minute : but on moving one
of the connecting wires so that only the four well-charged
troughs should be included in the circuit, they produced with the
same volta-electrometer $8\cdot4$ cubical inches of gas in the same
time.   Nearly seven-eighths of the power of the four troughs
had been lost, therefore, by their association with the fifth
trough.

1044. The same battery of fifty pairs of plates, after being
thus used, was connected with the volta-electrometer (711.), so
that by quickly shifting the wires of communication, the current of the whole of the battery, or of any portion of it, could
be made to pass through the instrument for given portions of
time in succession.   The whole of the battery evolved $0\cdot9$ of a

cubic inch of oxygen and hydrogen in half a minute ; the forty plates evolved 4·6 cubic inches in the same time; the whole then evolved 1 cubic inch in the half minute ; the ten weakly charged evolved 0·4 of a cubic inch in the time given : and finally the whole evolved 1·15 cubic inch in the standard time. The order of the observations was that given ; the results sufficiently show the extremely injurious effect produced by the mixture of strong and weak charges in the same battery*.

1045. In the same manner associations of *strong and weak* pairs of plates should be carefully avoided. A pair of copper and platina plates arranged in *accordance* with a pair of zinc and platina plates in dilute sulphuric acid, were found to stop the action of the latter, or even of two pairs of the latter, as effectually almost as an interposed plate of platina (1011.), or as if the copper itself had been platina. It, in fact, became an interposed decomposing plate, and therefore a retarding instead of an assisting pair.

1046. The *reversal,* by accident or otherwise, of the plates in a battery has an exceedingly injurious effect. It is not merely the counteraction of the current which the reversed plates can produce, but their effect also in retarding even as indifferent plates, and requiring decomposition to be effected upon their surface, in *accordance* with the course of the current, before the latter can pass. They oppose the current, therefore, in the first place, as interposed platina plates would do (1011—1018.) ; and to this they add a force of opposition as counter-voltaic plates. I find that, in a series of four pairs of zinc and platina plates in dilute sulphuric acid, if one pair be reversed, it very nearly neutralizes the power of the whole.

1047. There are many other causes of reaction, retardation, and irregularity in the voltaic battery. Amongst them is the not unusual one of precipitation of copper upon the zinc in the cells, the injurious effect of which has before been adverted to (1006.). But their interest is not perhaps sufficient to justify any increase of the length of this paper, which is rather in-

---

* The gradual increase in the action of the whole fifty pairs of plates was due to the elevation of temperature in the weakly charged trough by the passage of the current, in consequence of which the exciting energies of the fluid within were increased.

tended to be an investigation of the theory of the voltaic pile than a particular account of its practical application *.

*Note.*—Many of the views and experiments in this Series of my Experimental Researches will be seen at once to be corrections and extensions of the theory of electro-chemical decomposition, given in the Fifth and Seventh Series of these Researches. The expressions I would now alter are those which concern the independence of the evolved elements in relation to the poles or electrodes, and the reference of their evolution to powers entirely internal (524. 537. 661.). The present paper fully shows my present views; and I would refer to paragraphs 891. 904. 910. 917. 918. 947. 963. 1007. 1031. &c., as stating what they are. I hope this note will be considered as sufficient in the way of correction at present; for I would rather defer revising the whole theory of electro-chemical decomposition until I can obtain clearer views of the way in which the power under consideration can appear at one time as associated with particles giving them their chemical attraction, and at another as free electricity (493. 957.).—M. F.

*Royal Institution,*
    *March 31st,* 1834.

* For further practical results relating to these points of the philosophy of the voltaic battery, see Series X. § 17. 1136.—1160.—*Dec.* 1838.

# NINTH SERIES.

§ 15. *On the influence by induction of an Electric Current on itself:—and on the inductive action of Electric Currents generally.*

Received December 18, 1834,—Read January 29, 1835.

1048. The following investigations relate to a very remarkable inductive action of electric currents, or of the different parts of the same current (74.), and indicate an immediate connexion between such inductive action and the direct transmission of electricity through conducting bodies, or even that exhibited in the form of a spark.

1049. The inquiry arose out of a fact communicated to me by Mr. Jenkin, which is as follows. If an ordinary wire of short length be used as the medium of communication between the two plates of an electromotor consisting of a single pair of metals, no management will enable the experimenter to obtain an electric shock from this wire; but if the wire which surrounds an electro-magnet be used, a shock is felt each time the contact with the electromotor is broken, provided the ends of the wire be grasped one in each hand.

1050. Another effect is observed at the same time, which has long been known to philosophers, namely, that a bright electric spark occurs at the place of disjunction.

1051. A brief account of these results, with some of a corresponding character which I had observed in using long wires, was published in the Philosophical Magazine for 1834*; and I added to them some observations on their nature. Further investigations led me to perceive the inaccuracy of my first notions and ended in identifying these effects with the phenomena of induction which I had been fortunate enough to develop in the First Series of these Experimental Researches (1.—59.)†. Notwithstanding this identity, the extension and the peculiarity of the views respecting electric currents which

---

* Vol. v. pp. 349, 444.  † Philosophical Transactions, 1832, p. 126.

the results supply, lead me to believe that they will be found worthy of the attention of the Royal Society.

1052. The *electromotor* used consisted of a cylinder of zinc introduced between the two parts of a double cylinder of copper, and preserved from metallic contact in the usual way by corks. The zinc cylinder was eight inches high and four inches in diameter. Both it and the copper cylinder were supplied with stiff wires, surmounted by cups containing mercury ; and it was at these cups that the contacts of wires, helices, or electro-magnets, used to complete the circuit, were made or broken. These cups I will call G and E throughout the rest of this paper (1079.).

1053. Certain *helices* were constructed, some of which it will be necessary to describe. A pasteboard tube had four copper wires, one twenty-fourth of an inch in thickness, wound round it, each forming a helix in the same direction from end to end : the convolutions of each wire were separated by string, and the superposed helices prevented from touching by intervening calico. The lengths of the wires forming the helices were 48, 49·5, 48, and 45 feet. The first and third wires were united together so as to form one consistent helix of 96 feet in length ; and the second and fourth wires were similarly united to form a second helix, closely interwoven with the first, and 94·5 feet in length. These helices may be distinguished by the numbers i and ii. They were carefully examined by a powerful current of electricity and a galvanometer, and found to have no communication with each other.

1054. Another helix was constructed upon a similar pasteboard tube, two lengths of the same copper wire being used, each forty-six feet long. These were united into one consistent helix of ninety-two feet, which therefore was nearly equal in value to either of the former helices, but was not in close inductive association with them. It may be distinguished by the number iii.

1055. A fourth helix was constructed of very thick copper wire, being one fifth of an inch in diameter ; the length of wire used was seventy-nine feet, independent of the straight terminal portions.

1056. The principal *electro-magnet* employed consisted of a cylindrical bar of soft iron twenty-five inches long, and one inch and three quarters in diameter, bent into a ring, so that the ends nearly touched, and surrounded by three coils of thick copper wire, the similar ends of which were fastened together; each of these terminations was soldered to a copper rod, serving as a conducting continuation of the wire. Hence any electric current sent through the rods was divided in the helices surrounding the ring, into three parts, all of which, however, moved in the same direction. The three wires may therefore be considered as representing one wire, of thrice the thickness of the wire really used.

1057. Other electro-magnets could be made at pleasure by introducing a soft iron rod into any of the helices described (1053, &c.).

1058. The *galvanometer* which I had occasion to use was rough in its construction, having but one magnetic needle, and not at all delicate in its indications.

1059. The effects to be considered *depend on the conductor* employed to complete the communication between the zinc and copper plates of the electromotor; and I shall have to consider this conductor under four different forms: as the helix of an electro-magnet (1056.); as an ordinary helix (1053. &c.); as a *long* extended wire, having its course such that the parts can exert little or no mutual influence; and as a *short* wire. In all cases the conductor was of copper.

1060. The peculiar effects are best shown by the *electro-magnet* (1056.). When it was used to complete the communication at the electromotor, there was no sensible spark on *making* contact, but on *breaking* contact there was a very large and bright spark, with considerable combustion of the mercury. Then, again, with respect to the shock: if the hands were moistened in salt and water, and good contact between them and the wires retained, no shock could be felt upon *making* contact at the electromotor, but a powerful one on *breaking* contact.

1061. When the *helix* i or iii (1053. &c.) was used as the connecting conductor, there was also a good spark on breaking contact, but none (sensibly) on making contact. On trying to obtain the shock from these helices, I could not succeed at first. By joining the similar ends of i and ii so as to make the two helices equivalent to one helix, having wire of double thickness,

I could just obtain the sensation. Using the helix of thick wire (1055.) the shock was distinctly obtained. On placing the tongue between two plates of silver connected by wires with the parts which the hands had heretofore touched (1064.), there was a powerful shock on *breaking* contact, but none on *making* contact.

1062. The power of producing these phenomena exists therefore in the simple helix, as in the electro-magnet, although by no means in the same high degree.

1063. On putting a bar of soft iron into the helix, it became an electro-magnet (1057.), and its power was instantly and greatly raised. On putting a bar of copper into the helix, no change was produced, the action being that of the helix alone. The two helices i and ii, made into one helix of twofold length of wire, produced a greater effect than either i or ii alone.

1064. On descending from the helix to the mere *long wire*, the following effects were obtained. A copper wire, 0·18 of an inch in diameter, and 132 feet in length, was laid out upon the floor of the laboratory, and used as the connecting conductor (1059.) ; it gave no sensible spark on making contact, but produced a bright one on breaking contact, yet not so bright as that from the helix (1061.). On endeavouring to obtain the electric shock at the moment contact was broken, I could not succeed so as to make it pass through the hands ; but by using two silver plates fastened by small wires to the extremity of the principal wire used, and introducing the tongue between those plates, I succeeded in obtaining powerful shocks upon the tongue and gums, and could easily convulse a flounder, an eel, or a frog. None of these effects could be obtained directly from the electromotor, *i. e.* when the tongue, frog, or fish was in a similar, and therefore comparative manner, interposed in the course of the communication between the zinc and copper plates, separated everywhere else by the acid used to excite the combination, or by air. The bright spark and the shock, produced only on breaking contact, are therefore effects of the same kind as those produced in a higher degree by the helix, and in a still higher degree by the electro-magnet.

1065. In order to compare an extended wire with a helix, the helix i, containing ninety-six feet, and ninety-six feet of the same-sized wire lying on the floor of the laboratory, were used alternately as conductors: the former gave a much brighter spark at the moment of disjunction than the latter. Again, twenty-eight feet of copper wire were made up into a helix, and being used gave a good spark on disjunction at the electro-motor; being then suddenly pulled out and again employed, it gave a much smaller spark than before, although nothing but its spiral arrangement had been changed.

1066. As the superiority of a helix over a wire is important to the philosophy of the effect, I took particular pains to ascertain the fact with certainty. A wire of copper sixty-seven feet long was bent in the middle so as to form a double termination which could be communicated with the electromotor; one of the halves of this wire was made into a helix and the other remained in its extended condition. When these were used alternately as the connecting wire, the helix half gave by much the strongest spark. It even gave a stronger spark than when it and the extended wire were used conjointly as a double conductor.

1067. When a *short wire* is used, *all* these effects disappear. If it be only two or three inches long, a spark can scarcely be perceived on breaking the junction. If it be ten or twelve inches long and moderately thick, a small spark may be more easily obtained. As the length is increased, the spark becomes proportionately brighter, until from extreme length the resistance offered by the metal as a conductor begins to interfere with the principal result.

1068. The effect of elongation was well shown thus: 114 feet of copper wire, one eighteenth of an inch in diameter, were extended on the floor and used as a conductor; it remained cold, but gave a bright spark on breaking contact. Being crossed so that the two terminations were in contact near the extremities, it was again used as a conductor, only twelve inches now being included in the circuit: the wire became very hot from the greater quantity of electricity passing through it, and yet the spark on breaking contact was scarcely visible. The experiment was repeated with a wire one ninth of an inch in diameter and thirty-six feet long with the same results.

1069. That the effects, and also the action, in all these forms of the experiment are identical, is evident from the manner in which the former can be gradually raised from that produced by the shortest wire to that of the most powerful electro-magnet : and this capability of examining what will happen by the most powerful apparatus, and then experimenting for the same results, or reasoning from them, with the weaker arrangements, is of great advantage in making out the true principles of the phenomena.

1070. The action is evidently dependent upon the wire which serves as a conductor ; for it varies as that wire varies in its length or arrangement. The shortest wire may be considered as exhibiting the full effect of spark or shock which the electromotor can produce by its own direct power ; all the additional force which the arrangements described can excite being due to some affection of the current, either permanent or momentary, in the wire itself. That it is a *momentary* effect, produced only at the instant of breaking contact, will be fully proved (1089. 1100.).

1071. No change takes place in the quantity or intensity of the current during the time the latter is *continued,* from the moment after contact is made, up to that previous to disunion, except what depends upon the increased obstruction offered to the passage of the electricity by a long wire as compared to a short wire. To ascertain this point with regard to *quantity,* the helix i (1053.) and the galvanometer (1058.) were both made parts of the metallic circuit used to connect the plates of a small electromotor, and the deflection at the galvanometer was observed ; then a soft iron core was put into the helix, and as soon as the momentary effect was over, and the needle had become stationary, it was again observed, and found to stand exactly at the same division as before. Thus the quantity passing through the wire when the current was continued was the same either with or without the soft iron, although the peculiar effects occurring at the moment of disjunction were very different in degree under such variation of circumstances.

1072. That the quality of *intensity* belonging to the constant current did not vary with the circumstances favouring the peculiar results under consideration, so as to yield an explanation of those results, was ascertained in the following manner. The current excited by an electromotor was passed through short wires, and its intensity tried by subjecting different substances to its electrolyzing power (912. 966. &c.) ; it was then passed through the wires of the powerful electro-magnet (1056.), and again examined with respect to its intensity by the same means and found unchanged. Again, the constancy of the *quantity* passed in the above experiment (1071.) adds further proof that the intensity could not have varied; for had it been increased upon the introduction of the soft iron, there is every reason to believe that the quantity passed in a given time would also have increased.

1073. The fact is, that under many variations of the experiments, the permanent current *loses* in force as the effects upon breaking contact become *exalted*. This is abundantly evident in the comparative experiments with long and short wires (1068.); and is still more strikingly shown by the following variation. Solder an inch or two in length of fine platina wire (about one hundredth of an inch in diameter) on to one end of the long communicating wire, and also a similar length of the same platina wire on to one end of the short communication; then, in comparing the effects of these two communications, make and break contact between the platina terminations and the mercury of the cup G or E (1079.). When the short wire is used, the platina will be *ignited by the constant current*, because of the quantity of electricity, but the spark on breaking contact will be hardly visible; on using the longer communicating wire, which by obstructing will diminish the current, the platina will remain cold whilst the current passes, but give a bright spark at the moment it ceases: thus the strange result is obtained of a diminished spark and shock from the strong current, and increased effects from the weak one. Hence the spark and shock at the moment of disjunction, although resulting from great intensity and quantity of the current *at that moment*, are no direct indicators or measurers of the intensity or quantity of the constant current previously passing, and by which they are ultimately produced.

———————

1074. It is highly important in using the spark as an indication, by its relative brightness, of these effects, to bear in mind certain circumstances connected with its production and appearance (958.). An ordinary electric spark is understood to be the bright appearance of electricity passing suddenly through an interval of air, or other badly conducting matter.

A voltaic spark is sometimes of the same nature, but generally, is due to the ignition and even combustion of a minute portion of a good conductor; and that is especially the case when the electromotor consists of but one or few pairs of plates. This can be very well observed if either or both of the metallic surfaces intended to touch be solid and pointed. The moment they come in contact the current passes; it heats, ignites, and even burns the touching points, and the appearance is as if the spark passed on making contact, whereas it is only a case of ignition by the current, contact being previously made, and is perfectly analogous to the ignition of a fine platina wire connecting the extremities of a voltaic battery.

1075. When mercury constitutes one or both of the surfaces used, the brightness of the spark is greatly increased. But as this effect is due to the action on, and probable combustion of, the metal, such sparks must only be compared with other sparks also taken from mercurial surfaces, and not with such as may be taken, for instance, between surfaces of platina or gold, for then the appearances are far less bright, though the same quantity of electricity be passed. It is not at all unlikely that the commonly occurring circumstance of combustion may affect even the duration of the light; and that sparks taken between mercury, copper, or other combustible bodies, will continue for a period sensibly longer than those passing between platina or gold.

1076. When the end of a short clean copper wire, attached to one plate of an electromotor, is brought down carefully upon a surface of mercury connected with the other plate, a spark, almost continuous, can be obtained. This I refer to a succession of effects of the following nature: first, contact,—then ignition of the touching points,—recession of the mercury from the mechanical results of the heat produced at the place of contact, and the electro-magnetic condition of the parts at the moment*,—breaking of the contact and the production of the peculiar intense effect dependent thereon,—renewal of the contact by the returning surface of the undulating mercury,—and then a repetition of the same series of effects, and that with such rapidity as to present the appearance of a continued dis-

---

* Quarterly Journal of Science, vol. xii. p. 420.

charge.   If a long wire or an electro-magnet be used as the
connecting conductor instead of a short wire, a similar appearance may be produced by tapping the vessel containing the
mercury and making it vibrate ; but the sparks do not usually
follow each other so rapidly as to produce an apparently continuous spark, because of the time required, when the long wire
or electro-magnet is used, both for the full development of the
current (1101. 1106.) and for its complete cessation.

1077. Returning to the phenomena in question, the first
thought that arises in the mind is, that the electricity circulates
with something like *momentum or inertia* in the wire, and that
thus a long wire produces effects at the instant the current is
stopped, which a short wire cannot produce.   Such an explanation is, however, at once set aside by the fact, that the same
length of wire produces the effects in very different degrees,
according as it is simply extended, or made into a helix, or
forms the circuit of an electro-magnet (1069.).   The experiments to be adduced (1089.) will still more strikingly show that
the idea of momentum cannot apply.

1078. The bright spark at the electromotor, and the shock
in the arms, appeared evidently to be due to *one* current in the
long wire, divided into two parts by the double channel afforded
through the body and through the electromotor ; for that the
spark was evolved at the place of disjunction with the electromotor, not by any direct action of the latter, but by a force immediately exerted in the wire of communication, seemed to be
without doubt (1070.).   It followed, therefore, that by using a
better conductor in place of the human body, the *whole* of this
extra current might be made to pass at that place ; and thus
be separated from that which the electromotor could produce
by its immediate action, and its *direction* be examined apart
from any interference of the original and originating current.
This was found to be true ; for on connecting the ends of the
principal wire together by a cross wire two or three feet in
length, applied just where the hands had felt the shock, the
whole of the extra current passed by the new channel, and then
no better spark than one producible by a short wire was obtained
on disjunction at the electromotor.

1079. The *current* thus separated was examined by galva-

nometers and decomposing apparatus introduced into the
course of this wire. I will always speak of it as the current
in the cross wire or wires, so that no mistake, as to its place or
origin, may occur. In the wood-cut, Z
and C represent the zinc and copper
plates of the electromotor; G and E the
cups of mercury where contact is made
or broken (1052.); A and B the terminations of D, the long wire, the helix, or
the electro-magnet, used to complete the
circuit; N and P are the cross wires,
which can either be brought into contact
at $x$, or else have a galvanometer (1058.)
or an electrolyzing apparatus (312. 316.) interposed there.

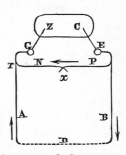

The production of the *shock* from the current in the cross
wire, whether D was a long extended wire, or a helix, or an
electro-magnet, has been already described (1064. 1061. 1060.).

1080. The *spark* of the cross-wire current could be produced
at $x$ in the following manner: D was made an electro-magnet;
the metallic extremities at $x$ were held close together, or rubbed
lightly against each other, whilst contact was broken at G or E.
When the communication was perfect at $x$, little or no spark
appeared at G or E. When the condition of vicinity at $x$ was
favourable for the result required, a bright spark would pass
there at the moment of disjunction, *none* occurring at G and
E: this spark was the luminous passage of the extra current
through the cross-wires. When there was no contact or passage of current at $x$, then the spark appeared at G or E, the
extra current forcing its way through the electromotor itself.
The same results were obtained by the use of the helix or the
extended wire at D in place of the electro-magnet.

1081. On introducing a fine platina wire at $x$, and employing
the electro-magnet at D, no visible effects occurred as long as
contact was continued; but on breaking contact at G or E, the
fine wire was instantly ignited and fused. A longer or thicker
wire could be so adjusted at $x$ as to show ignition, without
fusion, every time the contact was broken at G or E.

1082. It is rather difficult to obtain this effect with helices
or wires, and for very simple reasons: with the helices i, ii, or
iii, there was such retardation of the electric current, from the

length of wire used, that a full inch of platina wire one fiftieth of an inch in diameter could be retained ignited at the cross-wires during the *continuance of contact*, by the portion of electricity passing through it. Hence it was impossible to distinguish the particular effects at the moments of making or breaking contact from this constant effect. On using the thick wire helix (1055.), the same results ensued.

1083. Proceeding upon the known fact that electric currents of great quantity but low intensity, though able to ignite thick wires, cannot produce that effect upon thin ones, I used a very fine platina wire at $x$, reducing its diameter until a spark appeared at G or E, when contact was broken there. A quarter of an inch of such wire might be introduced at $x$ without being ignited by the *continuance* of contact at G or E; but when contact was broken at either place, this wire became red hot; proving, by this method, the production of the induced current at that moment.

1084. *Chemical decomposition* was next effected by the cross-wire current, an electro-magnet being used at D, and a decomposing apparatus, with solution of iodide of potassium in paper (1079.), employed at $x$. The conducting power of the connecting system A B D was sufficient to carry all the primary current, and consequently no chemical action took place at $x$ during the *continuance* of contact at G and E; but when contact was broken, there was instantly decomposition at $x$. The iodine appeared against the wire N, and not against the wire P; thus demonstrating that the current through the cross-wires, when contact was broken, was in the *reverse direction* to that marked by the arrow, or that which the electromotor would have sent through it.

1085. In this experiment a bright spark occurs at the place of disjunction, indicating that only a small part of the extra current passed the apparatus at $x$, because of the small conducting power of the latter.

1086. I found it difficult to obtain the chemical effects with the simple helices and wires, in consequence of the diminished inductive power of these arrangements, and because of the passage of a strong constant current at $x$ whenever a very active electromotor was used (1082.).

1087. The most instructive set of results was obtained, however, when the *galvanometer* was introduced at *x*. Using an electro-magnet at D, and continuing contact, a current was then indicated by the deflection, proceeding from P to N, in the direction of the arrow ; the cross-wire serving to carry one part of the electricity excited by the electromotor, and that part of the arrangement marked A B D, the other and far greater part, as indicated by the arrows. The magnetic needle was then forced back, by pins applied upon opposite sides of its two extremities, to its natural position when uninfluenced by a current ; after which, contact being *broken* at G or E, it was deflected strongly in the opposite direction ; thus showing, in accordance with the chemical effects (1084.), that the extra current followed a course in the cross-wires *contrary* to that indicated by the arrow, *i. e.* contrary to the one produced by the direct action of the electromotor*.

1088. With the *helix* only (1061.), these effects could scarcely be observed, in consequence of the smaller inductive force of this arrangement, the opposed action from induction in the galvanometer wire itself, the mechanical condition and tension of the needle from the effect of blocking (1087.) whilst the current due to continuance of contact was passing round it ; and because of other causes. With the *extended wire* (1064.) all these circumstances had still greater influence, and therefore allowed less chance of success.

1089. These experiments, establishing as they did, by the quantity, intensity, and even direction, a distinction between the primary or generating current and the extra current, led me to conclude that the latter was identical with the induced current described (6. 26. 74.) in the First Series of these Researches ; and this opinion I was soon able to bring to proof, and at the same times obtained not the partial (1078.) but entire separation of one current from the other.

1090. The double helix (1053.) was arranged so that it should form the connecting wire between the plates of the electromotor, ii being out of the current, and its ends unconnected. In this condition i acted very well, and gave a good spark at the time

---

* It was ascertained experimentally, that if a strong current was passed through the galvanometer only, and the needle restrained in one direction as above in its natural position, when the current was stopped, no vibration of the needle in the opposite direction took place.

and place of disjunction. The opposite ends of ii were then connected together so as to form an endless wire, i remaining unchanged; but now *no spark*, or one scarcely sensible, could be obtained from the latter at the place of disjunction. Then, again, the ends of ii were held so nearly together that any current running round that helix should be rendered visible as a spark; and in this manner a spark was obtained from ii when the junction of i with the electromotor was broken, in place of appearing at the disjointed extremity of i itself.

1091. By introducing a galvanometer or a decomposing apparatus into the circuit formed by the helix ii, I could easily obtain the deflections and decomposition occasioned by the induced current due to the breaking contact at helix i, or even to that occasioned by making contact of that helix with the electromotor; the results in both cases indicating the contrary directions of the two induced currents thus produced (26.).

1092. All these effects, except those of decomposition, were reproduced by two extended long wires, not having the form of helices, but placed close to each other; and thus it was proved that the *extra current* could be removed from the wire carrying the original current to a neighbouring wire, and was at the same time identified, in direction and every other respect, with the currents producible by induction (1089.). The case, therefore, of the bright spark and shock on disjunction may now be stated thus : If a current be established in a wire, and another wire, forming a complete circuit, be placed parallel to the first, at the moment the current in the first is stopped it induces a current in the *same* direction in the second, the first exhibiting then but a feeble spark; but if the second wire be away, disjunction of the first wire induces a current in itself in the same direction, producing a strong spark. The strong spark in the single long wire or helix, at the moment of disjunction, is therefore the equivalent of the current which would be produced in a neighbouring wire if such second current were permitted.

1093. Viewing the phenomena as the results of the induction of electrical currents, many of the principles of action, in the former experiments, become far more evident and precise. Thus the different effects of short wires, long wires, helices, and electro-magnets (1069.) may be comprehended. If the inductive action of a wire a foot long upon a collateral wire also a foot in length, be observed, it will be found very small; but if the same current be sent through a wire fifty feet long, it will induce in a neighbouring wire of fifty feet a far more powerful current at the moment of making or breaking contact, each successive foot of wire adding to the sum of action ; and by parity of reasoning, a similar effect should take place when the conducting wire is also that in which the induced current is formed (74.) : hence the reason why a long wire gives a brighter spark on breaking contact than a short one (1068.), although it carries much less electricity.

1094. If the long wire be made into a helix, it will then be still more effective in producing sparks and shocks on breaking contact ; for by the mutual inductive action of the convolutions each aids its neighbour, and will be aided in turn, and the sum of effect will be very greatly increased.

1095. If an electro-magnet be employed, the effect will be still more highly exalted ; because the iron, magnetized by the power of the continuing current, will lose its magnetism at the moment the current ceases to pass, and in so doing will tend to produce an electric current in the wire around it (37. 38.), in conformity with that which the cessation of current in the helix itself also tends to produce.

1096. By applying the laws of the induction of electric currents formerly developed (6. &c.), various new conditions of the experiments could be devised, which by their results should serve as tests of the accuracy of the view just given.   Thus, if a long wire be doubled, so that the current in the two halves shall have opposite actions, it ought not to give a sensible spark at the moment of disjunction : and this proved to be the case, for a wire forty feet long, covered with silk, being doubled and tied closely together to within four inches of the extremities, when used in that state, gave scarcely a perceptible spark ; but being opened out and the parts separated, it gave a very good one. The two helices i and ii being joined at their similar ends, and then used at their other extremities to connect the plates of the electromotor, thus constituted one long helix, of which one half was opposed in direction to the other half : under these circumstances it gave scarcely a sensible spark, even when the soft iron core was within, although containing nearly two hundred feet of wire. When it was made into one consistent helix of the same length of wire it gave a very bright spark.

1097. Similar proofs can be drawn from the mutual inductive action of two separate currents (1110.) ; and it is important for the general principles that the consistent action of two such currents should be established. Thus, two currents going in the same direction should, if simultaneously stopped, aid each other by their relative influence; or if proceeding in contrary directions should oppose each other under similar circumstances. I endeavoured at first to obtain two currents from two different electromotors, and passing them through the helices i and ii, tried to effect the disjunctions mechanically at the same moment. But in this I could not succeed ; one was always separated before the other, and in that case produced little or no spark, its inductive power being employed in throwing a current round the remaining complete circuit (1090.) : the current which was stopped last always gave a bright spark. If it were ever to become needful to ascertain whether two junctions were accurately broken at the same moment, these sparks would afford a test for the purpose, having an infinitesimal degree of perfection.

1098. I was able to prove the points by other expedients. Two short thick wires were selected to serve as terminations, by which contact could be made or broken with the electromotor. The compound helix, consisting of i and ii (1053.), was adjusted so that the extremities of the two helices could be placed in communication with the two terminal wires, in such a manner that the current moving through the thick wires should be divided into two equal portions in the two helices, these portions travelling, according to the mode of connexion, either in the same direction or in contrary directions at pleasure. In this manner two streams could be obtained, both of which could be stopped simultaneously, because the disjunction could be broken at G or F by removing a single wire. When the helices were in contrary directions, there was scarcely a sensible spark at the place of disjunction; but when they were in accordance there was a very bright one.

1099. The helix i was now used constantly, being sometimes associated, as above, with helix ii in an according direction, and sometimes with helix iii, which was placed at a little di-

stance.   The association i and ii, which presented two currents
able to affect each other by induction, because of their vicinity,
gave a brighter spark than the association i and iii, where the
two streams could not exert their mutual influence ; but the
difference was not so great as I expected.

1100.  Thus all the phenomena tend to prove that the effects
are due to an inductive action, occurring at the moment when
the principal current is stopped.   I at one time thought they
were due to an action continued during the *whole time* of the
current, and expected that a steel magnet would have an influence according to its position in the helix, comparable to that
of a soft iron bar, in assisting the effect.   This, however, is
not the case ; for hard steel, or a magnet in the helix, is not
so effectual as soft iron ; nor does it make any difference how
the magnet is placed in the helix, and for very simple reasons,
namely, that the effect does not depend upon a permanent state
of the core, but a *change of state* ; and that the magnet or hard
steel cannot sink through such a difference of state as soft iron,
at the moment contact ceases, and therefore cannot produce an
equal effect in generating a current of electricity by induction
(34. 37.).

---

1101.  As an electric current acts by induction with equal
energy at the moment of its commencement as at the moment of
its cessation (10. 26.), but in a contrary direction, the reference
of the effects under examination to an inductive action, would
lead to the conclusion that corresponding effects of an opposite
nature must occur in a long wire, a helix, or an electro-magnet,
every time that *contact is made* with the electromotor.   These
effects will tend to establish a resistance for the first moment
in the long conductor, producing a result equivalent to the reverse of a shock or a spark.   Now it is very difficult to devise
means fit for the recognition of such negative results ; but as
it is probable that some positive effect is produced at the time,
if we knew what to expect, I think the few facts bearing upon
this subject with which I am acquainted are worth recording.

1102.  The electro-magnet was arranged with an electrolyzing apparatus at *x*, as before described (1084.), except that
the intensity of the chemical action at the electromotor was increased until the electric current was just able to produce the

feeblest signs of decomposition whilst contact was continued at
G and E (1079.) ; (the iodine of course appearing against the
end of the cross wire P ;) the wire N was also separated from
A at *r*, so that contact there could be made or broken at pleasure.    Under these circumstances the following set of actions
was repeated several times : contact was broken at *r*, then
broken at G, next made at *r*, and lastly renewed at G ; thus
any current from N to P due to *breaking* of contact was avoided, but any additional force to the current from P to N due to
*making* contact could be observed.    In this way it was found,
that a much greater decomposing effect (causing the evolution
of iodine against P) could be obtained by a few completions of
contact than by the current which could pass in a much longer
time if the contact was *continued*.    This I attribute to the act
of induction in the wire A B D at the moment of contact rendering that wire a worse conductor, or rather retarding the
passage of the electricity through it for the instant, and so throwing a greater quantity of the electricity which the electromotor
could produce, through the cross wire passage N P.    The instant the induction ceased, A B D resumed its full power of
carrying a constant current of electricity, and could have it
highly increased, as we know by the former experiments (1060.)
by the opposite inductive action brought into activity at the
moment contact at Z or C was *broken*.

1103. A galvanometer was then introduced at *x*, and the
deflection of the needle noted whilst contact was continued at
G and E : the needle was then blocked as before in one direction
(1087.), so that it should not return when the current ceased,
but remain in the position in which the current could retain it.
Contact at G or E was broken, producing of course no visible
effect ; it was then renewed, and the needle was instantly deflected, passing from the blocking pins to a position still further
from its natural place than that which the constant current
could give, and thus showing, by the temporary excess of current in this cross communication, the temporary retardation in
the circuit A B D.

1104. On adjusting a platina wire at *x* (1081.) so that it
should not be ignited by the current passing through it whilst
contact at G and E was *continued*, and yet become red hot by
a current somewhat more powerful, I was readily able to pro-

duce its ignition upon *making contact*, and again upon *breaking contact*. Thus the momentary retardation in A B D on making contact was again shown by this result, as well also as the opposite result upon breaking contact. The two ignitions of the wire at *x* were of course produced by electric currents moving in opposite directions.

1105. Using the *helix* only, I could not obtain distinct deflections at *x*, due to the extra effect on making contact, for the reasons already mentioned (1088.). By using a very fine platina wire there (1083.), I did succeed in obtaining the igniting effect for making contact in the same manner, though by no means to the same degree, as with the electro-magnet (1104.).

1106. We may also consider and estimate the effect on *making contact*, by transferring the force of induction from the wire carrying the original current to a lateral wire, as in the cases described (1090.); and we then are sure, both by the chemical and galvanometrical results (1091.), that the forces upon making and breaking contact, like action and reaction, are equal in their strength but contrary in their direction. If, therefore, the effect on making contact resolves itself into a mere retardation of the current at the first moment of its existence, it must be, in its degree, equivalent to the high exaltation of that same current at the moment contact is broken.

1107. Thus the case, under the circumstances, is, that the intensity and quantity of electricity moving in a current are smaller when the current commences or is increased, and greater when it diminishes or ceases, than they would be if the inductive action occurring at these moments did not take place; or than they are in the original current wire if the inductive action be transferred from that wire to a collateral one (1090.).

1108. From the facility of transference to neighbouring wires, and from the effects generally, the inductive forces appear to be lateral, *i. e.* exerted in a direction perpendicular to the direction of the originating and produced currents; and they also appear to be accurately represented by the magnetic curves, and closely related to, if not identical with, magnetic forces.

1109. There can be no doubt that the current in one part of a wire can act by induction upon other parts of the *same* wire which are lateral to the first, *i. e.* in the same vertical section (74.), or in parts which are more or less oblique to it

(1112.), just as it can act in producing a current in a neighbouring wire or in a neighbouring coil of the same wire.   It is this which gives the appearance of the current acting upon itself ; but all the experiments and all analogy tend to show that the elements (if I may so say) of the currents do not act upon themselves, and so cause the effect in question, but produce it by exciting currents in conducting matter which is lateral to them.

1110. It is possible that some of the expressions I have used may seem to imply, that the inductive action is essentially the action of one current upon another, or of one element of a current upon another element of the same current.   To avoid any such conclusion I must explain more distinctly my meaning.   If an endless wire be taken, we have the means of generating a current in it which shall run round the circuit without adding any electricity to what was previously in the wire.    As far as we can judge, the electricity which appears as a current is the same as that which before was quiescent in the wire ; and though we cannot as yet point out the essential condition of difference of the electricity at such times, we can easily recognise the two states.    Now when a current acts by induction upon conducting matter lateral to it, it probably acts upon the electricity in that conducting matter whether it be in the form of a *current* or *quiescent*, in the one case increasing or diminishing the current according to its direction, in the other producing a current, and the *amount* of the inductive action is probably the same in both cases.    Hence, to say that the action of induction depended upon the mutual relation of two or more currents, would, according to the restricted sense in which the term current is understood at present (283. 517. 667.), be an error.

1111. Several of the effects, as, for instances, those with helices (1066.), with according or counter currents (1097. 1098.), and those on the production of lateral currents (1090.), appeared to indicate that a current could produce an effect of induction in a neighbouring wire more readily than in its own carrying wire, in which case it might be expected that some variation of result would be produced if a bundle of wires were used as a conductor instead of a single wire.   In consequence the following experiments were made.   A copper wire one twenty-third of an inch in diameter was cut into lengths of five feet each, and six of these being laid side by side in one bundle, had their opposite extremities soldered to two terminal pieces of copper. This arrangement could be used as a discharging wire, but the general current could be divided into six parallel streams, which might be brought close together, or, by the separation of the wires, be taken more or less out of each other's influence. A somewhat brighter spark was, I think, obtained on breaking contact when the six wires were close together than when held asunder.

1112. Another bundle, containing twenty of these wires, was eighteen feet long ; the terminal pieces were one-fifth of an inch in diameter, and each six inches long. This was compared with nineteen feet in length of copper wire one-fifth of an inch. in diameter. The bundle gave a smaller spark on breaking contact than the latter, even when its strands were held together by string ; when they were separated, it gave a still smaller spark. Upon the whole, however, the diminution of effect was not such as I expected ; and I doubt whether the results can be considered as any proof of the truth of the supposition which gave rise to them.

1113. The inductive force by which two elements of one current (1109. 1110.) act upon each other, appears to diminish as the line joining them becomes oblique to the direction of the current, and to vanish entirely when it is parallel. I am led by some results to suspect that it then even passes into the repulsive force noticed by Ampère* ; which is the cause of the elevations in mercury described by Sir Humphry Davy†, and which again is probably directly connected with the quality of intensity.

1114. Notwithstanding that the effects appear only at the making and breaking of contact, (the current remaining unaffected, seemingly, in the interval,) I cannot resist the impression that there is some connected and correspondent effect produced by this lateral action of the elements of the electric stream during the time of its continuance (60. 242.). An action of this kind, in fact, is evident in the magnetic relations of the parts of the current. But admitting (as we may do for the moment) the magnetic forces to constitute the power which produces such striking and different results at the commencement and termi-

* Recueil d'Observations Electro-Dynamiques, p. 285.
† Philosophical Transactions, 1823, p. 155.

nation of a current, still there appears to be a link in the chain of effects, a wheel in the physical mechanism of the action, as yet unrecognised.   If we endeavour to consider electricity and magnetism as the results of two forces of a physical agent, or a peculiar condition of matter, exerted in determinate directions perpendicular to each other, then, it appears to me, that we must consider these two states or forces as convertible into each other in a greater or smaller degree ; *i. e.* that an element of an electric current has not a determinate electric force and a determinate magnetic force constantly existing in the same ratio, but that the two forces are, to a certain degree, convertible by a process or change of condition at present unknown to us. How else can a current of a given intensity and quantity be able, by its direct action, to sustain a state which, when allowed to react, (at the cessation of the original current,) shall produce a second current, having an intensity and quantity far greater than the generating one?   This cannot result from a direct reaction of the electric force ; and if it result from a change of electrical into magnetic force, and a reconversion back again, it will show that they differ in something more than mere direction, as regards *that agent* in the conducting wire which constitutes their immediate cause.

1115. With reference to the appearance, at different times, of the contrary effects produced by the making and breaking contact, and their separation by an intermediate and indifferent state, this separation is probably more apparent than real.   If the conduction of electricity be effected by vibrations (283.), or by any other mode in which opposite forces are successively and rapidly excited and neutralized, then we might expect a peculiar and contrary development of force at the commencement and termination of the periods during which the conducting action should last (somewhat in analogy with the colours produced at the outside of an imperfectly developed solar spectrum) : and the intermediate actions, although not sensible in the same way, may be very important and, for instance, perhaps constitute the very essence of conductibility.   It is by views and reasons such as these, which seem to me connected with the fundamental laws and facts of electrical science, that I have been induced to enter, more minutely than I otherwise should have done, into the experimental examination of the phenomena described in this paper.

1116. Before concluding, I may briefly remark, that on using a voltaic battery of fifty pairs of plates instead of a single pair (1052.), the effects were exactly of the same kind. The spark on making contact, for the reasons before given, was very small (1101. 1107.) ; that on breaking contact, very excellent and brilliant. The *continuous* discharge did not seem altered in character, whether a short wire or the powerful electro-magnet were used as a connecting discharger.

1117. The effects produced at the commencement and end of a current, (which are separated by an interval of time when that current is supplied from a voltaic apparatus,) must occur at the same moment when a common electric discharge is passed through a long wire. Whether, if happening accurately at the same moment, they would entirely neutralize each other, or whether they would not still give some definite peculiarity to the discharge, is a matter remaining to be examined ; but it is very probable that the peculiar character and pungency of sparks drawn from a long wire depend in part upon the increased intensity given at the termination of the discharge by the inductive action then occurring.

1118. In the wire of the helix of magneto-electric machines, (as, for instance, in Mr. Saxton's beautiful arrangement,) an important influence of these principles of action is evidently shown. From the construction of the apparatus the current is permitted to move in a complete metallic circuit of great length during the first instants of its formation : it gradually rises in strength, and is then suddenly stopped by the breaking of the metallic circuit; and thus great intensity is given *by induction* to the electricity, which at that moment passes (1064. 1060.). This intensity is not only shown by the brilliancy of the spark and the strength of the shock, but also by the necessity which has been experienced of well insulating the convolutions of the helix, in which the current is formed ; and it gives to the current a force at these moments very far above that which the apparatus could produce if the principle which forms the subject of this paper were not called into play.

*Royal Institution,*
  *December 8th,* 1834.

## TENTH SERIES.

§ 16. *On an improved form of the Voltaic Battery.* § 17. *Some practical results respecting the construction and use of the Voltaic Battery.*

Received June 16,—Read June 18, 1835.

1119. I HAVE lately had occasion to examine the voltaic trough practically, with a view to improvements in its construction and use ; and though I do not pretend that the results have anything like the importance which attaches to the discovery of a new law or principle, I still think they are valuable, and may therefore, if briefly told, and in connexion with former papers, be worthy the approbation of the Royal Society.

### § 16. *On an improved form of the Voltaic Battery.*

1120. In a simple voltaic circuit (and the same is true of the battery) the chemical forces which, during their activity, give power to the instrument, are generally divided into two portions ; one of these is exerted locally, whilst the other is transferred round the circle (947. 996.) ; the latter constitutes the electric current of the instrument, whilst the former is altogether lost or wasted. The ratio of these two portions of power may be varied to a great extent by the influence of circumstances : thus, in a battery not closed, *all* the action is local ; in one of the ordinary construction, *much* is in circulation when the extremities are in communication ; and in the perfect one, which I have described (1010), *all* the chemical power circulates and becomes electricity. By referring to the quantity of zinc dissolved from the plates (865. 1126.), and the quantity of decomposition effected in the volta-electrometer (711. 1126.) or elsewhere, the proportions of the local and transferred actions under any particular circumstances can be ascertained, and the efficacy of the voltaic arrangement, or the waste of chemical power at its zinc plates, be accurately determined.

1121. If a voltaic battery were constructed of zinc and platina, the latter metal surrounding the former, as in the double copper arrangement, and the whole being excited by dilute sulphuric acid, then no insulating divisions of glass, porcelain, or air would be required between the contiguous platina surfaces ; and, provided these did not touch metallically, the same acid which, being between the zinc and platina, would excite the battery into powerful action, would, between the two surfaces of platina, produce no discharge of the electricity, nor cause any diminution of the power of the trough. This is a necessary consequence of the resistance to the passage of the current which I have shown occurs at the place of decomposition (1007. 1011.) ; for that resistance is fully able to stop the current, and therefore acts as insulation to the electricity of the contiguous plates, inasmuch as the current which tends to pass between them never has a higher intensity than that due to the action of a single pair.

1122. If the metal surrounding the zinc be copper (1045.), and if the acid be nitro-sulphuric acid (1020.), then a slight discharge between the two contiguous coppers does take place, provided there be no other channel open by which the forces may circulate ; but when such a channel is permitted, the return or back discharge of which I speak is exceedingly diminished, in accordance with the principles laid down in the Eighth Series of these Researches.

1123. Guided by these principles I was led to the construction of a voltaic trough, in which the coppers, passing round both surfaces of the zincs, as in Wollaston's construction, should not be separated from each other except by an intervening thickness of paper, or in some other way, so as to prevent metallic contact, and should thus constitute an instrument compact, powerful, economical, and easy of use. On examining, however, what had been done before, I found that the new trough was in all essential respects the same as that invented and described by Dr. Hare, Professor in the University of Pennsylvania, to whom I have great pleasure in referring it.

1124. Dr. Hare has fully described his trough*. In it the

---

* Philosophical Magazine, 1824, vol. lxiii. p. 241 ; or Silliman's Journal, vol. vii. See also a previous paper by Dr. Hare, Annals of Philosophy, 1821, vol. i. p. 329, in which he speaks of the non-necessity of insulation between the coppers.

contiguous copper plates are separated by thin veneers of wood, and the acid is poured on to, or off, the plates by a quarter revolution of an axis, to which both the trough containing the plates, and another trough to collect and hold the liquid, are fixed. This arrangement I have found the most convenient of any, and have therefore adopted it. My zinc plates were cut from rolled metal, and when soldered to the copper plates had the form delineated, fig. 1. These were then bent over a gauge

Fig. 1.

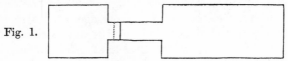

into the form fig. 2, and when packed in the wooden box constructed to receive them, were arranged as in fig. 3*, little plugs

Fig. 2.          Fig. 3.

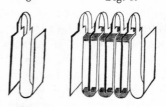

of cork being used to keep the zinc plates from touching the copper plates, and a single or double thickness of cartridge paper being interposed between the contiguous surfaces of copper to prevent them from coming in contact. Such was the facility afforded by this arrangement, that a trough of forty pairs of plates could be unpacked in five minutes, and repacked again in half an hour; and the whole series was not more than fifteen inches in length.

1125. This trough, of forty pairs of plates three inches square, was compared, as to the ignition of a platina wire, the discharge between points of charcoal, the shock on the human frame, &c., with forty pairs of four-inch plates having double coppers, and used in porcelain troughs divided into insulating cells, the strength of the acid employed to excite both being the same. In all these effects the former appeared quite equal to the latter.

* The papers between the coppers are, for the sake of distinctness, omitted in the figure.

On comparing a second trough of the new construction, containing twenty pairs of four-inch plates, with twenty pairs of four-inch plates in porcelain troughs, excited by acid of the same strength, the new trough appeared to surpass the old one in producing these effects, especially in the ignition of wire.

1126. In these experiments the new trough diminished in its energy much more rapidly than the one on the old construction, and this was a necessary consequence of the smaller quantity of acid used to excite it, which in the case of the forty pairs of new construction was only one-seventh part of that used for the forty pairs in the porcelain troughs. To compare, therefore, both forms of the voltaic trough in their decomposing powers, and to obtain accurate data as to their relative values, experiments of the following kind were made. The troughs were charged with a known quantity of acid of a known strength; the electric current was passed through a volta-electrometer (711.) having electrodes 4 inches long and 2·3 inches in width, so as to oppose as little obstruction as possible to the current; the gases evolved were collected and measured, and gave the quantity of water decomposed. Then the whole of the charge used was mixed together, and a known part of it analysed, by being precipitated and boiled with excess of carbonate of soda, and the precipitate well washed, dried, ignited, and weighed. In this way the quantity of metal oxidized and dissolved by the acid was ascertained; and the part removed from each zinc plate, or from all the plates, could be estimated and compared with the water decomposed in the volta-electrometer. To bring these to one standard of comparison, I have reduced the results so as to express the loss at the plates in equivalents of zinc for the equivalent of water decomposed at the volta-electrometer: I have taken the equivalent number of water as 9, and of zinc as 32·5, and have considered 100 cubic inches of the mixed oxygen and hydrogen, as they were collected over a pneumatic trough, to result from the decomposition of 12·68 grains of water.

1127. The acids used in these experiments were three,—sulphuric, nitric, and muriatic. The sulphuric acid was strong oil of vitriol; one cubical inch of it was equivalent to 486 grains of marble. The nitric acid was very nearly pure; one cubical inch dissolved 150 grains of marble. The muriatic acid was also nearly pure, and one cubical inch dissolved 108 grains of marble. These were always mixed with water by volumes, the standard of volume being a cubical inch.

1128. An acid was prepared consisting of 200 parts water, $4\frac{1}{2}$ parts sulphuric acid, and 4 parts nitric acid ; and with this both my trough containing forty pairs of three-inch plates, and four porcelain troughs, arranged in succession, each containing ten pairs of plates with double coppers four inches square, were charged. These two batteries were then used in succession, and the action of each was allowed to continue for twenty or thirty minutes, until the charge was nearly exhausted, the connexion with the volta-electrometer being carefully preserved during the whole time, and the acid in the troughs occasionally mixed together. In this way the former trough acted so well, that for each equivalent of water decomposed in the volta-electrometer only from 2 to 2·5 equivalents of zinc were dissolved from each plate. In four experiments the average was 2·21 equivalents for each plate, or 88·4 for the whole battery. In the experiments with the porcelain troughs, the equivalents of consumption at each plate were 3·54, or 141·6 for the whole battery. In a perfect voltaic battery of forty pairs of plates (991. 1001.) the consumption would have been one equivalent for each zinc plate, or forty for the whole.

1129. Similar experiments were made with two voltaic batteries, one containing twenty pairs of four-inch plates, arranged as I have described (1124.), and the other twenty pairs of four-inch plates in porcelain troughs. The average of five experiments with the former was a consumption of 3·7 equivalents of zinc from each plate, or 74 from the whole; the average of three experiments with the latter was 5·5 equivalents from each plate, or 110 from the whole : to obtain this conclusion, two experiments were struck out, which were much against the porcelain troughs, and in which some unknown deteriorating influence was supposed to be accidentally active. In all the experiments, care was taken not to compare *new* and *old* plates together, as that would have introduced serious errors into the conclusions (1146.).

1130. When ten pairs of the new arrangement were used, the consumption of zinc at each plate was 6·76 equivalents, or 67·6 for the whole. With ten pairs of the common construction, in a porcelain trough, the zinc oxidized was, upon an average, 15·5 equivalents each plate, or 155 for the entire trough.

1131. No doubt, therefore, can remain of the equality or even the great superiority of this form of voltaic battery over the best previously in use, namely, that with double coppers, in which the cells are insulated. The insulation of the coppers may therefore be dispensed with ; and it is that circumstance which principally permits of such other alterations in the construction of the trough as gives it its practical advantages.

1132. The advantages of this form of trough are very numerous and great. i. It is exceedingly compact, for 100 pairs of plates need not occupy a trough of more than three feet in length. ii. By Dr. Hare's plan of making the trough turn upon copper pivots which rest upon copper bearings, the latter afford *fixed* terminations ; and these I have found it very convenient to connect with two cups of mercury, fastened in the front of the stand of the instrument. These fixed terminations give the great advantage of arranging an apparatus to be used in connexion with the battery *before* the latter is put into action. iii. The trough is put into readiness for use in an instant, a single jug of dilute acid being sufficient for the charge of 100 pairs of four-inch plates. iv. On making the trough pass through a quarter of a revolution, it becomes active, and the great advantage is obtained of procuring for the experiment the effect of the *first contact* of the zinc and acid, which is twice or sometimes even thrice that which the battery can produce a minute or two after (1036. 1150.). v. When the experiment is completed, the acid can be at once poured from between the plates, so that the battery is never left to waste during an unconnected state of its extremities ; the acid is not unnecessarily exhausted ; the zinc is not uselessly consumed ; and, besides avoiding these evils, the charge is mixed and rendered uniform, which produces a great and good result (1039.) ; and, upon proceeding to a second experiment, the important effect of *first contact* is again obtained. vi. The saving of zinc is very great. It is not merely that, whilst in action, the zinc performs more voltaic duty (1128. 1129.), but *all* the destruction which takes place with the ordinary forms of battery between the experiments is prevented. This saving is of such extent, that I estimate the zinc in the new form of battery to

be thrice as effective as that in the ordinary form. vii. The
importance of this saving of metal is not merely that the value
of the zinc is saved, but that the battery is much lighter and
more manageable; and also that the surfaces of the zinc and
copper plates may be brought much nearer to each other when
the battery is constructed, and remain so until it is worn out:
the latter is a very important advantage (1148.). viii. Again,
as, in consequence of the saving, thinner plates will perform
the duty of thick ones, rolled zinc may be used; and I have
found rolled zinc superior to cast zinc in action; a superiority
which I incline to attribute to its greater purity (1144.). ix.
Another advantage is obtained in the economy of the acid
used, which is proportionate to the diminution of the zinc dissolved. x. The acid also is more easily exhausted, and is in such
small quantity that there is never any occasion to return an old
charge into use. The acid of old charges whilst out of use,
often dissolves portions of copper from the black flocculi usually
mingled with it, which are derived from the zinc; now any
portion of copper in solution in the charge does great harm,
because, by the *local* action of the acid and zinc, it tends to
precipitate upon the latter, and diminish its voltaic efficacy
(1145.). xi. By using a due mixture of nitric and sulphuric
acid for the charge (1139.), no gas is evolved from the troughs;
so that a battery of several hundred pairs of plates may, without inconvenience, be close to the experimenter. xii. If, during
a series of experiments, the acid becomes exhausted, it can be
withdrawn, and replaced by other acid with the utmost facility;
and after the experiments are concluded, the great advantage
of easily washing the plates is at command. And it appears to
me, that in place of making, under different circumstances,
mutual sacrifices of comfort, power, and economy, to obtain a
desired end, all are at once obtained by Dr. Hare's form of
trough.

1133. But there are some disadvantages which I have not
yet had time to overcome, though I trust they will finally be
conquered. One is the extreme difficulty of making a wooden
trough constantly water-tight under the alternations of wet and
dry to which the voltaic instrument is subject. To remedy this
evil, Mr. Newman is now engaged in obtaining porcelain
troughs. The other disadvantage is a precipitation of copper

on the zinc plates.   It appears to me to depend mainly on the circumstance that the papers between the coppers retain acid when the trough is emptied; and that this acid slowly acting on the copper, forms a salt, which gradually mingles with the next charge, and is reduced on the zinc plate by the local action (1120.) : the power of the whole battery is then reduced.   I expect that by using slips of glass or wood to separate the coppers at their edges, their contact can be sufficiently prevented, and the space between them be left so open that the acid of a charge can be poured and washed out, and so be removed from *every part* of the trough when the experiments in which the latter is used are completed.

1134. The actual superiority of the troughs which I have constructed on this plan, I believe to depend, first and principally, on the closer approximation of the zinc and copper surfaces;—in my troughs they are only one-tenth of an inch apart (1148.) ;—and, next, on the superior quality of the rolled zinc above the cast zinc used in the construction of the ordinary pile.   It cannot be that insulation between the contiguous coppers is a disadvantage, but I do not find that it is any advantage; for when, with both the forty pairs of three-inch plates and the twenty pairs of four-inch plates, I used papers well soaked in wax*, these being so large that when folded at the edges they wrapped over each other, so as to make cells as insulating as those of the porcelain troughs, still no sensible advantage in the chemical action was obtained.

1135. As, upon principle, there must be a discharge of part of the electricity from the edges of the zinc and copper plates at the sides of the trough, I should prefer, and intend having, troughs constructed with a plate or plates of crown glass at the sides of the trough : the bottom will need none, though to glaze that and the ends would be no disadvantage.   The plates need not be fastened in, but only set in their places; nor need they be in large single pieces.

§ 17. *Some practical results respecting the construction and use of the Voltaic Battery* (1034. &c.).

1136. The electro-chemical philosopher is well acquainted

---

* A single paper thus prepared could insulate the electricity of a trough of forty pairs of plates.

with some practical results obtained from the voltaic battery by
MM. Gay-Lussac and Thénard, and given in the first forty-five
pages of their ' Recherches Physico-Chimiques'.    Although
the following results are generally of the same nature, yet the
advancement made in this branch of science of late years, the
knowledge of the definite action of electricity, and the more accurate and philosophical mode of estimating the results by the
equivalents of zinc consumed, will be their sufficient justifi-
cation.

1137. *Nature and strength of the acid.*—My battery of forty
pairs of three-inch plates was charged with acid consisting of 200
parts water and 9 oil of vitriol.    Each plate lost, in the average
of the experiments, 4·66 equivalents of zinc for the equivalent
of water decomposed in the volta-electrometer, or the whole
battery 186·4 equivalents of zinc.    Being charged with a
mixture of 200 water and 16 of the muriatic acid, each plate
lost 3·8, equivalents of zinc for the water decomposed, or the
whole battery 152 equivalents of zinc.    Being charged with a
mixture of 200 water and 8 nitric acid, each plate lost 1·85,
equivalents of zinc for one equivalent of water decomposed, or
the whole battery 74·16 equivalents of zinc.    The sulphuric
and muriatic acids evolved much hydrogen at the plates in the
trough ; the nitric acid no gas whatever.    The relative strengths
of the original acids have already been given (1127.) ; but a difference in that respect makes no important difference in the
results when thus expressed by equivalents (1140.).

1138. Thus nitric acid proves to be the best for this purpose ;
its superiority appears to depend upon its favouring the electrolyzation of the liquid in the cells of the trough upon the principles already explained (905. 973. 1022.), and consequently
favouring the transmission of the electricity, and therefore the
production of transferable power (1120.).

1139. The addition of nitric acid might, consequently, be expected to improve sulphuric and muriatic acids.    Accordingly,
when the same trough was charged with a mixture of 200 water,
9 oil of vitriol, and 4 nitric acid, the consumption of zinc was
at each plate 2·786, and for the whole battery 111·5, equivalents.    When the charge was 200 water, 9 oil of vitriol, and
8 nitric acid, the loss per plate was 2·26, or for the whole battery 90·4, equivalents.    When the trough was charged with a

mixture of 200 water, 16 muriatic acid, and 6 nitric acid, the loss per plate was 2·11, or for the whole battery 84·4, equivalents. Similar results were obtained with my battery of twenty pairs of four-inch plates (1129.). Hence it is evident that the nitric acid was of great service when mingled with the sulphuric acid ; and the charge generally used after this time for ordinary experiments consisted of 200 water, 4½ oil of vitriol, and 4 nitric acid.

1140. It is not to be supposed that the different strengths of the acids produced the differences above; for within certain limits I found the electrolytic effects to be nearly as the strengths of the acids, so as to leave the expression of force, when given in equivalents, almost constant. Thus, when the trough was charged with a mixture of 200 water and 8 nitric acid, each plate lost 1·854 equivalent of zinc. When the charge was 200 water and 16 nitric acid, the loss per plate was 1·82 equivalent. When it was 200 water and 32 nitric acid, the loss was 2·1 equivalents. The differences here are not greater than happen from unavoidable irregularities, depending on other causes than the strength of acid.

1141. Again, when a charge consisting of 200 water, 4½ oil of vitriol, and 4 nitric acid was used, each zinc plate lost 2·16 equivalents ; when the charge with the same battery was 200 water, 9 oil of vitriol, and 8 nitric acid, each zinc plate lost 2·26 equivalents.

1142. I need hardly say that no copper is dissolved during the regular action of the voltaic trough. I have found that much ammonia is formed in the cells when nitric acid, either pure or mixed with sulphuric acid is used. It is produced in part as a secondary result at the cathodes (663.) of the different portions of fluid constituting the necessary electrolyte, in the cells.

1143. *Uniformity of the charge.*—This is a most important point, as I have already shown experimentally (1042. &c.). Hence one great advantage of Dr. Hare's mechanical arrangement of his trough.

1144. *Purity of the zinc.*—If pure zinc could be obtained, it would be very advantageous in the construction of the voltaic apparatus (998.). Most zincs, when put into dilute sulphuric acid, leave more or less of an insoluble matter upon the surface in the form of a crust, which contains various metals, as copper, lead, zinc, iron, cadmium, &c., in the metallic state. Such particles, by discharging part of the transferable power, render it, as to the whole battery, local; and so diminish the effect. As an indication connected with the more or less perfect action of the battery, I may mention that no gas ought to rise from the zinc plates. The more gas which is generated upon these surfaces, the greater is the local action and the less the transferable force. The investing crust is also inconvenient, by preventing the displacement and renewal of the charge upon the surface of the zinc. Such zinc as, dissolving in the cleanest manner in a dilute acid, dissolves also the slowest, is the best; zinc which contains much copper should especially be avoided. I have generally found rolled Liege or Mosselman's zinc the purest; and to the circumstance of having used such zinc in its construction attribute in part the advantage of the new battery (1134.).

1145. *Foulness of the zinc plates.*—After use, the plates of a battery should be cleaned from the metallic powder upon their surfaces, especially if they are employed to obtain the laws of action of the battery itself. This precaution was always attended to with the porcelain trough batteries in the experiments described (1125., &c.). If a few foul plates are mingled with many clean ones, they make the action in the different cells irregular, and the transferable power is accordingly diminished, whilst the local and wasted power is increased. No old charge containing copper should be used to excite a battery.

1146. *New and old plates.*—I have found voltaic batteries far more powerful when the plates were new than when they have been used two or three times; so that a new and an used battery cannot be compared together, or even a battery with itself on the first and after times of use. My trough of twenty pairs of four-inch plates, charged with acid consisting of 200 water, 4½ oil of vitriol, and 4 nitric acid, lost, upon the first time of being used, 2·32 equivalents per plate. When used after the fourth time with the same charge, the loss was from 3·26 to 4·47 equivalents per plate; the average being 3·7 equivalents. The first time the forty pair of plates (1124.) were used, the loss at each plate was only 1·65 equivalent; but afterwards it became 2·16, 2·17, 2·52. The first time twenty pair of four-inch plates in porcelain troughs

were used, they lost, per plate, only 3·7 equivalents; but after
that, the loss was 5·25, 5·36, 5·9 equivalents. Yet in all these
cases the zincs had been well cleaned from adhering copper, &c.,
before each trial of power.

1147. With the rolled zinc the fall in force soon appeared to
become constant, *i. e.* to proceed no further. But with the cast
zinc plates belonging to the porcelain troughs, it appeared to
continue, until at last, with the same charge, each plate lost
above twice as much zinc for a given amount of action as at first.
These troughs were, however, so irregular that I could not
always determine the circumstances affecting the amount of
electrolytic action.

1148. *Vicinity of the copper and zinc.*—The importance of
this point in the construction of voltaic arrangements, and the
greater power, as to immediate action, which is obtained when
the zinc and copper surfaces are near to each other than when
removed further apart, are well known. I find that the power
is not only greater on the instant, but also that the sum of
transferable power, in relation to the whole sum of chemical
action at the plates, is much increased. The cause of this gain
is very evident. Whatever tends to retard the circulation of
the transferable force, (*i. e.* the electricity,) diminishes the proportion of such force, and increases the proportion of that which
is local (996. 1120.). Now the liquid in the cells possesses this
retarding power, and therefore acts injuriously, in greater or
less proportion, according to the quantity of it between the zinc
and copper plates, *i. e.* according to the distances between their
surfaces. A trough, therefore, in which the plates are only
half the distance asunder at which they are placed in another,
will produce more transferable, and less local, force than the
latter; and thus, because the electrolyte in the cells can transmit the current more readily, both the intensity and quantity
of electricity is increased for a given consumption of zinc. To
this circumstance mainly I attribute the superiority of the trough
I have described (1134.).

1149. The superiority of *double coppers* over single plates
also depends in part upon diminishing the resistance offered by
the electrolyte between the metals. For, in fact, with double
coppers the sectional area of the interposed acid becomes nearly
double that with single coppers, and therefore it more freely

transfers the electricity.  Double coppers are, however, effective, mainly because they virtually double the acting surface of the zinc, or nearly so ; for in a trough with single copper plates and the usual construction of cells, that surface of zinc which is not opposed to a copper surface is thrown almost entirely out of voltaic action, yet the acid continues to act upon it and the metal is dissolved, producing very little more than local effect (947. 996.).   But when by doubling the copper, that metal is opposed to the second  surface of the zinc plate, then a great part of the action upon the latter is converted into transferable force, and thus the power of the trough as to quantity of electricity is highly exalted.

1150. *First immersion of the plates.*—The great effect produced at the first immersion of the plates, (apart from their being new or used (1146.),) I have attributed elsewhere to the unchanged condition of the acid in contact with the zinc plate (1003. 1037.) : as the acid becomes neutralized, its exciting power is proportionably diminished.  Hare's form of trough secures much advantage of this kind, by mingling the liquid, and bringing what may be considered as a fresh surface of acid against the plates every time it is used immediately after a rest.

1151. *Number of plates\*.*—The most advantageous number of plates in a battery used for chemical decomposition, depends almost entirely upon the resistance to be overcome at the place of action ; but whatever that resistance may be, there is a certain number which is more economical than either a greater or a less.   Ten pairs of four-inch plates in a porcelain trough of the ordinary construction, acting in the volta-electrometer (1126.) upon dilute sulphuric acid of spec. grav. 1·314, gave an average consumption of 15·4 equivalents per plate, or 154 equivalents on the whole.  Twenty pairs of the same plates, with the same acid, gave only a consumption of 5·5 per plate, or 110 equivalents upon the whole.  When forty pairs of the same plates were used, the consumption was 3·54 equivalents per plate, or 141·6 upon the whole battery.   Thus the consumption of zinc arranged as *twenty* plates was more advantageous than if arranged either as *ten* or as *forty*.

1152. Again, ten pairs of my four-inch plates (1129.) lost 6·76 each, or the whole ten 67·6 equivalents of zinc, in effect-

\* Gay-Lussac and Thénard, Recherches Physico-Chimiques, tom. i. p. 29.

ing decomposition; whilst twenty pairs of the same plates, excited by the same acid, lost 3·7 equivalents each, or on the whole 74 equivalents.    In other comparative experiments of numbers, ten pairs of the three-inch plates (1125.), lost 3·725, or 37·25 equivalents upon the whole; whilst twenty pairs lost 2·53 each, or 50·6 in all; and forty pairs lost on an average 2·21, or 88·4 altogether.    In both these cases, therefore, increase of numbers had not been advantageous as to the effective production of *transferable chemical power* from the *whole quantity of chemical force* active at the surfaces of excitation (1120.).

1153. But if I had used a weaker acid or a worse conductor in the volta-electrometer, then the number of plates which would produce the most advantageous effect would have risen; or if I had used a better conductor than that really employed in the volta-electrometer, I might have reduced the number even to one; as, for instance, when a thick wire is used to complete the circuit (865. &c.).    And the cause of these variations is very evident, when it is considered that each successive plate in the voltaic apparatus does not add anything to the *quantity* of transferable power or electricity which the first plate can put into motion, provided a good conductor be present, but tends only to exalt the *intensity* of that quantity, so as to make it more able to overcome the obstruction of bad conductors (994. 1158).

1154. *Large or small plates*\*.—The advantageous use of large or small plates for electrolyzations will evidently depend upon the facility with which the transferable power or electricity can pass.    If in a particular case the most effectual number of plates is known (1151.), then the addition of more zinc would be most advantageously made in increasing the *size* of the plates, and not their *number*.    At the same time, large increase in the size of the plates would raise in a small degree the most favourable number.

1155. Large and small plates should not be used together in the same battery: the small ones occasion a loss of the power of the large ones, unless they be excited by an acid proportionably more powerful; for with a certain acid they cannot transmit the same portion of electricity in a given time which the sam acid can evolve by action on the larger plates.

\* Gay-Lussac and Thénard, Recherches Physico-Chimiques, tom. i. p. 29.

1156. *Simultaneous decompositions.*—When the number of plates in a battery much surpasses the most favourable proportion (1151—1153.), two or more decompositions may be effected simultaneously with advantage. Thus my forty pairs of plates (1124.) produced in one volta-electrometer 22·8 cubic inches of gas. Being recharged exactly in the same manner, they produced in each of two volta-electrometers 21 cubical inches. In the first experiment the whole consumption of zinc was 88·4 equivalents, and in the second only 48·28 equivalents, for the whole of the water decomposed in both volta-electrometers.

1157. But when the twenty pairs of four-inch plates (1129.) were tried in a similar manner, the results were in the opposite direction. With one volta-electrometer 52 cubic inches of gas were obtained; with two, only 14·6 cubic inches from each. The quantity of charge was not the same in both cases, though it was of the same strength; but on rendering the results comparative by reducing them to equivalents (1126.), it was found that the consumption of metal in the first case was 74, and in the second case 97, equivalents for the *whole* of the water decomposed. These results of course depend upon the same circumstances of retardation, &c., which have been referred to in speaking of the proper number of plates (1151.).

1158. That the *transferring*, or, as it is usually called, *conducting, power* of an electrolyte which is to be decomposed, or other interposed body, should be rendered as good as possible *, is very evident (1020. 1120.). With a perfectly good conductor and a good battery, nearly all the electricity is passed, i. e. *nearly all* the chemical power becomes transferable, even with a single pair of plates (867.). With an interposed nonconductor, none of the chemical power becomes transferable. With an imperfect conductor more or less of the chemical power becomes transferable as the circumstances favouring the transfer of forces across the imperfect conductor are exalted or diminished: these circumstances are, actual increase or improvement of the conducting power, enlargement of the electrodes, approximation of the electrodes, and increased intensity of the passing current.

* Gay-Lussac and Thénard, Recherches Physico-Chimiques, tom. i. pp. 13, 15, 22.

1159. The introduction of common spring water in place of one of the volta-electrometers used with twenty pairs of four-inch plates (1156.) caused such obstruction as not to allow one fifteenth of the transferable force to pass which would have circulated without it. Thus fourteen fifteenths of the available force of the battery were destroyed, being converted into local force, (which was rendered evident by the evolution of gas from the zincs,) and yet the platina electrodes in the water were three inches long, nearly an inch wide, and not a quarter of an inch apart.

1160. These points, *i. e.* the increase of conducting power, the enlargement of the electrodes, and their approximation, should be especially attended to in *volta-electrometers*. The principles upon which their utility depend are so evident that there can be no occasion for further development of them here.

*Royal Institution,*
  *October 11th,* 1834.

## ELEVENTH SERIES.

§ 18. *On Induction.* ¶ i. *Induction an action of contiguous particles.* ¶ ii. *Absolute charge of matter.* ¶ iii. *Electrometer and inductive apparatus employed.* ¶ iv. *Induction in curved lines.* ¶ v. *Specific inductive capacity.* ¶ vi. *General results as to induction.*

Received November 30,—Read December 21, 1837.

¶ i. *Induction an action of contiguous particles.*

1161. THE science of electricity is in that state in which every part of it requires experimental investigation ; not merely for the discovery of new effects, but what is just now of far more importance, the development of the means by which the old effects are produced, and the consequent more accurate determination of the first principles of action of the most extraordinary and universal power in nature :—and to those philosophers who pursue the inquiry zealously yet cautiously, combining experiment with analogy, suspicious of their preconceived notions, paying more respect to a fact than a theory, not too hasty to generalize, and above all things, willing at every step to crossexamine their own opinions, both by reasoning and experiment, no branch of knowledge can afford so fine and ready a field for discovery as this. Such is most abundantly shown to be the case by the progress which electricity has made in the last thirty years : Chemistry and Magnetism have successively acknowledged its over-ruling influence ; and it is probable that every effect depending upon the powers of inorganic matter, and perhaps most of those related to vegetable and animal life, will ultimately be found subordinate to it.

1162. Amongst the actions of different kinds into which electricity has conventionally been subdivided, there is, I think, none which excels, or even equals in importance that called *Induction.* It is of the most general influence in electrical phenomena, appearing to be concerned in every one of them, and has in reality the character of a first, essential, and fundamental principle.  Its comprehension is so important, that I think we cannot proceed much further in the investigation of the laws of electricity without a more thorough understanding of its nature ;  how otherwise can we hope to comprehend the harmony and even unity of action which doubtless governs electrical excitement by friction, by chemical means, by heat, by magnetic influence, by evaporation, and even by the living being ?

1163.  In the long-continued course of experimental inquiry in which I have been  engaged, this  general result has pressed upon me constantly, namely, the necessity of admitting  two forces, or two forms or  directions of  a force (516. 517.), combined with the impossibility of separating these two forces  (or electricities) from  each other, either in the  phenomena of statical electricity or those of the current.   In association with this, the impossibility under  any circumstances, as yet, of absolutely charging matter of any kind with one or the other electricity only, dwelt on my mind, and  made me wish and search for a clearer view than any that  I  was  acquainted with, of the way in which  electrical powers and the  particles of matter are related ; especially in inductive actions, upon which almost all others appeared to rest.

1164.  When I discovered the  general fact that electrolytes refused to yield their elements to a current when in the solid state, though  they gave them forth freely if in the  liquid condition (380. 394. 402.), I thought I saw an opening to the elucidation of  inductive action, and the possible subjugation of many dissimilar phenomena to one law.   For let the electrolyte be water, a plate of ice being coated with platina foil on its two surfaces, and  these  coatings connected with  any continued source of  the two electrical powers, the ice will charge like a Leyden arrangement, presenting a case of common induction, but no current will pass.   If the ice be liquefied, the induction will fall to a certain degree, because a current can now pass ; but its passing is dependent upon a *peculiar molecular arrangement* of the particles consistent with the transfer of the elements of the electrolyte in opposite directions, the degree of discharge and the quantity of elements evolved being exactly proportioned to each other (377. 783.).   Whether the charging of the metallic coating be effected by a powerful electrical machine, a strong and large voltaic battery, or a single pair of plates, makes no difference in the principle, but only in the degree of action (360.). Common induction takes place in each case if the electrolyte be solid, or if fluid, chemical action and decomposition ensue, provided opposing actions do not interfere ; and it is of high importance occasionally thus to compare effects in their extreme degrees, for the purpose of enabling us to comprehend the nature of an action in its weak state, which may be only sufficiently evident to us in its stronger condition (451.). As, therefore, in the electrolytic action, *induction* appeared to be the *first* step, and *decomposition* the *second* (the power of separating these steps from each other by giving the solid or fluid condition to the electrolyte being in our hands) ; as the induction was the same in its nature as that through air, glass, wax, &c. produced by any of the ordinary means ; and as the whole effect in the electrolyte appeared to be an action of the particles thrown into a peculiar or polarized state, I was led to suspect that common induction itself was in all cases an *action of contiguous particles\**, and that electrical action at a distance (*i. e.* ordinary inductive action) never occurred except through the influence of the intervening matter.

1165. The respect which I entertain towards the names of Epinus, Cavendish, Poisson, and other most eminent men, all of whose theories I believe consider induction as an action at a distance and in straight lines, long indisposed me to the view I have just stated ; and though I always watched for opportunities to prove the opposite opinion, and made such experiments occasionally as seemed to bear directly on the point, as, for instance, the examination of electrolytes, solid and fluid, whilst under induction by polarized light (951. 955.), it is only of late, and by degrees, that the extreme generality of the subject has urged me still further to extend my experiments and publish my view. At present I believe ordinary induction in all cases to be an action of contiguous particles consisting in a species of polarity, instead of being an action of either particles or masses at sensible distances ; and if this be true, the di-

* The word *contiguous* is perhaps not the best that might have been used here and elsewhere ; for as particles do not touch each other it is not strictly correct. I was induced to employ it, because in its common acceptation it enabled me to state the theory plainly and with facility. By contiguous particles I mean those which are next.—*Dec.* 1838.

stinction and establishment of such a truth must be of the greatest consequence to our further progress in the investigation of the nature of electric forces. The linked condition of electrical induction with chemical decomposition; of voltaic excitement with chemical action; the transfer of elements in an electrolyte; the original cause of excitement in all cases; the nature and relation of conduction and insulation; of the direct and lateral or transverse action constituting electricity and magnetism; with many other things more or less incomprehensible at present, would all be affected by it, and perhaps receive a full explication in their reduction under one general law.

1166. I searched for an unexceptionable test of my view, not merely in the accordance of known facts with it, but in the consequences which would flow from it if true; especially in those which would not be consistent with the theory of action at a distance. Such a consequence seemed to me to present itself in the direction in which inductive action could be exerted. If in straight lines only, though not perhaps decisive, it would be against my view; but if in curved lines also, that would be a natural result of the action of contiguous particles, but, as I think, utterly incompatible with action at a distance, as assumed by the received theories, which, according to every fact and analogy we are acquainted with, is always in straight lines.

1167. Again, if induction be an action of contiguous particles, and also the first step in the process of electrolyzation (1164. 949.), there seemed reason to expect some particular relation of it to the different kinds of matter through which it would be exerted, or something equivalent to a *specific electric induction* for different bodies, which, if it existed, would unequivocally prove the dependence of induction on the particles; and though this, in the theory of Poisson and others, has never been supposed to be the case, I was soon led to doubt the received opinion, and have taken great pains in subjecting this point to close experimental examination.

1168. Another ever-present question on my mind has been, whether electricity has an actual and independent existence as a fluid or fluids, or was a mere power of matter, like what we conceive of the attraction of gravitation. If determined either way it would be an enormous advance in our knowledge; and as having the most direct and influential bearing on my notions, I have always sought for experiments which would in any way tend to elucidate that great inquiry.  It was in attempts to prove the existence of electricity separate from matter, by giving an independent charge of either positive or negative power only, to some one substance, and the utter failure of all such attempts, whatever substance was used or whatever means of exciting or *evolving* electricity were employed, that first drove me to look upon induction as an action of the particles of matter, each having *both* forces developed in it in exactly equal amount.   It is this circumstance, in connection with others, which makes me desirous of placing the remarks on absolute charge first, in the order of proof and argument, which I am about to adduce in favour of my view, that electric induction is an action of the contiguous particles of the insulating medium or *dielectric\**.

¶ ii.  *On the absolute charge of matter.*

1169. Can matter, either conducting or non-conducting, be charged with one electric force independently of the other, in any degree, either in a sensible or latent state ?

1170. The beautiful experiments of Coulomb upon the equality of action of *conductors*, whatever their substance, and the residence of *all* the electricity upon their surfaces †, are sufficient, if properly viewed, to prove that *conductors cannot be bodily charged* ; and as yet no means of communicating electricity to a conductor so as to place its particles in relation to one electricity, and not at the same time to the other in exactly equal amount, has been discovered.

1171. With regard to electrics or non-conductors, the conclusion does not at first seem so clear.  They may easily be electrified bodily, either by communication (1247.) or excitement ; but being so charged, every case in succession, when examined, came out to be a case of induction, and not of absolute charge.   Thus, glass within conductors could easily have parts not in contact with the conductor brought into an excited state ; but it was always found that a portion of the inner sur-

* I use the word *dielectric* to express that substance through or across which the electric forces are acting.—*Dec.* 1838.

† Mémoires de l'Académie, 1786, pp. 67. 69. 72 ; 1787, p. 452.

face of the conductor was in an opposite and equivalent state, or that another part of the glass itself was in an equally opposite state, an *inductive* charge and not an *absolute* charge having been acquired.

1172. Well-purified oil of turpentine, which I find to be an excellent liquid insulator for most purposes, was put into a metallic vessel, and, being insulated, an endeavour was made to charge its particles, sometimes by contact of the metal with the electrical machine, and at others by a wire dipping into the fluid within; but whatever the mode of communication, no electricity of one kind only was retained by the arrangement, except what appeared on the exterior surface of the metal, that portion being present there only by an inductive action through the air to the surrounding conductors. When the oil of turpentine was confined in glass vessels, there were at first some appearances as if the fluid did receive an absolute charge of electricity from the charging wire, but these were quickly reduced to cases of common induction jointly through the fluid, the glass, and the surrounding air.

1173. I carried these experiments on with air to a very great extent. I had a chamber built, being a cube of twelve feet. A slight cubical wooden frame was constructed, and copper wire passed along and across it in various directions, so as to make the sides a large net-work, and then all was covered in with paper, placed in close connexion with the wires, and supplied in every direction with bands of tin foil, that the whole might be brought into good metallic communication, and rendered a free conductor in every part. This chamber was insulated in the lecture-room of the Royal Institution; a glass tube about six feet in length was passed through its side, leaving about four feet within and two feet on the outside, and through this a wire passed from the large electrical machine (290.) to the air within. By working the machine, the air in this chamber could be brought into what is considered a highly electrified state (being, in fact, the same state as that of the air of a room in which a powerful machine is in operation), and at the same time the outside of the insulated cube was everywhere strongly charged. But putting the chamber in communication with the perfect discharging train described in a former series (292.), and working the machine so as to bring the air within to its utmost degree of charge if I quickly cut off the connexion with the machine, and at the same moment or instantly after insulated the cube, the air within had not the least power to communicate a further charge to it. If any portion of the air was electrified, as glass or other insulators may be charged (1171.), it was accompanied by a corresponding opposite action *within* the cube, the whole effect being merely a case of induction. Every attempt to charge air bodily and independently with the least portion of either electricity failed.

1174. I put a delicate gold-leaf electrometer within the cube, and then charged the whole by an *outside* communication, very strongly, for some time together; but neither during the charge or after the discharge did the electrometer or air within show the least signs of electricity. I charged and discharged the whole arrangement in various ways, but in no case could I obtain the least indication of an absolute charge; or of one by induction in which the electricity of one kind had the smallest superiority in quantity over the other. I went into the cube and lived in it, and using lighted candles, electrometers, and all other tests of electrical states, I could not find the least influence upon them, or indication of anything particular given by them, though all the time the outside of the cube was powerfully charged, and large sparks and brushes were darting off from every part of its outer surface. The conclusion I have come to is, that non-conductors, as well as conductors, have never yet had an absolute and independent charge of one electricity communicated to them, and that to all appearance such a state of matter is impossible.

1175. There is another view of this question which may be taken under the supposition of the existence of an electric fluid or fluids. It may be impossible to have one fluid or state in a free condition without its producing by induction the other, and yet possible to have cases in which an isolated portion of matter in one condition being uncharged, shall, by a change of state, evolve one electricity or the other: and though such evolved electricity might immediately induce the opposite state in its neighbourhood, yet the mere evolution of one electricity without the other in the *first instance*, would be a very important fact in the theories which assume a fluid or fluids; these

theories as I understand them assigning not the slightest reason why such an effect should not occur.

1176. But on searching for such cases I cannot find one.
Evolution by friction, as is well known, gives both powers in
equal proportion. So does evolution by chemical action, notwithstanding the great diversity of bodies which may be employed, and the enormous quantity of electricity which can in
this manner be evolved (371. 376. 861. 868. 961.). The more
promising cases of change of state, whether by evaporation,
fusion, or the reverse processes, still give both forms of the
power in *equal* proportion; and the cases of splitting of mica
and other crystals, the breaking of sulphur, &c., are subject to
the same law of limitation.

1177. As far as experiment has proceeded, it appears, therefore, impossible either to evolve or make disappear one electric
force without equal and corresponding change in the other. It
is also equally impossible experimentally to charge a portion
of matter with one electric force independently of the other.
Charge always implies *induction,* for it can in no instance be
effected without; and also the presence of the *two* forms of
power, equally at the moment of the development and afterwards. There is no *absolute* charge of matter with one fluid;
no latency of a single electricity. This though a negative result is an exceedingly important one, being probably the consequence of a natural impossibility, which will become clear to
us when we understand the true condition and theory of the
electric power.

1178. The preceding considerations already point to the following conclusions : bodies cannot be charged absolutely, but
only relatively, and by a principle which is the same with that
of *induction.* All *charge* is sustained by induction. All phenomena of *intensity* include the principle of induction. All *excitation* is dependent on or directly related to induction. All
*currents* involve previous intensity and therefore previous induction. INDUCTION appears to be the essential function both
in the first development and the consequent phenomena of
electricity.

¶ iii. *Electrometer and inductive apparatus employed.*

1179. Leaving for a time the further consideration of the

preceding facts until they can be collated with other results
bearing directly on the great question of the nature of induction, I will now describe the apparatus I have had occasion to
use ; and in proportion to the importance of the principles
sought to be established is the necessity of doing this so clearly,
as to leave no doubt of the results behind.

1180. *Electrometer.* The measuring instrument I have employed has been the torsion balance electrometer of Coulomb,
constructed, generally, according to his directions*, but with
certain variations and additions, which I will briefly describe.
The lower part was a glass cylinder eight inches in height and
eight inches in diameter ; the tube for the torsion thread was
seventeen inches in length. The torsion thread itself was not
of metal, but glass, according to the excellent suggestion of the
late Dr. Ritchie †. It was twenty inches in length, and of such
tenuity that when the shell-lac lever and attached ball, &c.
were connected with it, they made about ten vibrations in a
minute. It would bear torsion through four revolutions or
1440°, and yet, when released, return accurately to its position ;
probably it would have borne considerably more than this without injury. The repelled ball was of pith, gilt, and was 0·3 of
an inch in diameter. The horizontal stem or lever supporting
it was of shell-lac, according to Coulomb's direction, the arm
carrying the ball being 2·4 inches long, and the other only 1·2
inches : to this was attached the vane, also described by Coulomb, which I found to answer admirably its purpose of quickly
destroying vibrations. That the inductive action within the
electrometer might be uniform in all positions of the repelled
ball and in all states of the apparatus, two bands of tin foil,
about an inch wide each, were attached to the inner surface of
the glass cylinder, going entirely round it, at the distance of
0·4 of an inch from each other, and at such a height that the
intermediate clear surface was in the same horizontal plane with
the lever and ball. These bands were connected with each
other and with the earth, and, being perfect conductors, always
exerted a uniform influence on the electrified balls within, which
the glass surface, from its irregularity of condition at different
times, I found, did not. For the purpose of keeping the air

* Mémoires de l'Académie, 1785, p. 570.
† Philosophical Transactions, 1830.

within the electrometer in a constant state as to dryness, a glass dish, of such size as to enter easily within the cylinder, had a layer of fused potash placed within it, and this being covered with a disc of fine wire-gauze to render its inductive action uniform at all parts, was placed within the instrument at the bottom and left there.

1181. The moveable ball used to take and measure the portion of electricity under examination, and which may be called the *repelling,* or the *carrier,* ball, was of soft alder wood, well and smoothly gilt. It was attached to a fine shell-lac stem, and introduced through a hole into the electrometer according to Coulomb's method: the stem was fixed at its upper end in a block or vice, supported on three short feet; and on the surface of the glass cover above was a plate of lead with stops on it, so that when the carrier ball was adjusted in its right position, with the vice above bearing at the same time against these stops, it was perfectly easy to bring away the carrier-ball and restore it to its place again very accurately, without any loss of time.

1182. It is quite necessary to attend to certain precautions respecting these balls. If of pith alone they are bad; for when very dry, that substance is so imperfect a conductor that it neither receives nor gives a charge freely, and so, after contact with a charged conductor, it is liable to be in an uncertain condition. Again, it is difficult to turn pith so smooth as to leave the ball, even when gilt, so free from irregularities of form, as to retain its charge undiminished for a considerable length of time. When, therefore, the balls are finally prepared and gilt they should be examined; and being electrified, unless they can hold their charge with very little diminution for a considerable time, and yet be discharged instantly and perfectly by the touch of an uninsulated conductor, they should be dismissed.

1183. It is, perhaps, unnecessary to refer to the graduation of the instrument, further than to explain how the observations were made. On a circle or ring of paper on the outside of the glass cylinder, fixed so as to cover the internal lower ring of tinfoil, were marked four points corresponding to angles of 90°; four other points exactly corresponding to these points being marked on the upper ring of tinfoil within. By these

and the adjusting screws on which the whole instrument stands,
the glass torsion thread could be brought accurately into the
centre of the instrument and of the graduations on it.  From
one of the four points on the exterior of the cylinder a graduation of 90° was set off, and a corresponding graduation was
placed upon the upper tinfoil on the opposite side of the cylinder within; and a dot being marked on that point of the
surface of the repelled ball nearest to the side of the electrometer, it was easy, by observing the line which this dot made
with the lines of the two graduations just referred to, to ascertain accurately the position of the ball.  The upper end of the
glass thread was attached, as in Coulomb's original electrometer,
to an index, which had its appropriate graduated circle, upon
which the degree of torsion was ultimately to be read off.

1184. After the levelling of the instrument and adjustment
of the glass thread, the blocks which determine the place of
the *carrier ball* are to be regulated (1181.) so that when the
carrier arrangement is placed against them, the centre of the
ball may be in the radius of the instrument corresponding to 0°
on the lower graduation or that on the side of the electrometer,
and at the same level and distance from the centre as the *repelled
ball* on the suspended torsion lever.  Then the torsion index
is to be turned until the ball connected with it (the repelled ball)
is accurately at 30°, and finally the graduated arc belonging
to the torsion index is to be adjusted so as to bring 0° upon it
to the index.  This state of the instrument was adopted as that
which gave the most direct expression of the experimental results, and in the form having fewest variable errors; the angular
distance of 30° being always retained as the standard distance
to which the balls were in every case to be brought, and the
whole of the torsion being read off at once on the graduated
circle above.  Under these circumstances the distance of the
balls from each other was not merely the same in degree, but
their position in the instrument, and in relation to every part of
it, was actually the same every time that a measurement was
made; so that all irregularities arising from slight difference of
form and action in the instrument and the bodies around were
avoided.  The only difference which could occur in the position
of anything within, consisted in the deflection of the torsion
thread from a vertical position, more or less, according to the

force of repulsion of the balls ; but this was so slight as to cause
no interfering difference in the symmetry of form within the instrument, and gave no error in the amount of torsion force indicated on the graduation above.

1185. Although the constant angular distance of 30° between the centres of the balls was adopted, and found abundantly sensible, for all ordinary purposes, yet the facility of
rendering the instrument far more sensible by diminishing this
distance was at perfect command ; the results at different distances being very easily compared with each other either by
experiment, or, as they are inversely as the squares of the distances, by calculation.

1186. The Coulomb balance electrometer requires experience to be understood ; but I think it a very valuable instrument in the hands of those who will take pains by practice and
attention to learn the precautions needful in its use.   Its
insulating condition varies with circumstances, and should be
examined before it is employed in experiments.   In an ordinary
and fair condition, when the balls were so electrified as to give
a repulsive torsion force of 400° at the standard distance of 30°,
it took nearly four hours to sink to 50° at the same distance ;
the average loss from 400° to 300° being at the rate of 2°·7 per
minute, from 300° to 200° of 1°·7 per minute, from 200° to 100°
of 1°·3 per minute, and from 100° to 50° of 0°·87 per minute.
As a complete measurement by the instrument may be made in
much less than a minute, the amount of loss in that time is but
small, and can easily be taken into account.

1187. *The inductive apparatus.*—My object was to examine
inductive action carefully when taking place through different
media, for which purpose it was necessary to subject these
media to it in exactly similar circumstances, and in such quantities as should suffice to eliminate any variations they might present.   The requisites of the apparatus to be constructed were,
therefore, that the inducing surfaces of the conductors should
have a constant form and state, and be at a constant distance from
each other ; and that either solids, fluids, or gases might be
placed and retained between these surfaces with readiness and
certainty, and for any length of time.

1188. The apparatus used may be described in general terms

as consisting of two metallic spheres of unequal diameter, placed, the smaller within the larger, and concentric with it; the interval between the two being the space through which the induction was to take place. A section of it is given (Plate VII. fig. 104.) on a scale of one half: *a*, *a* are the two halves of a brass sphere, with an air-tight joint at *b*, like that of the Magdeburg hemispheres, made perfectly flush and smooth inside so as to present no irregularity; *c* is a connecting piece by which the apparatus is joined to a good stop-cock *d*, which is itself attached either to the metallic foot *e*, or to an air pump. The aperture within the hemisphere at *f* is very small; *g* is a brass collar fitted to the upper hemisphere, through which the shell-lac support of the inner ball and its stem passes; *h* is the inner ball, also of brass; it screws on to a brass stem *i*, terminated above by a brass ball B; *l*, *l* is a mass of shell-lac, moulded carefully on to *i*, and serving both to support and insulate it and its balls *h*, B. The shell-lac stem *l* is fitted into the socket *g*, by a little ordinary resinous cement, more fusible than shell-lac, applied at *m m* in such a way as to give sufficient strength and render the apparatus air-tight there, yet leave as much as possible of the lower part of the shell-lac stem untouched, as an insulation between the ball *h* and the surrounding sphere *a*, *a*. The ball *h* has a small aperture at *n*, so that when the apparatus is exhausted of one gas and filled with another, the ball *h* may itself also be exhausted and filled, that no variation of the gas in the interval *o* may occur during the course of an experiment.

1189. It will be unnecessary to give the dimensions of all the parts, since the drawing is to a scale of one half: the inner ball has a diameter of 2·33 inches, and the surrounding sphere an internal diameter of 3·57 inches. Hence the width of the intervening space, through which the induction is to take place, is 0·62 of an inch; and the extent of this place or plate, *i. e.* the surface of a medium sphere, may be taken as twenty-seven square inches, a quantity considered as sufficiently large for the comparison of different substances. Great care was taken in finishing well the inducing surfaces of the ball *h* and sphere *a*, *a*; and no varnish or lacquer was applied to them, or to any part of the metal of the apparatus.

1190. The attachment and adjustment of the shell-lac stem

was a matter requiring considerable care, especially as, in consequence of its cracking, it had frequently to be renewed. The best lac was chosen and applied to the wire *i*, so as to be in good contact with it everywhere, and in perfect continuity throughout its own mass. It was not smaller than is given by scale in the drawing, for when less it frequently cracked within a few hours after it was cold. I think that very slow cooling or annealing improved its quality in this respect. The collar *g* was made as thin as could be, that the lac might be as wide there as possible. In order that at every re-attachment of the stem to the upper hemisphere the ball *h* might have the same relative position, a gauge *p* (fig. 105.) was made of wood, and this being applied to the ball and hemisphere whilst the cement at *m* was still soft, the bearings of the ball at *q q*, and the hemisphere at *r r*, were forced home, and the whole left until cold. Thus all difficulty in the adjustment of the ball in the sphere was avoided.

1191. I had occasion at first to attach the stem to the socket by other means, as a band of paper or a plugging of white silk thread; but these were very inferior to the cement, interfering much with the insulating power of the apparatus.

1192. The retentive power of this apparatus was, when in good condition, better than that of the electrometer (1186.) *i. e.* the proportion of loss of power was less. Thus when the apparatus was electrified, and also the balls in the electrometer, to such a degree, that after the inner ball had been in contact with the top *k* of the ball of the apparatus, it caused a repulsion indicated by 600° of torsion force, then in falling from 600° to 400° the average loss was 8°·6 per minute; from 400° to 300° the average loss was 2°·6 per minute; from 300° to 200° it was 1°·7 per minute; from 200° to 170° it was 1° per minute. This was after the apparatus had been charged for a short time; at the first instant of charging there is an apparent loss of electricity, which can only be comprehended hereafter (1207. 1250.).

1193. When the apparatus loses its insulating power suddenly, it is almost always from a crack near to or within the brass socket. These cracks are usually transverse to the stem. If they occur at the part attached by common cement to the socket, the air cannot enter, and thus constituting vacua, they conduct away the electricity and lower the charge, as fast almost as if a piece of metal had been introduced there. Occasionally stems in this state, being taken out and cleared from the common cement, may by the careful application of the heat of a spirit-lamp, be so far softened and melted as to restore the perfect continuity of the parts; but if that does not succeed in replacing things in a good condition, the remedy is a new shell-lac stem.

1194. The apparatus when in order could easily be exhausted of air and filled with any given gas; but when that gas was acid or alkaline, it could not properly be removed by the air-pump, and yet required to be perfectly cleared away. In such cases the apparatus was opened and emptied of gas; and with respect to the inner ball $h$, it was washed out two or three times with distilled water introduced at the screw-hole, and then being heated above 212°, air was blown through to render the interior perfectly dry.

1195. The inductive apparatus described is evidently a Leyden phial, with the advantage, however, of having the *dielectric* or insulating medium changed at pleasure. The balls $h$ and B, with the connecting-wire $i$, constitute the charged conductor, upon the surface of which all the electric force is resident by virtue of induction (1178.). Now though the largest portion of this induction is between the ball $h$ and the surrounding sphere $a\,a$, yet the wire $i$ and the ball B determine a part of the induction from their surfaces towards the external surrounding conductors. Still, as all things in that respect remain the same, whilst the medium within at $o\,o$, may be varied, any changes exhibited by the whole apparatus will in such cases depend upon the variations made in the interior; and these were the changes I was in search of, the negation or establishment of such differences being the great object of my inquiry. I considered that these differences, if they existed, would be most distinctly set forth by having two apparatus of the kind described, precisely similar in every respect; and then, *different insulating media* being within, to charge one and measure it, and after dividing the charge with the other, to observe what the ultimate conditions of both were. If insulating media really had any specific differences in favouring or opposing inductive action through them, such differences, I conceived, could not fail of being developed by such a process.

1196. I will wind up this description of the apparatus, and explain the precautions necessary to their use, by describing the form and order of the experiments made to prove their equality when both contained common air. In order to facilitate reference I will distinguish the two by the terms App. i. and App. ii.

1197. The electrometer is first to be adjusted and examined (1184.), and the app. i. and ii. are to be perfectly discharged. A Leyden phial is to be charged to such a degree that it would give a spark of about one-sixteenth or one-twentieth of an inch in length between two balls of half an inch diameter; and the carrier ball of the electrometer being charged by this phial, is to be introduced into the electrometer, and the lever ball brought by the motion of the torsion index against it; the charge is thus divided between the balls, and repulsion ensues. It is useful then to bring the repelled ball to the standard distance of 30° by the motion of the torsion index, and observe the force in degrees required for this purpose; this force will in future experiments be called *repulsion of the balls*.

1198. One of the inductive apparatus, as, for instance, app. i., is now to be charged from the Leyden phial, the latter being in the state it was in when used to charge the balls; the carrier ball is to be brought into contact with the top of its upper ball (*k*, fig. 104.), then introduced into the electrometer, and the repulsive force (at the distance of 30°) measured. Again, the carrier should be applied to the app. i. and the measurement repeated; the apparatus i. and ii. are then to be joined, so as to *divide* the charge, and afterwards the force of each measured by the carrier ball, applied as before, and the results carefully noted. After this both i. and ii are to be discharged; then app. ii. charged, measured, divided with app. i., and the force of each again measured and noted. If in each case the half charges of app. i. and ii. are equal, and are together equal to the whole charge before division, then it may be considered as proved that the two apparatus are precisely equal in power, and fit to be used in cases of comparison between different insulating media or *dielectrics*.

1199. But the *precautions* necessary to obtain accurate results are numerous.    The apparatus i. and ii. must always be placed on a thoroughly uninsulating medium.    A mahogany table, for instance, is far from satisfactory in this respect, and therefore a sheet of tinfoil, connected with an extensive discharging train (292.), is what I have used.    They must be so placed also as not to be too near each other, and yet equally exposed to the inductive influence of surrounding objects ; and these objects, again, should not be disturbed in their position during an experiment, or else variations of induction upon the external ball B of the apparatus may occur, and so errors be introduced into the results.    The carrier ball, when receiving its portion of electricity from the apparatus, should always be applied at the same part of the ball, as, for instance, the summit $k$, and always in the same way ; variable induction from the vicinity of the head, hands, &c. being avoided, and the ball after contact being withdrawn upwards in a regular and constant manner.

1200. As the stem had occasionally to be changed (1190.), and the change might occasion slight variations in the position of the ball within, I made such a variation purposely, to the amount of an eighth of an inch (which is far more than ever could occur in practice), but did not find that it sensibly altered the relation of the apparatus, or its inductive condition *as a whole.*    Another trial of the apparatus was made as to the effect of dampness in the air, one being filled with very dry air, and the other with air from over water.    Though this produced no change in the result, except an occasional tendency to more rapid dissipation, yet the precaution was always taken when working with gases (1290.) to dry them perfectly.

1201. It is essential that the interior of the apparatus should be perfectly free from *dust or small loose particles,* for these very rapidly lower the charge and interfere on occasions when their presence and action would hardly be expected.    To breathe on the interior of the apparatus and wipe it out quietly with a clean silk handkerchief, is an effectual way of removing them ; but then the intrusion of other particles should be carefully guarded against, and a dusty atmosphere should for this and several other reasons be avoided.

1202. The shell-lac stem requires occasionally to be well wiped, to remove, in the first instance, the film of wax and adhering matter which is upon it; and afterwards to displace dirt and dust which will gradually attach to it in the course of experiments. I have found much to depend upon this precaution, and a silk handkerchief is the best wiper.

1203. But wiping and some other circumstances tend to give a charge to the surface of the shell-lac stem. This should be removed, for, if allowed to remain, it very seriously affects the degree of charge given to the carrier ball by the apparatus (1232.). This condition of the stem is best observed by discharging the apparatus, applying the carrier ball to the stem, touching it with the finger, insulating and removing it, and examining whether it has received any charge (by induction) from the stem; if it has, the stem itself is in a charged state. The best method of removing the charge I have found to be, to cover the finger with a single fold of a silk handkerchief, and breathing on the stem, to wipe it immediately after with the finger; the ball B and its connected wire, &c. being at the same time *uninsulated* : the wiping place of the silk must not be changed; it then becomes sufficiently damp not to excite the stem, and is yet dry enough to leave it in a clean and excellent insulating condition. If the air be dusty, it will be found that a single charge of the apparatus will bring on an electric state of the outside of the stem, in consequence of the carrying power of the particles of dust; whereas in the morning, and in a room which has been left quiet, several experiments can be made in succession without the stem assuming the least degree of charge.

1204. Experiments should not be made by candle or lamp light except with much care, for flames have great and yet unsteady powers of affecting and dissipating electrical charges.

1205. As a final observation on the state of the apparatus, they should retain their charges well and uniformly, and alike for both, and at the same time allow of a perfect and instantaneous discharge, giving afterwards no charge to the carrier ball, whatever part of the ball B it may be applied to (1218.).

1206. With respect to the balance electrometer, all the precautions that need be mentioned, are, that the carrier ball is to be preserved during the first part of an experiment in its electrified state, the loss of electricity which would follow upon its discharge being avoided; and that in introducing it into the electrometer through the hole in the glass plate above, care should be taken that it do not touch, or even come near to, the edge of the glass.

1207. When the whole charge in one apparatus is divided between the two, the gradual fall, apparently from dissipation, in the apparatus which has *received* the half charge is greater than in the one *originally* charged. This is due to a peculiar effect to be described hereafter (1250. 1251.), the interfering influence of which may be avoided to a great extent by going through the steps of the process regularly and quickly; therefore, after the original charge has been measured, in app. i. for instance, i. and ii. are to be symmetrically joined by their balls B, the carrier touching one of these balls at the same time; it is first to be removed, and then the apparatus separated from each other; app. ii. is next quickly to be measured by the carrier, then app. i.; lastly, ii. is to be discharged, and the discharged carrier applied to it to ascertain whether any residual effect is present (1205.), and app. i. being discharged is also to be examined in the same manner and for the same purpose.

1208. The following is an example of the division of a charge by the two apparatus, air being the dielectric in both of them. The observations are set down one under the other in the order in which they were taken, the left hand numbers representing the observations made on app. i., and the right hand numbers those on app. ii. App. i. is that which was originally charged, and after two measurements, the charge was divided with app. ii.

|  App. i. | | App. ii. |
|---|---|---|
| | Balls 160° | |
| | . . . . | 0° |
| 254° | . . . . | |
| 250 | . . . . | |
| | divided and instantly taken | |
| | . . . . | 122 |
| 124 | . . . . | |
| 1 | . . . . | after being discharged |
| | . . . . | 2 after being discharged. |

1209. Without endeavouring to allow for the loss which must have been gradually going on during the time of the experiment, let us observe the results of the numbers as they stand. As 1° remained in app. i. in an undischargeable state, 249° may be taken as the utmost amount of the transferable or divisible charge, the half of which is 124°·5. As app. ii. was free of charge in the first instance, and immediately after the division was found with 122°, this amount *at least* may be taken as what it had received. On the other hand 124° minus 1°, or 123°, may be taken as the half of the transferable charge retained by app. i. Now these do not differ much from each other, or from 124°·5, the half of the full amount of transferable charge; and when the gradual loss of charge evident in the difference between 254° and 250° of app. i. is also taken into account, there is every reason to admit the result as showing an equal division of charge, *unattended by any disappearance of power* except that due to dissipation.

1210. I will give another result, in which app. ii. was first charged, and where the residual action of that apparatus was greater than in the former case.

| App. i. | App. ii. | |
|---|---|---|
| Balls 150° | | |
| . . . . | 152° | |
| . . . . | 148 | |
| divided and instantly taken | | |
| 70° . . . . | | |
| . . . . | 78 | |
| . . . . | 5 | immediately after discharge. |
| 0 . . . . . . | | immediately after discharge. |

1211. The transferable charge being 148°—5°, its half is 71°·5, which is not far removed from 70°, the half charge of i. ; or from 73°, the half charge of ii. : these half charges again making up the sum of 143°, or just the amount of the whole transferable charge. Considering the errors of experiment, therefore, these results may again be received as showing that the apparatus were equal in inductive capacity, or in their powers of receiving charges.

1212. The experiments were repeated with charges of negative electricity with the same general results.

1213. That I might be sure of the sensibility and action of the apparatus, I made such a change in one as ought upon principle to increase its inductive force, *i. e.* I put a metallic lining into the lower hemisphere of app. i., so as to diminish the thickness of the intervening air in that part, from 0·62 to

0·435 of an inch : this lining was carefully shaped and rounded so that it should not present a sudden projection within at its edge, but a gradual transition from the reduced interval in the lower part of the sphere to the larger one in the upper.

1214. This change immediately caused app. i. to produce effects indicating that it had a greater aptness or capacity for induction than app. ii. Thus, when a transferable charge in app. ii. of 469° was divided with app. i., the former retained a charge of 225°, whilst the latter showed one of 227°, *i. e.* the former had lost 244° in communicating 227° to the latter : on the other hand, when app. i. had a transferable charge in it of 381° divided by contact with app. ii., it lost 181° only, whilst it gave to app. ii. as many as 194 :—the sum of the divided forces being in the first instance *less,* and in the second instance *greater* than the original undivided charge. These results are the more striking, as only one half of the interior of app. i. was modified, and they show that the instruments are capable of bringing out differences in inductive force from amongst the errors of experiment, when these differences are much less than that produced by the alteration made in the present instance.

¶ iv. *Induction in curved lines.*

1215. Amongst those results deduced from the molecular view of induction (1166.), which, being of a peculiar nature, are the best tests of the truth or error of the theory, the expected action in curved lines is, I think, the most important at present ; for, if shown to take place in an unexceptionable manner, I do not see how the old theory of action at a distance and in straight lines can stand, or how the conclusion that ordinary induction is an action of contiguous particles can be resisted.

1216. There are many forms of old experiments which might be quoted as favourable to, and consistent with the view I have adopted. Such are most cases of electro-chemical decomposition, electrical brushes, auras, sparks, &c. ; but as these might be considered equivocal evidence, inasmuch as they include a current and discharge, (though they have long been to me indications of prior molecular action (1230.) ) I endeavoured to devise such experiments for first proofs as should not include transfer, but relate altogether to the pure simple inductive action of statical electricity.

1217. It was also of importance to make these experiments in the simplest possible manner, using not more than one insulating medium or dielectric at a time, lest differences of slow conduction should produce effects which might erroneously be supposed to result from induction in curved lines. It will be unnecessary to describe the steps of the investigation minutely; I will at once proceed to the simplest mode of proving the facts, first in air and then in other insulating media.

1218. A cylinder of solid shell-lac, 0·9 of an inch in diameter and seven inches in length, was fixed upright in a wooden foot (fig. (106.) : it was made concave or cupped at its upper extremity so that a brass ball or other small arrangement could stand upon it. The upper half of the stem having been excited *negatively* by friction with warm flannel, a brass ball, B, 1 inch in diameter, was placed on the top, and then the whole arrangement examined by the carrier ball and Coulomb's electrometer (1180. &c.). For this purpose the balls of the electrometer were charged *positively* to about 360°, and then the carrier being applied to various parts of the ball B, the two were uninsulated whilst in contact or in position, then insulated*, separated, and the charge of the carrier examined as to its nature and force. Its electricity was always positive, and its force at the different positions *a*, *b*, *c*, *d*, &c. (figs. 106. and 107.) observed in succession, was as follows :

at *a* . . above 1000°

*b* it was . . . 149

*c* . . . . . 270

*d* . . . . . 512

*b* . . . . . 130

1219. To comprehend the full force of these results, it must first be understood, that all the charges of the ball B and the carrier are charges by induction, from the action of the excited surface of the shell-lac cylinder; for whatever electricity the ball B received by *communication* from the shell-lac, either in the first instance or afterwards, was removed by the uninsula-

---

* It can hardly be necessary for me to say here, that whatever general state the carrier ball acquired in any place where it was uninsulated and then insulated, it retained on removal from that place, notwithstanding that it might pass through other places that would have given to it, if uninsulated, a different condition.

ting contacts, only that due to induction remaining; and this
is shown by the charges taken from the ball in this its uninsulated state being always positive, or of the contrary character
to the electricity of the shell-lac.    In the next place, the charges
at *a*, *c*, and *d* were of such a nature as might be expected from
an inductive action in straight lines, but that obtained at *b* is
*not so*: it is clearly a charge by induction, but *induction* in *a*
*curved line*; for the carrier ball whilst applied to *b*, and after
its removal to a distance of six inches or more from B, could
not, in consequence of the size of B, be connected by a straight
line with any part of the excited and inducing shell-lac.

1220. To suppose that the upper part of the *uninsulated* ball
B, should in some way be retained in an electrified state by that
portion of the surface of the ball which is in sight of the shell-lac,
would be in opposition to what we know already of the subject.
Electricity is retained upon the surface of conductors only by
induction (1178.); and though some persons may not be prepared as yet to admit this with respect to insulated conductors,
all will as regards uninsulated conductors like the ball B; and
to decide the matter we have only to place the carrier ball at *e*
(fig. 107.), so that it shall not come in contact with B, uninsulate it by a metallic rod descending perpendicularly, insulate it,
remove it, and examine its state; it will be found charged with
the same kind of electricity as, and even to a *higher degree*
(1224.) than, if it had been in contact with the summit of B.

1221. To suppose, again, that induction acts in some way
*through or across* the metal of the ball, is negatived by the
simplest considerations; but a fact in proof will be better.    If
instead of the ball B a small disc of metal be used, the carrier
may be charged at, or above the middle of its upper surface:
but if the plate be enlarged to about $1\frac{1}{2}$ or 2 inches in diameter,
C (fig. 108.), then no charge will be given to the carrier at *f*,
though when applied nearer to the edge at *g*, or even *above the*
*middle* at *h*, a charge will be obtained; and this is true though
the plate may be a mere thin film of gold-leaf.    Hence it is clear
that the induction is not *through* the metal, but through the
surrounding air or *dielectric*, and that in curved lines.

1222. I had another arrangement, in which a wire passing
downwards through the middle of the shell-lac cylinder to the
earth, was connected with the ball B (fig. 109.) so as to keep

it in a constantly uninsulated state.   This was a very convenient form of apparatus, and the results with it were the same as
those just described.

1223.  In another case the ball B was supported by a shell-
lac stem, independently of the excited cylinder of shell-lac, and
at half an inch distance from it; but the effects were the same.
Then the brass ball of a charged Leyden jar was used in place
of the excited shell-lac to produce induction; but this caused
no alteration of the phenomena.   Both positive and negative
inducing charges were tried with the same general results.   Finally, the arrangement was inverted in the air for the purpose
of removing every possible objection to the conclusions, but
they came out exactly the same.

1224.  Some results obtained with a brass hemisphere instead
of the ball B were exceedingly interesting.   It was 1·36 of an
inch in diameter, (fig. 110.), and being placed on the top of the
excited shell-lac cylinder, the carrier ball was applied, as in
the former experiments (1218.), at the respective positions delineated in the figure.   At *i* the force was 112°, at *k* 108°, at *l*
65°, at *m* 35°; the inductive force gradually diminishing, as
might have been expected, to this point.   But on raising the
carrier to the position *n*, the charge increased to 87°; and on
raising it still higher to *o*, the charge still further increased to
105° : at a higher point still, *p*, the charge taken was smaller in
amount, being 98°, and continued to diminish for more elevated
positions.   Here the induction fairly turned a corner.   Nothing,
in fact, can better show both the curved lines or courses of the
inductive action, disturbed as they are from their rectilineal
form by the shape, position, and condition of the metallic hemisphere ; and also a *lateral tension,* so to speak, of these lines
on one another :—all depending, as I conceive, on induction
being an action of the contiguous particles of the dielectric,
which being thrown into a state of polarity and tension, are in
mutual relation by their forces in all directions.

1225.  As another proof that the whole of these actions were
inductive I may state a result which was exactly what might be
expected, namely, that if uninsulated conducting matter was
brought round and near to the excited shell-lac stem, then the
inductive force was directed towards it, and could not be found
on the top of the hemisphere.   Removing this matter the lines

of force resumed their former direction. The experiment affords proofs of the lateral tension of these lines, and supplies a warning to remove such matter in repeating the above investigation.

1226. After these results on curved inductive action in air I extended the experiments to other gases, using first carbonic acid and then hydrogen : the phenomena were precisely those already described. In these experiments I found that if the gases were confined in vessels they required to be very large, for whether of glass or earthenware, the conducting power of such materials is so great that the induction of the excited shell-lac cylinder towards them is as much as if they were metal ; and if the vessels be small, so great a portion of the inductive force is determined towards them that the lateral tension or mutual repulsion of the lines of force before spoken of (1224.), by which their inflexion is caused, is so much relieved in other directions, that no inductive charge will be given to the carrier ball in the positions $k$, $l$, $m$, $n$, $o$, $p$, (fig. 110.). A very good mode of making the experiment is to let large currents of the gases ascend or descend through the air, and carry on the experiments in these currents.

1227. These experiments were then varied by the substitution of a liquid dielectric, namely, *oil of turpentine*, in place of air and gases. A dish of thin glass well covered with a film of shell-lac, (1272.) which was found by trial to insulate well, had some highly rectified oil of turpentine put into it to the depth of half an inch, and being then placed upon the top of the brass hemisphere (fig. 110.), observations were made with the carrier ball as before (1224.). The results were the same, and the circumstance of some of the positions being within the fluid and some without, made no sensible difference.

1228. Lastly, I used a few solid dielectrics for the same purpose, and with the same results. These were shell-lac, sulphur, fused and cast borate of lead, flint glass well covered with a film of lac, and spermaceti. The following was the form of experiment with sulphur, and all were of the same kind. A square plate of the substance, two inches in extent and 0·6 of an inch in thickness, was cast with a small hole or depression in the middle of one surface to receive the carrier ball. This was placed upon the surface of the metal hemisphere (fig. 112.).

arranged on the excited lac as in former cases, and observations were made at *n, o, p,* and *q.*   Great care was required in these experiments to free the sulphur or other solid substance from any charge it might previously have received.   This was done by breathing and wiping (1203.), and the substance being found free from all electrical excitement, was then used in the experiment; after which it was removed and again examined, to ascertain that it had received no charge, but had acted really as a dielectric.   With all these precautions the results were the same: and it is thus very satisfactory to obtain the curved inductive action through *solid bodies,* as any possible effect from the translation of charged particles in fluids or gases, which some persons might imagine to be the case, is here entirely negatived.

1229. In these experiments with solid dielectrics, the degree of charge assumed by the carrier ball at the situations *n, o, p* (fig. 112.), was decidedly greater than that given to the ball at the same places when air only intervened between it and the metal hemisphere.   This effect is consistent with what will hereafter be found to be the respective relations of these bodies, as to their power of facilitating induction through them (1269. 1273. 1277.).

1230. I might quote *many* other forms of experiment, some old and some new, in which induction in curved or contorted lines take place, but think it unnecessary after the preceding results; I shall therefore mention but two.   If a conductor A, (fig. 111.) be electrified, and an uninsulated metallic ball B, or even a plate, provided the edges be not too thin, be held before it, a small electrometer at *c* or at *d,* uninsulated, will give signs of electricity, opposite in its nature to that of A, and therefore caused by induction, although the influencing and influenced bodies cannot be joined by a right line passing through the air.   Or if, the electrometers being removed, a point be fixed at the back of the ball in its uninsulated state as at C, this point will become luminous and discharge the conductor A. The latter experiment is described by Nicholson *, who, however, reasons erroneously upon it.   As to its introduction here, though it is a case of discharge, the discharge is preceded by induction, and that induction must be in curved lines.

* Encyclopædia Britannica, vol. vi. p. 504.

1231. As argument against the received theory of induction and in favour of that which I have ventured to put forth, I cannot see how the preceding results can be avoided. The effects are clearly inductive effects produced by electricity, not in currents but in its statical state, and this induction is exerted in lines of force which, though in many experiments they may be straight, are here curved more or less according to circumstances. I use the term *line of inductive force* merely as a temporary conventional mode of expressing the direction of the power in cases of induction ; and in the experiments with the hemisphere (1224.), it is curious to see how, when certain lines have terminated on the under surface and edge of the metal, those which were before lateral to them *expand and open out from each other*, some bending round and terminating their action on the upper surface of the hemisphere, and others meeting, as it were, above in their progress outwards, uniting their forces to give an increased charge to the carrier ball, at an *increased distance* from the source of power, and influencing each other so as to cause a second flexure in the contrary direction from the first one. All this appears to me to prove that the whole action is one of contiguous particles, related to each other, not merely in the lines which they may be conceived to form through the dielectric, between the *inductric* and the *inducteous* surfaces (1483.), but in other lateral directions also. It is this which gives an effect equivalent to a lateral repulsion or expansion in the lines of force I have spoken of, and enables induction to turn a corner (1304.). The power, instead of being like that of gravity, which causes particles to act on each other through straight lines, whatever other particles may be between them, is more analogous to that of a series of magnetic needles, or to the condition of the particles considered as forming the whole of a straight or a curved magnet. So that in whatever way I view it, and with great suspicion of the influence of favourite notions over myself, I cannot perceive how the ordinary theory applied to explain induction can be a correct representation of that great natural principle of electrical action.

1232. I have had occasion in describing the precautions necessary in the use of the inductive apparatus, to refer to one founded on induction in curved lines (1203.) ; and after the experiments already described, it will easily be seen how great an

influence the shell-lac stem may exert upon the charge of the
carrier ball when applied to the apparatus (1218.), unless that
precaution be attended to.

1233. I think it expedient, next in the course of these experimental researches, to describe some effects due to *conduction*,
obtained with such bodies as glass, lac, sulphur, &c., which had
not been anticipated. Being understood, they will make us
acquainted with certain precautions necessary in investigating
the great question of specific inductive capacity.

1234. One of the inductive apparatus already described
(1187, &c.) had a hemispherical cup of shell-lac introduced,
which being in the interval between the inner ball and the
lower hemisphere, nearly occupied the space there; consequently when the apparatus was charged, the lac was the dielectric or insulating medium through which the induction took
place in that part. When this apparatus was first charged
with electricity (1198.) up to a certain intensity, as 400°, measured by the Coulomb's electrometer (1180.), it sank much
faster from that degree than if it had been previously charged
to a higher point, and had gradually fallen to 400°; or than it
would do if the charge were, by a second application, raised up
again to 400°; all other things remaining the same. Again, if
after having been charged for some time, as fifteen or twenty
minutes, it was suddenly and perfectly discharged, even the
stem having all electricity removed from it (1203.), then the
apparatus being left to itself, would gradually recover a charge,
which in nine or ten minutes would rise up to 50° or 60°, and
in one instance to 80°.

1235. The electricity, which in these cases returned from an
apparently latent to a sensible state, was always of the same
kind as that which had been given by the charge. The return
took place at both the inducing surfaces; for if after the perfect discharge of the apparatus the whole was insulated, as the
inner ball resumed a positive state the outer sphere acquired a
negative condition.

1236. This effect was at once distinguished from that produced by the excited stem acting in curved lines of induction
(1203. 1232.), by the circumstance that all the returned electricity could be perfectly and instantly discharged. It appeared
to depend upon the shell-lac within, and to be, in some way,

due to electricity evolved from it in consequence of a previous condition into which it had been brought by the charge of the metallic coatings or balls.

1237. To examine this state more accurately, the apparatus, with the hemispherical cup of shell-lac in it, was charged for about forty-five minutes to above 600° with positive electricity at the balls *h* and B. (fig. 104.) above and within. It was then discharged, opened, the shell-lac taken out, and its state examined; this was done by bringing the carrier ball near the shell-lac, uninsulating it, insulating it, and then observing what charge it had acquired. As it would be a charge by induction, the state of the ball would indicate the opposite state of electricity in that surface of the shell-lac which had produced it. At first the lac appeared quite free from any charge; but gradually its two surfaces assumed opposite states of electricity, the concave surface, which had been next the inner and positive ball, assuming a positive state, and the convex surface, which had been in contact with the negative coating, acquiring a negative state; these states gradually increased in intensity for some time.

1238. As the return action was evidently greatest instantly after the discharge, I again put the apparatus together, and charged it for fifteen minutes as before, the inner ball positively. I then discharged it, instantly removing the upper hemisphere with the interior ball, and, leaving the shell-lac cup in the lower uninsulated hemisphere, examined its inner surface by the carrier ball as before (1237.). In this way I found the surface of the shell-lac actually *negative,* or in the reverse state to the ball which had been in it; this state quickly disappeared, and was succeeded by a positive condition, gradually increasing in intensity for some time, in the same manner as before. The first negative condition of the surface opposite the positive charging ball is a natural consequence of the state of things, the charging ball being in contact with the shell-lac only in a few points. It does not interfere with the general result and peculiar state now under consideration, except that it assists in illustrating in a very marked manner the ultimate assumption by the surfaces of the shell-lac of an electrified condition, similar to that of the metallic surfaces opposed to or against them.

1239. *Glass* was then examined with respect to its power of assuming this peculiar state. I had a thick flint-glass hemispherical cup formed, which would fit easily into the space *o* of the lower hemisphere (1188. 1189.) ; it had been heated and varnished with a solution of shell-lac in alcohol, for the purpose of destroying the conducting power of the vitreous surface (1254.). Being then well warmed and experimented with, I found it could also assume the *same state*, but not apparently to the same degree, the return action amounting in different cases to quantities from 6° to 18°.

1240. *Spermaceti* experimented with in the same manner gave striking results. When the original charge had been sustained for fifteen or twenty minutes at about 500°, the return charge was equal to 95° or 100°, and was about fourteen minutes arriving at the maximum effect. A charge continued for not more than two or three seconds was here succeeded by a return charge of 50° or 60°. The observations formerly made (1234.) held good with this substance. Spermaceti, though it will insulate a low charge for some time, is a better conductor than shell-lac, glass, and sulphur; and this conducting power is connected with the readiness with which it exhibits the particular effect under consideration.

1241. *Sulphur.*—I was anxious to obtain the amount of effect with this substance, first, because it is an excellent insulator, and in that respect would illustrate the relation of the effect to the degree of conducting power possessed by the dielectric (1247.) ; and in the next place, that I might obtain that body giving the smallest degree of the effect now under consideration, for the investigation of the question of specific inductive capacity (1277.).

1242. With a good hemispherical cup of sulphur cast solid and sound, I obtained the return charge, but only to an amount of 17° or 18°. Thus glass and sulphur, which are bodily very bad conductors of electricity, and indeed almost perfect insulators, gave very little of this return charge.

1243. I tried the same experiment having *air* only in the inductive apparatus. After a continued high charge for some time I could obtain a little effect of return action, but it was ultimately traced to the shell-lac of the stem.

1244. I sought to produce something like this state with one electric power and without induction; for upon the theory of an electric fluid or fluids, that did not seem impossible, and then I should have obtained an absolute charge (1169. 1177.), or something equivalent to it. In this I could not succeed. I excited the outside of a cylinder of shell-lac very highly for some time, and then quickly discharging it (1203.), waited and watched whether any return charge would appear, but such was not the case. This is another fact in favour of the inseparability of the two electric forces (1177.), and another argument for the view that induction and its concomitant phenomena depend upon a polarity of the particles of matter.

1245. Although inclined at first to refer these effects to a peculiar masked condition of a certain portion of the forces, I think I have since correctly traced them to known principles of electrical action. The effects appear to be due to an actual penetration of the charge to some distance within the electric, at each of its two surfaces, by what we call *conduction*; so that, to use the ordinary phrase, the electric forces sustaining the induction are not upon the metallic surfaces only, but upon and within the dielectric also, extending to a greater or smaller depth from the metal linings. Let $c$ (fig. 113.) be the section of a plate of any dielectric, $a$ and $b$ being the metallic coatings; let $b$ be uninsulated, and $a$ be charged positively; after ten or fifteen minutes, if $a$ and $b$ be discharged, insulated, and immediately examined, no electricity will appear in them; but in a short time, upon a second examination, they will appear charged in the same way, though not to the same degree, as they were at first. Now suppose that a portion of the positive force has, under the coercing influence of all the forces concerned, penetrated the dielectric and taken up its place at the line $p$, a corresponding portion of the negative force having also assumed its position at the line $n$; that in fact the electric at these two parts has become charged positive and negative; then it is clear that the induction of these two forces will be much greater one towards the other, and less in an external direction, now that they are at the small distance $n\,p$ from each other, than when they were at the larger interval $a\ b$. Then let $a$ and $b$ be discharged; the discharge destroys or neutralizes all external induction, and the coatings are therefore found by the carrier ball unelectrified but it also removes almost the whole of the forces by which the electric charge was driven into the dielectric, and though probably a part of that charge goes forward in its passage and terminates in what we call discharge, the greater portion returns on its course to the surfaces of *c*, and consequently to the conductors *a* and *b*, and constitutes the recharge observed.

1246. The following is the experiment on which ·I rest for the truth of this view. Two plates of spermaceti, *d* and *f* (fig. 114.), were put together to form the dielectric, *a* and *b* being the metallic coatings of this compound plate, as before. The system was charged, then discharged, insulated, examined, and found to give no indications of electricity to the carrier ball. The plates *d* and *f* were then separated from each other, and instantly *a* with *d* was found in a positive state, and *b* with *f* in a negative state, nearly all the electricity being in the linings *a* and *b*. Hence it is clear that, of the forces sought for, the positive was in one half of the compound plate and the negative in the other half; for when removed bodily with the plates from each other's inductive influence, they appeared in separate places, and resumed of necessity their power of acting by induction on the electricity of surrounding bodies. Had the effect depended upon a peculiar relation of the contiguous particles of matter only, then each half plate, *d* and *f*, should have shown positive force on one surface and negative on the other.

1247. Thus it would appear that the best solid insulators, such as shell-lac, glass and sulphur, have conductive properties to such an extent, that electricity can penetrate them bodily, though always subject to the overruling condition of induction (1178.). As to the depth to which the forces penetrate in this form of charge of the particles, theoretically, it should be throughout the mass, for what the charge of the metal does for the portion of dielectric next to it, should be done by the charged dielectric for the portion next beyond it again; but probably in the best insulators the sensible charge is to a very small depth only in the dielectric, for otherwise more would disappear in the first instance whilst the original charge is sustained, less time would be required for the assumption of the particular state, and more electricity would re-appear as return charge.

1248. The condition of *time* required for this penetration of the charge is important, both as respects the general relation of the cases to conduction, and also the removal of an objection that might otherwise properly be raised to certain results respecting specific inductive capacities, hereafter to be given (1269. 1277.).

1249. It is the assumption for a time of this charged state of the glass between the coatings in the Leyden jar, which gives origin to a well-known phenomenon, usually referred to the diffusion of electricity over the uncoated portion of the glass, namely, the *residual charge*. The extent of charge which can spontaneously be recovered by a large battery, after perfect uninsulation of both surfaces, is very considerable, and by far the largest portion of this is due to the return of electricity in the manner described. A plate of shell-lac six inches square, and half an inch thick, or a similar plate of spermaceti an inch thick, being coated on the sides with tinfoil as a Leyden arrangement, will show this effect exceedingly well.

---

1250. The peculiar condition of dielectrics which has now been described, is evidently capable of producing an effect interfering with the results and conclusions drawn from the use of the two inductive apparatus, when shell-lac, glass, &c. is used in one or both of them (1192. 1207.) ; for upon dividing the charge in such cases according to the method described (1198. 1207.), it is evident that the apparatus just receiving its half charge must fall faster in its tension than the other. For suppose app. i. first charged, and app. ii. used to divide with it ; though both may actually lose alike, yet app. i., which has been diminished one half, will be sustained by a certain degree of return action or charge (1234.), whilst app. ii. will sink the more rapidly from the coming on of the particular state. I have endeavoured to avoid this interference by performing the whole process of comparison as quickly as possible, and taking the force of app. ii. immediately after the division, before any sensible diminution of the tension arising from the assumption of the peculiar state could be produced ; and I have assumed that as about three minutes pass between the first charge of app. i. and the division, and three minutes between the division and discharge, when the force of the non-transferable electricity is measured, the contrary tendencies for those periods would keep that apparatus in a moderately steady and uniform condition for the latter portion of time.

1251. The particular action described occurs in the shell-lac of the stems, as well as in the *dielectric* used within the apparatus.   It therefore constitutes a cause by which the outside of the stems may in some operations become charged with electricity, independent of the action of dust or carrying particles (1203.).

¶ v.  *On specific induction, or specific inductive capacity.*

1252. I now proceed to examine the great question of specific inductive capacity, *i. e.* whether different dielectric bodies actually do possess any influence over the degree of induction which takes place through them.   If any such difference should exist, it appeared to me not only of high importance in the further comprehension of the laws and results of induction, but an additional and very powerful argument for the theory I have ventured to put forth, that the whole depends upon a molecular action, in contradistinction to one at sensible distances.

The question may be stated thus : suppose A an electrified plate of metal suspended in the air, and B and C two exactly similar plates, placed parallel to and on each side of A at equal distances and uninsulated ; A will then induce equally towards B and C.   If in this position of the plates some other dielectric than air, as shell-lac, be introduced between A and C, will the induction between them remain the same?   Will the relation of C and B to A be unaltered, notwithstanding the difference of the dielectrics interposed between them ? *

1253. As far as I recollect, it is assumed that no change will occur under such variation of circumstances, and that the relations of B and C to A depend entirely upon their distance. I only remember one experimental illustration of the question, and that is by Coulomb †, in which he shows that a wire surrounded by shell-lac took exactly the same quantity of electricity from a charged body as the same wire in air.   The ex-

* Refer for the practical illustration of this statement to the supplementary note commencing 1307, &c.—*Dec.* 1838.

† Mémoires de l'Académie, 1787, pp. 452, 453.

periment offered to me no proof of the truth of the supposition :
for it is not the mere films of dielectric substances surrounding
the charged body which have to be examined and compared,
but the *whole mass* between that body and the surrounding conductors at which the induction terminates. Charge depends
upon induction (1171. 1178.) ; and if induction is related to
the particles of the surrounding dielectric, then it is related to
*all* the particles of that dielectric inclosed by the surrounding
conductors, and not merely to the few situated next to the
charged body. Whether the difference I sought for existed
or not, I soon found reason to doubt the conclusion that might
be drawn from Coulomb's result ; and therefore had the apparatus made, which, with its use, has been already described
(1187, &c.), and which appears to me well suited for the investigation of the question.

1254. Glass, and many bodies which might at first be considered as very fit to test the principle, proved exceedingly unfit for that purpose. Glass, principally in consequence of the
alkali it contains, however well warmed and dried it may be,
has a certain degree of conducting power upon its surface, dependent upon the moisture of the atmosphere, which renders
it unfit for a test experiment. Resin, wax, naphtha, oil of turpentine, and many other substances were in turn rejected, because of a slight degree of conducting power possessed by them ;
and ultimately shell-lac and sulphur were chosen, after many
experiments, as the dielectrics best fitted for the investigation.
No difficulty can arise in perceiving how the possession of a
feeble degree of conducting power tends to make a body produce effects, which would seem to indicate that it had a greater
capability of allowing induction through it than another body
perfect in its insulation. This source of error has been that
which I have found most difficult to obviate in the proving experiments.

----

1255. *Induction through shell-lac.*—As a preparatory experiment, I first ascertained generally that when a part of the
surface of a thick plate of shell-lac was excited or charged,
there was no sensible difference in the character of the induction sustained by that charged part, whether exerted through

the air in the one direction, or through the shell-lac of the plate in the other; provided the second surface of the plate had not, by contact with conductors, the action of dust, or any other means, become charged (1203.). Its solid condition enabled it to retain the excited particles in a permanent position, but that appeared to be all; for these particles acted just as freely through the shell-lac on one side as through the air on the other. The same general experiment was made by attaching a disc of tinfoil to one side of the shell-lac plate, and electrifying it, and the results were the same. Scarcely any other solid substance than shell-lac and sulphur, and no liquid substance that I have tried will bear this examination. Glass in its ordinary state utterly fails; yet it was essentially necessary to obtain this prior degree of perfection in the dielectric used, before any further progress could be made in the principal investigation.

1256. *Shell-lac and air* were compared in the first place. For this purpose a thick hemispherical cup of shell-lac was introduced into the lower hemisphere of one of the inductive apparatus (1187, &c.), so as nearly to fill the lower half of the space *o*, *o* (fig. 104.) between it and the inner ball; and then charges were divided in the manner already described (1198. 1207.), each apparatus being used in turn to receive the first charge before its division by the other. As the apparatus were known to have equal inductive power when air was in both (1209. 1211.), any differences resulting from the introduction of the shell-lac would show a peculiar action in it, and if unequivocally referable to a specific inductive influence, would establish the point sought to be sustained. I have already referred to the precautions necessary in making the experiments (1199. &c.); and with respect to the error which might be introduced by the assumption of the peculiar state, it was guarded against, as far as possible, in the first place, by operating quickly (1248); and, afterwards, by using that dielectric as glass or sulphur, which assumed the peculiar state most slowly, and in the least degree (1239. 1241.).

1257. The shell-lac hemisphere was put into app. i., and app. ii. left filled with air. The results of an experiment in which the charge through air was divided and reduced by the shell-lac app. were as follows:

App. i. Lac.          App. ii. Air.
          Balls 255°.

0°   .   .   .   .

          .   .   .   304°

          .   .   .   297

Charge divided.

113   .   .   .   .

          .   .   .   121

0   .   .   .   .          after being discharged.

          .   .   .   .          7 after being discharged.

1258. Here 297°, minus 7°, or 290°, may be taken as the divisible charge of app. ii. (the 7° being fixed stem action (1203. 1232.)), of which 145° is the half. The lac. app. i. gave 113° as the power or tension it had acquired after division; and the air app. ii. gave 121°, minus 7°, or 114°, as the force it possessed from what it retained of the divisible charge of 290°. These two numbers should evidently be alike, and they are very nearly so, indeed far within the errors of experiment and observation. But these numbers differ very much from 145°, or the force which the half charge would have had if app. i. had contained air instead of shell-lac; and it appears that whilst in the division the induction through the air has lost 176° of force, that through the lac has only gained 113°.

1259. If this difference be assumed as depending entirely on the greater facility possessed by shell-lac of allowing or causing inductive action through its substance than that possessed by air, then this capacity for electric induction would be inversely as the respective loss and gain indicated above; and assuming the capacity of the air apparatus as 1, that of the shell-lac apparatus would be $\frac{176}{113}$ or 1·55.

1260. This extraordinary difference was so unexpected in its amount, as to excite the greatest suspicion of the general accuracy of the experiment, though the perfect discharge of app. i. after the division, showed that the 113° had been taken and given up readily. It was evident that, if it really existed, it ought to produce corresponding effects in the reverse order; and that when induction through shell-lac was converted into induction through air, the force or tension of the whole ought to be *increased*. The app. i. was therefore charged in the first place, and its force divided with app. ii.    The following were the results :

| App. i. Lac. | | | | App. ii. Air. |
|---|---|---|---|---|
| | . | . | . | 0° |
| 215° | . | . | . | |
| 204 | . | . | . | |
| Charge divided. | | | | |
| | . | . | . | 118 |
| 118 | . | . | . | |
| | . | . | . | 0 after being discharged. |
| 0 | . | . | . | after being discharged. |

1261. Here 204° must be the utmost of the divisible charge. The app. i. and app. ii. present 118° as their respective forces ; both now much *above* the half of the first force, or 102°, whereas in the former case they were below it.   The lac app. i. has lost only 86°, yet it has given to the air app. ii. 118°, so that the lac still appears much to surpass the air, the capacity of the lac app. i. to the air app. ii. being as 1·37 to 1.

1262. The difference of 1·55 and 1·37 as the expression of the capacity for the induction of shell-lac seems considerable, but is in reality very admissible under the circumstances, for both are in error in *contrary directions*.   Thus in the last experiment the charge fell from 215° to 204° by the joint effects of dissipation and absorption (1192. 1250.), during the time which elapsed in the electrometer operations, between the applications of the carrier ball required to give those two results. Nearly an equal time must have elapsed between the application of the carrier which gave the 204° result, and the division of the charge between the two apparatus ; and as the fall in force progressively decreases in amount (1192.), if in this case it be taken at 6° only, it will reduce the whole transferable charge at the time of division to 198° instead of 204° ; this diminishes the loss of the shell-lac charge to 80° instead of 86° ; and then the expression of specific capacity for it is increased, and, instead of 1·37, is 1·47 times that of air.

1263. Applying the same correction to the former experiment in which air was *first* charged, the result is of the *contrary* kind. No shell-lac hemisphere was then in the apparatus, and therefore the loss would be principally from dissipation, and not from absorption : hence it would be nearer to the degree of loss shown by the numbers 304° and 297°, and being assumed as 6° would reduce the divisible charge to 284°.   In that case the air would have lost 170°, and communicated only 113° to the shell-lac ; and the relative specific capacity of the latter would appear to be 1·50, which is very little indeed removed from 1·47, the expression given by the second experiment when corrected in the same way.

1264. The shell-lac was then removed from app. i. and put into app. ii. and the experiments of division again made.   I give the results, because I think the importance of the point justifies and even requires them.

App. i. Air.        App. ii. Lac.
Balls 200°.
. . . .        0°
286° . . . .
283 . . . .
Charge divided.
. . . . 110
109 . . . .
. . . .   0·25 after discharge.
Trace . . . .        after discharge.

Here app. i. retained 109°, having lost 174° in communicating 110° to app. ii. ; and the capacity of the air app. is to the lac app., therefore, as 1 to 1·58.   If the divided charge be corrected for an assumed loss of only 3°, being the amount of previous loss in the same time, it will make the capacity of the shell-lac app. 1·55 only.

1265. Then app. ii. was charged, and the charge divided thus :

App. i. Air.        App. ii. Lac.
0° . . . .
. . . . 256°
. . . . 251
Charge divided.
146 . . . .
. . . . 149
a little . . . .        after discharge.
. . . . a little after discharge.

Here app. i. acquired a charge of 146°, while app. ii. lost only 102° in communicating that amount of force; the capacities being, therefore, to each other as 1 to 1·43. If the whole transferable charge be corrected for a loss of 4° previous to division, it gives the expression of 1·49 for the capacity of the shell-lac apparatus.

1266. These four expressions of 1·47, 1·50, 1·55, and 1·49 for the power of the shell-lac apparatus, through the different variations of the experiment, are very near to each other; the average is close upon 1·5, which may hereafter be used as the expression of the result. It is a very important result; and, showing for this particular piece of shell-lac a decided superiority over air in allowing or causing the act of induction, it proved the growing necessity of a more close and rigid examination of the whole question.

1267. The shell-lac was of the best quality, and had been carefully selected and cleaned; but as the action of any conducting particles in it would tend, virtually, to diminish the quantity or thickness of the dielectric used, and produce effects as if the two inducing surfaces of the conductors in that apparatus were nearer together than in the one with air only, I prepared another shell-lac hemisphere, of which the material had been dissolved in strong spirit of wine, the solution filtered, and then carefully evaporated. This is not an easy operation, for it is difficult to drive off the last portions of alcohol without injuring the lac by the heat applied; and unless they be dissipated, the substance left conducts too well to be used in these experiments. I prepared two hemispheres this way, one of them unexceptionable; and with it I repeated the former experiments with all precautions. The results were exactly of the same kind; the following expressions for the capacity of the shell-lac apparatus, whether it were app. i. or ii., being given directly by the experiments, 1·46, 1·50, 1·52, 1·51; the average of these and several others being very nearly 1·5.

1268. As a final check upon the general conclusion, I then actually brought the surfaces of the air apparatus, corresponding to the place of the shell-lac in its apparatus, nearer together, by putting a metallic lining into the lower hemisphere of the one not containing the lac (1213.). The distance of the metal sur-

face from the carrier ball was in this way diminished from 0·62
of an inch to 0·435 of an inch, whilst the interval occupied by
the lac in the other apparatus remained 0·62 of an inch as
before.   Notwithstanding this change, the lac apparatus showed
its former superiority; and whether it or the air apparatus was
charged first, the capacity of the lac apparatus to the air apparatus was by the experimental results as 1·45 to 1.

1269. From all the experiments I have made, and their constant results, I cannot resist the conclusion that shell-lac does
exhibit a case of *specific inductive capacity*.   I have tried to
check the trials in every way, and if not remove, at least estimate,
every source of error.   That the final result is not due to common conduction is shown by the capability of the apparatus to
retain the communicated charge; that it is not due to the conductive power of inclosed small particles, by which they could
acquire a polarized condition as conductors, is shown by the
effects of the shell-lac purified by alcohol; and, that it is not
due to any influence of the charged state, formerly described
(1250.), first absorbing and then evolving electricity, is indicated by the *instantaneous* assumption and discharge of those
portions of the power which are concerned in the phenomena,
that instantaneous effect occurring in these cases, as in all others
of ordinary induction by charged conductors.   The latter argument is the more striking in the case where the air apparatus
is employed to divide the charge with the lac apparatus, for it
obtains its portion of electricity in an *instant*, and yet is charged
far above the *mean*.

1270. Admitting for the present the general fact sought to
be proved; then 1·5, though it expresses the capacity of the
apparatus containing the hemisphere of shell-lac, by no means
expresses the relation of lac to air.   The lac only occupies one
half of the space *o, o,* of the apparatus containing it, through
which the induction is sustained; the rest is filled with air, as
in the other apparatus; and if the effect of the two upper
halves of the globes be abstracted, then the comparison of the
shell-lac powers in the lower half of the one, with the power of
the air in the lower half of the other, will be as 2 : 1; and even
this must be less than the truth, for the induction of the upper
part of the apparatus, *i. e.* of the wire and ball B. (fig. 104.) to

external objects, must be the same in both, and considerably diminish the difference dependent upon, and really producible by, the influence of the shell-lac within.

1271. *Glass.*—I next worked with glass at the dielectric. It involved the possibility of conduction on its surface, but it excluded the idea of conducting particles within its substance (1267.) other than those of its own mass. Besides this it does not assume the charged state (1239.) so readily, or to such an extent as shell-lac.

1272. A thin hemispherical cup of glass being made hot was covered with a coat of shell-lac dissolved in alcohol, and after being dried for many hours in a hot place, was put into the apparatus and experimented with. It exhibited effects so slight, that, though they were in the direction indicating a superiority of glass over air, they were allowed to pass as possible errors of experiment; and the glass was considered as producing no sensible effect.

1273. I then procured a thick hemispherical flint glass cup resembling that of shell-lac (1239.), but not filling up the space *o, o,* so well. Its average thickness was 0·4 of an inch, there being an additional thickness of air, averaging 0·22 of an inch to make up the whole space of 0·62 of an inch between the inductive metallic surfaces. It was covered with a film of shell-lac as the former was, (1272.) and being made very warm, was introduced into the apparatus, also warmed, and experiments made with it as in the former instances (1257. &c.). The general results were the same as with shell-lac, *i. e.* glass surpassed air in its power of favouring induction through it. The two best results as respected the state of the apparatus for retention of charge, &c., gave, when the air apparatus was charged first 1·336, and when the glass apparatus was charged first 1·45, as the specific inductive capacity for glass, both being without correction. The average of nine results, four with the glass apparatus first charged, and five with the air apparatus first charged, gave 1·38 as the power of the glass apparatus; 1·22 and 1·46 being the minimum and maximum numbers with all the errors of experiment upon them. In all the experiments the glass apparatus took up its inductive charge instantly, and lost it as readily (1269.) ; and during the short time of each experiment, acquired the peculiar state in a small degree only, so that the influence of this state, and also of conduction upon the results, must have been small.

1274. Allowing specific inductive capacity to be proved and active in this case, and 1·38 as the expression for the glass apparatus, then the specific inductive capacity of flint glass will be above 1·76, not forgetting that this expression is for a piece of glass of such thickness as to occupy not quite two-thirds of the space through which the induction is sustained (1273. 1253.).

---

1275. *Sulphur.*—The same hemisphere of this substance was used in app. ii. as was formerly referred to (1242.). The experiments were well made, *i. e.* the sulphur itself was free from charge both before and after each experiment, and no action from the stem appeared (1203. 1232.), so that no correction was required on that account. The following are the results when the air apparatus was first charged and divided :

<pre>
      App. i. Air.        App. ii. Sulphur.
            Balls 280°.
       0°  .  .  .  .
            .  .  .  .      0°
      438  .  .  .  .
      434  .  .  .  .
            Charge divided.
            .  .  .  .    162
      164  .  .  .  .
            .  .  .  .    160
      162  .  .  .  .
            .  .  .  .    0 after discharge.
       0   .  .  .  .      after discharge.
</pre>

Here app. i. retained 164°, having lost 270° in communicating 162° to app. ii., and the capacity of the air apparatus is to that of the sulphur apparatus as 1 to 1·66.

1276. Then the sulphur apparatus was charged first, thus :

<pre>
            .  .  .  .      0°
       0°  .  .  .  .
            .  .  .  .    395
            .  .  .  .    388
</pre>

Charge divided.

237 . . . .

. . . . 238

0 . . . .        after discharge.

. . . .        0 after discharge.

Here app. ii. retained 238°, and gave up 150° in communicating a charge of 237° to app. i., and the capacity of the air
apparatus is to that of the sulphur apparatus as 1 to 1·58. These
results are very near to each other, and we may take the mean
1·62 as representing the specific inductive capacity of the sulphur apparatus : in which case the specific inductive capacity
of sulphur itself as compared to air = 1 (1270.) will be about
or above 2·24.

1277. This result with sulphur I consider as one of the most
unexceptionable. The substance when fused was perfectly
clear, pellucid, and free from particles of dirt (1267.), so that
no interference of small conducting bodies confused the result.
The substance when solid is an excellent insulator, and by
experiment was found to take up, with great slowness, that
state (1241. 1242.) which alone seemed likely to disturb the
conclusion. The experiments themselves, also, were free from
any need of correction. Yet notwithstanding these circumstances, so favourable to the exclusion of error, the result is a
higher specific inductive capacity for sulphur than for any other
body as yet tried ; and though this may in part be due to the
sulphur being in a better shape, *i. e.* filling up more completely
the space *o, o,* (fig. 104.) than the cups of shell-lac and glass,
still I feel satisfied that the experiments altogether fully prove
the existence of a difference between dielectrics as to their power
of favouring an inductive action through them ; which difference may, for the present, be expressed by the term *specific
inductive capacity.*

1278. Having thus established the point in the most favourable cases that I could anticipate, I proceeded to examine other
bodies amongst solids, liquids, and gases. These results I shall
give with all convenient brevity.

1279. *Spermaceti.*—A good hemisphere of spermaceti being
tried as to conducting power whilst its two surfaces were still
in contact with the tinfoil moulds used in forming it, was

found to conduct sensibly even whilst warm. On removing it from the moulds and using it in one of the apparatus, it gave results indicating a specific inductive capacity between 1·3 and 1·6 for the apparatus containing it. But as the only mode of operation was to charge the air apparatus, and then after a quick contact with the spermaceti apparatus, ascertain what was left in the former (1281.), no great confidence can be placed in the results. They are not in opposition to the general conclusion, but cannot be brought forward as argument in favour of it.

1280. I endeavoured to find some liquids which would insulate well, and could be obtained in sufficient quantity for these experiments. Oil of turpentine, native naphtha rectified, and the condensed oil gas fluid, appeared by common experiments to promise best as to insulation. Being left in contact with fused carbonate of potassa, chloride of lime, and quick lime for some days and then filtered, they were found much injured in insulating power; but after distillation acquired their best state, though even then they proved to be conductors when extensive metallic contact was made with them.

1281. *Oil of turpentine rectified.*—I filled the lower half of app. i. with the fluid: and as it would not hold a charge sufficiently to enable me first to measure and then divide it, I charged app. ii. containing air, and dividing its charge with app. i. by a quick contact, measured that remaining in app. ii.: for, theoretically, if a quick contact would divide up to equal tension between the two apparatus, yet without sensible loss from the conducting power of app. i.; and app. ii. were left charged to a degree of tension above half the original charge, it would indicate that oil of turpentine had less specific inductive capacity than air; or, if left charged below that mean state of tension, it would imply that the fluid had the greater inductive capacity. In an experiment of this kind, app. ii. gave as its charge 390° before division with app. i., and 175° afterwards, which is less than the half of 390°. Again, being at 175° before division, it was 79° after, which is also less than half the divided charge. Being at 79°, it was a third time divided, and then fell to 36°, less than the half of 79°. Such are the best results I could obtain; they are not inconsistent with the belief that oil of turpentine has a greater specific capacity than air, but they do not prove the fact, since the dis-appearance of more than half the charge may be due to the conducting power merely of the fluid.

1282. *Naphtha.*—This liquid gave results similar in their nature and direction to those with oil of turpentine.

---

1283. A most interesting class of substances, in relation to specific inductive capacity, now came under review, namely, the gases or aeriform bodies. These are so peculiarly consti-tuted, and are bound together by so many striking physical and chemical relations, that I expected some remarkable results from them : air in various states was selected for the first expe-riments.

1284. *Air, rare and dense.*—Some experiments of division (1208.) seemed to show that dense and rare air were alike in the property under examination. A simple and better process was to attach one of the apparatus to an air pump, to charge it, and then examine the tension of the charge when the air within was more or less rarefied. Under these circumstances it was found, that commencing with a certain charge, that charge did not change in its tension or force as the air was rare-fied, until the rarefaction was such that *discharge* across the space *o, o* (fig. 104.) occurred. This discharge was proportionate to the rarefaction; but having taken place, and lowered the tension to a certain degree, that degree was not at all affected by restoring the pressure and density of the air to their first quantities.

inches of mercury.

| | | | | |
|---|---|---|---|---|
| Thus at a pressure of | 30 | the charge was | . . . | 88° |
| Again . . . . . | 30 | the charge was | . . . | 88 |
| Again . . . . . | 30 | the charge was | . . . | 87 |
| Reduced to . . . . | 14 | the charge was | . . . | 87 |
| Raised again to . . | 30 | the charge was | . . . | 86 |
| Being now reduced to | 3·4 | the charge fell to. | . . | 81 |
| Raised again to . . | 30 | the charge was still | . . | 81 |

1285. The charges were low in these experiments, first that they might not pass off at low pressure, and next that little loss by dissipation might occur. I now reduced them still lower, that I might rarefy further, and for this purpose in the following experiment used a measuring interval in the electro-meter of only 15° (1185.). The pressure of air within the appa-ratus being reduced to 1·9 inches of mercury, the charge was found to be 29°; then letting in air till the pressure was 30 inches, the charge was still 29°.

1286. These experiments were repeated with pure oxygen with the same consequences.

1287. This result of *no variation* in the electric tension being produced by variation in the density or pressure of the air agrees perfectly with those obtained by Mr. Harris\*, and described in his beautiful and important investigations contained in the Phi-losophical Transactions ; namely that induction is the same in rare and dense air, and that the divergence of an electrometer under such variations of the air continues the same, provided no electricity pass away from it. The effect is one entirely in-dependent of that power which dense air has of causing a higher charge to be *retained* upon the surface of conductors in it than can be retained by the same conductors in rare air; a point I propose considering hereafter.

1288. I then compared *hot and cold air* together, by raising the temperature of one of the inductive apparatus as high as it could be without injury, and then dividing charges between it and the other apparatus containing cold air. The tempera-tures were about 50° and 200°. Still the power or capacity appeared to be unchanged ; and when I endeavoured to vary the experiment, by charging a cold apparatus and then warming it by a spirit lamp, I could obtain no proof that the inductive capacity underwent any alteration.

1289. I compared *damp and dry air* together, but could find no difference in the results.

---

1290. *Gases.*—A very long series of experiments was then undertaken for the purpose of comparing *different gases* one with another. They were all found to insulate well, except such as acted on the shell-lac of the supporting stem; these were chlorine, ammonia, and muriatic acid. They were all dried by appropriate means before being introduced into the apparatus. It would have been sufficient to have compared each with air ; but, in consequence of the striking result which came out,

* Philosophical Transactions, 1834, pp. 223, 224, 237, 244.

namely, that *all had the same power of* or *capacity for,* sustaining induction through them, (which perhaps might have been expected after it was found that no variation of density or pressure produced any effect,) I was induced to compare them, experimentally, two and two in various ways, that no difference might escape me, and that the sameness of result might stand in full opposition to the contrast of property, composition, and condition which the gases themselves presented.

1291. The experiments were made upon the following pairs of gases.

| | | |
|---|---|---|
| 1. | Nitrogen and . . | Oxygen. |
| 2. | Oxygen . . . . | Air. |
| 3. | Hydrogen . . . | Air. |
| 4. | Muriatic acid gas . | Air. |
| 5. | Oxygen . . . . | Hydrogen. |
| 6. | Oxygen . . . . | Carbonic acid. |
| 7. | Oxygen . . . . | Olefiant gas. |
| 8. | Oxygen . . . . | Nitrous gas. |
| 9. | Oxygen . . . . | Sulphurous acid. |
| 10. | Oxygen . . . . | Ammonia. |
| 11. | Hydrogen . . . | Carbonic acid. |
| 12. | Hydrogen . . . | Olefiant gas. |
| 13. | Hydrogen . . . | Sulphurous acid. |
| 14. | Hydrogen . . . | Fluo-silicic acid. |
| 15. | Hydrogen . . . | Ammonia. |
| 16. | Hydrogen . . . | Arseniuretted hydrogen. |
| 17. | Hydrogen . . . | Sulphuretted hydrogen. |
| 18. | Nitrogen . . . . | Olefiant gas. |
| 19. | Nitrogen . . . . | Nitrous gas. |
| 20. | Nitrogen . . . . | Nitrous oxide. |
| 21. | Nitrogen . . . . | Ammonia. |
| 22. | Carbonic oxide . . | Carbonic acid. |
| 23. | Carbonic oxide . . | Olefiant gas. |
| 24. | Nitrous oxide . . | Nitrous gas. |
| 25. | Ammonia. . . . | Sulphurous acid. |

1292. Notwithstanding the striking contrasts of all kinds which these gases present of property, of density, whether simple or compound, anions or cathions (665.), of high or low pressure (1284. 1286.), hot or cold (1288.), not the least difference in their capacity to favour or admit electrical induction through them could be perceived. Considering the point established, that in all these gases induction takes place by an action of contiguous particles, this is the more important, and adds one to the many striking relations which hold between bodies having the gaseous condition and form. Another equally important electrical relation, which will be examined in the next paper*, is that which the different gases have to each other at the *same pressure* of causing the retention of the *same or different degrees of charge* upon conductors in them. These two results appear to bear importantly upon the subject of electrochemical excitation and decomposition; for as *all* these phenomena, different as they seem to be, must depend upon the electrical forces of the particles of matter, the very distance at which they seem to stand from each other will do much, if properly considered, to illustrate the principle by which they are held in one common bond, and subject, as they must be, to one common law.

1293. It is just possible that the gases may differ from each other in their specific inductive capacity, and yet by quantities so small as not to be distinguished in the apparatus I have used. It must be remembered, however, that in the gaseous experiments the gases occupy all the space *o, o,* (fig. 104.) between the inner and the outer ball, except the small portion filled by the stem; and the results, therefore, are twice as delicate as those with solid dielectrics.

1294. The insulation was good in all the experiments recorded, except Nos. 10, 15, 21, and 25, being those in which ammonia was compared with other gases. When shell-lac is put into ammoniacal gas its surface gradually acquires conducting power, and in this way the lac part of the stem within was so altered, that the ammonia apparatus could not retain a charge with sufficient steadiness to allow of division. In these experiments, therefore, the other apparatus was charged; its charge measured and divided with the ammonia apparatus by a quick contact, and what remained untaken away by the division again measured (1281.). It was so nearly one half of the original charge, as to authorize, with this reservation, the insertion of

---

* See in relation to this point 1382, &c.—*Dec.* 1838.

ammoniacal gas amongst the other gases, as having equal power with them.

¶ vi. *General results as to induction.*

1295. Thus *induction* appears to be essentially an action of contiguous particles, through the intermediation of which the electric force, originating or appearing at a certain place, is propagated to or sustained at a distance, appearing there as a force of the same kind exactly equal in amount, but opposite in its direction and tendencies (1164.). Induction requires no sensible thickness in the conductors which may be used to limit its extent; an uninsulated leaf of gold may be made very highly positive on one surface, and as highly negative on the other, without the least interference of the two states whilst the inductions continue. Nor is it affected by the nature of the limiting conductors, provided time be allowed, in the case of those which conduct slowly, for them to assume their final state (1170.).

1296. But with regard to the *dielectrics* or insulating media, matters are very different (1167.). Their thickness has an immediate and important influence on the degree of induction. As to their quality, though all gases and vapours are alike, whatever their state; yet amongst solid bodies, and between them and gases, there are differences which prove the existence of *specific inductive capacities,* these differences being in some cases very great.

1297. The direct inductive force, which may be conceived to be exerted in lines between the two limiting and charged conducting surfaces, is accompanied by a lateral or transverse force equivalent to a dilatation or repulsion of these representative lines (1224.); or the attractive force which exists amongst the particles of the dielectric in the direction of the induction is accompanied by a repulsive or a diverging force in the transverse direction (1304.).

1298. Induction appears to consist in a certain polarized state of the particles, into which they are thrown by the electrified body sustaining the action, the particles assuming positive and negative points or parts, which are symmetrically arranged with respect to each other and the inducting surfaces or particles*.

* The theory of induction which I am stating does not pretend to decide

The state must be a forced one, for it is originated and sustained only by force, and sinks to the normal or quiescent state when that force is removed. It can be *continued* only in insulators by the same portion of electricity, because they only can retain this state of the particles (1304.).

1299. The principle of induction is of the utmost generality in electric action. It constitutes charge in every ordinary case, and probably in every case; it appears to be the cause of all excitement, and to precede every current. The degree to which the particles are affected in this their forced state, before discharge of one kind or another supervenes, appears to constitute what we call *intensity*.

1300. When a Leyden jar is *charged*, the particles of the glass are forced into this polarized and constrained condition by the electricity of the charging apparatus. *Discharge* is the return of these particles to their natural state from their state of tension, whenever the two electric forces are allowed to be disposed of in some other direction.

1301. All charge of conductors is on their surface, because being essentially inductive, it is there only that the medium capable of sustaining the necessary inductive state begins. If the conductors are hollow and contain air or any other dielectric, still no *charge* can appear upon that internal surface, because the dielectric there cannot assume the polarized state throughout, in consequence of the opposing actions in different directions.

1302. The known influence of *form* is perfectly consistent with the corpuscular view of induction set forth. An electrified cylinder is more affected by the influence of the surrounding conductors (which complete the condition of charge) at the ends than at the middle, because the ends are exposed to a greater sum of inductive forces than the middle ; and a point is brought to a higher condition than a ball, because by relation to the conductors around, more inductive force terminates on its surface than on an equal surface of the ball with which it is compared. Here, too, especially, can be perceived the influence of the lateral or transverse force (1297.), which, being

whether electricity be a fluid or fluids, or a mere power or condition of recognized matter. That is a question which I may be induced to consider in the next or following series of these researches.

a power of the nature of or equivalent to repulsion, causes such a disposition of the lines of inductive force in their course across the dielectric, that they must accumulate upon the point, the end of the cylinder, or any projecting part.

1303. The influence of *distance* is also in harmony with the same view. There is perhaps no distance so great that induction cannot take place through it* ; but with the same constraining force (1298.) it takes place the more easily, according as the extent of dielectric through which it is exerted is lessened. And as it is assumed by the theory that the particles of the dielectric, though tending to remain in a normal state, are thrown into a forced condition during the induction ; so it would seem to follow that the fewer there are of these intervening particles opposing their tendency to the assumption of the new state, the greater degree of change will they suffer, *i. e.* the higher will be the condition they assume, and the larger the amount of inductive action exerted through them.

1304. I have used the phrases *lines of inductive force* and *curved lines* of force (1231. 1297. 1298. 1302.) in a general sense only, just as we speak of the lines of magnetic force. The lines are imaginary, and the force in any part of them is of course the resultant of compound forces, every molecule being related to every other molecule in *all* directions by the tension and reaction of those which are contiguous. The transverse force is merely this relation considered in a direction oblique to the lines of inductive force, and at present I mean no more than that by the phrase. With respect to the term *polarity* also, I mean at present only a disposition of force by which the same molecule acquires opposite powers on different parts. The particular way in which this disposition is made will come into consideration hereafter, and probably varies in different bodies, and so produces variety of electrical relation†. All I am anxious about at present is, that a more particular meaning should not be attached to the expressions used

---

* I have traced it experimentally from a ball placed in the middle of the large cube formerly described (1173.) to the sides of the cube six feet distant, and also from the same ball placed in the middle of our large lecture-room to the walls of the room at twenty-six feet distance, the charge sustained upon the ball in these cases being solely due to induction through these distances.

† See now 1685. &c.—*Dec.* 1838.

than I contemplate.  Further inquiry, I trust, will enable us
by degrees to restrict the sense more and more, and so render
the explanation of electrical phenomena day by day more and
more definite.

1305. As a test of the probable accuracy of my views, I have
throughout this experimental examination compared them with
the conclusions drawn by M. Poisson from his beautiful mathematical inquiries*.   I am quite unfit to form a judgment of
these admirable papers; but as far as I can perceive, the
theory I have set forth and the results I have obtained are not
in opposition to such of those conclusions as represent the
final disposition and state of the forces in the limited number
of cases he has considered.   His theory assumes a very different mode of action in induction to that which I have ventured to support, and would probably find its mathematical
test in the endeavour to apply it to cases of induction in curved
lines.  To my feeling it is insufficient in accounting for the retention of electricity upon the surface of conductors by the
pressure of the air, an effect which I hope to show is simple
and consistent according to the present view†; and it does
not touch voltaic electricity, or in any way associate it and
what is called ordinary electricity under one common principle.

I have also looked with some anxiety to the results which
that indefatigable philosopher Harris has obtained in his investigation of the laws of induction‡, knowing that they were
experimental, and having a full conviction of their exactness;
but I am happy in perceiving no collision at present between
them and the views I have taken.

1306. Finally, I beg to say that I put forth my particular
view with doubt and fear, lest it should not bear the test of
general examination, for unless true it will only embarrass the
progress of electrical science.   It has long been on my mind,
but I hesitated to publish it until the increasing persuasion of
its accordance with all known facts, and the manner in which
it linked together effects apparently very different in kind,

* Mémoires de l'Institut, 1811, tom. xii. the first page 1, and the second
paging 163.
† Refer to 1377, 1378, 1379, 1398.—*Dec.* 1838.
‡ Philosophical Transactions, 1834, p. 213.

urged me to write the present paper.  I as yet see no inconsistency between it and nature, but, on the contrary, think I
perceive much new light thrown by it on her operations ; and
my next papers will be devoted to a review of the phenomena
of conduction, electrolyzation, current, magnetism, retention,
discharge, and some other points, with an application of the
theory to these effects, and an examination of it by them.

*Royal Institution,*
   *November* 16, 1837.

---

*Supplementary Note to Experimental Researches in Electricity.*
*Eleventh Series.*

Received March 29, 1838.

1307. I have recently put into an experimental form that
general statement of the question of *specific inductive capacity*
which is given at No. 1252 of Series XI., and the result is such
as to lead me to hope the Council of the Royal Society will authorize its addition to the paper in the form of a supplementary
note.    Three circular brass plates, about five inches in diameter, were mounted side by side upon insulating pillars ; the
middle one, A, was a fixture, but the outer plates B and C were
moveable on slides, so that all three could be brought with
their sides almost into contact, or separated to any required distance.    Two gold leaves were suspended in a glass jar from
insulated wires ; one of the outer plates B was connected with
one of the gold leaves, and the other outer plate with the other
leaf.    The outer plates B and C were adjusted at the distance
of an inch and a quarter from the middle plate A, and the
gold leaves were fixed at two inches apart ; A was then slightly
charged with electricity, and the plates B and C, with their
gold leaves, thrown out of insulation *at the same time,* and then
left insulated.    In this state of things A was charged positive
inductrically, and B and C negative inducteously ; the same
dielectric, air, being in the two intervals, and the gold leaves
hanging, of course, parallel to each other in a relatively unelectrified state.

1308. A plate of shell-lac three quarters of an inch in thickness, and four inches square, suspended by clean white silk
thread, was very carefully deprived of all charge (1203.) (so
that it produced no effect on the gold leaves if A were uncharged) and then introduced between plates A and B ; the
electric relation of the three plates was immediately altered,
and the gold leaves attracted each other. On removing the
shell-lac this attraction ceased ; on introducing it between A
and C it was renewed ; on removing it the attraction again
ceased ; and the shell-lac when examined by a delicate Coulomb
electrometer was still without charge.

1309. As A was positive, B and C were of course negative ;
but as the specific inductive capacity of shell-lac is about twice
that of air (1270.), it was expected that when the lac was introduced between A and B, A would induce more towards B
than towards C ; that therefore B would become more negative
than before towards A, and, consequently, because of its insulated condition, be positive externally, as at its back or at the
gold leaves ; whilst C would be less negative towards A, and
therefore negative outwards or at the gold leaves. This was
found to be the case ; for on whichever side of A the shell-lac
was introduced the external plate at that side was positive, and
the external plate on the other side negative towards each
other, and also to uninsulated external bodies.

1310. On employing a plate of sulphur instead of shell-lac,
the same results were obtained ; consistent with the conclusions
drawn regarding the high specific inductive capacity of that
body already given (1276.).

1311. These effects of specific inductive capacity can be
exalted in various ways, and it is this capability which makes
the great value of the apparatus. Thus I introduced the shell-
lac between A and B, and then for a moment connected B and
C, uninsulated them, and finally left them in the insulated state ;
the gold leaves were of course hanging parallel to each other.
On removing the shell-lac the gold leaves attracted each other ;
on introducing the shell-lac between A and C this attraction
was *increased,* (as had been anticipated from theory,) and the
leaves came together, though not more than four inches long,
and hanging three inches apart.

1312. By simply bringing the gold leaves nearer to each other

I was able to show the difference of specific inductive capacity
when only thin plates of shell-lac were used, the rest of the
dielectric space being filled with air.   By bringing B and C
nearer to A another great increase of sensibility was made.
By enlarging the size of the plates still further power was
gained.   By diminishing the extent of the wires, &c. connected
with the gold leaves, another improvement resulted.   So that
in fact the gold leaves became, in this manner, as delicate a
test of *specific inductive action* as they are, in Bennet's and
Singer's electrometers, of ordinary electrical charge.

1313. It is evident that by making the three plates the sides
of cells, with proper precautions as regards insulation, &c.,
this apparatus may be used in the examination of gases, with
far more effect than the former apparatus (1187. 1290.), and
may, perhaps, bring out differences which have as yet escaped
me (1292. 1293.).

1314. It is also evident that two metal plates are quite sufficient to form the instrument; the state of the single inducteous
plate when the dielectric is changed, being examined either by
bringing a body excited in a known manner towards its gold
leaves, or, what I think will be better, employing a carrier ball
in place of the leaf, and examining that ball by the Coulomb
electrometer (1180.).   The inductive and inducteous surfaces
may even be balls; the latter being itself the carrier ball of the
Coulomb's electrometer (1181. 1229.).

1315. To increase the effect, a small condenser may be used
with great advantage.   Thus if, when two inducteous plates
are used, a little condenser were put in the place of the gold
leaves, I have no doubt the three principal plates might be reduced to an inch or even half an inch in diameter.   Even the
gold leaves act to each other for the time as the plates of a condenser.   If only two plates were used, by the proper application of the condenser the same reduction might take place.
This expectation is fully justified by an effect already observed
and described (1229.).

1316. In that case the application of the instrument to very
extensive research is evident.   Comparatively small masses of
dielectrics could be examined, as diamonds and crystals.   An
expectation, that the specific inductive capacity of crystals will
vary in different directions, according as the lines of inductive

force (1304.) are parallel to, or in other positions in relation to the axes of the crystals, can be tested* : I purpose that these and many other thoughts which arise respecting specific inductive action and the polarity of the particles of dielectric matter, shall be put to the proof as soon as I can find time.

1317. Hoping that this apparatus will form an instrument of considerable use, I beg to propose for it (at the suggestion of a friend) the name of *Differential Inductometer*.

*Royal Institution,*
 *March* 29, 1838.

  * Refer for this investigation to 1689—1698.—*Dec.* 1838.

## TWELFTH SERIES.

§ 18. *On Induction (continued).* ¶ vii. *Conduction, or conductive discharge.* ¶ viii. *Electrolytic discharge.* ¶ ix. *Disruptive discharge—Insulation—Spark—Brush—Difference of discharge at the positive and negative surfaces of conductors.*

Received January 11,—Read February 8, 1838.

1318. I proceed now, according to my promise, to examine, by the great facts of electrical science, that theory of induction which I have ventured to put forth (1165. 1295. &c.). The principle of induction is so universal that it pervades all electrical phenomena; but the general case which I purpose at present to go into consists of insulation traced into and terminating with discharge, with the accompanying effects. This case includes the various *modes* of discharge, and also the condition and characters of a current; the elements of magnetic action being amongst the latter. I shall necessarily have occasion to speak theoretically, and even hypothetically; and though these papers profess to be experimental researches, I hope that, considering the facts and investigations contained in the last series in support of the particular view advanced, I shall not be considered as taking too much liberty on the present occasion, or as departing too far from the character which they ought to have, especially as I shall use every opportunity which presents itself of returning to that strong test of truth, experiment.

1319. Induction has as yet been considered in these papers only in cases of insulation; opposed to insulation is *discharge*. The action or effect which may be expressed by the general term *discharge*, may take place, as far as we are aware at present, in several modes. Thus, that which is called simply *conduction* involves no chemical action, and apparently no displacement of the particles concerned. A second mode may

be called *electrolytic discharge* ; in it chemical action does
occur, and particles must, to a certain degree, be displaced.
A third mode, namely, that by sparks or brushes, may, because of its violent displacement of the particles of the
*dielectric* in its course, be called the *disruptive discharge*;
and a fourth may, perhaps, be conveniently distinguished for a
time by the words *convection,* or *carrying discharge,* being
that in which discharge is effected either by the carrying
power of solid particles, or those of gases and liquids.   Hereafter, perhaps, all these modes may appear as the result of
one common principle, but at present they require to be considered apart ; and I will now speak of the *first* mode, for
amongst all the forms of discharge that which we express by
the term conduction appears the most simple and the most
directly in contrast with insulation.

¶ vii. *Conduction, or conductive discharge.*

1320. Though assumed to be essentially different, yet neither Cavendish nor Poisson attempt to explain by, or even
state in, their theories, what the essential difference between
insulation and conduction is.   Nor have I anything, perhaps,
to offer in this respect, *except* that, according to my view of induction, insulation and conduction depend upon the same molecular action of the dielectrics concerned ; are only extreme degrees of *one common condition* or effect ; and in any sufficient
mathematical theory of electricity must be taken as cases of
the same kind.   Hence the importance of the endeavour to
show the connection between them under my theory of the
electrical relations of contiguous particles.

1321. Though the action of the insulating dielectric in the
charged Leyden jar, and that of the wire in discharging it,
may seem very different, they may be associated by numerous
intermediate links, which carry us on from one to the other,
leaving, I think, no necessary connection unsupplied.   We
may observe some of these in succession for information respecting the whole case.

1322. Spermaceti has been examined and found to be a dielectric, through which induction can take place (1240. 1246.),

its specific inductive capacity being about or above 1·8 (1279.), and the inductive action has been considered in it, as in all other substances, an action of contiguous particles.

1323. But spermaceti is also a *conductor*, though in so low a degree that we can trace the process of conduction, as it were, step by step through the mass (1247.) ; and even when the electric force has travelled through it to a certain distance, we can, by removing the coercitive (which is at the same time the inductive) force, cause it to return upon its path and reappear in its first place (1245. 1246.). Here induction appears to be a necessary preliminary to conduction. It of itself brings the contiguous particles of the dielectric into a certain condition, which, if retained by them, constitutes *insulation*, but if lowered by the communication of power from one particle to another, constitutes *conduction*.

1324. If *glass* or *shell-lac* be the substances under consideration, the same capabilities of suffering either induction or conduction through them appear (1233. 1239. 1247.), but not in the same degree. The conduction almost disappears (1239. 1242.) ; the induction therefore is sustained, *i. e.* the polarized state into which the inductive force has brought the contiguous particles is retained, there being little discharge action between them, and therefore the *insulation* continues. But, what discharge there is, appears to be consequent upon that condition of the particles into which the induction throws them ; and thus it is that ordinary insulation and conduction are closely associated together or rather are extreme cases of one common condition.

1325. In ice or water we have a better conductor than spermaceti, and the phenomena of induction and insulation therefore rapidly disappear, because conduction quickly follows upon the assumption of the inductive state. But let a plate of cold ice have metallic coatings on its sides, and connect one of these with a good electrical machine in work, and the other with the ground, and it then becomes easy to observe the phenomena of induction through the ice, by the electrical tension which can be obtained and continued on both the coatings (419. 426.). For although that portion of power which at one moment gave the inductive condition to the particles is at the next lowered by the consequent discharge due to the conductive act, it is succeeded by another portion of force from the machine to restore the inductive state. If the ice be converted into water the same succession of actions can be just as easily proved, provided the water be distilled, and (if the machine be not powerful enough) a voltaic battery be employed.

1326. All these considerations impress my mind strongly with the conviction, that insulation and ordinary conduction cannot be properly separated when we are examining into their nature; that is, into the general law or laws under which their phenomena are produced. They appear to me to consist in an action of contiguous particles dependent on the forces developed in electrical excitement; these forces bring the particles into a state of tension or polarity, which constitutes both *induction* and *insulation*; and being in this state, the continuous particles have a power or capability of communicating their forces one to the other, by which they are lowered, and discharge occurs. Every body appears to discharge (444. 987.); but the possession of this capability in a *greater or smaller degree* in different bodies, makes them better or worse conductors, worse or better insulators; and both *induction* and *conduction* appear to be the same in their principle and action (1320.), except that in the latter an effect common to both is raised to the highest degree, whereas in the former it occurs in the best cases, in only an almost insensible quantity.

1327. That in our attempts to penetrate into the nature of electrical action, and to deduce laws more general than those we are at present acquainted with, we should endeavour to bring apparently opposite effects to stand side by side in harmonious arrangement, is an opinion of long standing, and sanctioned by the ablest philosophers. I hope, therefore, I may be excused the attempt to look at the highest cases of conduction as analogous to, or even the same in kind with, those of induction and insulation.

1328. If we consider the slight penetration of sulphur (1241. 1242.) or shell-lac (1234.) by electricity, or the feebler insulation sustained by spermaceti (1279. 1240.), as essential consequences and indications of their *conducting* power, then may we look on the resistance of metallic wires to the passage of electricity through them as *insulating* power. Of the numerous well-known cases fitted to show this resistance in what are called the perfect conductors, the experiments of Professor Wheatstone best serve my present purpose, since they were carried to such an extent as to show that *time* entered as an element into the conditions of conduction* even in metals.  When discharge was made through a copper wire 2640 feet in length, and $\frac{1}{15}$th of an inch in diameter, so that the luminous sparks at each end of the wire, and at the middle, could be observed in the same place, the latter was found to be sensibly behind the two former in time, they being by the conditions of the experiment simultaneous.  Hence a proof of retardation; and what reason can be given why this retardation should not be of the same kind as that in spermaceti, or in lac, or sulphur?  But as, in them, retardation is insulation, and insulation is induction, why should we refuse the same relation to the same exhibitions of force in the metals?

1329.  We learn from the experiment, that if *time* be allowed the retardation is gradually overcome; and the same thing obtains for the spermaceti, the lac, and glass (1248.); give but time in proportion to the retardation, and the latter is at last vanquished.  But if that be the case, and all the results are alike in kind, the only difference being in the length of time, why should we refuse to metals the previous inductive action, which is admitted to occur in the other bodies?  The diminution of *time* is no negation of the action; nor is the lower degree of tension requisite to cause the forces to traverse the metal, as compared to that necessary in the cases of water, spermaceti, or lac.  These differences would only point to the conclusion, that in metals the particles under induction can transfer their forces when at a lower degree of tension or polarity, and with greater facility than in the instances of the other bodies.

1330.  Let us look at Mr. Wheatstone's beautiful experiment in another point of view.  If, leaving the arrangement at the middle and two ends of the long copper wire unaltered, we remove the two intervening portions and replace them by wires of iron or platina, we shall have a much greater retardation of the middle spark than before.  If, removing the iron,

* Philosophical Transactions, 1834, p. 583.

we were to substitute for it only five or six feet of water in a
cylinder of the same diameter as the metal, we should have
still greater retardation.  If from water we passed to spermaceti, either directly or by gradual steps through other bodies,
(even though we might vastly enlarge the bulk, for the purpose of evading the occurrence of a spark elsewhere (1331.)
than at the three proper intervals,) we should have still
greater retardation, until at last we might arrive, by degrees
so small as to be inseparable from each other, at actual and
permanent insulation.   What, then, is to separate the principle of these two extremes, perfect conduction and perfect
insulation, from each other ; since the moment we leave in the
smallest degree perfection at either extremity, we involve the
element of perfection at the opposite end ?   Especially too, as
we have not in nature the case of perfection either at one
extremity or the other, either of insulation or conduction.

1331. Again, to return to this beautiful experiment in the
various forms which may be given to it : the forces are not all
in the wire (after they have left the Leyden jar) during the whole
time (1328.) occupied by the discharge ; they are disposed in
part through the surrounding dielectric under the well-known
form of induction ; and if that dielectric be air, induction takes
place from the wire through the air to surrounding conductors,
until the ends of the wire are electrically related through its
length, and discharge has occurred, *i. e.* for the *time* during
which the middle spark is retarded beyond the others.   This
is well shown by the old experiment, in which a long wire is
so bent that two parts (Plate VIII. fig. 115.) *a. b.* near its extremities shall approach within a short distance, as a quarter of
an inch, of each other in the air.   If the discharge of a Leyden
jar, charged to a sufficient degree, be sent through such a wire,
by far the largest portion of the electricity will pass as a spark
across the air at the interval, and not by the metal.   Does not
the middle part of the wire, therefore, act here as an insulating
medium, though it be of metal ?   and is not the spark through
the air an indication of the tension (simultaneous with *induction*)
of the electricity in the ends of this single wire ?   Why should
not the wire and the air both be regarded as dielectrics ; and the
action at its commencement, and whilst there is tension, as an inductive action ?   If it acts through the contorted lines of the wire,

so it also does in curved and contorted lines through air (1219. 1224. 1231.), and other insulating dielectrics (1228.) ; and we can apparently go so far in the analogy, whilst limiting the case to the inductive action only, as to show that amongst insulating dielectrics some lead away the lines of force from others (1229.), as the wire will do from worse conductors, though in it the principal effect is no doubt due to the ready discharge between the particles whilst in a low state of tension.   The retardation is for the time insulation ; and it seems to me we may just as fairly compare the air at the interval *a, b.* (fig. 115.) and the wire in the circuit, as two bodies of the same kind and acting upon the same principles, as far as the first inductive pheno- mena are concerned, notwithstanding the different forms of dis- charge which ultimately follow *, as we may compare, according to Coulomb's investigations †, *different lengths* of different in- sulating bodies required to produce the same amount of in- sulating effect.

1332. This comparison is still more striking when we take into consideration the experiment of Mr. Harris, in which he stretched a fine wire across a glass globe, the air within being rarefied ‡.   On sending a charge through the joint arrangement of metal and rare air, as much, if not more, electricity passed by the latter as by the former.   In the air, rarefied as it was, there can be no doubt the discharge was preceded by induction (1284.) ; and to my mind all the circumstances indicate that the same was the case with the metal; that, in fact, both sub- stances are dielectrics, exhibiting the same effects in conse- quence of the action of the same causes, the only variation being one of degree in the different substances employed.

1333. Judging on these principles, velocity of discharge through the *same wire* may be varied greatly by attending to the circumstances which cause variations of discharge through spermaceti or sulphur.   Thus, for instance, it must vary with the tension or intensity of the first urging force (1234. 1240.), which tension is charge and induction.   So if the two ends of the wire, in Professor Wheatstone's experiment, were immedi- ately connected with two large insulated metallic surfaces ex-

* These will be examined hereafter (1348, &c.).

† Mémoires de l'Académie, 1785, p. 612. or Ency. Britann. First. Supp. vol. i. p. 611.

‡ Philosophical Transactions, 1834, p. 242.

posed to the air, so that the primary act of induction, after making the contact for discharge, might be in part removed from the internal portion of the wire at the first instant, and disposed for the moment on its surface jointly with the air and surrounding conductors, then I venture to anticipate that the middle spark would be more retarded than before ; and if these two plates were the inner and outer coating of a large jar or a Leyden battery, then the retardation of that spark would be still greater.

1334. Cavendish was perhaps the first to show distinctly that discharge was not always by one channel*, but, if several are present, by many at once. We may make these different channels of different bodies, and by proportioning their thicknesses and lengths, may include such substances as air, lac, spermaceti, water, protoxide of iron, iron and silver, and by *one* discharge make each convey its proportion of the electric force. Perhaps the air ought to be excepted, as its discharge by conduction is questionable at present (1336.) ; but the others may all be limited in their mode of discharge to pure conduction. Yet several of them suffer previous induction, precisely like the induction through the air, it being a necessary preliminary to their discharging action. How can we therefore separate any one of these bodies from the others, as to the *principles and mode* of insulating and conducting, except by mere degree ? All seem to me to be dielectrics acting alike, and under the same common laws.

1335. I might draw another argument in favour of the general sameness, in nature and action, of good and bad conductors (and all the bodies I refer to are conductors more or less), from the perfect equipoise in action of very different bodies when opposed to each other in magneto-electric inductive action, as formerly described (213.), but am anxious to be as brief as is consistent with the clear examination of the probable truth of my views.

1336. With regard to the possession by the gases of any conducting power of the simple kind now under consideration, the question is a very difficult one to determine at present. Experiments seem to indicate that they do insulate certain low degrees of tension perfectly, and that the effects which may have appeared to be occasioned by *conduction* have been the

* Philosophical Transactions, 1776, p. 197.

result of the carrying power of the charged particles, either of the air or of dust, in it. It is equally certain, however, that with higher degrees of tension or charge the particles discharge to one another, and that is conduction. If the gases possess the power of insulating a certain low degree of tension continuously and perfectly, such a result may be due to their peculiar physical state, and the condition of separation under which their particles are placed. But in that, or in any case, we must not forget the fine experiments of Cagniard de la Tour*, in which he has shown that liquids and their vapours can be made to pass gradually into each other, to the entire removal of any marked distinction of the two states. Thus, hot dry steam and cold water pass by insensible gradations into each other; yet the one is amongst the gases as an insulator, and the other a comparatively good conductor. As to conducting power, therefore, the transition from metals even up to gases is gradual; substances make but one series in this respect, and the various cases must come under one condition and law (444.). The specific differences of bodies as to conducting power only serves to strengthen the general argument, that conduction, like insulation, is a result of induction, and is an action of contiguous particles.

1337. I might go on now to consider induction and its concomitant, *conduction,* through mixed dielectrics, as, for instance, when a charged body, instead of acting across air to a distant uninsulated conductor, acts jointly through it and an interposed insulated conductor. In such a case, the air and the conducting body are the mixed dielectrics; and the latter assumes a polarized condition as a mass, like that which my theory assumes *each particle* of the air to possess at the same time (1679.). But I fear to be tedious in the present condition of the subject, and hasten to the consideration of other matter.

1338. To sum up, in some degree, what has been said, I look upon the first effect of an excited body upon neighbouring matters to be the production of a polarized state of their particles, which constitutes *induction*; and this arises from its action upon the particles in immediate contact with it, which again act upon those contiguous to them, and thus the forces are transferred to a distance. If the induction remain undiminished, then perfect insulation is the consequence; and the higher the

* Annales de Chimie, xxi. pp. 127, 178; or Quarterly Journal of Science, xv. 145.

polarized condition which the particles can acquire or maintain, the higher is the intensity which may be given to the acting forces. If, on the contrary, the contiguous particles, upon acquiring the polarized state, have the power to communicate their forces, then conduction occurs, and the tension is lowered, conduction being a distinct act of discharge between neighbouring particles. The lower the state of tension at which this discharge between the particles of a body takes place, the better conductor is that body. In this view, insulators may be said to be bodies whose particles can retain the polarized state; whilst conductors are those whose particles cannot be permanently polarized. If I be right in my view of induction, then I consider the reduction of these two effects (which have been so long held distinct) to an action of contiguous particles obedient to one common law, as a very important result; and, on the other hand, the identity of character which the two acquire when viewed by the theory (1326.), is additional presumptive proof in favour of the correctness of the latter.

1339. That heat has great influence over simple conduction is well known (445.), its effect being, in some cases, almost an entire change of the characters of the body (432. 1340.). Harris has, however, shown that it in no respect affects gaseous bodies, or at least air*; and Davy has taught us that, as a class, metals have their conducting power *diminished* by it†.

1340. I formerly described a substance, sulphuret of silver, whose conducting power was increased by heat (433. 437. 438.); and I have since then met with another as strongly affected in the same way: this is fluoride of lead. When a piece of that substance, which had been fused and cooled, was introduced into the circuit of a voltaic battery, it stopped the current. Being heated, it acquired conducting powers before it was visibly red hot in daylight; and even sparks could be taken against it whilst still solid. The current alone then raised its temperature (as in the case of sulphuret of silver) until it fused, after which it seemed to conduct as well as the metallic vessel containing it; for whether the wire used to complete the circuit touched the fused fluoride only, or was in contact with the platina on which it was supported, no sensible difference in the

---

* Philosophical Transactions, 1834, p. 230.　　† Ibid. 1821, p. 431.

force of the current was observed.   During all the time there
was scarcely a trace of decomposing action on the fluoride, and
what did occur, seemed referable to the air and moisture of the
atmosphere, and not to electrolytic action.

1341. I have now very little doubt that periodide of mercury
(414. 448. 691.) is a case of the same kind, and also corrosive
sublimate (692.).   I am also inclined to think, since making the
above experiments, that the anomalous action of the protoxide
of antimony, formerly observed and described (693. 801.), may
be referred in part to the same cause.

1342. I have no intention at present of going into the particular relation of heat and electricity, but we may hope hereafter to discover by experiment the law which probably holds
together all the above effects with those of the *evolution* and
the *disappearance* of heat by the current, and the striking and
beautiful results of thermo-electricity, in one common bond.

¶ viii. *Electrolytic discharge.*

1343. I have already expressed in a former paper (1164.),
the view by which I hope to associate ordinary induction and
electrolyzation.   Under that view, the discharge of electric
forces by electrolyzation is rather an effect superadded, in a
certain class of bodies, to those already described as constituting induction and insulation, than one independent of and distinct from these phenomena.

1344. Electrolytes, as respects their insulating and conducting forces, belong to the general category of bodies (1320.
1334.) ; and if they are in the solid state (as nearly all can assume that state), they retain their place, presenting then no
new phenomenon (426. &c.) ; or if one occur, being in so small
a proportion as to be almost unimportant.   When liquefied,
they also belong to the same list whilst the electric intensity is
below a certain degree; but at a given intensity (910. 912.
1007.), fixed for each, and very low in all known cases, they
play a new part, causing discharge in proportion (783.) to the
development of certain chemical effects of combination and decomposition ; and at this point, move out from the general class
of insulators and conductors, to form a distinct one by themselves.   The former phenomena have been considered (1320.
1338.) ; it is the latter which have now to be revised, and used
as a test of the proposed theory of induction.

1345. The theory assumes, that the particles of the dielectric (now an electrolyte) are in the first instance brought, by ordinary inductive action, into a polarized state, and raised to a certain degree of tension or intensity before discharge commences; the inductive state being, in fact, a *necessary preliminary* to discharge.    By taking advantage of those circumstances which bear upon the point, it is not difficult to increase the tension indicative of this state of induction, and so make the state itself more evident.    Thus, if distilled water be employed, and a long narrow portion of it placed between the electrodes of a powerful voltaic battery, we have at once indications of the intensity which can be sustained at these electrodes by the inductive action through the water as a dielectric, for sparks may be obtained, gold leaves diverged, and Leyden bottles charged at their wires.    The water is in the condition of the spermaceti (1322. 1323.), a bad conductor and a bad insulator; but what it does insulate is by virtue of inductive action, and that induction is the preparation for and precursor of discharge (1338.).

1346. The induction and tension which appear at the limits of the portion of water in the direction of the current, are only the sums of the induction and tension of the contiguous particles between those limits; and the limitation of the inductive tension, to a certain degree shows (time entering in each case as an important element of the result), that when the particles have acquired a certain relative state, *discharge,* or a transfer of forces equivalent to ordinary conduction, takes place.

1347. In the inductive condition assumed by water before discharge comes on, the particles polarized are the particles of the *water,* that being the dielectric used*; but the discharge between particle and particle is not, as before, a mere interchange of their powers or forces at the polar parts, but an actual separation of them into their two elementary particles, the oxygen travelling in one direction, and carrying with it its amount of the force it had acquired during the polarization, and the hydrogen doing the same thing in the other direction, until they each meet the next approaching particle, which is in the same electrical state with that they have left, and by association of their forces with it, produce what constitutes discharge.

* See 1699—1708.—*Dec.* 1838.

This part of the action may be regarded as a carrying one (1319. 1572. 1622.), performed by the constituent particles of the dielectric. The latter is always a compound body (664. 823.) ; and by those who have considered the subject and are acquainted with the philosophical view of transfer which was first put forth by Grotthuss*, its particles may easily be compared to a series of metallic conductors under inductive action, which, whilst in that state, are divisible into these elementary moveable halves.

1348. Electrolytic discharge depends, of necessity, upon the non-conduction of the dielectric as a whole, and there are two steps or acts in the process : first a polarization of the molecules of the substance, and then a lowering of the forces by the separation, advance in opposite directions, and recombination of the elements of the molecules, these being, as it were, the halves of the originally polarized conductors or particles.

1349. These views of the decomposition of electrolytes and the consequent effect of discharge, which, as to the particular case, are the same with those of Grotthuss (481.) and Davy (482.), though they differ from those of Biot (487.), De la Rive (490.), and others, seem to me to be fully in accordance not merely with the theory I have given of induction generally (1165.), but with all the known *facts* of common induction, conduction, and electrolytic discharge ; and in that respect help to confirm in my mind the truth of the theory set forth. The new mode of discharge which electrolyzation presents must surely be an evidence of the *action of contiguous particles* ; and as this appears to depend directly upon a previous inductive state, which is the same with common induction, it greatly strengthens the argument which refers induction in all cases to an action of contiguous particles also (1295, &c.).

1350. As an illustration of the condition of the polarized particles in a dielectric under induction, I may describe an experiment. Put into a glass vessel some clear rectified oil of turpentine, and introduce two wires passing through glass tubes where they coincide with the surface of the fluid, and terminating either in balls or points. Cut some very clean dry white silk into small particles, and put these also into the liquid :

* Annales de Chimie, lviii. 60. and lxiii. 20.

then electrify one of the wires by an ordinary machine and discharge by the other.   The silk will immediately gather from all
parts of the liquid, and form a band of particles reaching from
wire to wire, and if touched by a glass rod will show considerable tenacity ; yet the moment the supply of electricity ceases,
the band will fall away and disappear by the dispersion of its
parts.   The *conduction* by the silk is in this case very small;
and after the best examination I could give to the effects, the
impression on my mind is, that the adhesion of the whole is
due to the polarity which each filament acquires, exactly as the
particles of iron between the poles of a horse-shoe magnet are
held together in one mass by a similar disposition of forces.
The particles of silk therefore represent to me the condition of
the molecules of the dielectric itself, which I assume to be
polar, just as that of the silk is.   In all cases of conductive discharge the contiguous polarized particles of the body are able
to effect a neutralization of their forces with greater or less
facility, as the silk does also in a very slight degree.   Further
we are not able to carry the parallel, except in imagination ;
but if we could divide each particle of silk into two halves, and
let each half travel until it met and united with the next half
in an opposite state, it would then exert its carrying power
(1347.), and so far represent electrolytic discharge.

1351. Admitting that electrolytic discharge is a consequence
of previous induction, then how evidently do its numerous
cases point to induction in curved lines (521. 1216.), and to
the divergence or lateral action of the lines of inductive force
(1231.), and so strengthen that part of the general argument
in the former paper !   If two balls of platina, forming the
electrodes of a voltaic battery, are put into a large vessel
of dilute sulphuric acid, the whole of the surfaces are covered
with the respective gases in beautifully regulated proportions,
and the mind has no difficulty in conceiving the direction
of the curved lines of discharge, and even the intensity of
force of the different lines, by the quantity of gas evolved upon
the different parts of the surface.   From this condition of the
lines of inductive force arise the general effects of diffusion ;
the appearance of the anions or cathions round the edges
and on the further side of the electrodes when in the form of
plates ; and the manner in which the current or discharge will

follow all the forms of the electrolyte, however contorted. Hence, also, the effects which Nobili has so well examined and described* in his papers on the distribution of currents in conducting masses. All these effects indicate the curved direction of the currents or discharges which occur in and through the dielectrics, and these are in every case *preceded* by equivalent inductive actions of the contiguous particles.

1352. Hence also the advantage, when the exciting forces are weak or require assistance, of enlarging the mass of the electrolyte; of increasing the size of the electrodes; of making the coppers surround the zincs:—all is in harmony with the view of induction which I am endeavouring to examine; I do not perceive as yet one fact against it.

1353. There are many points of *electrolytic discharge* which ultimately will require to be very closely considered, though I can but slightly touch upon them. It is not that, as far as I have investigated them, they present any contradiction to the view taken (for I have carefully, though unsuccessfully, sought for such cases,) but simply want of time as yet to pursue the inquiry, which prevents me from entering upon them here.

1354. One point is, that different electrolytes or dielectrics require different initial intensities for their decomposition (912.). This may depend upon the degree of polarization which the particles require before electrolytic discharge commences. It is in direct relation to the chemical affinity of the substances concerned; and will probably be found to have a relation or analogy to the specific inductive capacity of different bodies (1252. 1296.). It thus promises to assist in causing the great truths of those extensive sciences, which are occupied in considering the forces of the particles of matter, to fall into much closer order and arrangement than they have heretofore presented.

1355. Another point is the facilitation of electrolytic conducting power or discharge by the addition of substances to the dielectric employed. This effect is strikingly shown where water is the body whose qualities are improved, but, as yet, no general law governing all the phenomena has been

* Bibliothèque Universelle, 1835, lix. 263. 416.

detected.  Thus some acids, as the sulphuric, phosphoric,
oxalic, and nitric, increase the power of water enormously;
whilst others, as the tartaric and citric acids, give but little
power; and others, again, as the acetic and boracic acids, do
not produce a change sensible to the voltameter (739.).  Ammonia produces no effect, but its carbonate does.  The caustic
alkalies and their carbonates produce a fair effect.  Sulphate
of soda, nitre (753.), and many soluble salts produce much effect.
Percyanide of mercury and corrosive sublimate produce no effect;
nor does iodine, gum, or sugar, the test being a voltameter.
In many cases the added substance is acted on either directly
or indirectly, and then the phenomena are more complicated;
such substances are muriatic acid (758.), the soluble proto-
chlorides (766.), and iodides (769.), nitric acid (752.), &c.  In
other cases the substance added is not, when alone, subject to
or a conductor of the powers of the voltaic battery, and yet
both gives and receives power when associated with water.
M. de la Rive has pointed this result out in sulphurous acid*,
iodine and bromine†; the chloride of arsenic produces the
same effect.  A far more striking case, however, is presented
by that very influential body sulphuric acid (681.) : and probably phosphoric acid also is in the same peculiar relation.

1356. It would seem in the cases of those bodies which
suffer no change themselves, as sulphuric acid (and perhaps in
all), that they affect water in its conducting power only as an
electrolyte; for whether little or much improved, the decomposition is proportionate to the quantity of electricity passing
(727. 730.), and the transfer is therefore due to electrolytic
discharge.  This is in accordance with the fact already
stated as regards water (984.), that the conducting power is
not improved for electricity of force below the electrolytic
intensity of the substance acting as the dielectric; but both
facts (and some others) are against the opinion which I formerly gave, that the power of salts, &c. might depend upon
their assumption of the liquid state by solution in the water

* Quarterly Journal, xxvii. 407. or Bibliothèque Universelle, xl. 205.
Kemp says sulphurous acid is a very good conductor, Quarterly Journal, 1831,
p. 613.
   † Quarterly Journal, xxiv. 465. or Annales de Chimie, xxxv. 161.

employed (410.). It occurs to me that the effect may perhaps be related to, and have its explanation in differences of specific inductive capacities.

1357. I have described in the last paper, cases, where shell-lac was rendered a conductor by absorption of ammonia (1294.). The same effect happens with muriatic acid ; yet both these sub-stances, when gaseous, are non-conductors ; and the ammonia, also when in strong solution (748.). Mr. Harris has men-tioned instances\* in which the conducting power of metals is seriously altered by a very little alloy. These may have no relation to the former cases, but nevertheless should not be overlooked in the general investigation which the whole question requires.

1358. Nothing is perhaps more striking in that class of dielectrics which we call electrolytes, than the extraordinary and almost complete suspension of their peculiar mode of effecting discharge when they are rendered *solid* (380. &c.), even though the intensity of the induction acting through them may be increased a hundredfold or more (419.). It not only establishes a very general relation between the physical properties of these bodies and electricity acting by induction through them, but draws both their physical and chemical relations so near together, as to make us hope we shall shortly arrive at the full comprehension of the influence they mutually possess over each other.

¶ ix. *Disruptive discharge and insulation.*

1359. The next form of discharge has been distinguished by the adjective *disruptive* (1319.), as it in every case displaces more or less the particles amongst and across which it suddenly breaks. I include under it, discharge in the form of sparks, brushes, and glow (1405.), but exclude the cases of currents of air, fluids, &c., which, though frequently accompanying the former, are essentially distinct in their nature.

1360. The conditions requisite for the production of an electric spark in its simplest form are well known. An insu-lating dielectric must be interposed between two conducting surfaces in opposite states of electricity, and then if the

---

\* Philosophical Transactions, 1827, p. 22.

actions be continually increased in strength, or otherwise
favoured, either by exalting the electric state of the two conductors, or bringing them nearer to each other, or diminishing
the density of the dielectric, a *spark* at last appears, and the
two forces are for the time annihilated, for *discharge* has
occurred.

1361. The conductors (which may be considered as the
termini of the inductive action) are in ordinary cases most
generally metals, whilst the dielectrics usually employed are
common air and glass. In my view of induction, however,
every dielectric becomes of importance, for as the results are
considered essentially dependent on these bodies, it was to be
expected that differences of action never before suspected
would be evident upon close examination, and so at once give
fresh confirmation of the theory, and open new doors of discovery into the extensive and varied fields of our science. This
hope was especially entertained with respect to the gases, because of their high degree of insulation, their uniformity in
physical condition, and great difference in chemical properties.

1362. All the effects prior to the discharge are inductive;
and the degree of tension which it is necessary to attain before
the spark passes is therefore, in the examination I am now
making of the new view of induction, a very important point.
It is the limit of the influence which the dielectric exerts in
resisting discharge; it is a measure, consequently, of the
conservative power of the dielectric, which in its turn may be
considered as becoming a measure, and therefore a representative of the intensity of the electric forces in activity.

1363. Many philosophers have examined the circumstances
of this limiting action in air, but, as far as I know, none have
come near Mr. Harris as to the accuracy with, and the extent to, which he has carried on his investigations*. Some
of his results I must very briefly notice, premising that they
are all obtained with the use of air as the *dielectric* between
the conducting surfaces.

1364. First as to the *distance* between the two balls used,
or in other words, the *thickness* of the dielectric across which

* Philosophical Transactions, 1834, p. 225.

the induction was sustained. The quantity of electricity, measured by a unit jar, or otherwise on the same principle with the unit jar, in the charged or inductive ball, necessary to produce spark discharge, was found to vary exactly with the distance between the balls, or between the discharging points, and that under very varied and exact forms of experiment *.

1365. Then with respect to variation in the *pressure* or *density* of the air. The quantities of electricity required to produce discharge across a *constant* interval varied exactly with variations of the density; the quantity of electricity and density of the air being in the same simple ratio. Or, if the quantity was retained the same, whilst the interval and density of the air were varied, then these were found in the inverse simple ratio of each other, the same quantity passing across twice the distance with air rarefied to one half †.

1366. It must be remembered that these effects take place without any variation of the *inductive* force by condensation or rarefaction of the air. That force remains the same in air ‡, and in all gasses (1284. 1292.), whatever their rarefaction may be.

1367. Variations of the *temperature* of the air produced no variation of the quantity of electricity required to cause discharge across a given interval §.

Such are the general results, which I have occasion for at present, obtained by Mr. Harris, and they appear to me to be unexceptionable.

1368. In the theory of induction founded upon a molecular action of the dielectric, we have to look to the state of that body principally for the cause and determination of the above effects. Whilst the induction continues, it is assumed that the particles of the dielectric are in a certain polarized state, the tension of this state rising higher in each particle as the induction is raised to a higher degree, either by approximation of the inducing surfaces, variation of form, increase of the original force, or other means; until at last, the tension of the particles having reached the utmost degree which they can sus-

---

* Philosophical Transactions, 1834, p. 225.     † Ibid. p. 229.
‡ Ibid. pp. 237, 244.     § Ibid. p. 230.

tain without subversion of the whole arrangement, discharge immediately after takes place.

1369. The theory does not assume, however, that *all* the particles of the dielectric subject to the inductive action are affected to the same amount, or acquire the same tension. What has been called the lateral action of the lines of inductive force (1231. 1297.), and the diverging and occasionally curved form of these lines is against such a notion. The idea is, that any section taken through the dielectric across the lines of inductive force, and including *all of them,* would be equal, in the sum of the forces, to the sum of the forces in any other section; and that, therefore, the whole amount of tension for each such section would be the same.

1370. Discharge probably occurs, not when all the particles have attained to a certain degree of tension, but when that particle which is most affected has been exalted to the subverting or turning point (1410.). For though *all* the particles in the line of induction resist charge, and are associated in their actions so as to give a sum of resisting force, yet when any one is brought up to the overturning point, *all* must give way in the case of a spark between ball and ball. The breaking down of that one must of necessity cause the whole barrier to be overturned, for it was at its utmost degree of resistance when it possessed the aiding power of that one particle, in addition to the power of the rest, and the power of that one is now lost. Hence *tension* or *intensity**\** may, according to the theory, be considered as represented by the particular condition of the particles, or the amount in them of forced variation from their normal state (1298. 1368.).

1371. The whole effect produced by a charged conductor on a distant conductor, insulated or not, is by my theory assumed to be due to an action propagated from particle to particle of the intervening and insulating dielectric, all the particles being considered as thrown for the time into a forced condition, from which they endeavoured to return to their normal or natural state. The theory, therefore, seems to supply an easy

---

\* See Harris on proposed particular meaning of these terms, Philosophical Transactions, 1834, p. 222.

explanation of the influence of *distance* in affecting induction
(1303. 1364.).  As the distance is diminished induction increases;
for there are then fewer particles in the line of inductive force to
oppose their united resistance to the assumption of the forced or
polarized state, and *vice versâ*.  Again, as the distance diminishes,
discharge across happens with a lower charge of electricity ;
for if, as in Harris's experiments (1364.), the interval be diminished to one half, then half the electricity required to discharge across the first interval is sufficient to strike across the
second ; and it is evident, also, that at that time there are only
half the number of interposed molecules uniting their forces to
resist the discharge.

1372. The effect of enlarging the conducting surfaces which
are opposed to each other in the act of induction, is, if the
electricity be limited in its supply, to lower the intensity of action ; and this follows as a very natural consequence from the
increased area of the dielectric across which the induction is
effected.   For by diffusing the inductive action, which at first
was exerted through one square inch of sectional area of the
dielectric, over two or three square inches of such area, twice
or three times the number of molecules of the dielectric are
brought into the polarized condition, and employed in sustaining
the inductive action, and consequently the tension belonging to
the smaller number on which the limited force was originally
accumulated, must fall in a proportionate degree.

1373. For the same reason diminishing these opposing surfaces must increase the intensity, and the effect will increase
until the surfaces become points.   But in this case, the tension
of the particles of the dielectric next the points is higher than
that of particles midway, because of the lateral action and consequent bulging, as it were, of the lines of inductive force at
the middle distance (1369.).

1374. The more exalted effects of induction on a point *p*, or
any small surface, as the rounded end of a rod, when it is
opposed to a large surface, as that of a ball or plate, rather than
to another point or end, the distance being in both cases the
same, fall into harmonious relation with my theory (1302.).  For
in the latter case, the small surface *p* is affected only by those
particles which are brought into the inductive condition by the

equally small surface of the opposed conductor, whereas when
that is a ball or plate the lines of inductive force from the
latter, are concentrated, as it were, upon the end *p*.  Now
though the molecules of the dielectrics against the large surface
may have a much lower state of tension than those against the
corresponding smaller surface, yet they are also far more numerous, and, as the lines of inductive force converge towards
a point, are able to communicate to the particles contained in
any cross section (1369.) nearer the small surface an amount of
tension equal to their own, and consequently much higher for
each individual particle ; so that at the surface of the smaller
conductor, the tension of a particle rises much, and if that conductor were to terminate in a point, the tension would rise to
an infinite degree, except that it is limited, as before (1368.),
by discharge.  The nature of the discharge from small surfaces and points under induction will be resumed hereafter
(1425. &c.).

1375. *Rarefaction* of the air does not alter the *intensity* of
inductive action (1284. 1287.) ; nor is there any reason, as far
as I can perceive, why it should.  If the quantity of electricity
and the distance remain the same, and the air be rarefied one
half, then, though one half of the particles of the dielectric are
removed, the other half assume a double degree of tension in
their polarity, and therefore the inductive forces are balanced,
and the result remains unaltered as long as the induction and
insulation are sustained.  But the case of *discharge* is very different ; for as there are only half the number of dielectric particles in the rarefied atmosphere, so these are brought up to
the discharging intensity by half the former quantity of electricity ; discharge, therefore, ensues, and such a consequence of
the theory is in perfect accordance with Mr. Harris's results
(1365.).

1376. The *increase* of electricity required to cause discharge
over the same distance, when the pressure of the air or its
density is increased, flows in a similar manner, and on the same
principle (1375.), from the molecular theory.

1377. Here I think my view of induction has a decided advantage over others, especially over that which refers the retention of electricity on the surface of conductors in air to the

*pressure of the atmosphere* (1305.).   The latter is the view
which, being adopted by Poisson and Biot*, is also, I believe,
that generally received; and it associates two such dissimilar
things, as the ponderous air and the subtile and even hypothetical fluid or fluids of electricity, by gross mechanical relations;
by the bonds of mere static pressure.   My theory, on the contrary, sets out at once by connecting the electric forces with the
particles of matter; it derives all its proofs, and even its origin
in the first instance, from experiment; and then, without any
further assumption, seems to offer at once a full explanation of
these and many other singular, peculiar, and, I think, heretofore unconnected effects.

1378. An important assisting experimental argument may
here be adduced, derived from the difference of specific inductive capacity of different dielectrics (1269. 1274. 1278.).   Consider an insulated sphere electrified positively and placed in
the centre of another and larger sphere uninsulated, a uniform
dielectric, as air, intervening.   The case is really that of my
apparatus (1187.), and also, in effect, that of any ball electrified in a room and removed to some distance from irregularly-
formed conductors.   Whilst things remain in this state the
electricity is distributed (so to speak) uniformly over the surface
of the electrified sphere.   But introduce such a dielectric as
sulphur or lac, into the space between the two conductors on
one side only, or opposite one part of the inner sphere, and
immediately the electricity on the latter is diffused unequally
(1229. 1270. 1309.), although the form of the conducting surfaces, their distances, and the *pressure* of the atmosphere remain perfectly unchanged.

1379. Fusinieri took a different view from that of Poisson,
Biot, and others, of the reason why rarefaction of air caused
easy diffusion of electricity.   He considered the effect as due
to the removal of the *obstacle* which the air presented to the
expansion of the substances from which the electricity passed†.
But platina balls show the phenomena in vacuo as well as vola-
tile metals and other substances; besides which, when the

* Encyclopædia Britannica, Supplement, vol. iv. Article Electricity, pp. 76,
81, &c.
† Bibl. Univ. 1831. xlviii. 375.

rarefaction is very considerable, the electricity passes with scarcely any resistance, and the production of no sensible heat; so that I think Fusinieri's view of the matter is likely to gain but few assents.

1380. I have no need to remark upon the discharging or collecting power of flame or hot air. I believe, with Harris, that the mere heat does nothing (1367.), the rarefaction only being influential. The effect of rarefaction has been already considered generally (1375.) ; and that caused by the heat of a burning light, with the pointed form of the wick, and the carrying power of the carbonaceous particles which for the time are associated with it, are fully sufficient to account for all the effects.

1381. We have now arrived at the important question, how will the inductive tension requisite for insulation and disruptive discharge be sustained in gases, which, having the same physical state and also the *same pressure* and the *same temperature* as *air,* differ from it in specific gravity, in chemical qualities, and it may be in peculiar relations, which not being as yet recognized are purely electrical (1361.) ?

1382. Into this question I can enter now only as far as is essential for the present argument, namely, that insulation and inductive tension do not depend merely upon the charged conductors employed, but also, and essentially, upon the interposed dielectric, in consequence of the molecular action of its particles (1292.).

1383. A glass vessel *a* (fig. 127.)* was ground at the top and bottom so as to be closed by two ground brass plates, *b* and *c*; *b* carried a stuffing box, with a sliding rod *d* terminated by a brass ball *s* below and a ring above. The lower plate was connected with a foot, stop-cock, and socket, *e, f* and *g*; and also with a brass ball *l*, which by means of a stem attached to it and entering the socket *g*, could be fixed at various heights. The metallic parts of this apparatus were not varnished, but the glass was well covered with a coat of shell-lac previously dissolved in alcohol. On exhausting the vessel at the air-pump it could be filled with any other gas than air, and,

* The drawing is to a scale of ⅙.

in such cases, the gas so passed in was dried whilst entering by fused chloride of calcium.

1384. The other part of the apparatus consisted of two insulating pillars, *h* and *i*, to which were fixed two brass balls, and through these passed two sliding rods, *k* and *m*, terminated at each end by brass balls ; *n* is the end of an insulated conductor, which could be rendered either positive or negative from an electrical machine ; *o* and *p* are wires connecting it with the two parts previously described, and *q* is a wire which, connecting the two opposite sides of the collateral arrangements, also communicates with a good discharging train *r* (292.).

1385. It is evident that the discharge from the machine electricity may pass either between *s* and *l*, or S and L. The regulation adopted in the first experiments was to keep *s* and *l* with their distance *unchanged*, but to introduce first one gas and then another into the vessel *a*, and then balance the discharge at the one place against that at the other ; for by making the interval at *u* sufficiently small, all the discharge would pass there, or making it sufficiently large it would all occur at the interval *v* in the receiver. On principle it seemed evident, that in this way the varying interval *u* might be taken as a measure, or rather indication of the resistance to discharge through the gas at the constant interval *v*. The following are the constant dimensions.

Ball *s* . . . . . . . 0·93 of an inch.
Ball S . . . . . . . 0·96 of an inch.
Ball *l* . . . . . . . 2·02 of an inch.
Ball L . . . . . . . 1·95 of an inch.
Interval *v* . . . . . . 0·62 of an inch.

1386. On proceeding to experiment it was found that when air or any gas was in the receiver *a*, the interval *u* was not a fixed one ; it might be altered through a certain range of distance, and yet sparks pass either there or at *v* in the receiver. The extremes were therefore noted, *i. e.* the greatest distance short of that at which the discharge *always* took place at *v* in the gas, and the least distance short of that at which it *always* took place at *u* in the air. Thus, with air in the receiver, the extremes at *u* were 0·56 and 0·79 of an inch, the range of 0·23 between these distances including intervals at which sparks passed occasionally either at one place or the other.

1387. The small balls *s* and S could be rendered either positive or negative from the machine, and as gases were expected and were found to differ from each other in relation to this change (1399.), the results obtained under these differences of charge were also noted.

1388. The following is a Table of results; the gas named is that in the vessel *a*. The smallest, greatest, and mean interval at *u* in air is expressed in parts of an inch, the interval *v* being constantly 0·62 of an inch.

|  | Smallest. | Greatest. | Mean. |
|---|---|---|---|
| Air, *s* and S, pos. . . . . | 0·60 | 0·79 | 0·695 |
| Air, *s* and S, neg. . . . . | 0·59 | 0·68 | 0·635 |
| Oxygen, *s* and S, pos. . . . | 0·41 | 0·60 | 0·505 |
| Oxygen, *s* and S, neg. . . . | 0·50 | 0·52 | 0·510 |
| Nitrogen, *s* and S, pos. . . | 0·55 | 0·68 | 0·615 |
| Nitrogen, *s* and S, neg. . . | 0·59 | 0·70 | 0·645 |
| Hydrogen, *s* and S, pos. . . | 0·30 | 0·44 | 0·370 |
| Hydrogen, *s* and S, neg. . . | 0·25 | 0·30 | 0·275 |
| Carbonic acid, *s* and S, pos. . | 0·56 | 0·72 | 0·640 |
| Carbonic acid, *s* and S, neg. . | 0·58 | 0·60 | 0·590 |
| Olefiant gas, *s* and S, pos. . | 0·64 | 0·86 | 0·750 |
| Olefiant gas, *s* and S, neg. . | 0·69 | 0·77 | 0·730 |
| Coal gas, *s* and S, pos. . . | 0·37 | 0·61 | 0·490 |
| Coal gas, *s* and S, neg. . . | 0·47 | 0·58 | 0·525 |
| Muriatic acid gas, *s* and S, pos. | 0·89 | 1·32 | 1·105 |
| Muriatic acid gas, *s* and S, neg. | 0·67 | 0·75 | 0·720 |

1389. The above results were all obtained at one time. On other occasions other experiments were made, which gave generally the same results as to order, though not as to numbers. Thus :

|  | | | |
|---|---|---|---|
| Hydrogen, *s* and S, pos. . . . | 0·23 | 0·57 | 0·400 |
| Carbonic acid, *s* and S, pos. . | 0·51 | 1·05 | 0·780 |
| Olefiant gas, *s* and S, pos. . . | 0·66 | 1·27 | 0·965 |

I did not notice the difference of the barometer on the days of experiment*.

* Similar experiments in different gases are described at 1507. 1508.—*Dec.* 1838.

1390. One would have expected only two distances, one for each interval, for which the discharge might happen either at one or the other; and that the least alteration of either would immediately cause one to predominate constantly over the other. But that under common circumstances is not the case. With air in the receiver, the variation amounted to 0·2 of an inch nearly on the smaller interval of 0·6, and with muriatic acid gas, the variation was above 0·4 on the smaller interval of 0·9. Why is it that when a fixed interval (the one in the receiver) will pass a spark that cannot go across 0·6 of air at one time, it will immediately after, and apparently under exactly similar circumstances, not pass a spark that can go across 0·8 of air?

1391. It is probable that part of this variation will be traced to particles of dust in the air drawn into and about the circuit (1568.). I believe also that part depends upon a variable charged condition of the surface of the glass vessel *a*. That the whole of the effect is not traceable to the influence of circumstances in the vessel *a*, may be deduced from the fact, that when sparks occur between balls in free air they frequently are not straight, and often pass otherwise than by the shortest distance. These variations in air itself, and at different parts of the very same balls, shows the presence and influence of circumstances which are calculated to produce effects of the kind now under consideration.

1392. When a spark had passed at either interval, then, generally, more tended to appear at the *same* interval, as if a preparation had been made for the passing of the latter sparks. So also on continuing to work the machine quickly the sparks generally followed at the same place. This effect is probably due in part to the warmth of the air heated by the preceding spark, in part to dust, and I suspect in part to something unperceived as yet in the circumstances of discharge.

1393. A very remarkable difference, which is *constant* in its direction, occurs when the electricity communicated to the balls *s* and S is changed from positive to negative, or in the contrary direction. It is that the range of variation is always greater when the small balls are positive than when they are negative. This is exhibited in the following Table, drawn from the former experiments.

|                              | Pos. | Neg. |
|------------------------------|------|------|
| In Air the range was . . .   | 0·19 | 0·09 |
| Oxygen. . . . . . .          | 0·19 | 0·02 |
| Nitrogen . . . . . .         | 0·13 | 0·11 |
| Hydrogen . . . . . .         | 0·14 | 0·05 |
| Carbonic acid. . . . .       | 0·16 | 0·02 |
| Olefiant gas . . . . .       | 0·22 | 0·08 |
| Coal gas . . . . . .         | 0·24 | 0·12 |
| Muriatic acid. . . . .       | 0·43 | 0·08 |

I have no doubt these numbers require considerable correction, but the general result is striking, and the differences in several cases very great.

---

1394. Though, in consequence of the variation of the striking distance (1386.), the interval in air fails to be a measure, as yet, of the insulating or resisting power of the gas in the vessel, yet we may for present purposes take the mean interval as representing in some degree that power. On examining these mean intervals as they are given in the third column (1388.), it will be very evident, that gases, when employed as dielectrics, have peculiar electrical relations to insulation, and therefore to induction, very distinct from such as might be supposed to depend upon their mere physical qualities of specific gravity or pressure.

1395. First, it is clear that at the *same pressure* they are not alike, the difference being as great as 37 and 110. When the small balls are charged positively, and with the same surfaces and the same pressure, muriatic acid gas has three times the insulating or restraining power (1362.) of hydrogen gas, and nearly twice that of oxygen, nitrogen, or air.

1396. Yet it is evident that the difference is not due to specific gravity, for though hydrogen is the lowest, and therefore lower than oxygen, oxygen is much beneath nitrogen, or than olefiant gas; and carbonic acid gas, though considerably heavier than olefiant gas or muriatic acid gas, is lower than either. Oxygen as a heavy, and olefiant as a light gas, are in strong contrast with each other; and if we may reason of olefiant gas from Harris's results with air (1365.), then it might be rarefied to two-thirds its usual density, or to a specific gravity of 9·3 (hydrogen being 1), and having neither the same density nor pressure as oxygen, would have equal insulating powers with it, or equal tendency to resist discharge.

1397. Experiments have already been described (1291. 1292.) which show that the gases are sensibly alike in their inductive capacity. This result is not in contradiction with the existence of great differences in their restraining power. The same point has been observed already in regard to dense and rare air (1375.).

1398. Hence arises a new argument proving that it cannot be mere pressure of the atmosphere which prevents or governs discharge (1377. 1378.), but a specific electric quality or relation of the gaseous medium. Hence also additional argument for the theory of molecular inductive action.

---

1399. Other specific differences amongst the gases may be drawn from the preceding series of experiments, rough and hasty as they are. Thus the positive and negative series of mean intervals do not give the same differences. It has been already noticed that the negative numbers are lower than the positive (1393.), but, besides that, the *order* of the positive and negative results is not the same. Thus, on comparing the mean numbers (which represent for the present insulating tension,) it appears that in air, hydrogen, carbonic acid, olefiant gas and muriatic acid, the tension rose higher when the smaller ball was made positive than when rendered negative, whilst in oxygen, nitrogen, and coal gas, the reverse was the case. Now though the numbers cannot be trusted as exact, and though air, oxygen, and nitrogen should probably be on the same side, yet some of the results, as, for instance, those with muriatic acid, fully show a peculiar relation and difference amongst gases in this respect. This was further proved by making the interval in air 0·8 of an inch whilst muriatic acid gas was in the vessel *a* ; for on charging the small balls *s* and S positively, *all* the discharge took place through the *air* ; but on charging them negatively, *all* the discharge took place through the *muriatic acid gas*.

1400. So also, when the conductor *n* was connected *only* with the muriatic acid gas apparatus, it was found that the discharge was more facile when the small ball *s* was negative than when positive ; for in the latter case, much of the electricity passed

off as brush discharge through the air from the connecting wire
*p* ; but in the former case it all seemed to go through the muriatic acid.

1401. The consideration, however, of positive and negative
discharge across air and other gases will be resumed in the further part of this, or in the next paper (1465. 1525.).

1402. Here for the present I must leave this part of the subject, which had for its object only to observe how far gases
agreed or differed as to their power of retaining a charge on
bodies acting by induction through them. All the results con-
spire to show that Induction is an action of contiguous molecules (1295. &c.) ; but besides confirming this, the first principle placed for proof in the present inquiry, they greatly assist
in developing the specific properties of each gaseous dielectric,
at the same time showing that further and extensive experimental investigation is necessary, and holding out the promise
of new discovery as the reward of the labour required.

1403. When we pass from the consideration of dielectrics
like the gases to that of bodies having the liquid and solid condition, then our reasonings in the present state of the subject
assume much more of the character of mere supposition. Still
I do not perceive anything adverse to the theory, in the phenomena which such bodies present. If we take three insulating
dielectrics, as air, oil of turpentine and shell-lac, and use the
same balls or conductors at the same intervals in these three
substances, increasing the intensity of the induction until discharge take place, we shall find that it must be raised much
higher in the fluid than for the gas, and higher still in the solid
than for the fluid. Nor is this inconsistent with the theory ;
for with the liquid, though its molecules are free to move almost
as easily as those of the gas, there are many more particles introduced into the given interval ; and such is also the case when
the solid body is employed. Besides that with the solid, the
cohesive force of the body used will produce some effect ; for
though the production of the polarized states in the particle of
a solid may not be obstructed, but, on the contrary, may in some
cases be even favoured (1164. 1344.) by its solidity or other
circumstances, yet solidity may well exert an influence on the

point of final subversion, (just as it prevents discharge in an electrolyte,) and so enable inductive intensity to rise to a much higher degree.

1404. In the cases of solids and liquids too, bodies may, and most probably do, possess specific differences as to their ability of assuming the polarized state, and also as to the extent to which that polarity must rise before discharge occurs. An analogous difference exists in the specific inductive capacities already pointed out in a few substances (1278.) in the last paper. Such a difference might even account for the various degrees of insulating and conducting power possessed by different bodies, and, if it should be found to exist, would add further strength to the argument in favour of the molecular theory of inductive action.

———————

1405. Having considered these various cases of sustained insulation in non-conducting dielectrics up to the highest point which they can attain, we find that they terminate at last in *disruptive discharge*; the peculiar condition of the molecules of the dielectric which was necessary to the continuous induction, being equally essential to the occurrence of that effect which closes all the phenomena. This discharge is not only in its appearance and condition different to the former modes by which the lowering of the powers was effected (1320. 1343.), but, whilst really the same in principle, varies much from itself in certain characters, and thus presents us with the forms of *spark*, *brush*, and *glow* (1359.). I will first consider *the spark*, limiting it for the present to the case of discharge between two oppositely electrified conducting surfaces.

### *The electric spark or flash.*

1406. The *spark* is consequent upon a discharge or lowering of the polarized inductive state of many dielectric particles, by a particular action of a few of the particles occupying a very small and limited space ; all the previously polarized particles returning to their first or normal condition in the inverse order in which they left it, and uniting their powers meanwhile to produce, or rather to continue, (1417.—1436.) the discharge effect in the place where the subversion of force first occurred.

My impression is, that the few particles situated where discharge occurs are not merely pushed apart, but assume a peculiar state, a highly exalted condition for the time, *i. e.* have thrown upon them all the surrounding forces in succession, and rising up to a proportionate intensity of condition, perhaps equal to that of chemically combining atoms, discharge the powers, possibly in the same manner as they do theirs, by some operation at present unknown to us ; and so the end of the whole. The ultimate effect is exactly as if a metallic wire had been put into the place of the discharging particles ; and it does not seem impossible that the principles of action in both cases, may, hereafter, prove to be the same.

1407. The *path of the spark,* or of the discharge, depends on the degree of tension acquired by the particles in the line of discharge, circumstances, which in every common case are very evident and by the theory easy to understand, rendering it higher in them than in their neighbours, and, by exhalting them first to the requisite condition, causing them to determine the course of the discharge.   Hence the selection of the path, and the solution of the wonder which Harris has so well described* as existing under the old theory.   All is prepared amongst the molecules beforehand, by the prior induction, for the path either of the electric spark or of lightning itself.

1408. The same difficulty is expressed as a principle by Nobili for voltaic electricity, almost in Mr. Harris's words, namely †, " electricity directs itself towards the point where it can most easily discharge itself," and the results of this as a principle he has well wrought out for the case of voltaic currents.   But the *solution* of the difficulty, or the proximate cause of the effects, is the same; induction brings the particles up to or towards a certain degree of tension (1370.) ; and by those which first attain it, is the discharge first and most efficiently performed.

1409. The *moment* of discharge is probably determined by that molecule of the dielectric which, from the circumstances has its tension most quickly raised up to the maximum intensity.   In all cases where the discharge passes from conductor to conductor this molecule must be on the surface of one of

* Nautical Magazine, 1834, p. 229.
† Bibliothèque Universelle, 1835, lix. 275.

them; but when it passes between a conductor and a non-conductor, it is, perhaps, not always so (1453.). When this particle has acquired its maximum tension, then the whole barrier of resistance is broken down in the line or lines of inductive action originating at it, and disruptive discharge occurs (1370.) : and such an inference, drawn as it is from the theory, seems to me in accordance with Mr. Harris's facts and conclusions respecting the resistance of the atmosphere, namely, that it is not really greater at any one discharging distance than another*.

1410. It seems probable, that the tension of a particle of the same dielectric, as air, which is requisite to produce discharge, is a *constant quantity,* whatever the shape of the part of the conductor with which it is in contact, whether ball or point; whatever the thickness or depth of dielectric throughout which induction is exerted ; perhaps, even, whatever the state, as to rarefaction or condensation of the dielectric ; and whatever the nature of the conductor, good or bad, with which the particle is for the moment associated. In saying so much, I do not mean to exclude small differences which may be caused by the reaction of neighbouring particles on the deciding particle, and indeed, it is evident that the intensity required in a particle must be related to the condition of those which are contiguous. But if the expectation should be found to approximate to truth, what a generality of character it presents ! and, in the definiteness of the power possessed by a particular molecule, may we not hope to find an immediate relation to the force which, being electrical, is equally definite and constitutes chemical affinity ?

1411. Theoretically it would seem that, at the moment of discharge by the spark in one line of inductive force, not merely would all the other lines throw their forces into this one (1406.), but the lateral effect, equivalent to a repulsion of these lines (1224. 1297.) would be relieved and, perhaps, followed by a contrary action, amounting to a collapse or attraction of these parts. Having long sought for some transverse force in statical electricity, which should be the equivalent to magnetism or the transverse force of current electricity, and conceiving that it might be connected with the transverse action of the lines of inductive force already described (1297.), I was desi-

* Philosophical Transactions, 1834, pp. 227, 229.

rous, by various experiments, of bringing out the effect of such a force, and making it tell upon the phenomena of electro-magnetism and magneto-electricity*.

1412. Amongst other results, I expected and sought for the mutual affection, or even the lateral coalition of two similar sparks, if they could be obtained simultaneously side by side, and sufficiently near to each other. For this purpose, two similar Leyden jars were supplied with rods of copper projecting from their balls in a horizontal direction, the rods being about 0·2 of an inch thick, and rounded at the ends. The jars were placed upon a sheet of tinfoil, and so adjusted that their rods, *a* and *b*, were near together, in the position represented in plan at fig. 116; *c* and *d* were two brass balls connected by a brass rod and insulated : *e* was also a brass ball connected, by a wire, with the ground and with the tinfoil upon which the Leyden jars were placed. By laying an insulated metal rod across from *a* to *b*, charging the jars, and removing the rod, both the jars could be brought up to the same intensity of charge (1370.). Then, making the ball *e* approach the ball *d*, at the moment the spark passed there, two sparks passed between the rods *n*, *o*, and the ball *c*; and as far as the eye could judge, or the conditions determine, they were simultaneous.

1413. Under these circumstances two modes of discharge took place ; either each end had its own particular spark to the ball, or else one end only was associated by a spark with the ball, but was at the same time related to the other end by a spark between the two.

1414. When the ball *c* was about an inch in diameter, the ends *n* and *o*, about half an inch from it, and about 0·4 of an inch from each other, the two sparks to the ball could be obtained. When, for the purpose of bringing the sparks nearer together, the ends, *n* and *o*, were brought closer to each other, then, unless very carefully adjusted, only one end had a spark with the ball, the other having a spark to it; and the least variation of position would cause either *n* or *o* to be the end which, giving the direct spark to the ball, was also the one through, or by means of which, the other discharged its electricity.

1415. On making the ball *c* smaller, I found that then it was

* See further investigations of this subject, 1658—1666, 1709—1735.— *Dec.* 1838.

needful to make the interval between the ends *n* and *o* larger in proportion to the distance between them and the ball *c*. On making *c* larger, I found I could diminish the interval, and so bring the two simultaneous separate sparks closer together, until, at last, the distance between them was not more at the widest part than 0·6 of their whole length.

1416. Numerous sparks were then passed and carefully observed. They were very rarely straight, but either curved or bent irregularly. In the average of cases they were, I think, decidedly convex towards each other ; perhaps two-thirds presented more or less of this effect, the rest bulging more or less outwards. I was never able, however, to obtain sparks which, separately leaving the ends of the wires *n* and *o*, conjoined into one spark before they reached or communicated with the ball *c*. At present, therefore, though I think I saw a tendency in the sparks to unite, I cannot assert it as a fact.

1417. But there is one very interesting effect here, analogous to, and it may be in part the same with, that I was searching for : I mean the increased facility of discharge where the spark passes. For instance, in the cases where one end, as *n*, discharged the electricity of both ends to the ball *c*, fig. 116, the electricity of the other end *o*, had to pass through an interval of air 1·5 times as great as that which it might have taken, by its direct passage between the end and the ball itself. In such cases, the eye could not distinguish, even by the use of Wheatstone's means\*, that the spark from the end *n*, which contained both portions of electricity, was a double spark. It could not have consisted of two sparks taking separate courses, for such an effect would have been visible to the eye ; but it is just possible, that the spark of the first end *n* and its jar, passing at the smallest interval of time before that of the other *o*, had heated and expanded the air in its course, and made it so much more favourable to discharge, that the electricity of the end *o* preferred leaping across to it and taking a very circuitous route, rather than the more direct one to the ball. It must, however, be remarked, in answer to this supposition, that the one spark between *d* and *e* would, by its influence, tend to produce simultaneous discharges at *n* and *o*, and certainly did so,

* Philosophical Transactions, 1834, pp. 584, 585.

when no preponderance was given to one wire over the other,
as to the previous inductive effect (1414.).

1418. The fact, however, is, that the disruptive discharge is
favourable to itself. It is at the outset a case of tottering equilibrium : and if *time* be an element in discharge, in however
minute a proportion (1436.), then the commencement of the act
at any point favours its continuance and increase there, and
portions of power will be discharged by a course which they
would not otherwise have taken.

1419. The mere heating and expansion of the air itself by the
first portion of electricity which passes, must have a great influence in producing this result.

1420. As to the result itself, we see its effect in every
electric spark; for it is not the whole quantity which passes
that determines the discharge, but merely that small portion of
force which brings the deciding molecule (1370.) up to its
maximum tension ; then, when its forces are subverted and discharge begins, all the rest passes by the same course, from the
influence of the favouring circumstances just referred to ; and
whether it be the electricity on a square inch, or a thousand
square inches of charged glass, the discharge is complete.
Hereafter we shall find the influence of this effect in the formation of brushes (1435.) ; and it is not impossible that we may
trace it producing the jagged spark and the forked lightning.

----

1421. The characters of the electric spark in *different gases*
vary, and the variation *may* be due simply to the effect of the
heat evolved at the moment. But it may also be due to that
specific relation of the particles and the electric forces which I
have assumed as the basis of a theory of induction; the facts
do not oppose such a view ; and in that view, the variation
strengthens the argument for molecular action, as it would
seem to show the influence of the latter in every part of the
electrical effect (1423. 1454.).

1422. The appearances of the sparks in different gases have
often been observed and recorded\*, but I think it not out of

\* See Van Marum's description of the Teylerian machine, vol. i. p. 112.,
and vol. ii. p. 196.; also Ency. Britan., vol. vi., Article Electricity, pp. 505, 507.

place to notice briefly the following results : they were obtained with balls of brass, (platina surfaces would have been better,) and at common pressures.  In *air,* the sparks have that intense light and bluish colour which are so well known, and often have faint or dark parts in their course, when the quantity of electricity passing is not great.  In *nitrogen,* they are very beautiful, having the same general appearance as in air, but have decidedly more colour of a bluish or purple character, and I thought were remarkably sonorous.  In *oxygen,* the sparks were whiter than in air or nitrogen, and I think not so brilliant.  In *hydrogen,* they had a very fine crimson colour, not due to its rarity, for the character passed away as the atmosphere was rarefied (1459.)\*.  Very little sound was produced in this gas ; but that is a consequence of its physical condition†.  In *carbonic acid gas,* the colour was similar to that of the spark in air, but with a little green in it : the sparks were remarkably irregular in form, more so than in common air : they could also, under similar circumstances as to size of ball, &c., be obtained much longer than in air, the gas showing a singular readiness to cause the discharge in the form of a spark.  In *muriatic acid gas,* the spark was nearly white : it was always bright throughout, never presenting those dark parts which happen in air, nitrogen, and some other gases.  The gas was dry, and during the whole experiment the surface of the glass globe within remained quite dry and bright.  In *coal gas,* the spark was sometimes green, sometimes red, and occasionally one part was green and another red : black parts also occur very suddenly in the line of the spark, *i. e.* they are not connected by any dull part with bright portions, but the two seem to join directly one with the other.

1423. These varieties of character impress my mind with a feeling, that they are due to a direct relation of the electric powers to the particles of the dielectric through which the discharge occurs, and are not the mere results of a casual ignition or a secondary kind of action of the electricity, upon

* Van Marum says they are about four times as large in hydrogen as in air, vol. i. p. 122.

† Leslie.  Cambridge Phil. Transactions, 267.

the particles which it finds in its course and thrusts aside in its passage (1454.).

1424. The spark may be obtained in media which are far denser than air, as in oil of turpentine, olive oil, resin, glass, &c. : it may also be obtained in bodies which being denser likewise approximate to the condition of conductors, as spermaceti, water, &c.   But in these cases, nothing occurs which, as far as I can perceive, is at all hostile to the general views I have endeavoured to advocate.

### *The electrical brush.*

1425. The *brush* is the next form of disruptive discharge which I shall consider.   There are many ways of obtaining it, or rather of exalting its characters ; and all these ways illustrate the principles upon which it is produced.   If an insulated conductor, connected with the positive conductor of an electrical machine, have a metal rod 0·3 of an inch in diameter projecting from it outwards from the machine, and terminating by a rounded end or a small ball, it will generally give good brushes ; or, if the machine be not in good action, then many ways of assisting the formation of the brush can be resorted to ; thus, the hand or any *large* conducting surface may be approached towards the termination to increase inductive force (1374.) : or the termination may be smaller and of badly conducting matter, as wood : or sparks may be taken between the prime conductor of the machine and the secondary conductor to which the termination giving brushes belongs ; or, which gives to the brushes exceedingly fine characters and great magnitude, the air around the termination may be rarefied more or less, either by heat or the air pump ; the former favourable circumstances being also continued.

1426. The brush when obtained by a powerful machine on a ball about 0·7 of an inch in diameter, at the end of a long brass rod attached to the positive prime conductor, had the general appearance as to form represented in fig. 117. : a short conical bright part or root appeared at the middle part of the ball projecting directly from it, which, at a little distance from the ball, broke out suddenly into a wide brush of pale ramifications having a quivering motion, and being accompanied at the same time with a low dull chattering sound.

1427. At first the brush seems continuous, but Professor Wheatstone has shown that the whole phenomenon consists of successive intermittent discharges*. If the eye be passed rapidly, not by a motion of the head, but of the eyeball itself, across the direction of the brush, by first looking steadfastly about 10° or 15° above, and then instantly as much below it, the general brush will be resolved into a number of individual brushes, standing in a row upon the line which the eye passed over ; each elementary brush being the result of a single discharge, and the space between them representing both the time during which the eye was passing over that space, and that which elapsed between one discharge and another.

1428. The single brushes could easily be separated to eight or ten times their own width, but were not at the same time extended, *i. e.* they did not become more indefinite in shape, but, on the contrary, less so, each being more distinct in form, ramification, and character, because of its separation from the others, in its effects upon the eye. Each, therefore, was instantaneous in its existence (1436.). Each had the conical root complete (1426.).

1429. On using a smaller ball, the general brush was smaller, and the sound, though weaker, more continuous. On resolving the brush into its elementary parts, as before, these were found to occur at much shorter intervals of time than in the former case, but still the discharge was intermitting.

1430. Employing a wire with a round end, the brush was still smaller, but, as before, separable into successive discharges. The sound, though feebler, was higher in pitch, being a distinct musical note.

1431. The sound is, in fact, due to the recurrence of the noise of each separate discharge, and these, happening at intervals nearly equal under ordinary circumstances, cause a definite note to be heard, which, rising in pitch with the increased rapidity and regularity of the intermitting discharges, gives a ready and accurate measure of the intervals, and so may be used in any case when the discharge is heard, even though the appearances

* Philosophical Transactions, 1834, p. 586.

may not be seen, to determine the element of *time*. So when, by bringing the hand towards a projecting rod or ball, the pitch of the tone produced by a brushy discharge increases, the effect informs us that we have increased the induction (1374.), and by that means increased the rapidity of the alternations of charge and discharge.

1432. By using wires with finer terminations, smaller brushes were obtained, until they could hardly be distinguished as brushes ; but as long as *sound* was heard, the discharge could be ascertained by the eye to be intermitting ; and when the sound ceased, the light became *continuous* as a glow (1359. 1405. 1526—1543.).

1433. To those not accustomed to use the eye in the manner I have described, or, in cases where the recurrence is too quick for any unassisted eye, the beautiful revolving mirror of Professor Wheatstone\* will be useful for such developments of condition as those mentioned above. Another excellent process is to produce the brush or other luminous phenomenon on the end of a rod held in the hand opposite to a charged positive or negative conductor, and then move the rod rapidly from side to side whilst the eye remains still. The successive discharges occur of course in different places, and the state of things before, at, and after a single coruscation or brush can be exceedingly well separated.

1434. The *brush* is in reality a discharge between a bad or a non-conductor and either a conductor or another non-conductor. Under common circumstances, the brush is a discharge between a conductor and air, and I conceive it to take place in something like the following manner. When the end of an electrified rod projects into the middle of a room, induction takes place between it and the walls of the room, across the dielectric, air ; and the lines of inductive force accumulate upon the end in greater quantity than elsewhere, or the particles of air at the end of the rod are more highly polarized than those at any other part of the rod, for the reasons already given (1374.). The particles of air situated in sections across these lines of force are least polarized in the sections towards the walls, and most polarized in those nearer

\* Philosophical Transactions, 1834, pp. 584, 585.

to the end of the wires (1369.) : thus, it may well happen, that a particle at the end of the wire is at a tension that will immediately terminate in discharge, whilst in those even only a few inches off, the tension is still beneath that point. But suppose the rod to be charged positively, a particle of air A, fig. 118. next it, being polarized, and having of course its negative force directed towards the rod and its positive force outwards; the instant that discharge takes place between the positive force of the particle of the rod opposite the air and the negative force of the particle of air towards the rod, the whole particle of air becomes positively electrified; and when, the next instant, the discharged part of the rod resumes its positive state by conduction from the surface of metal behind, it not only acts on the particles beyond A, by throwing A into a polarized state again, but A itself, because of its charged state, exerts a distinct inductive act towards these further particles, and the tension is consequently so much exalted between A and B, that discharge takes place there also, as well as again between the metal and A.

1435. In addition to this effect, it has been shown, that, the act of discharge having once commenced, the whole operation, like a case of unstable equilibrium, is hastened to a conclusion (1370. 1418.), the rest of the act being facilitated in its occurrence, and other electricity than that which caused the first necessary tension hurrying to the spot. When, therefore, disruptive discharge has once commenced at the root of a brush, the electric force which has been accumulating in the conductor attached to the rod, finds a more ready discharge there than elsewhere, and will at once follow the course marked out as it were for it, thus leaving the conductor in a partially discharged state, and the air about the end of the wire in a charged condition; and the time necessary for restoring the full charge of the conductor, and the dispersion of the charged air in a greater or smaller degree, by the joint forces of repulsion from the conductor and attraction towards the walls of the room, to which its inductive action is directed, is just that time which forms the interval between brush and brush (1420. 1427. 1431. 1447.).

1436. The words of this description are long, but there is nothing in the act or the forces on which it depends to prevent

the discharge being *instantaneous,* as far as we can estimate
and measure it.   The consideration of *time* is, however, important in several points of view (1418.), and in reference to disruptive discharge, it seemed from theory far more probable
that it might be  detected in a brush than in a spark ; for in a
brush, the particles in the line through which the discharge
passes are in very different states as to intensity, and the discharge is already complete in its act at the root of the brush,
before the particles at the extremity of the ramifications have
yet attained their maximum intensity.

1437. I consider *brush* discharge as, probably a successive
effect in this way.   Discharge begins at the root (1426. 1553.),
and, extending itself in succession to all parts of the single
brush, continues to go on at the root and the previously formed
parts until the whole brush is complete ; then, by the fall in
intensity and power at the conductor, it ceases at once in all
parts, to be renewed, when that power has risen again to a sufficient degree.   But in a *spark,* the particles in the line of discharge being, from the circumstances, nearly alike in their intensity of polarization, suffer discharge so nearly at the same
moment as to make the time quite insensible to us.

1438. Mr. Wheatstone has already made experiments which
fully illustrate this point.   He found that the brush generally
had a sensible duration, but that with its highest capabilities
he could not detect any such effect in the spark *.   I repeated
his experiment on the brush, though with more imperfect means,
to ascertain whether I could distinguish a longer duration in
the stem or root of the brush than in the extremities, and the
appearances were such as to make me think an effect of this
kind was produced.

1439. That the discharge breaks into several ramifications,
and by them passes through portions of air alike, or nearly
alike, as to polarization and the degree of tension the particles
there have acquired, is a very natural result of the previous
state of things, and rather to be expected than that the discharge should continue to go straight out into space in a single
line amongst those particles which, being at a distance from
the end of the rod, are in a lower state of tension than those
which are near : and whilst we cannot but conclude, that those

* Philosophical Transactions, 1836, pp. 586, 590.

parts where the branches of a single brush appear, are more favourably circumstanced for discharge than the darker parts between the ramifications, we may also conclude, that in those parts where the light of concomitant discharge is equal, there the circumstances are nearly equal also. The single successive brushes are by no means of the same particular shape even when they are observed without displacement of the rod or surrounding objects (1427. 1433.), and the successive discharges may be considered as taking place into the mass of air around, through different roads at each brush, according as minute circumstances, such as dust, &c. (1391. 1392.) may have favoured the course by one set of particles rather than another.

1440. Brush discharge does not essentially require any current of the medium in which the brush appears : the current almost always occurs, but is a consequence of the brush, and will be considered hereafter (1562.—1610.). On holding a blunt point positively charged towards uninsulated water, a star or glow appeared on the point, a current of air passed from it, and the surface of the water was depressed; but on bringing the point so near that sonorous brushes passed, then the current of air instantly ceased, and the surface of the water became level.

1441. The discharge by a brush is not to all the particles of air that are near the electrified conductor from which the brush issues; only those parts where the ramifications pass are electrified : the air in the central dark parts between them receives no charge, and, in fact, at the time of discharge, has its electric and inductive tension considerably lowered. For consider fig. 128, to represent a single positive brush ;—the induction before the discharge is from the end of the rod outwards, in diverging lines towards the distant conductors, as the walls of the room, &c., and a particle at *a* has polarity of a certain degree of tension, and tends with a certain force to become charged; but at the moment of discharge, the air in the ramifications *b* and *d*, acquiring also a positive state, opposes its influence to that of the positive conductor on *a*, and the tension of the particle at *a* is therefore diminished rather than increased. The charged particles at *b* and *d* are now inductive bodies, but their lines of inductive action are still outwards towards the walls of the room ; the direction of the polarity and the tendency of other particles to charge from these, being governed by, or in conformity with, these lines of force.

1442. The particles that are charged are probably very highly charged, but the medium being a non-conductor, they cannot communicate that state to their neighbours. They travel, therefore, under the influence of the repulsive and attractive forces, from the charged conductor towards the nearest uninsulated conductor, or the nearest body in a different state to themselves, just as charged particles of dust would travel, and are then discharged; each particle acting, in its course, as a centre of inductive force upon any bodies near which it may come. The travelling of these charged particles when they are numerous, causes wind and currents, but these will come into consideration under *carrying discharge* (1319. 1562. &c.).

1443. When air is said to be electrified, and it frequently assumes this state near electrical machines, it consists, according to my view, of a mixture of electrified and unelectrified particles, the latter being in very large proportion to the former. When we gather electricity from air, by a flame or by wires, it is either by the actual discharge of these particles, or by effects dependent on their inductive action, a case of either kind being produceable at pleasure. That the law of equality between the two forces or forms of force in inductive action is as strictly preserved in these as in other cases, is fully shown by the fact, formerly stated (1173. 1174.), that, however strongly air in a vessel might be charged positively, there was an exactly equal amount of negative force on the inner surface of the vessel itself, for no residual portion of either the one or the other electricity could be obtained.

1444. I have nowhere said, nor does it follow, that the air is charged only where the luminous brush appears. The charging may extend beyond those parts which are visible, *i. e.* particles to the right or left of the lines of light may receive electricity, the parts which are luminous being so only because much electricity is passing by them to other parts (1437.); just as in a spark discharge the light is greater as more electricity passes, though it has no necessary relation to the quantity required to commence discharge (1370. 1420.). Hence the form we see in a brush may by no means represent the whole quantity of air electrified; for an invisible portion, clothing the visible form to a certain depth, may, at the same time, receive its charge (1552.).

1445. Several effects which I have met with in muriatic acid gas tend to make me believe, that that gaseous body allows of a dark discharge. At the same time, it is quite clear from theory, that in some gases, the reverse of this may occur, *i. e.* that the charging of the air may not extend even so far as the light. We do not know as yet enough of the electric light to be able to state on what it depends, and it is very possible that, when electricity bursts forth into air, all the particles of which are in state of tension, light may be evolved by such as, being very near to, are not of, those which actually receive a charge at the time.

1446. The further a brush extends in a gas, the further no doubt is the charge or discharge carried forward; but this may vary between different gases, and yet the intensity required for the first moment of discharge not vary in the same, but in some other proportion. Thus with respect to nitrogen and muriatic acid gases, the former, as far as my experiments have proceeded, produces far finer and larger brushes than the latter (1458. 1462.), but the intensity required to commence discharge is much higher for the muriatic acid than the nitrogen (1395.). Here again, therefore, as in many other qualities, specific differences are presented by different gaseous dielectrics, and so prove the special relation of the latter to the act and the phenomena of induction.

1447. To sum up these considerations respecting the character and condition of the brush, I may state that it is a spark to air; a diffusion of electric force to matter, not by conduction, but disruptive discharge; a dilute spark which, passing to very badly conducting matter, frequently discharges but a small portion of the power stored up in the conductor; for as the air charged reacts on the conductor, whilst the conductor, by loss of electricity, sinks in its force (1435.), the discharge quickly ceases, until by the dispersion of the charged air and the renewal of the excited conditions of the conductor, circumstances have risen up to their first effective condition, again to cause discharge, and again to fall and rise.

1448. The brush and spark gradually pass into one another.

Making a small ball positive by a good electrical machine with
a large prime conductor, and approaching a large uninsulated
discharging ball towards it, very beautiful variations from the
spark to the brush may be obtained. The drawings of long and
powerful sparks, given by Van Marum*, Harris †, and others,
also indicate the same phenomena. As far as I have observed,
whenever the spark has been brushy in air of common pressures, the whole of the electricity has not been discharged, but
only portions of it, more or less according to circumstances;
whereas, whenever the effect has been a distinct spark throughout the whole of its course, the discharge has been perfect,
provided no interruption had been made to it elsewhere, in the
discharging circuit, than where the spark occurred.

1449. When an electrical brush from an inch to six inches
in length or more is issuing into free air, it has the form given,
fig. 117. But if the hand, a ball, or any knobbed conductor be
brought near, the extremities of the coruscations turn towards
it and each other, and the whole assumes various forms according to circumstances, as in figs. 119, 120, and 121. The influence of the circumstances in each case is easily traced, and I
might describe it here, but that I should be ashamed to occupy
the time of the Society in things so evident. But how beautifully does the curvature of the ramifications illustrate the curved form of the lines of inductive force existing previous to the
discharge! for the former are consequences of the latter, and
take their course, in each discharge, where the previous inductive tension had been raised to the proper degree. They
represent these curves just as well as iron filings represent magnetic curves, the visible effects in both cases being the consequences of the action of the forces in *the places where* the effects appear. The phenomena, therefore, constitute additional
and powerful testimony (1216. 1230.) to that already given in
favour both of induction through dielectrics in curved lines
(1231.), and of the lateral relation of these lines, by an effect
equivalent to a repulsion producing divergence, or, as in the
cases figured, the bulging form.

1450. In reference to the theory of molecular inductive ac-

* Description of the Teylerian machine, vol. i. pp. 28. 32.; vol. ii. p. 226,
&c.

† Philosophical Transactions, 1834, p. 243.

tion, I may also add, the proof deducible from the long brushy ramifying spark which may be obtained between a small ball on the positive conductor of an electrical machine, and a larger one at a distance (1448. 1504.).   What a fine illustration that spark affords of the previous condition of *all* the particles of the dielectric between the surfaces of discharge, and how unlike the appearances are to any which would be deduced from the theory which assumes inductive action to be action at a distance, in straight lines only ; and charge, as being electricity retained upon the surface of conductors by the mere pressure of the atmosphere !

1451. When the brush is obtained in rarefied air, the appearances vary greatly, according to circumstances, and are exceedingly beautiful.   Sometimes a brush may be formed of only six or seven branches, these being broad and highly luminous, of a purple colour, and in some parts an inch or more apart :—by a spark discharge at the prime conductor (1455.) single brushes may be obtained at pleasure.   Discharge in the form of a brush is favoured by rarefaction of the air, in the same manner and for the same reason as discharge in the form of a spark (1375.) ; but in every case there is previous induction and charge through the dielectric, and polarity of its particles (1437.), the induction being, as in any other instance, alternately raised by the machine and lowered by the discharge. In certain experiments the rarefaction was increased to the utmost degree, and the opposed conducting surfaces brought as near together as possible without producing glow (1529.) : the brushes then contracted in their lateral dimensions, and recurred so rapidly as to form an apparently continuous arc of light from metal to metal.   Still the discharge could be observed to intermit (1427.), so that even under these high conditions, induction preceded each single brush, and the tense polarized condition of the contiguous particles was a necessary preparation for the discharge itself.

1452. The brush form of disruptive discharge may be obtained not only in air and gases, but also in much denser media.   I procured it in *oil of turpentine* from the end of a wire going through a glass tube into the fluid contained in a metal vessel.   The brush was small and very difficult to obtain ; the ramifications were simple, and stretched out from each other, diverging very much. The light was exceedingly feeble, a perfectly dark room being required for its observation. When a few solid particles, as of dust or silk, were in the liquid, the brush was produced with much greater facility.

1453. The running together or coalescence of different lines of discharge (1412.) is very beautifully shown in the brush in air. This point may present a little difficulty to those who are not accustomed to see in every discharge an equal exertion of power in opposite directions, a positive brush being considered by such (perhaps in consequence of the common phrase *direction of a current*) as indicating a breaking forth in different directions of the original force, rather than a tendency to convergence and union in one line of passage. But the ordinary case of the brush may be compared, for its illustration, with that in which, by holding the knuckle opposite to highly excited glass, a discharge occurs, the ramifications of a brush then leading from the glass and converging into a spark on the knuckle. Though a difficult experiment to make, it is possible to obtain discharge between highly excited shell-lac and the excited glass of a machine : when the discharge passes, it is, from the nature of the charged bodies, brush at each end and spark in the middle, beautifully illustrating that tendency of discharge to facilitate like action, which I have described in a former page (1418.).

1454. The brush has *specific characters* in different gases, indicating a relation to the particles of these bodies even in a stronger degree than the spark (1422. 1423.). This effect is in strong contrast with the non-variation caused by the use of different substances as *conductors* from which the brushes are to originate. Thus, using such bodies as wood, card, charcoal, nitre, citric acid, oxalic acid, oxide of lead, chloride of lead, carbonate of potassa, potassa fusa, strong solution of potash, oil of vitriol, sulphur, sulphuret of antimony, and hæmatite, no variation in the character of the brushes was obtained, except that (dependent upon their effect as better or worse conductors) of causing discharge with more or less readiness and quickness from the machine *.

---

* Exception must, of course, be made of those cases where the root of the brush, becoming a spark, causes a little diffusion or even decomposition of the matter there, and so gains more or less of a particular colour at that part.

1455. The following are a few of the effects I observed in different gases at the positively charged surfaces, and with atmospheres varying in their pressure. The general effect of rarefaction was the same for all the gases : at first, sparks passed ; these gradually were converted into brushes, which became larger and more distinct in their ramifications, until, upon further rarefaction, the latter began to collapse and draw in upon each other, till they formed a stream across from conductor to conductor : then a few lateral streams shot out towards the glass of the vessel from the conductors ; these became thick and soft in appearance, and were succeeded by the full constant glow which covered the discharging wire. The phenomena varied with the size of the vessel (1477.), the degree of rarefaction, and the discharge of electricity from the machine. When the latter was in successive sparks, they were most beautiful, the effect of a spark from a small machine being equal to, and often surpassing, that produced by the *constant* discharge of a far more powerful one.

1456. *Air.*—Fine positive brushes are easily obtained in air at common pressures, and possess the well-known purplish light. When the air is rarefied, the ramifications are very long, filling the globe (1477.) ; the light is greatly increased, and is of a beautiful purple colour, with an occasional rose tint in it.

1457. *Oxygen.*—At common pressures, the brush is very close and compressed, and of a dull whitish colour. In rarefied oxygen, the form and appearance are better, the colour somewhat purplish, but all the characters very poor compared to those in air.

1458. *Nitrogen* gives brushes with great facility at the positive surface, far beyond any other gas I have tried : they are almost always fine in form, light, and colour, and in rarefied nitrogen are magnificent. They surpass the discharges in any other gas as to the quantity of light evolved.

1459. *Hydrogen,* at common pressures, gave a better brush than oxygen, but did not equal nitrogen ; the colour was greenish gray. In rarefied hydrogen, the ramifications were very fine in form and distinctness, but pale in colour, with a soft and velvety appearance, and not at all equal to those in nitrogen. In the rarest state of the gas, the colour of the light was a pale gray green.

1460. *Coal gas.*—The brushes were rather difficult to produce, the contrast with nitrogen being great in this respect. They were short and strong, generally of a greenish colour, and possessing much of the spark character : for, occurring on both the positive and negative terminations, often when there was a dark interval of some length between the two brushes, still the quick, sharp sound of the spark was produced, as if the discharge had been sudden through this gas, and partaking, in that respect, of the character of a spark. In rare coal gas, the brush forms were better, but the light very poor and the colour gray.

1461. *Carbonic acid gas* produces a very poor brush at common pressures, as regards either size, light, or colour ; and this is probably connected with the tendency which this gas has to discharge the electricity as a spark (1422.). In rarefied carbonic acid, the brush is better in form, but weak as to light, being of a dull greenish or purplish hue, varying with the pressure and other circumstances.

1462. *Muriatic acid gas.*—It is very difficult to obtain the brush in this gas at common pressures. On gradually increasing the distance of the rounded ends, the sparks suddenly ceased when the interval was about an inch, and the discharge, which was still through the gas in the globe, was silent and dark. Occasionally a very short brush could for a few moments be obtained, but it quickly disappeared. Even when the intermitting spark current (1455.) from the machine was used, still I could only with difficulty obtain a brush, and that very short, though I used rods with rounded terminations (about $0.25$ of an inch in diameter) which had before given them most freely in air and nitrogen. During the time of this difficulty with the muriatic gas, magnificent brushes were passing off from different parts of the machine into the surrounding air. On rarefying the gas, the formation of the brush was facilitated, but it was generally of a low squat form, very poor in light, and very similar on both the positive and negative surfaces. On rarefying the gas still more, a few large ramifications were obtained of a pale bluish colour, utterly unlike those in nitrogen.

1463. In all the gases, the different forms of disruptive discharge may be linked together and gradually traced from one extreme to the other, *i. e.* from the spark to the glow (1405. 1526.), or, it may be, to a still further condition to be called dark discharge (1544—1560.); but it is nevertheless very surprising to see what a specific character each keeps whilst under the predominance of the general law. Thus, in muriatic acid, the brush is very difficult to obtain, and there comes in its place almost a dark discharge, partaking of the readiness of the spark action. Moreover, in muriatic acid, I have *never* observed the spark with any dark interval in it. In nitrogen, the spark readily changes its character into that of brush. In carbonic acid gas, there seems to be a facility to occasion spark discharge, whilst yet that gas is unlike nitrogen in the facility of the latter to form brushes, and unlike muriatic acid in its own facility to continue the spark. These differences add further force, first to the observations already made respecting the spark in various gases (1422. 1423.), and then, to the proofs deducible from it, of the relation of the electrical forces to the particles of matter.

1464. The peculiar characters of nitrogen in relation to the electric discharge (1422. 1458.) must, evidently, have an important influence over the form and even the occurrence of lightning. Being that gas which most readily produces coruscations, and, by them, extends discharge to a greater distance than any other gas tried, it is also that which constitutes four-fifths of our atmosphere; and as in atmospheric electrical phenomena, one, and sometimes both the inductive forces are resident on the particles of the air, which, though probably affected as to conducting power by the aqueous particles in it, cannot be considered as a good conductor; so the peculiar power possessed by nitrogen, to originate and effect discharge in the form of a brush or of ramifications, has, probably, an important relation to its electrical service in nature, as it most seriously affects the character and condition of the discharge when made. The whole subject of discharge from and through gases is of great interest, and, if only in reference to atmospheric electricity, deserves extensive and close experimental investigation.

*Difference of discharge at the positive and negative conducting surfaces.*

1465. I have avoided speaking of this well-known phenomenon more than was quite necessary, that I might bring together here what I have to say on the subject. When the
brush discharge is observed in air at the positive and negative
surfaces, there is a very remarkable difference, the true and full
comprehension of which would, no doubt, be of the utmost importance to the physics of electricity; it would throw great light
on our present subject, *i. e.* the molecular action of dielectrics
under induction, and its consequences ; and seems very open to,
and accessible by, experimental inquiry.

1466. The difference in question used to be expressed in
former times by saying, that a point charged positively gave
brushes into the air, whilst the same point charged negatively
gave a star. This is true only of bad conductors, or of metallic
conductors charged intermittingly, or otherwise controlled by
collateral induction. If metallic points project *freely* into the
air, the positive and negative light upon them differ very little
in appearance, and the difference can be observed only upon
close examination.

1467. The effect varies exceedingly under different circumstances, but, as we must set out from some position, may perhaps be stated thus : if a metallic wire with a rounded termination in free air be used to produce the brushy discharge, then
the brushes obtained when the wire is charged negatively are
very poor and small, by comparison with those produced when
the charge is positive. Or if a large metal ball connected with
the electrical machine be charged *positively*, and a fine uninsulated point be gradually brought towards it, a star appears
on the point when at a considerable distance, which, though it
becomes brighter, does not change its form of a star until it is
close up to the ball : whereas, if the ball be charged negatively,
the point at a considerable distance has a star on it as before ;
but when brought nearer, (in my case to the distance of $1\frac{1}{2}$
inch,) a brush formed on it, extending to the negative ball ;
and when still nearer, (at $\frac{1}{8}$ of an inch distance,) the brush
ceased, and bright sparks passed. These variations, I believe,

include the whole series of differences, and they seem to show
at once, that the negative surface tends to retain its discharging
character unchanged, whilst the positive surface, under similar
circumstances, permits of great variation.

1468. There are several points in the character of the negative discharge to air which it is important to observe.    A metal
rod, 0·3 of an inch in diameter, with a rounded end projecting
into the air, was charged negatively, and gave a short noisy
brush (fig. 122.).    It was ascertained both by sight (1427. 1433.)
and sound (1431.), that the successive discharges were very
rapid in their recurrence, being seven or eight times more numerous in the same period than those produced when the rod was
charged positively to an equal degree.    When the rod was positive, it was easy, by working the machine a little quicker, to
replace the brush by a glow (1405. 1463.), but when it was
negative no efforts could produce this change.    Even by bringing the hand opposite the wire, the only effect was to increase
the number of brush discharges in a given period, raising at the
same time the sound to a higher pitch.

1469. A point opposite the negative brush exhibited a star,
and as it was approximated caused the size and sound of the
negative brush to diminish, and at last, to cease, leaving the
negative end silent and dark, yet effective as to discharge.

1470. When the round end of a smaller wire (fig. 123.) was
advanced towards the negative brush, it (becoming positive by
induction) exhibited the quiet glow at 8 inches distance, the
negative brush continuing.    When nearer, the pitch of the
sound of the negative brush rose, indicating quicker intermit-
tences (1431.) ; still nearer the positive end threw off ramifications and distinct brushes ; at the same time the negative
brush contracted in its lateral directions and collected together,
giving a peculiar narrow longish brush, in shape like a hair pen-
cil, the two brushes existing at once, but very different in their
form and appearance, and especially in the more rapid recurrence of the negative discharges than of the positive.    On using
a smaller positive wire for the same experiment, the glow first
appeared on it, and then the brush, the negative brush being
affected at the same time ; and the two at one distance became
exceedingly alike in appearance, and the sounds, I thought, were
in unison ; at all events they were in harmony, so that the inter-

missions of discharge were either isochronous, or a simple ratio existed between the intervals. With a higher action of the machine, the wires being retained unaltered, the negative surface became dark and silent, and a glow appeared on the positive one. A still higher action changed the latter into a spark. Finer positive wires gave other variations of these effects, the description of which I must not allow myself to go into here.

1471. A thinner rod was now connected with the negative conductor in place of the larger one (1468.), its termination being gradually diminished to a blunt point, as in fig. 124; and it was beautiful to observe that, notwithstanding the variation of the brush, the same general order of effects was produced. The end gave a small sonorous negative brush, which the approach of the hand or a large conducting surface did not alter, until it was so near as to produce a spark. A fine point opposite to it was luminous at a distance; being nearer it did not destroy the light and sound of the negative brush, but only tended to have a brush produced on itself, which, at a still less distance, passed into a spark joining the two surfaces.

1472. When the distinct negative and positive brushes are produced simultaneously in relation to each other in air, the former almost always has a contracted form, as in fig. 125., very much indeed resembling the figure which the positive brush itself has when influenced by the lateral vicinity of positive parts acting by induction. Thus a brush issuing from a point in the re-entering angle of a positive conductor has the same compressed form (fig. 126.).

1473. The character of the negative brush is not affected by the chemical nature of the substances of the conductors (1454). but only by their possession of the conducting power in a greater or smaller degree.

1474. Rarefaction of common air about a negative ball or blunt point facilitated the development of the negative brush, the effect being, I think, greater than on a positive brush, though great on both. Extensive ramifications could be obtained from a ball or end electrified negatively to the plate of the air-pump on which the jar containing it stood.

1475. A very important variation of the relative forms and conditions of the positive and negative brush takes place on varying the dielectric in which they are produced. The differ-

ence is so very great that it points to a specific relation of this
form of discharge to the particular gas in which it takes place,
and opposes the idea that gases are but obstructions to the
discharge, acting one like another and merely in proportion to
their pressure (1377.).

1476. In *air*, the superiority of the positive brush is well
known (1467. 1472.). In *nitrogen*, it is as great or even greater
than in air (1458.). In *hydrogen*, the positive brush loses a part
of its superiority, not being so good as in nitrogen or air;
whilst the negative brush does not seem injured (1459.). In
*oxygen*, the positive brush is compressed and poor (1457);
whilst the negative did not become less : the two were so alike
that the eye frequently could not tell one from the other, and
this similarity continued when the oxygen was gradually rarefied. In *coal gas*, the brushes are difficult of production as
compared to nitrogen (1460.), and the positive not much superior to the negative in its character, either at common or low
pressures. In *carbonic acid gas*, this approximation of character also occurred. In *muriatic acid gas*, the positive brush
was very little better than the negative, and both difficult to
produce (1462.) as compared with the facility in nitrogen or air.

1477. These experiments were made with rods of brass about
a quarter of an inch thick having rounded ends, these being
opposed in a glass globe 7 inches in diameter, containing the gas
to be experimented with. The electric machine was used to communicate directly, sometimes the positive, and sometimes the
negative, state, to the rod in connection with it.

1478. Thus we see that, notwithstanding there is a general
difference in favour of the superiority of the positive brush
over the negative, that difference is at its maximum in nitrogen
and air; whilst in carbonic acid, muriatic acid, coal gas, and
oxygen, it diminishes, and at last almost disappears. So that
in this particular effect, as in all others yet examined, the evidence is in favour of that view which refers the results to a direct relation of the electric forces with the molecules of the
matter concerned in the action (1421. 1423. 1463.). Even
when special phenomena arise under the operation of the general law, the theory adopted seems fully competent to meet
the case.

1479. Before I proceed further in tracing the probable

cause of the difference between the positive and negative brush discharge, I wish to know the results of a few experiments which are in course of preparation : and thinking this Series of Researches long enough, I shall here close it with the expectation of being able in a few weeks to renew the inquiry, and entirely redeem my pledge (1306.).

*Royal Institution,*
 *December 23rd, 1837.*

# THIRTEENTH SERIES.

§ 18. *On Induction (continued).* ¶ ix. *Disruptive discharge (continued)—Peculiarities of positive and negative discharge either as spark or brush—Glow discharge—Dark discharge.* ¶ x. *Convection, or carrying discharge.* ¶ xi. *Relation of a vacuum to electrical phenomena.* § 19. *Nature of the electrical current.*

Received February 22,—Read March 15, 1838.

¶ ix. *Disruptive discharge (continued).*

1480. LET us now direct our attention to the general difference of the positive and negative disruptive discharge, with the object of tracing, as far as possible, the cause of that difference, and whether it depends on the charged conductors principally, or on the interposed dielectric; and as it appears to be great in air and nitrogen (1476.), let us observe the phenomena in air first.

1481. The general case is best understood by a reference to surfaces of considerable size rather than to points, which involve (as a secondary effect) the formation of currents (1562.). My investigation, therefore, was carried on with balls and terminations of different diameters, and the following are some of the principal results.

1482. If two balls of very different dimensions, as for instance one half an inch, and the other three inches, in diameter, be arranged at the ends of rods so that either can be electrified by a machine and made to discharge by sparks to the other, which is at the same time uninsulated; then, as is well known, far longer sparks are obtained when the small ball is positive and the large ball negative, than when the small ball is negative and the large ball positive. In the former case, the sparks are 10 or 12 inches in length; in the latter, an inch or an inch and a half only.

1483. But previous to the description of further experiments, I will mention two words, for which with many others I am indebted to a friend, and which I think it would be expedient to introduce and use. It is important in ordinary inductive action, to distinguish at which charged surface the induction originates and is sustained: *i. e.* if two or more metallic balls, or other masses of matter, are in inductive relation, to express which are charged originally, and which are brought by them into the opposite electrical condition. I propose to call those bodies which are originally charged, *inductric* bodies; and those which assume the opposite state, in consequence of the induction, *inducteous* bodies. This distinction is not needful because there is any difference between the sums of the *inductric* and the *inducteous* forces; but principally because, when a ball A is inductric, it not merely brings a ball B, which is opposite to it, into an inducteous state, but also many other surrounding conductors, though some of them may be a considerable distance off, and the consequence is, that the balls do not bear the same precise relation to each other when, first one, and then the other, is made the inductric ball; though, in each case, the *same ball* be made to assume the *same state*.

1484. Another liberty which I may also occasionally take in language I will explain and limit. It is that of calling a particular spark or brush, *positive* or *negative,* according as it may be considered as *originating* at a positive or a negative surface. We speak of the brush as positive or negative when it shoots out from surfaces previously in those states; and the experiments of Mr. Wheatstone go to prove that it *really begins* at the charged surface, and from thence extends into the air (1437. 1438.) or other dielectric. According to my view, *sparks* also originate or are determined at one particular spot (1370.), namely, that where the tension first rises up to the maximum degree; and when this can be determined, as in the simultaneous use of large and small balls, in which case the discharge begins or is determined by the latter, I would call that discharge which passes *at once,* a positive spark, if it was at the positive surface that the maximum intensity was first obtained; or a negative spark, if that necessary intensity was first obtained at the negative surface.

1485. An apparatus was arranged, as in fig. 129 (Plate VIII.) : A and B, were brass balls of very different diameters attached to metal rods, moving through sockets on insulating pillars, so that the distance between the balls could be varied at pleasure. The large ball A, 2 inches in diameter, was connected with an insulated brass conductor, which could be rendered positive or negative directly from a cylinder machine : the small ball B, 0·25 of an inch in diameter, was connected with a discharging train (292.) and perfectly uninsulated. The brass rods sustaining the balls were 0·2 of an inch in thickness.

1486. When the large ball was *positive* and inductric (1483.), negative sparks occurred until the interval was 0·49 of an inch; then mixed brush and spark between that and 0·51; and from 0·52 and upwards, negative brush alone. When the large ball was made *negative* and inductric, then positive spark alone occurred until the interval was as great as 1·15 inches; spark and brush from that up to 1·55; and to have the positive brush alone, it required an interval of at least 1·65 inches.

1487. The balls A and B were now changed for each other. Then making the small ball B inductric *positively*, the positive sparks alone continued only up to 0·67; spark and brush occurred from 0·68 up to 0·72; and positive brush alone from 0·74 and upwards. Rendering the small ball B inductric and *negative*, negative sparks alone occurred up to 0·40; then spark and brush at 0·42; whilst from 0·44 and upwards the noisy negative brush alone took place.

1488. We thus find a great difference as the balls are rendered inductric or inducteous; the small ball rendered *positive* inducteously giving a spark nearly twice as long as that produced when it was charged positive inductrically, and a corresponding difference, though not, under the circumstances, to the same extent, was manifest, when it was rendered *negative*.[*]

1489. Other results are, that the small ball rendered positive gives a much longer spark than when it is rendered negative, and that the small ball rendered negative gives a brush

[*] For similar experiments on different gases, see 1518.—*Dec.* 1838.

more readily than when positive, in relation to the effect produced by increasing the distance between the two balls.

1490. When the interval was below 0·4 of an inch, so that the small ball should give sparks, whether positive or negative, I could not observe that there was any constant difference, either in their ready occurrence or the number which passed in a given time. But when the interval was such that the small ball when negative gave a brush, then the discharges from it, as separate negative brushes, were far more numerous than the corresponding discharges from it when rendered positive, whether those positive discharges were as sparks or brushes.

1491. It is, therefore, evident that, when a ball is discharging electricity in the form of brushes, the brushes are far more numerous, and each contains or carries off far less electric force when the electricity so discharged is negative, than when it is positive.

1492. In all such experiments as those described, the point of change from spark to brush is very much governed by the working state of the electrical machine and the size of the conductor connected with the discharging ball. If the machine be in strong action and the conductor large, so that much power is accumulated quickly for each discharge, then the interval is greater at which the sparks are replaced by brushes ; but the general effect is the same.*

1493. These results, though indicative of very striking and peculiar relations of the electric force or forces, do not show the relative degrees of charge which the small ball acquires before discharge occurs, *i. e.* they do not tell whether it acquires a higher condition in the negative, or in the positive state, immediately preceding that discharge. To illustrate this important point I arranged two places of discharge as represented, fig. 130. A and D are brass balls 2 inches in diameter, B and C are smaller brass balls 0·25 of an inch in diameter ; the forks L and R supporting them were of brass wire 0·2 of an inch in diameter : the space between the large and small ball on the same fork was 5 inches, that the two places of discharge *n* and *o* might be sufficiently removed from each other's influence.

---

* For similar experiments in different gases, see 1510—1517.—*Dec.* 1838.

The fork L was connected with a projecting cylindrical conductor, which could be rendered positive or negative at pleasure, by an electrical machine, and the fork R was attached to another conductor, but thrown into an uninsulated state by connection with a discharging train (292.). The two intervals or places of discharge *n* and *o* could be varied at pleasure, their extent being measured by the occasional introduction of a diagonal scale. It is evident, that, as the balls A and B connected with the same conductor are always charged at once, and that discharge may take place to either of the balls connected with the discharging train, the intervals of discharge *n* and *o* may be properly compared to each other, as respects the influence of large and small balls when charged positively and negatively in air.

1494. When the intervals *n* and *o* were each made = 0·9 of an inch, and the balls A and B inductive *positively*, the discharge was all at *n* from the small ball of the conductor to the large ball of the discharging train, and mostly by positive brush, though once by a spark. When the balls A and B were made inductric *negatively*, the discharge was still from the same small ball, at *n*, by a constant negative brush.

1495. I diminished the intervals *n* and *o* to 0·6 of an inch. When A and B were inductric *positively*, all the discharge was at *n* as a positive brush : when A and B were inductric *negatively*, still all the discharge was at *n*, as a negative brush.

1496. The facility of discharge at the positive and negative small balls, therefore, did not appear to be very different. If a difference had existed, there were always two small balls, one in each state, that the discharge might happen at that most favourable to the effect. The only difference was, that one was in the inductric, and the other in the inducteous state, but whichsoever happened for the time to be in that state, whether positive or negative, had the advantage.

1497. To counteract this interfering influence, I made the interval *n* = 0·79 and interval *o* = 0·58 of an inch. Then, when the balls A and B were *inductric positive*, the discharge was about equal at both intervals. When, on the other hand, the balls A and B were inductric *negative*, there was discharge, still at both, but most at *n*, as if the small ball *negative* could discharge a little easier than the same ball *positive*.

1498. The small balls and terminations used in these and similar experiments may very correctly be compared, in their action, to the same balls and ends when electrified in free air at a much greater distance from conductors, than they were in those cases from each other. In the first place, the discharge, even when as a spark, is, according to my view, determined, and, so to speak, begins at a spot on the surface of the small ball (1374.), occurring when the intensity there has risen up to a certain maximum degree (1370.) ; this determination of discharge at a particular spot first, being easily traced from the spark into the brush, by increasing the distance, so as, at last, even to render the time evident which is necessary for the production of the effect (1436. 1438.). In the next place, the large balls which I have used might be replaced by larger balls at a still greater distance, and so, by successive degrees, may be considered as passing into the sides of the rooms; these being under general circumstances the inducteous bodies, whilst the small ball rendered either positive or negative is the inductric body.

1499. But, as has long been recognised, the small ball is only a blunt end, and, electrically speaking, a point only a small ball; so that when a point or blunt end is throwing out its brushes into the air, it is acting exactly as the small balls have acted in the experiments already described, and by virtue of the same properties and relations.

1500. It may very properly be said with respect to the experiments, that the large negative ball is as essential to the discharge as the small positive ball, and also that the large negative ball shows as much superiority over the large positive ball (which is inefficient in causing a spark from its opposed small negative ball) as the small positive ball does over the small negative ball; and probably when we understand the real cause of the difference, and refer it rather to the condition of the particles of the dielectric than to the sizes of the conducting balls, we may find much importance in such an observation. But for the present, and whilst engaged in investigating the point, we may admit, what is the fact, that the forces are of higher intensity at the surfaces of the smaller balls than at those of the larger (1372. 1374.) ; that the former, therefore, determine the discharge, by first rising up to that exalted condition which is necessary for it; and that, whether brought to this condition by induction towards the walls of a room or the large balls I have used, these may fairly be compared one with the other in their influence and actions.

1501. The conclusions I arrive at are: first, that when two equal small conducting surfaces equally placed in air are electrified, one positively and the other negatively, that which is negative can discharge to the air at a tension a little lower than that required for the positive ball: second, that when discharge does take place, much more passes at each time from the positive than from the negative surface (1491.). The last conclusion is very abundantly proved by the optical analysis of the positive and negative brushes already described (1468.), the latter set of discharges being found to recur five or six times oftener than the former*.

1502. If, now, a small ball be made to give brushes or brushy sparks by a powerful machine, we can, in some measure, understand and relate the difference perceived when it is rendered positive or negative. It is known to give when positive a much larger and more powerful spark than when negative, and with greater facility (1482.); in fact, the spark, although it takes away so much more electricity at once, commences at a tension higher only in a small degree, if at all. On the other hand, if rendered negative, though discharge may commence at a lower degree, it continues but for a very short period, very little electricity passing away each time. These circumstances are directly related; for the extent to which the positive spark can reach, and the size and extent of the positive brush, are consequences of the capability which exists of much electricity passing off at one discharge from the positive surface (1468. 1501.).

1503. But to refer these effects only to the form and size of the conductor, would, according to my notion of induction, be a very imperfect mode of viewing the whole question (1523. 1600.). I apprehend that the effects are due altogether to the mode in which the particles of the interposed dielectric polarize, and I have already given some experimental indications of

---

* A very excellent mode of examining the relation of small positive and negative surfaces would be by the use of drops of gum water, solutions, or other liquids. See onwards (1581. 1593.).

the differences presented by different electrics in this respect (1475. 1476.).   The modes of polarization, as I shall have occasion hereafter to show, may be very diverse in different dielectrics.   With respect to common air, what seems to be the consequence of a superiority in the positive force at the surface of the small ball, may be due to the more exalted condition of the negative polarity of the particles of air, or of the nitrogen in it (the negative part being, perhaps, more compressed, whilst the positive part is more diffuse, or *vice versâ* (1687. &c.)) ; for such a condition could determine certain effects at the positive ball which would not take place to the same degree at the negative ball, just as well as if the positive ball had possessed some special and independent power of its own.

1504. The opinion, that the effects are more likely to be dependent upon the dielectric than the ball, is supported by the character of the two discharges.   If a small positive ball be throwing off brushes with ramifications ten inches long, how can the ball affect that part of a ramification which is five inches from it ?   Yet the portion beyond that place has the same character as that preceding it, and no doubt has that character impressed by the same general principle and law. Looking upon the action of the contiguous particles of a dielectric as fully proved, I see, in such a ramification, a propagation of discharge from particle to particle, each doing for the one next it what was done for it by the preceding particle, and what was done for the first particle by the charged metal against which it was situated.

1505. With respect to the general condition and relations of the positive and negative brushes in dense or rare air, or in other media and gases, if they are produced at different times and places, they are of course independent of each other.   But when they are produced from opposed ends or balls at the same time, in the same vessel of gas (1470. 1477.), they are frequently related ; and circumstances may be so arranged that they shall be isochronous, occurring in equal numbers in equal times ; or shall occur in multiples, *i. e.* with two or three negatives to one positive ; or shall alternate, or be quite irregular. All these variations I have witnessed ; and when it is considered that the air in the vessel, and also the glass of the vessel, can

take a momentary charge, it is easy to comprehend their general nature and cause.

1506. Similar experiments to those in air (1485. 1493.) were
made in different gases, the results of which I will describe as
briefly as possible. The apparatus is represented fig. 131.,
consisting of a bell-glass eleven inches in diameter at the widest
part, and ten and a half inches high up to the bottom of the
neck. The balls are lettered, as in fig. 130., and are in the
same relation to each other; but A and B were on separate
sliding wires, which, however, were generally joined by a cross
wire, *w*, above, and that connected with the brass conductor,
which received its positive or negative charge from the machine. The rods of A and B were graduated at the part
moving through the stuffing-box, so that the application of a
diagonal scale applied there, told what was the distance between these balls and those beneath them. As to the position
of the balls in the jar, and their relation to each other, C and
D were three and a quarter inches apart, their height above
the pump plate five inches, and the distance between any of
the balls and the glass of the jar one inch and three quarters
at least, and generally more. The balls A and D were two
inches in diameter, as before (1493.); the balls B and C only
0·15 of an inch in diameter.

Another apparatus was occasionally used in connection with
that just described, being an open discharger (fig. 132.), by
which a comparison of the discharge in air and that in gases
could be obtained. The balls E and F, each 0·6 of an inch in
diameter, were connected with sliding rods and other balls, and
were insulated. When used for comparison, the brass conductor was associated at the same time with the balls A and
B of figure 131 and ball E of this apparatus (fig. 132); whilst
the balls C, D and F were connected with the discharging train.

1507. I will first tabulate the results as to the *restraining
power* of the gases over discharge. The balls A and C (fig.
131.) were thrown out of action by distance, and the effects
at B and D, or the interval *n* in the gas, compared with those
at the interval *p* in the air, between E and F (fig. 132.). The
Table sufficiently explains itself. It will be understood that
all discharge was in the air, when the interval there was less

than that expressed in the first or third columns of figures ;
and all the discharge in the gas, when the interval in air was
greater than that in the second or fourth column of figures.
At intermediate distances the discharge was occasionally at
both places, *i. e.* sometimes in the air, sometimes in the gas.

| Constant interval *n* between B and D = 1 inch. | Interval *p* in parts of an inch. | | | |
|---|---|---|---|---|
| | When the small ball B was inductric and *positive* the discharge was all | | When the small ball B was inductric and *negative* the discharge was all | |
| | at *p* in air before. | at *n* in the gas after. | at *p* in air before. | at *n* in the gas after. |
| | *p* = | *p* = | *p* = | *p* = |
| In Air.............. | 0·40 | 0·50 | 0·28 | 0·33 |
| In Nitrogen......... | 0·30 | 0·65 | 0·31 | 0·40 |
| In Oxygen .......... | 0·33 | 0·52 | 0·27 | 0·30 |
| In Hydrogen ........ | 0·20 | 0·40 | 0·22 | 0·24 |
| In Coal gas . ........ | 0·20 | 0·90 | 0·20 | 0·27 |
| In Carbonic acid  .... | 0·64 | 1·30 | 0·30 | 0·45 |

1508. These results are the same generally, as far as they
go, as those of the like nature in the last series (1388.), and
confirm the conclusion that different gases restrain discharge
in very different proportions.  They are probably not so good
as the former ones, for the glass jar not being varnished, acted
irregularly, sometimes taking a certain degree of charge as a
non-conductor, and at other times acting as a conductor in the
conveyance and derangement of that charge.  Another cause
of difference in the ratios is, no doubt, the relative sizes of the
discharge balls in air; in the former case they were of very
different size, here they were alike.

1509. In future experiments intended to have the character
of accuracy, the influence of these circumstances ought to be
ascertained, and, above all things, the gases themselves ought
to be contained in vessels of metal, and not of glass.

———

1510. The next set of results are those obtained when the
intervals *n* and *o* (fig. 131.) were made equal to each other, and
relate to the greater facility of discharge at the small ball, when
rendered positive or negative (1493.). .

1511. In *air*, with the intervals = 0·4 of an inch, A and B
being inductric and positive, discharge was nearly equal at *n*
and *o* ; when A and B were inductric and negative, the discharge was mostly at *n* by negative brush.   When the intervals

were = 0·8 of an inch, with A and B inductric positively, all discharge was at *n* by positive brush; with A and B inductric negatively, all the discharge was at *n* by a negative brush. It is doubtful, therefore, from these results, whether the negative ball has any greater facility than the positive.

1512. *Nitrogen.*—Intervals *n* and *o* = 0·4 of an inch : A, B inductric positive, discharge at both intervals, most at *n*, by positive sparks; A, B inductric negative, discharge equal at *n* and *o*. The intervals made = 0·8 of an inch : A, B inductric positive, discharge all at *n* by positive brush; A, B inductric negative, discharge most at *o* by positive brush. In this gas, therefore, though the difference is not decisive, it would seem that the positive small ball caused the most ready discharge.

1513. *Oxygen.*—Intervals *n* and *o* = 0·4 of an inch : A, B inductric positive, discharge nearly equal; inductric negative, discharge mostly at *n* by negative brush. Made the intervals = 0·8 of an inch : A, B inductric positive, discharge both at *n* and *o*; inductric negative, discharge all at *o* by negative brush. So here the negative small ball seems to give the most ready discharge.

1514. *Hydrogen.*—Intervals *n* and *o* = 0·4 of an inch : A, B inductric positive, discharge nearly equal : inductric negative, discharge mostly at *o*. Intervals = 0·8 of an inch : A and B inductric positive, discharge mostly at *n*, as positive brush; inductric negative, discharge mostly at *o*, as positive brush. Here the positive discharge seems most facile.

1515. *Coal gas.*—*n* and *o* = 0·4 of an inch : A, B inductric positive, discharge nearly all at *o* by negative spark : A, B inductric negative, discharge nearly all at *n* by negative spark. Intervals = 0·8 of an inch, and A, B inductric positive, discharge mostly at *o* by negative brush : A, B inductric negative, discharge all at *n* by negative brush. Here the negative discharge most facile.

1516. *Carbonic acid gas.*—*n* and *o* = 0·4 of an inch : A, B inductric positive, discharge nearly all at *o*, or negative : A, B inductric negative, discharge nearly all at *n*, or negative. Intervals = 0·8 of an inch : A, B inductric positive, discharge mostly at *o*, or negative : A, B inductric negative, discharge all at *n*, or negative. In this case the negative had a decided advantage in facility of discharge.

1517. Thus, if we may trust this form of experiment, the

negative small ball has a decided advantage in facilitating disruptive discharge over the positive small ball in some gases,
as in carbonic acid gas and coal gas, (1399.), whilst in others
that conclusion seems more doubtful; and in others, again,
there seems a probability that the positive small ball may be
superior.  All these results were obtained at very nearly the
same pressure of the atmosphere.

1518. I made some experiments in these gases whilst in the
air jar (fig. 131.), as to the change from spark to brush, analogous to those in the open air already described (1486. 1487.).
I will give, in a Table, the results as to when brush began to
appear mingled with the spark ; but the after results were so
varied, and the nature of the discharge in different gases so
different, that to insert the results obtained without further investigation, would be of little use.  At intervals less than those
expressed the discharge was always by spark.

| | Discharge between balls B and D. | | Discharge between balls A and C. | |
|---|---|---|---|---|
| | Small ball B inductric *pos.* | Small ball B inductric *neg.* | Large ball A inductric *pos.* | Large ball A inductric *neg.* |
| Air ........ | 0·55 | 0·30 | 0·40 | 0·75 |
| Nitrogen .... | 0·30 | 0·40 | 0·52 | 0·41 |
| Oxygen .... | 0·70 | 0·30 | 0·45 | 0·82 |
| Hydrogen .. | 0·20 | 0·10 | | |
| Coal gas .... | 0·13 | 0·30 | 0·30 | 0·14 |
| Carbonic acid | 0·82 | 0·43 | 1·60 | { above 1·80; had not space. |

1519. It is to be understood that sparks occurred at much
higher intervals than these ; the table only expresses that distance beneath which all discharge was as spark.  Some curious
relations of the different gases to discharge are already dis-
cernible, but it would be useless to consider them until illustrated by further experiments.

1520. I ought not to omit noticing here, that Professor Belli
of Milan has published a very valuable set of experiments on
the relative dissipation of positive and negative electricity in the
air* ; he finds the latter far more ready, in this respect, than
the former.

* Bibliothèque Universelle, 1836, September, p. 152.

1521. I made some experiments of a similar kind, but with sustained high charges ; the results were less striking than those of Signore Belli, and I did not consider them as satisfactory. I may be allowed to mention, in connexion with the subject, an interfering effect which embarrassed me for a long time. When I threw positive electricity from a given point into the air, a certain intensity was indicated by an electrometer on the conductor connected with the point, but as the operation continued this intensity rose several degrees ; then making the conductor negative with the same point attached to it, and all other things remaining the same, a certain degree of tension was observed in the first instance, which also gradually rose as the operation proceeded.    Returning the conductor to the positive state, the tension was at first low, but rose as before ; and so also when again made negative.

1522. This result appeared to indicate that the point which had been giving off one electricity, was, by that, more fitted for a short time to give off the other.    But on closer examination I found the whole depended upon the inductive reaction of that air, which being charged by the point, and gradually increasing in quantity before it, as the positive or negative issue was continued, diverted and removed a part of the inductive action of the surrounding wall, and thus apparently affected the powers of the point, whilst really it was the dielectric itself that was causing the change of tension.

1523. The results connected with the different conditions of positive and negative discharge will have a far greater influence on the philosophy of electrical science than we at present imagine, especially if, as I believe, they depend on the peculiarity and degree of polarized condition which the molecules of the dielectrics concerned acquire (1503. 1600.)    Thus, for instance, the relation of our atmosphere and the earth within it, to the occurrence of spark or brush, must be especial and not accidental (1464.).    It would not else consist with other meteorological phenomena, also of course dependent on the special properties of the air, and which being themselves in harmony the most perfect with the functions of animal and vegetable life, are yet restricted in their actions, not by loose regulations, but by laws the most precise.

1524. Even in the passage through air of the voltaic current

we see the peculiarities of positive and negative discharge at
the two charcoal points , and if these discharges are made to
take place simultaneously to mercury, the distinction is still
more remarkable, both as to the sound and the quantity of vapour produced.

1525. It seems very possible that the remarkable difference
recently observed and described by my friend Professor Daniell\*,
namely, that when a zinc and a copper ball, the same in size,
were placed respectively in copper and zinc spheres, also the
same in size, and excited by electrolytes or dielectrics of the
same strength and nature, the zinc ball far surpassed the zinc
sphere in action, may also be connected with these phenomena ;
for it is not difficult to conceive how the polarity of the particles
shall be affected by the circumstance of the positive surface,
namely the zinc, being the larger or the smaller of the two inclosing the electrolyte.   It is even possible, that with different
electrolytes or dielectrics the ratio may be considerably varied,
or in some cases even inverted.

*Glow discharge.*

1526. That form of disruptive discharge which appears as a
*glow* (1359. 1405.), is very peculiar and beautiful : it seems to
depend on a quick and almost continuous charging of the air
close to, and in contact with, the conductor.

1527. *Diminution of the charging surface* will produce it.
Thus, when a rod 0·3 of an inch in diameter, with a rounded
termination, was rendered positive in free air, it gave fine brushes
from the extremity, but occasionally these disappeared, and a
quiet phosphorescent continuous glow took their place, covering the whole of the end of the wire, and extending a very small
distance from the metal into the air.   With a rod 0·2 of an inch
in diameter the glow was more readily produced.   With still
smaller rods, and also with blunt conical points, it occurred still
more readily ; and with a fine point I could not obtain the brush
in free air, but only this glow.   The positive glow and the
positive star are, in fact, the same.

1528. *Increase of power in the machine* tends to produce the
glow ; for rounded terminations which will give only brushes

\* Philosophical Transactions, 1838, p. 47.

when the machine is in weak action, will readily give the glow when it is in good order.

1529. *Rarefaction of the air* wonderfully favours the glow phenomena.    A brass ball, two and a half inches in diameter, being made positively inductric in an air-pump receiver, became covered with glow over an area of two inches in diameter, when the pressure was reduced to 4·4 inches of mercury.    By a little adjustment the ball could be covered all over with this light.    Using a brass ball 1·25 inches in diameter, and making it inducteously positive by an inductric negative point, the phenomena, at high degrees of rarefaction, were exceedingly beautiful.    The glow came over the positive ball, and gradually increased in brightness, until it was at last very luminous ; and it also stood up like a low flame, half an inch or more in height. On touching the sides of the glass jar this lambent flame was affected, assumed a ring form, like a crown on the top of the ball, appeared flexible, and revolved with a comparatively slow motion, *i. e.* about four or five times in a second.    This ringshape and revolution are beautifully connected with the mechanical currents (1576.) taking place within the receiver. These glows in rarefied air are often highly exalted in beauty by a spark discharge at the conductor (1551. *Note*.).

1530. To obtain a *negative glow* in air at common pressures is difficult.    I did not procure it on the rod 0·3 of an inch in diameter by my machine, nor on much smaller rods ; and it is questionable as yet, whether, even on fine points, what is called the negative star is a very reduced and minute, but still intermitting brush, or a glow similar to that obtained on a positive point.

1531. In rarefied air the negative glow can easily be obtained. If the rounded ends of two metal rods, about 0·2 of an inch in diameter, are introduced into a globe or jar (the air within being rarefied), and being opposite to each other, are about four inches apart, the glow can be obtained on both rods, covering not only the ends, but an inch or two of the part behind.    On using *balls* in the air-pump jar, and adjusting the distance and exhaustion, the negative ball could be covered with glow, whether it were the inductric or the inducteous surface.

1532. When rods are used it is necessary to be aware that, if placed concentrically in the jar or globe, the light on one rod is often reflected by the sides of the vessel on to the other rod, and makes it apparently luminous, when really it is not so. This effect may be detected by shifting the eye at the time of observation, or avoided by using blackened rods.

1533. It is curious to observe the relation of *glow, brush,* and *spark* to each other, as produced by positive or negative surfaces; thus, beginning with spark discharge, it passes into brush much sooner when the surface at which the discharge commences (1484.) is negative, than it does when positive; but proceeding onwards in the order of change, we find that the positive brush passes into *glow* long before the negative brush does. So that, though each presents the three conditions in the same general order, the series are not precisely the same. It is probable that, when these points are minutely examined, as they must be shortly, we shall find that each different gas or dielectric presents its own peculiar results, dependent upon the mode in which its particles assume polar electric condition.

1534. The glow occurs in all gases in which I have looked for it. These are air, nitrogen, oxygen, hydrogen, coal gas, carbonic acid, muriatic acid, sulphurous acid and ammonia. I thought also that I obtained it in oil of turpentine, but if so it was very dull and small.

1535. The glow is always accompanied by a wind proceeding either directly out from the glowing part, or directly towards it; the former being the most general case. This takes place even when the glow occurs upon a ball of considerable size : and if matters be so arranged that the ready and regular access of air to a part exhibiting the glow be interfered with or prevented, the glow then disappears.

1536. I have never been able to analyse or separate the glow into visible elementary intermitting discharges (1427. 1433.), nor to obtain the other evidence of intermitting action, namely an audible sound (1431.). The want of success, as respects trials made by ocular means, may depend upon the large size of the glow preventing the separation of the visible images : and, indeed, if it does intermit, it is not likely that all parts intermit at once with a simultaneous regularity.

1537. All the effects tend to show, that *glow* is due to a continuous charge or discharge of air; in the former case being accompanied by a current from, and in the latter by one to, the place of the glow. As the surrounding air comes up to the charged conductor, on attaining that spot at which the tension of the particles is raised to the sufficient degree (1370. 1410.), it becomes charged, and then moves off, by the joint action of the forces to which it is subject; and, at the same time that it makes way for other particles to come and be charged in turn, actually helps to form that current by which they are brought into the necessary position. Thus, through the regularity of the forces, a constant and quiet result is produced; and that result is, the charging of successive portions of air, the production of a current, and of a continuous glow.

1538. I have frequently been able to make the termination of a rod, which, when left to itself, would produce a brush, produce in preference a glow, simply by aiding the formation of a current of air at its extremity; and, on the other hand, it is not at all difficult to convert the glow into brushes, by affecting the current of air (1574. 1579.) or the inductive action near it.

1539. The transition from glow, on the one hand, to brush and spark, on the other, and, therefore, their connexion, may be established in various ways. Those circumstances which tend to facilitate the charge of the air by the excited conductor, and also those which tend to keep the tension at the same degree notwithstanding the discharge, assist in producing the glow; whereas those which tend to resist the charge of the air or other dielectric, and those which favour the accumulation of electric force prior to discharge, which, sinking by that act, has to be exalted before the tension can again acquire the requisite degree, favour intermitting discharge, and, therefore, the production of brush or spark. Thus, rarefaction of the air, the removal of large conducting surfaces from the neighbourhood of the glowing termination, the presentation of a sharp point towards it, help to sustain or produce the glow : but the condensation of the air, the presentation of the hand or other large surface, the gradual approximation of a discharging ball, tend to convert the glow into brush or even spark. All these circumstances may be traced and reduced, in a manner easily comprehensible, to their relative power of assisting to produce, either a *continuous* discharge to the air, which gives the glow; or an *interrupted* one, which produces the brush, and, in a more exalted condition, the spark.

1540. The rounded end of a brass rod, 0·3 of an inch in diameter, was covered with a positive glow by the working of an
electrical machine : on stopping the machine, so that the charge
of the connected conductor should fall, the glow changed for a
moment into brushes just before the discharge ceased altogether, illustrating the necessity for a certain high continuous
charge, for a certain sized termination.   Working the machine
so that the intensity should be just low enough to give continual
brushes from the end in free air, the approach of a fine point
changed these brushes into a glow.   Working the machine so
that the termination presented a continual glow in free air, the
gradual approach of the hand caused the glow to contract at
the very end of the wire, then to throw out a luminous point,
which, becoming a foot stalk (1426.) finally produced brushes
with large ramifications.   All these results are in accordance
with what is stated above (1539.).

1541. Greasing the end of a rounded wire will immediately
make it produce brushes instead of glow. A ball having a blunt
point which can be made to project more or less beyond its surface, at pleasure, can be made to produce every gradation from
glow, through brush, to spark.

1542. It is also very interesting and instructive to trace the
transition from spark to glow, through the intermediate condition of stream, between ends in a vessel containing air more
or less rarefied ; but I fear to be prolix.

1543. All the effects show, that the glow is in its nature exactly the same as the luminous part of a brush or ramification,
namely a charging of air ; the only difference being, that the
glow has a continuous appearance from the constant renewal
of the same action in the same place, whereas the ramification
is due to a momentary, independent and intermitting action of
the same kind.

*Dark discharge.*

1544. I will now notice a very remarkable circumstance in
the luminous discharge accompanied by negative glow, which
may, perhaps, be correctly traced hereafter into discharges of
much higher intensity.   Two brass rods, 0·3 of an inch in diameter, entering a glass globe on opposite sides, had their ends

brought into contact, and the air about them very much rarefied. A discharge of electricity from the machine was then
made through them, and whilst that was continued the ends
were separated from each other. At the moment of separation
a continuous glow came over the end of the negative rod, the
positive termination remaining quite dark. As the distance
was increased, a purple stream or haze appeared on the end of
the positive rod, and proceeded directly outwards towards the
negative rod ; elongating as the interval was enlarged, but
never joining the negative glow, there being always a short
dark space between. This space, of about $\frac{1}{16}$th or $\frac{1}{20}$th of an
inch, was apparently invariable in its extent and its position,
relative to the negative rod ; nor did the negative glow vary.
Whether the negative end were inductric or inducteous, the
same effect was produced. It was strange to see the positive
purple haze diminish or lengthen as the ends were separated,
and yet this dark space and the negative glow remain unaltered
(fig. 133.).

1545. Two balls were then used in a large air pump receiver,
and the air rarefied. The usual transitions in the character of
the discharge took place; but whenever the luminous stream,
which appears after the spark and the brush have ceased, was
itself changed into glow at the balls, the dark space occurred,
and that whether the one or the other ball was made inductric,
or positive, or negative.

1546. Sometimes when the negative ball was large, the machine in powerful action, and the rarefaction high, the ball
would be covered over half its surface with glow, and then,
upon a hasty observation, would seem to exhibit no dark space :
but this was a deception, arising from the overlapping of the
convex termination of the negative glow and the concave termination of the positive stream. More careful observation and
experiment have convinced me, that when the negative glow
occurs, it never visibly touches the luminous part of the positive discharge, but that the dark space is always there.

1547. This singular separation of the positive and negative
discharge, as far as concerns their luminous character, under
circumstances which one would have thought very favourable
to their coalescence, is probably connected with their differences when in the form of brush, and is perhaps even de-

pendent on the same cause. Further, there is every likelihood
that the dark parts which occur in feeble sparks are also connected with these phenomena*. To understand them would
be very important, for it is quite clear that in many of the experiments, indeed in all that I have quoted, discharge is taking
place across the dark part of the dielectric to an extent quite
equal to what occurs in the luminous part. This difference in
the result would seem to imply a distinction in the modes by
which the two electric forces are brought into equilibrium in
the respective parts; and looking upon all the phenomena as
giving additional proofs, that it is to the condition of the particles of the dielectric we must refer for the principles of induction and discharge, so it would be of great importance if we
could know accurately in what the difference of action in the
dark and the luminous parts consisted.

1548. The dark discharge through air (1552.), which in the
case mentioned is very evident (1544.), leads to the inquiry,
whether the particles of air are generally capable of effecting
discharge from one to another without becoming luminous; and
the inquiry is important, because it is connected with that degree of tension which is necessary to originate discharge (1368.
1370.). Discharge between *air and conductors* without luminous appearances are very common; and non-luminous discharges by carrying currents of air and other fluids (1562. 1595.)
are also common enough : but these are not cases in point, for
they are not discharges between insulating particles.

1549. An arrangement was made for discharge between two
balls (1485.) (fig. 129.) but, in place of connecting the inducteous
ball directly with the discharging train, it was put in communication with the inside coating of a Leyden jar, and the discharging train with the outside coating. Then working the
machine, it was found that whenever sonorous and luminous
discharge occurred at the balls A B, the jar became charged;
but that when these did not occur, the jar acquired no charge :
and such was the case when small rounded terminations were
used in place of the balls, and also in whatever manner they
were arranged. Under these circumstances, therefore, discharge even between the air and conductors was always luminous.

* See Professor Johnson's experiments. Silliman's Journal, xxv. p. 57.

1550. But in other cases, the phenomena are such as to make it almost certain, that dark discharge can take place across air. If the rounded end of a metal rod, 0·15 of an inch in diameter, be made to give a good negative brush, the approach of a smaller end or a blunt point opposite to it will, at a certain distance, cause a diminution of the brush, and a glow will appear on the positive inducteous wire, accompanied by a current of air passing from it. Now, as the air is being charged both at the positive and negative surfaces, it seems a reasonable conclusion, that the charged portions meet somewhere in the interval, and there discharge to each other, without producing any luminous phenomena. It is possible, however, that the air electrified positively at the glowing end may travel on towards the negative surface, and actually form that atmosphere into which the visible negative brushes dart, in which case dark discharge need not, of necessity, occur. But I incline to the former opinion, and think, that the diminution in size of the negative brush, as the positive glow comes on to the end of the opposed wire, is in favour of that view.

1551. Using rarefied air as the dielectric, it is very easy to obtain luminous phenomena as brushes, or glow, upon both conducting balls or terminations, whilst the interval is dark, and that, when the action is so momentary that I think we cannot consider currents as effecting discharge across the dark part. Thus if two balls, about an inch in diameter, and 4 or more inches apart, have the air rarefied about them, and are then interposed in the course of discharge, an interrupted or spark current being produced at the machine*, each termination may be made to show luminous phenomena, whilst more or less of the interval is quite dark. The discharge will pass as suddenly as a retarded spark (295. 334.), *i. e.* in an interval of time almost inappreciably small, and in such a case, I think it must have passed across the dark part as true disruptive discharge, and not by convection.

1552. Hence I conclude that dark disruptive discharge may occur (1547. 1550.) ; and also, that, in the luminous brush, the

* By spark current I mean one passing in a series of spark between the conductor of the machine and the apparatus: by a continuous current one that passes through metallic conductors, and in that respect without interruption at the same place.

visible ramifications may not show the full extent of the disruptive discharge (1444. 1452.), but that each may have a dark outside, enveloping, as it were, every part through which the discharge extends. It is probable, even, that there are such things as dark discharges analogous in form to the brush and the spark, but not luminous in any part (1445.).

1553. The occurrence of dark discharge in any case shows at how low a tension disruptive discharge may occur (1548.), and indicates that the light of the ultimate brush or spark is in no relation to the intensity required (1368. 1370.). So to speak, the discharge begins in darkness, and the light is a mere consequence of the quantity which, after discharge has commenced, flows to that spot and there finds its most facile passage (1418. 1435.). As an illustration of the growth generally of discharge, I may remark that, in the experiments on the transition in oxygen of the discharge from spark to brush (1518.), every spark was immediately preceded by a short brush.

1554. The phenomena relative to dark discharge in other gases, though differing in certain characters from those in air, confirm the conclusions drawn above. The two rounded terminations (1544.) (fig. 133.), were placed in *muriatic acid gas* (1445. 1463.) at the pressure of 6·5 inches of mercury, and a continuous machine current of electricity sent through the apparatus : bright sparks occurred until the interval was about or above an inch, when they were replaced by squat brushy intermitting glows upon both terminations, with a dark part between. When the current at the machine was in spark, then each spark caused a discharge across the muriatic acid gas, which, with a certain interval, was bright ; with a larger interval, was straight across and flamy, like a very exhausted and sudden, but not a dense sharp spark ; and with a still larger interval, produced a feeble brush on the inductric positive end, and a glow on the inducteous negative end, the dark part being between (1544.) ; and at such times, the spark at the conductor, instead of being sudden and sonorous, was dull and quiet (334.).

1555. On introducing more muriatic acid gas, until the pressure was 29·97 inches, the same terminations gave bright sparks within at small distances ; but when they were about an inch or more apart, the discharge was generally with very small brushes and glow, and frequently with no light at all, though electricity had passed through the gas.    Whenever the bright spark did pass through the muriatic acid gas at this pressure, it was bright throughout, presenting no dark or dull space.

1556. In *coal gas*, at common pressures, when the distance was about an inch, the discharge was accompanied by short brushes on the ends, and a dark interval of half an inch or more between them, notwithstanding the discharge had the sharp quick sound of a dull spark, and could not have depended in the dark part on *convection* (1562.).

1557. This gas presents several curious points in relation to the bright and dark parts of spark discharge.    When bright sparks passed between the rod ends 0·3 of an inch in diameter (1544.), very sudden dark parts would occur next to the brightest portions of the spark.    Again, with these ends and also with balls (1422.), the bright sparks would be sometimes red, sometimes green, and occasionally green and red in different parts of the same spark.    Again, in the experiments described (1518.), at certain intervals a very peculiar pale, dull, yet sudden discharge would pass, which, though apparently weak, was very direct in its course, and accompanied by a sharp snapping noise, as if quick in its occurrence.

1558. *Hydrogen* frequently gave peculiar sparks, one part being bright red, whilst the other was a dull pale gray, or else the whole spark was dull and peculiar.

1559. *Nitrogen* presented a very remarkable discharge, between two balls of the respective diameters of 0·15 and 2 inches (1506. 1518.), the smaller one being rendered negative either directly or inducteously.    The peculiar discharge occurs at intervals between 0·42 and 0·68, and even at 1·4 inches when the large ball was inductric positively; it consisted of a little brushy part on the small negative ball, then a dark space, and lastly a dull straight line on the large positive ball (fig. 134.). The position of the dark space was very constant, and is probably in direct relation to the dark space described when negative glow was produced (1544.).    When by any circumstance a bright spark was determined, the contrast with the peculiar spark described was very striking; for it always had a faint purple part, but the place of this part was constantly near the positive ball.

1560. Thus dark discharge appears to be decidedly established. But its establishment is accompanied by proofs that it occurs in different degrees and modes in different gases. Hence then another specific action, added to the many (1296. 1398. 1399. 1423. 1454. 1503.) by which the electrical relations of insulating dielectrics are distinguished and established, and another argument in favour of that molecular theory of induction, which is at present under examination*.

1561. What I have had to say regarding disruptive discharge has extended to some length, but I hope will be excused in consequence of the importance of the subject. Before concluding my remarks, I will again intimate in the form of a query, whether we have not reason to consider the tension or retention and after discharge in air or other insulating dielectrics, as the same thing with retardation and discharge in a metal wire, differing only, but almost infinitely, in degree (1334. 1336.). In other words, can we not, by a gradual chain of association, carry up discharge from its occurrence in air, through spermaceti and water, to solutions, and then on to chlorides, oxides and metals, without any essential change in its character; and, at the same time, connecting the insensible conduction of air, through muriatic acid gas and the dark discharge, with the better conduction of spermaceti, water, and the all but perfect conduction of the metals, associate the phenomena at both extremes? and may it not be, that the retardation and ignition of a wire are effects exactly correspondent in their nature to the retention of charge and spark in air? If so, here again the two extremes in property amongst dielectrics will be found to be in intimate relation, the whole difference probably depending upon the mode and degree in which their particles polarize under the influence of inductive actions (1338. 1603. 1610.).

¶ x. *Convection, or carrying discharge.*

1562. The last kind of discharge which I have to consider is that effected by the motion of charged particles from place to

* I cannot resist referring here by a note to Biot's philosophical view of the nature of the light of the electric discharge, Annales de Chimie, liii. p. 321.

place. It is apparently very different in its nature to any of the former modes of discharge (1319.), but, as the result is the same, may be of great importance in illustrating, not merely the nature of discharge itself, but also of what we call the electric current. It often, as before observed, in cases of brush and glow (1440. 1535.), joins its effect to that of disruptive discharge, to complete the act of neutralization amongst the electric forces.

1563. The particles which being charged, then travel, may be either of insulating or conducting matter, large or small. The consideration in the first place of a large particle of conducting matter may perhaps help our conceptions.

1564. A copper boiler 3 feet in diameter was insulated and electrified, but so feebly, that dissipation by brushes or disruptive discharge did not occur at its edges or projecting parts in a sensible degree. A brass ball, 2 inches in diameter, suspended by a clean white silk thread, was brought towards it, and it was found that, if the ball was held for a second or two near any part of the charged surface of the boiler, at such distance (two inches more or less) as not to receive any direct charge from it, it became itself charged, although insulated the whole time; and its electricity was the *reverse* of that of the boiler.

1565. This effect was the strongest opposite the edges and projecting parts of the boiler, and weaker opposite the sides, or those extended portions of the surface which, according to Coulomb's results, have the weakest charge. It was very strong opposite a rod projecting a little way from the boiler. It occurred when the copper was charged negatively as well as positively: it was produced also with small balls down to 0·2 of an inch and less in diameter, and also with smaller charged conductors than the copper. It is, indeed, hardly possible in some cases to carry an insulated ball within an inch or two of a charged plane or convex surface without its receiving a charge of the contrary kind to that of the surface.

1566. This effect is one of induction between the bodies, not of communication. The ball, when related to the positive charged surface by the intervening dielectric, has its opposite sides brought into contrary states, that side towards the boiler being negative and the outer side positive. More inductric

action is directed towards it than would have passed across the
same place if the ball had not been there, for several reasons ;
amongst others, because, being a conductor, the resistance of
the particles of the dielectric, which otherwise would have been
there, is removed (1298.) ; and also, because the reacting positive surface of the ball being projected further out from the
boiler than when there is no introduction of conducting matter,
is more free therefore to act through the rest of the dielectric
towards surrounding conductors, and so favours the exaltation
of that inductric polarity which is directed in its course.    It is,
as to the exaltation of force upon its outer surface beyond that
upon the inductric surface of the boiler, as if the latter were
itself protuberant in that direction.    Thus it acquires a state
like, but higher than, that of the surface of the boiler which
causes it ; and sufficiently exalted to discharge at its positive
surface to the air, or to affect small particles, as it is itself
affected by the boiler, and they flying to it, take a charge and
pass off; and so the ball, as a whole, is brought into the contrary inducteous state.    The consequence is, that, if free to
move, its tendency, under the influence of all the forces, to approach the boiler is increased, whilst it at the same time becomes more and more exalted in its condition, both of polarity
and charge, until at a certain distance, discharge takes place, it
acquires the same state as the boiler, is repelled, and passing
to that conductor most favourably circumstanced to discharge
it, there resumes its first indifferent condition.

1567. It seems to me, that the manner in which inductric
bodies affect uncharged floating or moveable conductors near
them, is very frequently of this nature, and generally so when
it ends in a carrying operation (1562. 1602.).    The manner in
which, whilst the dominant inductric body cannot give off its
electricity to the air, the inducteous body *can* effect the discharge
of the same kind of force, is curious, and, in the case of elongated
or irregularly shaped conductors, such as filaments or particles
of dust, the effect will often be very ready, and the consequent
attraction immediate.

1568. The effect described is also probably influential in
causing those variations in spark discharge referred to in the
last series (1386. 1390. 1391.) : for if a particle of dust were
drawn towards the axis of induction between the balls, it would

tend, whilst at some distance from that axis, to commence discharge at itself, in the manner described (1566.), and that commencement might so far facilitate the act (1417. 1420.) as to make the complete discharge, as spark, pass through the particle, though it might not be the shortest course from ball to ball. So also, with equal balls at equal distances, as in the experiments of comparison already described (1493. 1506.), a particle being between one pair of balls would cause discharge there in preference ; or even if a particle were between each, difference of size or shape would give one for the time a predominance over the other.

1569. The power of particles of dust to carry off electricity in cases of high tension is well known, and I have already mentioned some instances of the kind in the use of the inductive apparatus (1201.). The general operation is very well shown by large light objects, as the toy called the electrical spider ; or, if smaller ones are wanted for philosophical investigation, by the smoke of a glowing green wax taper, which, presenting a successive stream of such particles, makes their course visible.

1570. On using oil of turpentine as the dielectric, the action and course of small conducting carrying particles in it can be well observed. A few short pieces of thread will supply the place of carriers, and their progressive action is exceedingly interesting.

1571. A very striking effect was produced on oil of turpentine, which, whether it was due to the carrying power of the particles in it, or to any other action of them, is perhaps as yet doubtful. A portion of that fluid in a glass vessel had a large uninsulated silver dish at the bottom, and an electrified metal rod with a round termination dipping into it at the top. The insulation was very good, and the attraction and other phenomena striking. The rod end, with a drop of gum water attached to it, was then electrified in the fluid ; the gum water soon spun off in fine threads, and was quickly dissipated through the oil of turpentine. By the time that four drops had in this way been commingled with a pint of the dielectric, the latter had lost by far the greatest portion of its insulating power ; no sparks could be obtained in the fluid ; and all the phenomena dependent upon insulation had sunk to a low degree. The fluid was very slightly turbid. Upon being filtered through paper only, it resumed its first clearness, and now insulated as well as before. The water, therefore, was merely diffused through the oil of turpentine, not combined with or dissolved in it: but whether the minute particles acted as carriers, or whether they were not rather gathered together in the line of highest inductive tension (1350.), and there, being drawn into elongated forms by the electric forces, combined their effects to produce a band of matter having considerable conducting power, as compared with the oil of turpentine, is as yet questionable.

1572. The analogy between the action of solid conducting carrying particles and that of the charged particles of fluid insulating substances, acting as dielectrics, is very evident and simple; but in the latter case the result is, necessarily, currents in the mobile media. Particles are brought by inductric action into a polar state; and the latter, after rising to a certain tension (1370.), is followed by the communication of a part of the force originally on the conductor; the particles consequently become charged, and then, under the joint influence of the repellant and attractive forces, are urged towards a discharging place, or to that spot where these inductric forces are most easily compensated by the contrary inducteous forces.

1573. Why a point should be so exceedingly favourable to the production of currents in a fluid insulating dielectric, as air, is very evident. It is at the extremity of the point that the intensity necessary to charge the air is first acquired (1374.); it is from thence that the charged particle recedes; and the mechanical force which it impresses on the air to form a current is in every way favoured by the shape and position of the rod, of which the point forms the termination. At the same time, the point, having become the origin of an active mechanical force, does, by the very act of causing that force, namely, by discharge, prevent any other part of the rod from acquiring the same necessary condition, and so preserves and sustains its own predominance.

1574. The very varied and beautiful phenomena produced by sheltering or enclosing the point, illustrate the production of the current exceedingly well, and justify the same conclu-

sions ; it being remembered that in such cases the effect upon
the discharge is of two kinds.  For the current may be interfered with by stopping the access of fresh uncharged air, or retarding the removal of that which has been charged, as when
a point is electrified in a tube of insulating matter closed at one
extremity ; or the *electric condition* of the point itself may be
altered by the relation of other parts in its neighbourhood,
also rendered electric, as when the point is in a metal tube,
by the metal itself, or when it is in the glass tube, by a similar action of the charged parts of the glass, or even by the
surrounding air which has been charged, and which cannot
escape.

1575. Whenever it is intended to observe such inductive
phenomena in a fluid dielectric as have a direct relation to, and
dependence upon, the fluidity of the medium, such, for instance,
as discharge from points, or attractions and repulsions, &c.,
then the mass of the fluid should be great, and in such proportion to the distance between the inductric and inducteous
surfaces as to include all the *lines of inductive force* (1369.)
between them ; otherwise, the effects of currents, attraction,
&c., which are the resultants of all these forces, cannot be obtained.   The phenomena which occur in the open air, or in
the middle of a globe filled with oil of turpentine, will not take
place in the same media if confined in tubes of glass, shell-lac,
sulphur, or other such substances, though they be excellent
insulating dielectrics ; nor can they be expected ; for in such
cases, the polar forces, instead of being all dispersed amongst
fluid particles, which tend to move under their influence, are
now associated in many parts with particles that, notwithstanding their tendency to motion, are constrained by their solidity
to remain quiescent.

1576. The varied circumstances under which, with conductors
differently formed and constituted, currents can occur, all illustrate the same simplicity of production.  A *ball*, if the intensity
be raised sufficiently on its surface, and that intensity be greatest
on a part consistent with the production of a current of air up
to and off from it, will produce the effect like a point (1537.) ;
such is the case whenever the glow occurs upon a ball, the
current being essential to that phenomenon. If as large a sphere
as can well be employed with the production of glow be used,

the glow will appear at the place where the current leaves the ball, and that will be the part directly opposite to the connection of the ball and rod which supports it; but by increasing the tension elsewhere, so as to raise it above the tension upon that spot, which can easily be effected inductively, then the place of the glow and the direction of the current will also change, and pass to that spot which for the time is most favourable for their production (1591.).

1577. For instance, approaching the hand towards the ball will tend to cause brush (1539.), but by increasing the supply of electricity the condition of glow may be preserved; then on moving the hand about from side to side the position of the glow will very evidently move with it.

1578. A point brought towards a glowing ball would at twelve or fourteen inches distance make the glow break into brush, but when still nearer glow was reproduced, probably dependent upon the discharge of wind or air passing from the point to the ball, and this glow was very obedient to the motion of the point, following it in every direction.

1579. Even a current of wind could affect the place of the glow; for a varnished glass tube being directed sideways towards the ball, air was sometimes blown through it at the ball, and sometimes not. In the former case, the place of the glow was changed a little, as if it were blown away by the current, and this is just the result which might have been anticipated. All these effects illustrate beautifully the general causes and relations, both of the glow and the current of air accompanying it (1574.)

1580. Flame facilitates the production of a current in the dielectric surrounding it. Thus, if a ball which would not occasion a current in the air have a flame, whether large or small, formed on its surface, the current is produced with the greatest ease; but not the least difficulty can occur in comprehending the effective action of the flame in this case, if its relation, as part of the surrounding dielectric, to the electrified ball, be but for a moment considered (1375. 1380.).

---

1581. Conducting fluid terminations, instead of rigid points, illustrate in a very beautiful manner the formation of the currents, with their effects and influence in exalting the conditions under which they were commenced. Let the rounded end of a brass rod, 0.3 of an inch or thereabouts in diameter, point downwards in free air; let it be amalgamated, and have a drop of mercury suspended from it; and then let it be powerfully electrized. The mercury will present the phenomenon of *glow*; a current of air will rush along the rod, and set off from the mercury directly downwards; and the form of the metallic drop will be slightly effected, the convexity at a small part near the middle and lower part becoming greater, whilst it diminishes all round at places a little removed from this spot. The change is from the form of *a* (fig. 135.) to that of *b*, and is due almost, if not entirely, to the mechanical force of the current of air sweeping over its surface.

1582. As a comparative observation, let it be noticed, that a ball gradually brought towards it converts the glow into brushes, and ultimately sparks pass from the most projecting part of the mercury. A point does the same, but at much smaller distances.

1583. Take next a drop of strong solution of muriate of lime; being electrified, a part will probably be dissipated, but a considerable portion, if the electricity be not too powerful, will remain, forming a conical drop (fig. 136.), accompanied by a strong current. If glow be produced, the drop will be smooth on the surface. If a short low brush is formed, a minute tremulous motion of the liquid will be visible; but both effects coincide with the principal one to be observed, namely, the regular and successive charge of air, the formation of a wind or current, and the form given by that current to the fluid drop. If a discharge ball be gradually brought toward the cone, sparks will at last pass, and these will be from the apex of the cone to the approached ball, indicating a considerable degree of conducting power in this fluid.

1584. With a drop of water, the effects were of the same kind, and were best obtained when a portion of gum water or of syrup hung from a ball (fig. 137.) When the machine was worked slowly, a fine large quiet conical drop, with concave lateral outline, and a small rounded end, was produced, on which the glow appeared, whilst a steady wind issued, in a direction from the point of the cone, of sufficient force to depress the urface of uninsulated water held opposite to the termination. When the machine was worked more rapidly some of the water was driven off; the smaller pointed portion left was roughish on the surface, and the sound of successive brush discharges was heard. With still more electricity, more water was dispersed; that which remained was elongated and contracted, with an alternating motion; a stronger brush discharge was heard, and the vibrations of the water and the successive discharges of the individual brushes were simultaneous. When water from beneath was brought towards the drop, it did not indicate the same regular strong contracted current of air as before; and when the distance was such that sparks passed, the water beneath was *attracted* rather than driven away, and the current of air *ceased*.

1585. When the discharging ball was brought near the drop in its first quiet glowing state (1582.), it converted that glow into brushes, and caused the vibrating motion of the drop. When still nearer, sparks passed, but they were always from the metal of the rod, over the surface of the water, to the point, and then across the air to the ball. This is a natural consequence of the deficient conducting power of the fluid (1584. 1585.).

1586. Why the drop vibrated, changing its form between the periods of discharging brushes, so as to be more or less acute at particular instants, to be most acute when the brush issued forth, and to be isochronous in its action, and how the quiet glowing liquid drop, on assuming the conical form, facilitated, as it were, the first action, are points, as to theory, so evident, that I will not stop to speak of them. The principal thing to observe at present is, the formation of the carrying current of air, and the manner in which it exhibits its existence and influence by giving form to the drop.

1587. That the drop, when of water, or a better conductor than water, is formed into a cone principally by the current of air, is shown amongst other ways (1594.) thus. A sharp point being held opposite the conical drop, the latter soon lost its pointed form; was retracted and became round; the current of air from it ceased, and was replaced by one from the point beneath, which, if the latter were held near enough to the drop, actually blew it aside, and rendered it concave in form.

1588. It is hardly necessary to say what happened with stil worse conductors than water, as oil, or oil of turpentine; the fluid itself was then spun out into threads and carried off, not only because the air rushing over its surface, helped to sweep it away, but also because its insulating particles assumed the same charged state as the particles of air, and, not being able to discharge to them in a much greater degree than the air particles themselves could do, were carried off by the same causes which urged these in their course.  A similar effect with melted sealing-wax on a metal-point forms an old and well-known experiment.

1589. A drop of gum water in the exhausted receiver of the air-pump was not sensibly affected in its form when electrified. When air was let in, it began to show change of shape when the pressure was ten inches of mercury.  At the pressure of fourteen or fifteen inches the change was more sensible, and as the air increased in density the effects increased, until they were the same as those in the open atmosphere.  The diminished effect in the rare air I refer to the relative diminished energy of its current ; that diminution depending, in the first place, on the lower electric condition of the electrified ball in the rarefied medium, and in the next, on the attenuated condition of the dielectric, the cohesive force of water in relation to rarefied air being something like that of mercury to dense air (1581.), whilst that of water in dense air may be compared to that of mercury in oil of turpentine (1597.).

1590. When a ball is covered with a thick conducting fluid, as treacle or syrup, it is easy by inductive action to determine the wind from almost any part of it  (1577.) ; the experiment, which before was of rather difficult performance, being rendered facile in consequence of the fluid enabling that part, which at first was feeble in its action, to rise into an exalted condition by assuming a pointed form.

1591. To produce the current, the electric intensity must rise and continue at *one spot*, namely, at the origin of the current, higher than elsewhere, and then, air having a uniform and ready access, the current is produced.  If no current be allowed (1574.), then discharge may take place by brush or spark. But whether it be by brush or spark, or wind, it seems very probable that the initial intensity or tension at which a particle of a given gaseous dielectric charges, or commences discharge, is, under the conditions before expressed, always the same (1410.).

1592. It is not supposed that all the air which enters into motion is electrified; on the contrary, much that is not charged is carried on into the stream. The part which is really charged may be but a small proportion of that which is ultimately set in motion (1442.).

1593. When a drop of gum water (1584.) is made *negative*, it presents a larger cone than when made positive; less of the fluid is thrown off, and yet, when a ball is approached, sparks can hardly be obtained, so pointed is the cone, and so free the discharge. A point held opposite to it did not cause the retraction of the cone to such an extent as when it was positive. All the effects are so different from those presented by the positive cone, that I have no doubt such drops would present a very instructive method of investigating the difference of positive and negative discharge in air and other dielectrics (1480. 1501.).

1594. That I may not be misunderstood (1587.), I must observe here that I do not consider the cones produced as the result *only* of the current of air or other insulating dielectric over their surface. When the drop is of badly conducting matter, a part of the effect is due to the electrified state of the particles, and this part constitutes almost the whole when the matter is melted sealing-wax, oil of turpentine, and similar insulating bodies (1588.). But even when the drop is of good conducting matter, as water, solutions, or mercury, though the effect above spoken of will then be insensible (1607.), still it is not the mere current of air or other dielectric which produces all the change of form; for a part is due to those attractive forces by which the charged drop, if free to move, would travel along the line of strongest induction, and not being free to move, has its form elongated until the sum of the different forces tending to produce this form is balanced by the cohesive attraction of the fluid. The effect of the attractive forces are well shown when treacle, gum water, or syrup is used; for the long threads which spin out, at the same time that they form the axes of the currents of air, which may still be considered as determined at their points, are like flexible conductors, and show by their directions in what way the attractive forces draw them.

1595. When the phenomena of currents are observed in dense insulating dielectrics, they present us with extraordinary degrees of mechanical force. Thus, if a pint of well-rectified and filtered (1571.) oil of turpentine be put into a glass vessel, and two wires be dipped into it in different places, one leading to the electrical machine, and the other to the discharging train, on working the machine the fluid will be thrown into violent motion throughout its whole mass, whilst at the same time it will rise two, three, or four inches up the machine wire, and dart off in jets from it into the air.

1596. If very clean uninsulated mercury be at the bottom of the fluid, and the wire from the machine be terminated either by a ball or a point, and also pass through a glass tube extending both above and below the surface of the oil of turpentine, the currents can be better observed, and will be seen to rush down the wire, proceeding directly from it towards the mercury, and there, diverging in all directions, will ripple its surface strongly, and mounting up at the sides of the vessel, will return to re-enter upon their course.

1597. A drop of mercury being suspended from an amalgamated brass ball, preserved its form almost unchanged in air (1581.) ; but when immersed in the oil of turpentine it became very pointed, and even particles of the metal could be spun out and carried off by the currents of the dielectric. The form of the liquid metal was just like that of the syrup in air (1584.) the point of the cone being quite as fine, though not so long. By bringing a sharp uninsulated point towards it, it could also be effected in the same manner as the syrup drop in air (1587.), though not so readily, because of the density and limited quantity of the dielectric.

1598. If the mercury at the bottom of the fluid be connected with the electrical machine, whilst a rod is held in the hand terminating in a ball three quarters of an inch, less or more, in diameter, and the ball be dipped into the electrified fluid, very striking appearances ensue. When the ball is raised again so as to be at a level nearly out of the fluid, large portions of the latter will seem to cling to it (fig. 138.). If it be raised higher, a column of the oil of turpentine will still connect it with that

in the basin below (fig. 139.).    If the machine be excited into
more powerful action, this will become more bulky, and may
then also be raised higher, assuming the form (fig. 140); and
all the time that these effects continue, currents and counter-
currents, sometimes running very close together, may be observed in the raised column of fluid.

1599. It is very difficult to decide by sight the direction of
the currents in such experiments as these.    If particles of silk
are introduced they cling about  the  conductors;  but  using
drops of water and mercury the course of the fluid dielectric
seems well indicated.    Thus, if a drop of water be placed at
the end of a rod (1571.) over the uninsulated mercury, it is soon
swept away in particles streaming downwards towards the mercury.    If another drop be placed on the mercury beneath the
end of the rod, it is quickly dispersed in all  directions  in  the
form of streaming particles, the attractive forces drawing it into
elongated portions, and the currents carrying them away.    If
a drop of mercury be hung from  a ball used to raise  a column
of the fluid (1598.), then the shape of the drop seems  to  show
currents travelling in the fluid in the direction indicated by the
arrows (fig. 141.).

1600. A very remarkable effect is produced on these phenomena, connected  with  positive  and  negative  charge  and  discharge, namely, that a ball charged positively raises a much
higher and larger column of the oil of turpentine than when
charged negatively.    There can be no doubt that this is connected with the  difference of positive and negative action already spoken of (1480. 1525.), and tends much to strengthen
the idea that such difference is referable to the particles of the
dielectric rather than to the  charged conductors, and  is  dependent  upon  the  mode  in  which these  particles  polarize
(1503. 1523.).

1601. Whenever currents travel in insulating dielectrics they
really effect discharge ; and it is important to observe, though
a very natural result, that it is indifferent which way the current or particles travel, as with reversed direction their state
is reversed.    The change is easily made, either in air or oil of
turpentine, between two opposed rods, for an insulated  ball
being placed in connexion with either rod and brought near its

extremity, will cause the current to set towards it from the opposite end.

1602. The two currents often occur at once, as when both terminations present brushes, and frequently when they exhibit the glow (1531.). In such cases, the charged particles, or many of them, meet and mutually discharge each other (1548. 1612.). If a smoking wax taper be held at the end of an insulating rod towards a charged prime conductor, it will very often happen that two currents will form, and be rendered visible by its vapour, one passing as a fine filament of smoky particles directly to the charged conductor, and the other passing as directly from the same taper wick outwards, and from the conductor; the principles of inductric action and charge, which were referred to in considering the relation of a carrier ball and a conductor (1566.), being here also called into play.

---

1603. The general analogy and, I think I may say, identity of action found to exist as to insulation and conduction (1338. 1561.) when bodies, the best and the worst in the classes of insulators or conductors, were compared, led me to believe that the phenomena of *convection* in badly conducting media were not without their parallel amongst the best conductors, such even as the metals. Upon consideration, the cones produced by Davy* in fluid metals, as mercury and tin, seemed to be cases in point, and probably also the elongation of the metallic medium through which a current of electricity was passing, described by Ampère (1113.) †; for it is not difficult to conceive, that the diminution of convective effect, consequent upon the high conducting power of the metallic media used in these experiments, might be fully compensated for by the enormous quantity of electricity passing. In fact it is impossible not to expect *some* effect, whether sensible or not, of the kind in question, when such a current is passing through a fluid offering a sensible resistance to the passage of the electricity, and, thereby giving proof of a certain degree of insulating power (1328.).

1604. I endeavoured to connect the convective currents in air, oil of turpentine, &c. and those in metals, by intermediate cases, but found this not easy to do. On taking bodies, for in-

* Philosophical Transactions, 1823, p. 155.
† Bibliothèque Universelle, xxi. 47.

stance, which, like water, acids, solutions, fused salts or chlorides, &c., have intermediate conducting powers, the minute
quantity of electricity which the common machine can supply
(371. 861.) is exhausted instantly, so that the cause of the phenomenon is kept either very low in intensity, or the instant of
time during which the effect lasts is so small, that one cannot
hope to observe the result sought for. If a voltaic battery be
used, these bodies are all electrolytes, and the evolution of gas,
or the production of other changes, interferes and prevents
observation of the effect required.

1605. There are, nevertheless, some experiments which illustrate the connection. Two platina wires, forming the electrodes of a powerful voltaic battery, were placed side by side,
near each other, in distilled water, hermetically sealed up in a
strong glass tube, some minute vegetable fibres being present
in the water. When, from the evolution of gas and the consequent increased pressure, the bubbles formed on the electrodes
were so small as to produce but feebly ascending currents, then
it could be observed that the filaments present were attracted
and repelled between the two wires, as they would have been
between two oppositely charged surfaces in air or oil of turpentine, moving so quickly as to displace and disturb the bubbles
and the currents which these tended to form. Now I think it
cannot be doubted, that uuder similar circumstances, and with
an abundant supply of electricity, of sufficient tension also,
convective currents might have been formed; the attractions
and repulsions of the filaments were, in fact, the elements of
such currents (1572.), and therefore water, though almost infinitely above air or oil of turpentine as a conductor, is a medium
in which similar currents can take place.

1606. I had an apparatus made (fig. 142.) in which $a$ is a
plate of shell-lac, $b$ a fine platina wire passing through it, and
having only the section of the wire exposed above; $c$ a ring of
bibulous paper resting on the shell-lac, and $d$ distilled water
retained by the paper in its place, and just sufficient in quantity
to cover the end of the wire $b$; another wire, $e$, touched a piece
of tinfoil lying in the water, and was also connected with a discharging train; in this way it was easy, by rendering $b$ either
positive or negative, to send a current of electricity by its extremity into the fluid, and so away by the wire $e$.

1607. On connecting *b* with the conductor of a powerful electrical machine, not the least disturbance of the level of the fluid over the end of the wire during the working of the machine could be observed; but at the same time there was not the smallest indication of electrical charge about the conductor or of the machine, so complete was the discharge. I conclude that the quantity of electricity passed in a *given time* had been too small, when compared with the conducting power of the fluid to produce the desired effect.

1608. I then charged a large Leyden battery (291.), and discharged it through the wire *b*, interposing, however, a wet thread, two feet long, to prevent a spark in the water, and to reduce what would else have been a sudden violent discharge into one of more moderate character, enduring for a sensible length of time (334.). I now did obtain a very brief elevation of the water over the end of the wire; and though a few minute bubbles of gas were at the same time formed there, so as to prevent me from asserting that the effect was unequivocally the same as that obtained by DAVY in the metals, yet, according to my best judgement, it was partly, and I believe principally, of that nature.

1609. I employed a voltaic battery of 100 pair of four-inch plates for experiments of a similar nature with electrolytes. In these cases the shell-lac was cupped, and the wire *b* 0·2 of an inch in diameter. Sometimes I used a positive amalgamated zinc wire in contact with dilute sulphuric acid; at others, a negative copper wire in a solution of sulphate of copper; but, because of the evolution of gas, the precipitation of copper, &c., I was not able to obtain decided results. It is but right to mention, that when I made use of mercury, endeavouring to repeat DAVY's experiment, the battery of 100 pair was not sufficient to produce the elevations*.

1610. The latter experiments (1609.) may therefore be considered as failing to give the hoped-for proof, but I have much confidence in the former (1605. 1608.), and in the considerations (1603.) connected with them. If I have rightly viewed

* In the experiments at the Royal Institution, Sir H. Davy used, I think, 500 or 600 pairs of plates. Those at the London Institution were made with the apparatus of Mr. Pepys (consisting of an enormous single pair of plates) described in the Philosophical Transactions for 1823, p. 187.

them, and we may be allowed to compare the currents at points and surfaces in such extremely different bodies as air and the metals, and admit that they are effects of the *same* kind, differing only in degree and in proportion to the insulating or conducting power of the dielectric used, what great additional argument we obtain in favour of that theory, which in the phenomena of insulation and conduction also, as in these, would link *the same* apparently dissimilar substances together (1336. 1561.); and how completely the general view, which refers all the phenomena to the direct action of the molecules of matter, seems to embrace the various isolated phenomena as they successively come under consideration !

---

1611. The connection of this convective or carrying effect, which depends upon a certain degree of insulation, with conduction; *i. e.* the occurrence of both in so many of the substances referred to, as, for instance, the metals, water, air, &c., would lead to many very curious theoretical generalizations, which I must not indulge in here.   One point, however, I shall venture to refer to.    Conduction appears to be essentially an action of contiguous particles, and the considerations just stated, together with others formerly expressed (1326. 1336, &c.), lead to the conclusion, that all bodies conduct, and by the same process, air as well as metals ; the only difference being in the necessary degree of force or tension between the particles which must exist before the act of conduction or transfer from one particle to another can take place.

1612. The question then arises, what is this limiting condition which separates, as it were, conduction and insulation from each other ?   Does it consist in a difference between the two contiguous particles, or the contiguous poles of these particles, in the nature and amount of positive and negative force, no communication or discharge occurring unless that difference rises up to a certain degree, variable for different bodies, but always the same for the same body ?   Or is it true that, however small the difference between two such particles, if *time* be allowed, equalization of force will take place, even with the particles of such bodies as air, sulphur, or lac ?   In the first case, insulating power in any particular body would be proportionate to the degree of the assumed necessary difference of force ; in the second, to the *time* required to equalize equal degrees of difference in different bodies.    With regard to airs, one is almost led to expect a permanent difference of force ; but in all other bodies, time seems to be quite sufficient to ensure, ultimately, complete conduction.    The difference in the modes by which insulation may be sustained, or conduction effected, is not a mere fanciful point, but one of great importance, as being essentially connected with the molecular theory of induction, and the manner in which the particles of bodies assume and retain their polarized state.

---

¶ xi. *Relation of a vacuum to electrical phenomena.*

1613. It would seem strange, if a theory which refers all the phenomena of insulation and conduction. *i. e.* all electrical phenomena, to the action of contiguous particles, were to omit to notice the assumed possible case of a *vacuum*.    Admitting that a vacuum can be produced, it would be a very curious matter indeed to know what its relation to electrical phenomena would be ;    and as shell-lac and metal are directly opposed to each other, whether a vacuum would be opposed to them both, and allow neither of induction or conduction across it.    Mr. Morgan* has said that a vacuum does not conduct.    Sir H. Davy concluded from his investigations, that as perfect a vacuum as could be made† did conduct, but does not consider the prepared spaces which he used as absolute vacua.    In such experiments I think I have observed the luminous discharge to be principally on the inner surface of the glass ; and it does not appear at all unlikely, that, if the vacuum refused to conduct, still the surface of glass next it might carry on that action.

1614. At one time, when I thought inductive force was exerted in right lines, I hoped to illustrate this important question by making experiments on induction with metallic mirrors (used only as conducting vessels) exposed towards a very clear sky at night time, and of such concavity that nothing but the firmament could be visible from the lowest part of the concave

* Philosophical Transactions, 1785, p. 272.          † Ibid. 1822, p. 64.

*n*, fig. 143. Such mirrors, when electrified, as by connexion with a Leyden jar, and examined by a carrier ball, readily gave electricity at the lowest part of their concavity if in a room ; but I was in hopes of finding that, circumstanced as before stated, they would give little or none at the same spot, if the atmosphere above really terminated in a vacuum. I was disappointed in the conclusion, for I obtained as much electricity there as before ; but on discovering the action of induction in curved lines (1231.), found a full and satisfactory explanation of the result.

1615. My theory, as far as I have ventured it, does not pretend to decide upon the consequences of a vacuum. It is not at present limited sufficiently, or rendered precise enough, either by experiments relating to spaces void of matter, or those of other kinds, to indicate what would happen in the vacuum case. I have only as yet endeavoured to establish, what all the facts seem to prove, that when electrical phenomena, as those of induction, conduction, insulation, and discharge occur, they depend on, and are produced by the action of *contiguous* particles of matter, the next existing particle being considered as the contiguous one; and I have further assumed, that these particles are polarized ; that each exhibits the two forces, or the force in two directions (1295. 1298.) ; and that they act at a distance, only by acting on the *contiguous* and intermediate particles.

1616. But assuming that a perfect vacuum were to intervene in the course of the lines of inductive action (1304), it does not follow from this theory, that the particles on opposite sides of such a vacuum could not act on each other. Suppose it possible for a positively electrified particle to be in the centre of a vacuum an inch in diameter, nothing in my present views forbids that the particle should act at the distance of half an inch on all the particles forming the inner superfices of the bounding sphere, and with a force consistent with the well known law of the squares of the distance. But suppose the sphere of an inch were full of insulating matter, the electrified particle would not then, according to my notion, act directly on the distant particles, but on those in immediate association with it, employing *all* its power in polarizing them; producing in them negative force equal in amount to its own positive force and directed towards the latter, and positive force of equal amount directed outwards and acting in the same manner upon the layer of particles next in succession.   So that ultimately, those particles in the surface of a sphere of half an inch radius, which were acted on *directly* when that sphere was a vacuum, will now be acted on *indirectly* as respects the central particle or source of action, *i. e.* they will be polarized in the same way, and with the same amount of force.

§ 19.  *Nature of the electric current.*

1617.  The word *current* is so expressive in common language, that when applied in the consideration of electrical phenomena we can hardly divest it sufficiently of its meaning, or prevent our minds from being prejudiced by it (283. 511.).   I shall use it in its common electrical sense, namely, to express generally a certain condition and relation of electrical forces supposed to be in progression.

1618.  A current is produced both by excitement and discharge ; and whatsoever the variation of the two general causes may be, the effect remains the same.   Thus excitement may occur in many ways, as by friction, chemical action, influence of heat, change of condition, induction, &c. ;  and discharge has the forms of conduction, electrolyzation, disruptive discharge, and convection ; yet the current connected with these actions, when it occurs, appears in all cases to be the same.   This constancy in the character of the current, notwithstanding the particular and great variations which may be made in the mode of its occurrence, is exceedingly striking and important ; and its investigation and development promise to supply the most open and advantageous road to a true and intimate understanding of the nature of electrical forces.

1619.  As yet the phenomena of the current have presented nothing in opposition to the view I have taken of the nature of induction as an action of contiguous particles.   I have endeavoured to divest myself of prejudices and to look for contradictions, but I have not perceived any in conductive, electrolytic, convective, or disruptive discharge.

1620. Looking at the current as a *cause*, it exerts very extraordinary and diverse powers, not only in its course and on the bodies in which it exists, but collaterally, as in inductive or magnetic phenomena.

1621. *Electrolytic action.*—One of its direct actions is the exertion of pure chemical force, this being a result which has now been examined to a considerable extent. The effect is found to be *constant* and *definite* for the quantity of electric force discharged (783, &c.); and beyond that, the *intensity* required is in relation to the intensity of the affinity or forces to be overcome (904. 906. 911.). The current and its consequences are here proportionate; the one may be employed to represent the other; no part of the effect of either is lost or gained; so that the case is a strict one, and yet it is the very case which most strikingly illustrates the doctrine that induction is an action of contiguous particles (1164. 1343.).

1622. The process of electrolytic discharge appears to me to be in close analogy, and perhaps in its nature identical with another process of discharge, which at first seems very different from it, I mean *convection* (1347. 1572.). In the latter case the particles may travel for yards across a chamber; they may produce strong winds in the air, so as to move machinery; and in fluids, as oil of turpentine, may even shake the hand, and carry heavy metallic bodies about *; and yet I do not see that the force, either in kind or action, is at all different to that by which a particle of hydrogen leaves one particle of oxygen to go to another, or by which a particle of oxygen travels in the contrary direction.

1623. Travelling particles of the air can effect chemical changes just as well as the contact of a fixed platina electrode, or that of a combining electrode, or the ions of a decomposing electrolyte (453. 471.); and in the experiment formerly described, where eight places of decomposition were rendered active by one current (469.), and where charged particles of air in motion were the only electrical means of connecting these

* If a metallic vessel three or four inches deep, containing oil of turpentine, be insulated and electrified, and a rod with a ball (an inch or more in diameter) at the end have the ball immersed in the fluid whilst the end is held in the hand, the mechanical force generated when the ball is moved to and from the sides of the vessel will soon be evident to the experimenter.

parts of the current, it seems to me that the action of the particles of the electrolyte and of the air were essentially the same. A particle of air was rendered positive; it travelled in a certain determinate direction, and coming to an electrolyte, communicated its powers; an equal amount of positive force was accordingly acquired by another particle (the hydrogen), and the latter, so charged, travelled as the former did, and in the same direction, until it came to another particle, and transferred its power and motion, making that other particle active. Now, though the particle of air travelled over a visible and occasionally a large space, whilst the particle of the electrolyte moved over an exceedingly small one; though the air particle might be oxygen, nitrogen, or hydrogen, receiving its charge from force of high intensity, whilst the electrolytic particle of hydrogen had a natural aptness to receive the positive condition with extreme facility; though the air particle might be charged with very little electricity at a very high intensity by one process, whilst the hydrogen particle might be charged with much electricity at a very low intensity by another process; these are not differences of kind, as relates to the final discharging action of these particles, but only of degree; not essential differences which make things unlike, but such differences as give to things, similar in their nature, that great variety which fits them for their office in the system of the universe.

1624. So when a particle of air, or of dust in it, electrified at a negative point, moves on through the influence of the inductive forces (1572.) to the next positive surface, and after discharge passes away, it seems to me to represent exactly that particle of oxygen which, having been rendered negative in the electrolyte, is urged by the same disposition of inductive forces, and going to the positive platina electrode, is there discharged, and then passes away, as the air or dust did before it.

1625. *Heat* is another direct effect of the *current* upon substances in which it occurs, and it becomes a very important question, as to the relation of the electric and heating forces, whether the latter is always definite in amount *. There are many cases, even amongst bodies which conduct without change, that at present are irreconcileable with the assumption that it

---

* See De la Rive's Researches, Bib. Universelle, 1829. xl. p. 40.

is\*; but there are also many which indicate that, when proper limitations are applied, the heat produced is definite. Harris has shown this for a given length of current in a metallic wire, using common electricity†; and De la Rive has proved the same point for voltaic electricity by his beautiful application of Breguet's thermometer‡.

1626. When the production of heat is observed in electrolytes under decomposition, the results are still more complicated. But important steps have been taken in the investigation of this branch of the subject by De la Rive § and others; and it is more than probable that, when the right limitations are applied, constant and definite results will here also be obtained.

———————

1627. It is a most important part of the character of the current, and essentially connected with its very nature, that it is always the same. The two forces are everywhere in it. There is never one current of force or one fluid only. Any one part of the current may, as respects the presence of the two forces there, be considered as precisely the same with any other part; and the numerous experiments which imply their possible separation, as well as the theoretical expressions which, being used daily, assume it, are, I think in contradiction with facts (511, &c.). It appears to me to be as impossible to assume a current of positive or a current of negative force alone, or of the two at once with any predominance of one over the other, as it is to give an absolute charge to matter (516. 1169. 1177.).

1628. The establishment of this truth, if, as I think, it be a truth, or on the other hand the disproof of it, is of the greatest consequence. If, as a first principle, we can establish, that the centres of the two forces, or elements of force, never can be separated to any sensible distance, or at all events not further than the space between two contiguous particles (1615.), or if we can establish the contrary conclusion, how much more clear

———————

* Amongst others, Davy, Philosophical Transactions, 1821, p. 438. Pelletier's important results, Annales de Chimie, 1834, lvi. p. 371, and Becquerel's non-heating current, Bib. Universelle, 1835, lx. 218.

† Philosophical Transactions, 1824, pp. 225. 228.

‡ Annales de Chimie, 1836, lxii. 177.

§ Bib. Universelle, 1829, xl. 49; and Ritchie, Phil. Trans. 1832, p. 296.

is our view of what lies before us, and how much less embarrassed the ground over which we have to pass in attaining to it, than if we remain halting between two opinions! And if, with that feeling, we rigidly test every experiment which bears upon the point, as far as our prejudices will let us (1161.), instead of permitting them with a theoretical expression to pass too easily away, are we not much more likely to attain the real truth, and from that proceed with safety to what is at present unknown?

1629. I say these things, not, I hope, to advance a particular view, but to draw the strict attention of those who are able to investigate and judge of the matter, to what must be a turning point in the theory of electricity; to a separation of two roads, one only of which can be right; and I hope I may be allowed to go a little further into the facts which have driven me to the view I have just given.

1630. When a wire in the voltaic circuit is heated, the temperature frequently rises first, or most at one end. If this effect were due to any relation of positive or negative as respects the current, it would be exceedingly important. I therefore examined several such cases; but when, keeping the contacts of the wire and its position to neighbouring things unchanged, I altered the direction of the current, I found that the effect remained unaltered, showing that it depended, not upon the direction of the current, but on other circumstances. So there is here no evidence of a difference between one part of the circuit and another.

1631. The same point, *i. e.* uniformity in every part, may be illustrated by what may be considered as the inexhaustible nature of the current when producing particular effects; for these effects depend upon transfer only, and do not consume the power. Thus a current which will heat one inch of platina wire will heat a hundred inches (853. note). If a current be sustained in a constant state, it will decompose the fluid in one voltameter only, or in twenty others if they be placed in the circuit, in each to an amount equal to that in the single one.

1632. Again, in cases of disruptive discharge, as in the spark, there is frequently a dark part (1422.) which, by Professor Johnson, has been called the neutral point*; and this has given

* Silliman's Journal, 1834, xxv. p. 57.

rise to the use of expressions implying that there are two electricities existing separately, which, passing to that spot, there
combine and neutralize each other*. But if such expressions
are understood as correctly indicating that positive electricity
alone is moving between the positive ball and that spot, and
negative electricity only between the negative ball and that spot,
then what strange conditions these parts must be in; conditions, which to my mind are every way unlike those which really
occur! In such a case, one part of a current would consist of
positive electricity only, and that moving in one direction; another part would consist of negative electricity only, and that
moving in the other direction; and a third part would consist
of an accumulation of the two electricities, not moving in either
direction, but mixing up together, and being in a relation to
each other utterly unlike any relation which could be supposed
to exist in the two former portions of the discharge. This does
not seem to me to be natural. In a current, whatever form the
discharge may take, or whatever part of the circuit or current
is referred to, as much positive force as is there exerted in one
direction, so much negative force is there exerted in the other.
If it were not so we should have bodies electrified not merely
positive and negative, but on occasions in a most extraordinary
manner, one being charged with five, ten, or twenty times as
much of both positive and negative electricity in equal quantities as another. At present, however, there is no known fact
indicating such states.

1633. Even in cases of convection, or carrying discharge, the
statement that the current is everywhere the same must in effect
be true (1627.); for how, otherwise could the results formerly
described occur? When currents of air constituted the mode of
discharge between the portions of paper moistened with iodide
of potassium or sulphate of soda (465. 469.), decomposition
occurred; and I have since ascertained that, whether a current
of positive air issued from a spot, or one of negative air passed
towards it, the effect of the evolution of iodine or of acid was
the same, whilst the reversed currents produced alkali. So
also in the magnetic experiments (307.) whether the discharge
was effected by the introduction of a wire, or the occurrence of
a spark, or the passage of convective currents either one way

* Thomson on Heat and Electricity, p. 471.

or the other, (depending on the electrified state of the particles) the result was the same, being in all cases dependent upon the perfect current.

1634. Hence, the section of a current compared with other sections of the same current must be a constant quantity, if the actions exerted be of the same kind ; or if of different kinds, then the forms under which the effects are produced are equivalent to each other, and experimentally convertible at pleasure. It is in sections, therefore, we must look for identity of electrical force, even to the sections of sparks and carrying actions, as well as those of wires and electrolytes.

1635. In illustration of the utility and importance of establishing that which may be the true principle, I will refer to a few cases. The doctrine of unipolarity, as formerly stated, and I think generally understood*, is evidently inconsistent with my view of a current (1627.) ; and the later singular phenomena of poles and flames described by Erman and others † partake of the same inconsistency of character. If a unipolar body could exist, *i. e.* one that could conduct the one electricity and not the other, what very new characters we should have a right to expect in the currents of single electricities passing through them, and how greatly ought they to differ, not only from the common current which is supposed to have both electricities travelling in opposite directions in equal amount at the same time, but also from each other ! The facts, which are excellent, have, however, gradually been more correctly explained by Becquerel ‡, Andrews §, and others ; and I understand that Professor Ohms ‖ has perfected the work, in his close examination of all

---

* Erman, Annales de Chimie, 1807, lxi. p. 115. Davy's Elements, p. 168. Biot, Ency. Brit. Supp. iv. p. 444. Becquerel, Traité, i. p. 167. De la Rive, Bib. Univ. 1837. vii. 392.

† Erman, Annales de Chimie, 1824, xxv. 278. Becquerel, Ibid. xxxvi. p. 329.

‡ Becquerel, Annales de Chimie, 1831, xlvi. p. 283.

§ Andrews, Philosophical Magazine, 1836, ix. 182.

‖ Schweigger's Jahrbuch der Chimie, &c. 1830. Heft 8. Not understanding German, it is with extreme regret I confess I have not access, and cannot do justice, to the many most valuable papers in experimental electricity published in that language. I take this opportunity also of stating another circumstance which occasions me great trouble, and, as I find by experience, may make me seemingly regardless of the labours of others :—it is a gradual loss of memory for some years past ; and now, often when I read a memoir, I rethe phenomena; and after showing that similar phenomena can take place with good conductors, proves that with soap, &c. many of the effects are the mere consequences of the bodies evolved by electrolytic action.

1636. I conclude, therefore, that the *facts* upon which the doctrine of unipolarity was founded are not adverse to that unity and indivisibility of character which I have stated the current to possess, any more than the phenomena of the pile itself, (which might well bear comparison with those of unipolar bodies,) are opposed to it. Probably the effects which have been called effects of unipolarity, and the peculiar differences of the positive and negative surface when discharging into air, gases, or other dielectrics (1480. 1525.) which have been already referred to, may have considerable relation to each other\*.

---

1637. M. de la Rive has recently described a peculiar and remarkable effect of heat on a current when passing between electrodes and a fluid †. It is, that if platina electrodes dip into acidulated water, no change is produced in the passing current by making the positive electrode hotter or colder; whereas making the negative electrode hotter increased the deflexion of a galvanometer affected by the current, from $12°$ to $30°$ and even $45°$, whilst making it colder diminished the current in the same high proportions.

1638. That one electrode should have this striking relation to heat whilst the other remained absolutely without, seem to me as incompatible with what I conceived to be the character of a current as unipolarity (1627. 1635.), and it was therefore with some anxiety that I repeated the experiment. The electrodes which I used were platina; the electrolyte, water containing about one sixth of sulphuric acid by weight: the voltaic battery consisted of two pairs of amalgamated zinc and platina plates in dilute sulphuric acid, and the galvanometer in the circuit was one with two needles, and gave when the arrangement was complete a deflexion of $10°$ or $12°$.

member that I have seen it before, and would have rejoiced if at the right time I could have recollected and referred to it in the progress of my own papers.—M. F.

\* See also Hare in Silliman's Journal, 1833, xxiv. 246.

† Bibliothèque Universelle, 1837, vii. 388.

1639. Under these circumstances heating either electrode increased the current ; heating both produced still more effect. When both were heated, if either were cooled, the effect on the current fell in proportion. The proportion of effect due to heating this or that electrode varied, but on the whole heating the negative seemed to favour the passage of the current somewhat more than heating the positive. Whether the application of heat were by a flame applied underneath, or one directed by a blowpipe from above, or by a hot iron or coal, the effect was the same.

1640. Having thus removed the difficulty out of the way of my views regarding a current, I did not pursue this curious experiment further. It is probable, that the difference between my results and those of M. de la Rive may depend upon the relative values of the currents used ; for I employed only a weak one resulting from two pairs of plates two inches long and half an inch wide, whilst M. de la Rive used four pairs of plates of sixteen square inches in surface.

1641. Electric discharges in the atmosphere in the form of balls of fire have occasionally been described. Such phenomena appear to me to be incompatible with all that we know of electricity and its modes of discharge. As *time* is an element in the effect (1418. 1436.) it is possible perhaps that an electric discharge might really pass as a ball from place to place ; but as every thing shows that its velocity must be almost infinite, and the time of its duration exceedingly small, it is impossible that the eye should perceive it as anything else than a line of light. That phenomena of balls of fire may appear in the atmosphere, I do not mean to deny ; but that they have anything to do with the discharge of ordinary electricity, or are at all related to lightning or atmospheric electricity, is much more than doubtful.

1642. All these considerations, and many others, help to confirm the conclusion, drawn over and over again, that the current is an indivisible thing ; an axis of power, in every part of which both electric forces are present in equal amount* (517.

* I am glad to refer here to the results obtained by Mr. Christie with mag-

1627.).   With conduction and electrolyzation, and even discharge by spark, such a view will harmonize without hurting any of our preconceived notions ; but as relates to convection, a more startling result appears, which must therefore be considered.

1643. If two balls A and B be electrified in opposite states and held within each other's influence, the moment they move towards each other, a current, or those effects which are understood by the word current, will be produced.   Whether A move towards B, or B move in the opposite direction towards A, a current, and in both cases having the same *direction,* will result.   If A and B move from each other, then a *current* in the opposite direction, or equivalent effects, will be produced.

1644. Or, as charge exists only by induction (1178. 1299.), and a body when electrified is necessarily in relation to other bodies in the opposite state ; so, if a ball be electrified positively in the middle of a room and be then moved in any direction, effects will be produced, as if a *current* in the same direction (to use the conventional mode of expression) had existed : or, if the ball be negatively electrified, and then moved, effects as if a current in a direction contrary to that of the motion had been formed, will be produced.

1645. I am saying of a single particle or of two what I have before said, in effect, of many (1633.).   If the former account of currents be true, then that just stated must be a necessary result.   And, though the statement may seem startling at first, it is to be considered that, according to my theory of induction, the charged conductor or particle is related to the distant conductor in the opposite state, or that which terminates the extent of the induction, by all the intermediate particles (1165. 1295.), these becoming polarized exactly as the particles of a solid electrolyte do when interposed between the two electrodes. Hence the conclusion regarding the unity and identity of the current in the case of convection, jointly with the former cases, is not so strange as it might at first appear.

---

1646. There is a very remarkable phenomenon or effect of the electrolytic discharge, first pointed out, I believe, by Mr.

neto-electricity, Philosophical Transactions, 1833, p. 113. note.   As regards the current in a wire, they confirm everything that I am contending for.

Porrett, of the accumulation of fluid under decomposing action in the current on one side of an interposed diaphragm\*.   It is a mechanical result; and as the liquid passes from the positive towards the negative electrode in all the known cases, it seems to establish a relation to the polar condition of the di-electric in which the current exists (1164. 1525.).   It has not as yet been sufficiently investigated by experiment; for De la Rive says †, it requires that the water should be a bad con-ductor, as, for instance, distilled water, the effect not happen-ing with strong solutions; whereas, Dutrochet says ‡ the con-trary is the case, and that, the effect is not directly due to the electric current.

1647. Becquerel, in his Traité de l'Electricité, has brought together the considerations which arise for and against the opinion, that the effect generally is an electric effect §.   Though I have no decisive fact to quote at present, I cannot refrain from venturing an opinion, that the effect is analogous both to combination and convection (1623.), being a case of carrying due to the relation of the diaphragm and the fluid in contact with it, through which the electric discharge is jointly effected; and further, that the peculiar relation of positive and negative small and large surfaces already referred to (1482. 1503, 1525.), may be the direct cause of the fluid and the diaphragm travel-ling in contrary but determinate directions.   A very valuable experiment has been made by M. Becquerel with particles of clay ‖, which will probably bear importantly on this point.

————————

1648. *As long as* the terms *current* and *electro-dynamic* are used to express those relations of the electric forces in which progression of either fluids or effects are supposed to occur (283.), *so long* will the idea of velocity be associated with them; and this will, perhaps, be more especially the case if the hypo-thesis of a fluid or fluids be adopted.

1649. Hence has arisen the desire of estimating this velocity either directly or by some effect dependent on it; and amongst

————————

\* Annals of Philosophy, 1816, viii. p. 75.
† Annales de Chimie, 1835, xxviii. p. 196.
‡ Annales de Chimie, 1832, xlix. p. 423.
§ Vol. iv. pp. 192, 197.
‖ Traité de l'Electricité, i. p. 285.

the endeavours to do this correctly, may be mentioned especially those of Dr. Watson * in 1748, and of Professor Wheatstone† in 1834; the electricity in the early trials being supposed to travel from end to end of the arrangement, but in the later investigations a distinction occasionally appearing to be made between the transmission of the effect and of the supposed fluid by the motion of whose particles that effect is produced.

1650. Electrolytic action has a remarkable bearing upon this question of the velocity of the current, especially as connected with the theory of an electric fluid or fluids. In it there is an evident transfer of power with the transfer of each particle of the ánion or cathion present, to the next particles of the cathion or anion; and as the amount of power is definite, we have in this way a means of localizing as it were the force, identifying it by the particle and dealing it out in successive portions, which leads, I think, to very striking results.

1651. Suppose, for instance, that water is undergoing decomposition by the powers of a voltaic battery. Each particle of hydrogen as it moves one way, or of oxygen as it moves in the other direction, will transfer a certain amount of electrical force associated with it in the form of chemical affinity (822. 852. 918.) onwards through a distance, which is equal to that through which the particle itself has moved. This transfer will be accompanied by a corresponding movement in the electrical forces throughout every part of the circuit formed (1627. 1634.), and its effects may be estimated, as, for instance, by the heating of a wire (853.) at any particular section of the current however distant. If the water be a cube of an inch in the side, the electrodes touching, each by a surface of one square inch, and being an inch apart, then, by the time that a tenth of it, or 25· 25 grains, is decomposed, the particles of oxygen and hydrogen throughout the mass may be considered as having moved relatively to each other in opposite directions, to the amount of the tenth of an inch; *i. e.* that two particles at first in combination will after the motion be the tenth of an inch apart. Other motions which occur in the fluid will not at all interfere with this result; for they have no power of accelerating or retarding the electric discharge, and possess in fact no relation to it.

* Philosophical Transactions, 1748. † Ibid. 1834, p. 583.

1652. The quantity of electricity in 25·25 grains of water is, according to an estimate of the force which I formerly made (861.), equal to above 24 millions of charges of a large Leyden battery; or it would have kept any length of a platina wire $\frac{1}{104}$ of an inch in diameter red hot for an hour and a half (853.). This result, though given only as an approximation, I have seen no reason as yet to alter, and it is confirmed generally by the experiments and results of M. Pouillet*. According to Mr. Wheatstone's experiments, the influence or effects of the current would appear at a distance of 576,000 miles in a second †. We have, therefore, in this view of the matter, on the one hand, an enormous quantity of power equal to a most destructive thunder storm appearing instantly at the distance of 576,000 miles from its source, and on the other, a quiet effect, in producing which the power had taken an hour and a half to travel through the tenth of an inch: yet these are the equivalents to each other, being effects observed at the sections of one and the same current (1634.).

---

1653. It is time that I should call attention to the lateral or transverse forces of the *current*. The great things which have been achieved by Oersted, Arago, Ampère, Davy, De la Rive, and others, and the high degree of simplification which has been introduced into their arrangement by the theory of Ampère, have not only done their full service in advancing most rapidly this branch of knowledge, but have secured to it such attention that there is no necessity for urging on its pursuit. I refer of course to magnetic action and its relations; but though this is the only recognised lateral action of the current, there is great reason for believing that others exist and would by their discovery reward a close search for them (951.).

1654. The magnetic or transverse action of the current seems to be in a most extraordinary degree independent of those variations or modes of action which it presents directly in its course; it consequently is of the more value to us, as it gives us a higher relation of the power than any that might have varied with each mode of discharge. This discharge,

---

* Becquerel, Traité de l'Electricité, v. p. 278.
† Philosophical Transactions, 1834, p. 589.

whether it be by conduction through a wire with infinite velocity (1652.), or by electrolyzation with its corresponding and
exceeding slow motion (1651.), or by spark, and probably even
by convection, produces a transverse magnetic action always
the same in kind and direction.

1655. It has been shown by several experimenters, that whilst
the discharge is of the *same kind* the amount of lateral or magnetic force is very constant (216. 366. 367. 368. 376.). But
when we wish to compare discharge of different kinds, for the
important purpose of ascertaining whether the same amount of
current will in its *different forms* produce the same amount of
transverse action, we find the data very imperfect. Davy noticed, that when the electric current was passing through an
aqueous solution it affected a magnetic needle*, and Dr. Ritchie
says, that the current in the electrolyte is as magnetic as that
in a metallic wire†, and has caused water to revolve round a
magnet as a wire carrying the current would revolve.

1656. Disruptive discharge produces its magnetic effects : a
strong spark, passed transversely to a steel needle, will magnetise it as well as if the electricity of the spark were conducted
by a metallic wire occupying the line of discharge ; and Sir H.
Davy has shown that the discharge of a voltaic battery in vacuo
is affected and has motion given to it by approximated magnets ‡.

1657. Thus the three very different modes of discharge,
namely, conduction, electrolyzation, and disruptive discharge,
agree in producing the important transverse phenomenon of
magnetism. Whether convection or carrying discharge will
produce the same phenomenon has not been determined, and
the few experiments I have as yet had time to make do not enable me to answer in the affirmative.

1658. Having arrived at this point in the consideration of the
current and in the endeavour to apply its phenomena as tests
of the truth or fallacy of the theory of induction which I have
ventured to set forth, I am now very much tempted to indulge
in a few speculations respecting its lateral action and its possi-

* Philosophical Transactions, 1821, p. 426.      † Ibid. 1832, p. 294.
‡ Philosophical Transactions, 1821, p. 427.

ble connexion with the transverse condition of the lines of ordinary induction (1165. 1304.)*.    I have long sought and still seek for an effect or condition which shall be to statical electricity what magnetic force is to current electricity (1411.) ; for as the lines of discharge are associated with a certain transverse effect, so it appeared to me impossible but that the lines of tension or of inductive action, which of necessity precede that discharge, should also have their correspondent transverse condition or effect (951.).

1659. According to the beautiful theory of Ampère, the transverse force of a current may be represented by its attraction for a similar current and its repulsion of a contrary current. May not then the equivalent transverse force of static electricity be represented by that lateral tension or repulsion which the lines of inductive action appear to possess (1304.) ?  Then again, when current or discharge occurs between two bodies, previously under inductrical relations to each other, the lines of inductive force will weaken and fade away, and, as their lateral repulsive tension diminishes, will contract and ultimately disappear in the line of discharge.    May not this be an effect identical with the attractions of similar currents ? *i. e.* may not the passage of static electricity into current electricity, and that of the lateral tension of the lines of inductive force into the lateral attraction of lines of similar discharge, have the same relation and dependences, and run parallel to each other?

1660. The phenomena of induction amongst currents which I had the good fortune to discover some years ago (6. &c. 1048.) may perchance here form a connecting link in the series of effects.    When a current is first formed, it tends to produce a current in the contrary direction in all the matter around it; and if that matter have conducting properties and be fitly circumstanced, such a current is produced.    On the contrary, when the original current is stopped, one in the same direction tends to form all around it, and, in conducting matter properly arranged, will be excited.

1661. Now though we perceive the effects only in that portion of matter which, being in the neighbourhood, has conducting properties, yet hypothetically it is probable, that the nonconducting matter has also its relations to, and is affected by,

* Refer for further investigations to 1709.—1736.—*Dec.* 1838.

the disturbing cause, though we have not yet discovered them. Again and again the relation of conductors and non-conductors has been shown to be one not of opposition in kind, but only of degree (1334. 1603.) ; and therefore, for this, as well as for other reasons, it is probable, that what will affect a conductor will affect an insulator also ; producing perhaps what may deserve the term of the electrotonic state (60. 242. 1114.).

1662. It is the feeling of the necessity of some lateral connexion between the lines of electric force (1114.) ; of some link in the chain of effects as yet unrecognised, that urges me to the expression of these speculations. The same feeling has led me to make many experiments on the introduction of insulating dielectrics having different inductive capacities (1270. 1277.) between magnetic poles and wires carrying currents, so as to pass across the lines of magnetic force. I have employed such bodies both at rest and in motion, without, as yet, being able to detect any influence produced by them ; but I do by no means consider the experiments as sufficiently delicate, and intend, very shortly, to render them more decisive*.

1663. I think the hypothetical question may at present be put thus : can such considerations as those already generally expressed (1658.) account for the transverse effects of electrical currents ? are two such currents in relation to each other merely by the inductive condition of the particles of matter between them, or are they in relation by some higher quality and condition (1654.), which, acting at a distance and not by the intermediate particles, has, like the force of gravity, no relation to them ?

1664. If the latter be the case, then, when electricity is acting upon and in matter, its direct and its transverse action are essentially different in their nature ; for the former, if I am correct, will depend upon the contiguous particles, and the latter will not. As I have said before, this may be so, and I incline to that view at present ; but I am desirous of suggesting considerations why it may not, that the question may be thoroughly sifted.

1665. The transverse power has a character of polarity impressed upon it. In the simplest forms it appears as attraction

---

* See onwards 1711.—1726.—*Dec.* 1838.

or repulsion, according as the currents are in the same or different directions : in the current and the magnet it takes up the condition of tangenital forces ; and in magnets and their particles produces poles.   Since the experiments have been made which have persuaded me that the polar forces of electricity, as in induction and electrolytic action (1298. 1343.), show effects at a distance only by means of the polarized contiguous and intervening particles, I have been led to expect that *all polar forces* act in the same general manner; and the other kinds of phenomena which one can bring to bear upon the subject seem fitted to strengthen that expectation.   Thus in crystallizations the effect is transmitted from particle to particle ; and in this manner, in acetic acid or freezing water a crystal a few inches or even a couple of feet in length will form in less than a second, but progressively and by a transmission of power from particle to particle. And, as far as I remember, no case of polar action, or partaking of polar action, except the one under discussion, can be found which does not act by contiguous particles*.   It is apparently of the nature of polar forces that such should be the case, for the one force either finds or develops the contrary force near to it, and has, therefore, no occasion to seek for it at a distance.

1666. But leaving these hypothetical notions respecting the nature of the lateral action out of sight, and returning to the direct effects, I think that the phenomena examined and reasoning employed in this and the two preceding papers tend to confirm the view first taken (1164.), namely, that ordinary inductive action and the effects dependent upon it are due to an action of the contiguous particles of the dielectric interposed between the charged surfaces or parts which constitute, as it were, the terminations of the effect.   The great point of distinction and power (if it have any) in the theory is, the making the dielectric of essential and specific importance, instead of leaving it as it were a mere accidental circumstance or the simple representative of space, having no more influence over the phenomena than the space occupied by it.   I have still certain other results and views respecting the nature of the electrical forces and exci-

---

* I mean by contiguous particles those which are next to each other, not that there is *no* space between them.   See (1616.).

tation, which are connected with the present theory; and, unless upon further consideration they sink in my estimation, I shall very shortly put them into form as another series of these electrical researches.

*Royal Institution,*
*February 14th, 1838.*

1679. The particles of an insulating dielectric whilst under induction may be compared to a series of small magnetic needles, or more correctly still to a series of small insulated conductors. If the space round a charged globe were filled with a mixture of an insulating dielectric, as oil of turpentine or air, and small globular conductors, as shot, the latter being at a little distance from each other so as to be insulated, then these would in their condition and action exactly resemble what I consider to be the condition and action of the particles of the insulating dielectric itself (1337.). If the globe were charged, these little conductors would all be polar; if the globe were discharged, they would all return to their normal state, to be polarized again upon the recharging of the globe. The state developed by induction through such particles on a mass of conducting matter at a distance would be of the contrary kind, and exactly equal in amount to the force in the inductric globe. There would be a lateral diffusion of force (1224. 1297.), because each polarized sphere would be in an active or tense relation to all those contiguous to it, just as one magnet can affect two or more magnetic needles near it, and these again a still greater number beyond them. Hence would result the production of curved lines of inductive force if the inducteous body in such a mixed dielectric were an uninsulated metallic ball (1219. &c.) or other properly shaped mass. Such curved lines are the consequences of the two electric forces arranged as I have assumed them to be : and, that the inductive force can be directed in such curved lines is the strongest proof of the presence of the two powers and the polar condition of the dielectric particles.

1680. I think it is evident, that in the case stated, action at a distance can only result through an action of the contiguous conducting particles. There is no reason why the inductive body should polarize or affect *distant* conductors and leave those *near* it, namely the particles of the dielectric, unaffected : and everything in the form of fact and experiment with conducting masses or particles of a sensible size contradicts such a supposition.

1681. A striking character of the electric power is that it is limited and exclusive, and that the two forces being always present are exactly equal in amount. The forces are related in one of two ways, either as in the natural normal condition of an uncharged insulated conductor; or as in the charged state, the latter being a case of induction.

1682. Cases of induction are easily arranged so that the two forces being limited in their direction shall present no phenomena or indications external to the apparatus employed. Thus, if a Leyden jar, having its external coating a little higher than the internal, be charged and then its charging ball and rod removed, such jar will present no electrical appearances so long as its outside is uninsulated. The two forces which may be said to be in the coatings, or in the particles of the dielectric contiguous to them, are entirely engaged to each other by induction through the glass; and a carrier ball (1181.) applied either to the inside or outside of the jar will show no signs of electricity. But if the jar be insulated, and the charging ball and rod, in an uncharged state and suspended by an insulating thread of white silk, be restored to their place, then the part projecting above the jar will give electrical indications and charge the carrier, and at the same time the *outside* coating of the jar will be found in the opposite state and inductric towards external surrounding objects.

1683. These are simple consequences of the theory. Whilst the charge of the inner coating could induce only through the glass towards the outer coating, and the latter contained no more of the contrary force than was equivalent to it, no induction external to the jar could be perceived; but when the inner coating was extended by the rod and ball so that it could induce through the air towards external objects, then the tension of the polarized glass molecules would, by their tendency to return to the normal state, fall a little, and a portion of the charge passing to the surface of this new part of the inner conductor, would produce inductive action through the air towards distant objects, whilst at the same time a part of the force in the outer coating previously directed inwards would now be at liberty, and indeed be constrained to induct outwards through the air, producing in that outer coating what is sometimes called, though I think very improperly, free charge. If a small Leyden jar be converted into that form of apparatus usually known by the name of the electric well, it will illustrate this action very completely.

1684. The terms *free charge* and *dissimulated electricity* convey therefore erroneous notions if they are meant to imply any difference as to the mode or kind of action. The charge upon an insulated conductor in the middle of a room is in the same relation to the walls of that room as the charge upon the inner coating of a Leyden jar is to the outer coating of the same jar. The one is not more *free* or more *dissimulated* than the other; and when sometimes we make electricity appear where it was not evident before, as upon the outside of a charged jar, when, after insulating it, we touch the inner coating, it is only because we divert more or less of the inductive force from one direction into another; for not the slighest change is in such circumstances impressed upon the character or action of the force.

1685. Having given this general theoretical view, I will now notice particular points relating to the nature of the assumed electric polarity of the insulating dielectric particles.

1686. The polar state may be considered in common induction as a forced state, the particles tending to return to their normal condition. It may probably be raised to a very high degree by approximation of the inductric and inducteous bodies or by other circumstances ; and the phenomena of electrolyzation (861. 1652. 1706.) seem to imply that the quantity of power which can thus be accumulated on a single particle is enormous. Hereafter we may be able to compare corpuscular forces, as those of gravity, cohesion, electricity, and chemical affinity, and in some way or other from their effects deduce their relative equivalents ; at present we are not able to do so, but there seems no reason to doubt that their electrical, which are at the same time their chemical forces (891. 918.), will be by far the most energetic.

1687. I do not consider the powers when developed by the polarization as limited to two distinct points or spots on the surface of each particle to be considered as the poles of an axis, but as resident on large portions of that surface, as they are upon the surface of a conductor of sensible size when it is thrown into a polar state. But it is very probable, notwithstanding, that the particles of different bodies may present specific differences in this respect, the powers not being equally diffused though equal in quantity ; other circumstances also, as form and quality, giving to each a peculiar polar relation. It is perhaps to the existence of some such differences as these that we may attribute the specific actions of the different dielectrics in relation to discharge (1394. 1508.). Thus with respect to oxygen and nitrogen singular contrasts were presented when spark and brush discharge were made to take place in these gases, as may be seen by reference to the Table in paragraph 1518 of the Thirteenth Series ; for with nitrogen, when the small negative or the large positive ball was rendered inductric, the effects corresponded with those which in oxygen were produced when the small positive or the large negative ball was rendered inductric.

1688. In such solid bodies as glass, lac, sulphur, &c., the particles appear to be able to become polarized in all directions, for a mass when experimented upon so as to ascertain its inductive capacity in three or more directions (1690.), gives no indication of a difference. Now as the particles are fixed in the mass, and as the direction of the induction through them must change with its change relative to the mass, the constant effect indicates that they can be polarized electrically in any direction. This accords with the view already taken of each particle as a whole being a conductor (1669.), and, as an experimental fact, helps to confirm that view.

1689. But though particles may thus be polarized in *any* direction under the influence of powers which are probably of extreme energy (1686.), it does not follow that each particle may not tend to polarize to a greater degree, or with more facility, in one direction than another ; or that different kinds may not have specific differences in this respect, as they have differences of conducting and other powers (1296. 1326. 1395.). I sought with great anxiety for a relation of this nature ; and selecting crystalline bodies as those in which all the particles are symmetrically placed, and therefore best fitted to indicate any result which might depend upon variation of the direction of the forces to the direction of the particles in which they were developed, experimented very carefully with them. I was the more strongly stimulated to this inquiry by the beautiful electrical condition of the crystalline bodies tourmaline and boracite, and hoped also to discover a relation between electric polarity and that of crystallization, or even of cohesion itself (1316.). My experiments have not established any connexion of the kind sought for. But as I think it of equal importance to show either that there is or is not such a relation, I shall briefly describe the results.

1690. The form of experiment was as follows.  A brass ball
0·73 of an inch in diameter, fixed at the end of a horizontal
brass rod, and that at the end of a brass cylinder, was by
means of the latter connected with a large Leyden battery
(291.) by perfect metallic communications, the object being to
keep that ball, by its connexion with the charged battery in an
electrified state, very nearly uniform, for half an hour at a time.
This was the inductric ball.  The inducteous ball was the carrier of the torsion electrometer (1229. 1314.) ; and the dielectric between them was a cube cut from a crystal, so that two
of its faces should be perpendicular to the optical axis, whilst
the other four were parallel to it.  A small projecting piece of
shell-lac was fixed on the inductric ball at that part opposite
to the attachment of the brass rod, for the purpose of preventing actual contact between the ball and the crystal cube.  A
coat of shell-lac was also attached to that side of the carrier
ball which was to be towards the cube, being also that side

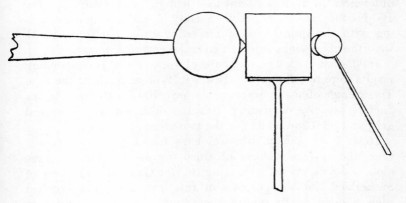

which was furthest from the repelled ball in the electrometer
when placed in its position in that instrument.  The cube was
covered with a thin coat of shell-lac dissolved in alcohol, to
prevent the deposition of damp upon its surface from the air.
It was supported upon a small table of shell-lac fixed on the
top of a stem of the same substance, the latter being of sufficient strength to sustain the cube, and yet flexible enough
from its length to act as a spring, and allow the cube to bear,
when in its place, against the shell-lac on the inductric ball.

1691. Thus it was easy to bring the inducteous ball always to the same distance from the inductric ball, and to uninsulate and insulate it again in its place; and then, after measuring the force in the electrometer (1181.), to return it to its place opposite to the inductric ball for a second observation. Or it was easy by revolving the stand which supported the cube to bring four of its faces in succession towards the inductric ball, and so observe the force when the lines of inductive action (1304.) coincided with, or were transverse to, the direction of the optical axis of the crystal. Generally from twenty to twenty-eight observations were made in succession upon the four vertical faces of a cube, and then an average expression of the inductive force was obtained, and compared with similar averages obtained at other times, every precaution being taken to secure accurate results.

1692. The first cube used was of *rock crystal*; it was 0·7 of an inch in the side. It presented a remarkable and constant difference, the average of not less than 197 observations, giving 100 for the specific inductive capacity in the direction coinciding with the optical axis of the cube, whilst 93·59 and 93·31 were the expressions for the two transverse directions.

1693. But with a second cube of rock crystal corresponding results were not obtained. It was 0·77 of an inch in the side. The average of many experiments gave 100 for the specific inductive capacity coinciding with the direction of the optical axis, and 98·6 and 99·92 for the two other directions.

1694. Lord Ashley, whom I have found ever ready to advance the cause of science, obtained for me the loan of three globes of rock crystal belonging to Her Grace the Duchess of Sutherland for the purposes of this investigation. Two had such fissures as to render them unfit for the experiments (1193. 1698.). The third, which was very superior, gave me no indications of any difference in the inductive force for different directions.

1695. I then used cubes of Iceland spar. One 0·5 of an inch in diameter gave 100 for the axial direction, and 98·66 and 95·74 for the two cross directions. The other, 0·8 of an inch in the side, gave 100 for the axial direction, whilst 101·73 and 101·86 were the numbers for the cross direction.

1696. Besides these differences there were others, which I do not think it needful to state, since the main point is not con-

firmed. For though the experiments with the first cube raised
great expectation, they have not been generalized by those
which followed. I have no doubt of the results as to that
cube, but they cannot as yet be referred to crystallization.
There are in the cube some faintly coloured layers parallel to
the optical axis, and the matter which colours them may have
an influence; but then the layers are also nearly parallel to a
cross direction, and if at all influential should show some effect
in that direction also, which they did not.

1697. In some of the experiments one half or one part of a
cube showed a superiority to another part, and this I could
not trace to any charge the different parts had received. It
was found that the varnishing of the cubes prevented any communication of charge to them, except (in a few experiments) a
small degree of the negative state, or that which was contrary
to the state of the inductric ball (1564. 1566.).

1698. I think it right to say that, as far as I could perceive,
the insulating character of the cubes used was perfect, or at
least so nearly perfect, as to bear a comparison with shell-lac,
glass, &c. (1255.). As to the cause of the differences, other than
regular crystalline structure, there may be several. Thus minute
fissures in the crystal insensible to the eye may be so disposed
as to produce a sensible electrical difference (1193.). Or the
crystallization may be irregular; or the substance may not be
quite pure; and if we consider how minute a quantity of
matter will alter greatly the conducting power of water, it will
seem not unlikely that a little extraneous matter diffused
through the whole or part of a cube, may produce effects sufficient to account for all the irregularities of action that have
been observed.

1699. An important inquiry regarding the electrical polarity
of the particles of an insulating dielectric, is, whether it be the
molecules of the particular substance acted on, or the component or ultimate particles, which thus act the part of insulated
conducting polarizing portions (1669.).

1700. The conclusion I have arrived at is, that it is the
molecules of the substance which polarize as wholes (1347.);
and that however complicated the composition of a body may
be, all those particles or atoms which are held together by
chemical affinity to form one molecule of the resulting body,

act as one conducting mass or particle when inductive phenomena and polarization are produced in the substance of which
it is a part.

1701. This conclusion is founded on several considerations.
Thus if we observe the insulating and conducting power of
elements when they are used as dielectrics, we find some, as
sulphur, phosphorus, chlorine, iodine, &c., whose particles insulate, and therefore polarize in a high degree; whereas others,
as the metals, give scarcely any indication of possessing a sensible proportion of this power (1328.), their particles freely conducting one to another. Yet when these enter into combination they form substances having no direct relation apparently,
in this respect, to their elements; for water, sulphuric acid,
and such compounds formed of insulating elements, conduct by
comparison freely; whilst oxide of lead, flint glass, borate of
lead, and other metallic compounds containing very high proportions of conducting matter, insulate excellently well. Taking
oxide of lead therefore as the illustration, I conceive that it is
not the particles of oxygen and lead which polarize separately
under the act of induction, but the molecules of oxide of lead
which exhibit this effect, all the elements of one particle of the
resulting body, being held together as parts of one conducting
individual by the bonds of chemical affinity; which is but another term for electrical force (918.).

1702. In bodies which are electrolytes we have still further
reason for believing in such a state of things. Thus when
water, chloride of tin, iodide of lead, &c. in the solid state are
between the electrodes of the voltaic battery, their particles
polarize as those of any other insulating dielectric do (1164.);
but when the liquid state is conferred on these substances, the
polarized particles divide, the two halves, each in a highly
charged state, travelling onwards until they meet other particles in an opposite and equally charged state, with which they
combine, to the neutralization of their chemical, *i. e.* their
electrical forces, and the reproduction of compound particles,
which can again polarize as wholes, and again divide to repeat
the same series of actions (1347.).

1703. But though electrolytic particles polarize as wholes,
it would appear very evident that in them it is not a matter of
entire indifference *how* the particle polarizes (1689.), since,
when free to move (380, &c.) the polarities are ultimately dis-

tributed in reference to the elements; and sums of force equivalent to the polarities, and very definite in kind and amount, separate, as it were, from each other, and travel onwards with the elementary particles.   And though I do not pretend to know what an atom is, or how it is associated or endowed with electrical force, or how this force is arranged in the cases of combination and decomposition, yet the strong belief I have in the electrical polarity of particles when under inductive action, and the bearing of such an opinion on the general effects of induction, whether ordinary or electrolytic, will be my excuse, I trust, for a few hypothetical considerations.

1704. In electrolyzation it appears that the polarized particles would (because of the gradual change which has been induced upon the chemical, *i. e.* the electrical forces of their elements (918.)) rather divide than discharge to each other without division (1348.); for if their division, *i. e.* their decomposition and recombination, be prevented by giving them the solid state, then they will insulate electricity perhaps a hundredfold more intense than that necessary for their electrolyzation (419, &c.).   Hence the tension necessary for direct conduction in such bodies appears to be much higher than that for decomposition (419. 1164. 1344.).

1705. The remarkable stoppage of electrolytic conduction by solidification (380. 1358.), is quite consistent with these views of the dependence of that process on the polarity which is common to all insulating matter when under induction, though attended by such peculiar electro-chemical results in the case of electrolytes. Thus it may be expected that the first effect of induction is so to polarize and arrange the particles of water that the positive or hydrogen pole of each shall be from the positive electrode and towards the negative electrode, whilst the negative or oxygen pole of each shall be in the contrary direction; and thus when the oxygen and hydrogen of a particle of water have separated, passing to and combining with other hydrogen and oxygen particles, unless these new particles of water could turn round they could not take up that position necessary for their successful electrolytic polarization.   Now solidification, by fixing the water particles and preventing them from assuming that essential preliminary position, prevents also their electrolysis (413.); and so the transfer of forces in that manner being prevented (1347. 1703.), the substance acts as an

ordinary insulating dielectric (for it is evident by former experiments (419. 1704.) that the insulating tension is higher
than the electrolytic tension), induction through it rises to a
higher degree, and the polar condition of the molecules as
wholes, though greatly exalted, is still securely maintained.

1706. When decomposition happens in a fluid electrolyte, I
do not suppose that all the molecules in the same sectional
plane (1634.) part with and transfer their electrified particles
or elements at once. Probably the *discharge force* for that
plane is summed up on one or a few particles, which decomposing, travelling and recombining, restore the balance of forces,
much as in the case of spark disruptive discharge (1406.) ; for
as those molecules resulting from particles which have just
transferred power must by their position (1705.) be less favourably circumstanced than others, so there must be some which
are most favourably disposed, and these, by giving way first,
will for the time lower the tension and produce discharge.

1707. In former investigations of the action of electricity
(821. &c.) it was shown, from many satisfactory cases, that the
quantity of electric power transferred onwards was in proportion to and was definite for a given quantity of matter moving
as anion or cathion onwards in the electrolytic line of action ;
and there was strong reason to believe that each of the particles of matter then dealt with, had associated with it a definite
amount of electrical force, constituting its force of chemical
affinity, the chemical equivalents and the electro-chemical equivalents being the same (836.). It was also found with few, and
I may now perhaps say with no exceptions (1341.), that only
those compounds containing elements in single proportions
could exhibit the characters and phenomena of electrolytes
(697.) ; oxides, chlorides, and other bodies containing more
than one proportion of the electro negative element refusing to
decompose under the influence of the electric current.

1708. Probable reasons for these conditions and limitations
arise out of the molecular theory of induction. Thus when a
liquid dielectric, as chloride of tin, consists of molecules, each
composed of a single particle of each of the elements, then as
these can convey equivalent opposite forces by their separation
in opposite directions, both decomposition and transfer can result. But when the molecules, as in the bichloride of tin, consist of one particle or atom of one element, and two of the other,

then the simplicity with which the particles may be supposed to be arranged and to act, is destroyed.    And, though it may be conceived that when the molecules of bichloride of tin are polarized as wholes by the induction across them, the positive polar force might accumulate on the one particle of tin whilst the negative polar force accumulated on the two particles of chlorine associated with it, and that these might respectively travel right and left to unite with other two of chlorine and one of tin, in analogy with what happens in cases of compounds consisting of single proportions, yet this is not altogether so evident or probable.    For when a particle of tin combines with two of chlorine, it is difficult to conceive that there should not be some relation of the three in the resulting molecule analogous to fixed position, the one particle of metal being perhaps symmetrically placed in relation to the two of chlorine : and, it is not difficult to conceive of such particles that they could not assume that position dependent both on their polarity and the relation of their elements, which appears to be the first step in the process of electrolyzation (1345. 1705.).

### §. 21. *Relation of the electric and magnetic forces.*

1709. I have already ventured a few speculations respecting the probable relation of magnetism, as the transverse force of the current, to the divergent or transverse force of the lines of inductive action belonging to static electricity (1658, &c.).

1710. In the further consideration of this subject it appeared to me to be of the utmost importance to ascertain, if possible, whether this lateral action which we call magnetism, or sometimes the induction of electrical currents (26. 1048, &c.), is extended to a distance *by the action of the intermediate particles* in analogy with the induction of static electricity, or the various effects, such as conduction, discharge, &c., which are dependent on that induction ; or, whether its influence at a distance is altogether independent of such intermediate particles (1662.).

1711. I arranged two magneto-electric helices with iron cores end to end, but with an interval of an inch and three quarters between them, in which interval was placed the end or pole of a bar magnet.    It is evident, that on moving the magnetic pole from one core towards the other, a current would tend to form

in both helices, in the one because of the lowering, and in the
other because of the strengthening of the magnetism induced
in the respective soft iron cores.   The helices were connected
together, and also with a galvanometer, so that these two currents should coincide in direction, and tend by their joint force
to deflect the needle of the instrument.   The whole arrangement was so effective and delicate, that moving the magnetic
pole about the eighth of an inch to and fro two or three times,
in periods equal to those required for the vibrations of the galvanometer needle, was sufficient to cause considerable vibration in the latter; thus showing readily the consequence of
strengthening the influence of the magnet on the one core and
helix, and diminishing it on the other.

1712. Then without disturbing the distances of the magnet
and cores, plates of substances were interposed.   Thus calling
the two cores A and B, a plate of shell-lac was introduced between the magnetic pole and A for the time occupied by the
needle in swinging one way; then it was withdrawn for the time
occupied in the return swing; introduced again for another equal
portion of time; withdrawn for another portion, and so on eight
or nine times; but not the least effect was observed on the needle.
In other cases the plate was alternated, *i. e.* it was introduced
between the magnet and A for one period of time, withdrawn
and introduced between the magnet and B for the second period,
withdrawn and restored to its first place for the third period,
and so on, but with no effect on the needle.

1713. In these experiments *shell-lac* in plates 0·9 of an inch
in thickness, *sulphur* in a plate 0·9 of an inch in thickness, and
*copper* in a plate 0·7 of an inch in thickness were used without
any effect.   And I conclude that bodies, contrasted by the extremes of conducting and insulating power, and opposed to each
other as strongly as metals, air, and sulphur, show no difference
with respect to magnetic forces when placed in their lines of
action, at least under the circumstances described.

1714. With a plate of iron, or even a small piece of that
metal, as the head of a nail, a very different effect was produced,
for then the galvanometer immediately showed its sensibility,
and the perfection of the general arrangement.

1715. I arranged matters so that a plate of *copper* 0·2 of an
inch in thickness, and ten inches in diameter, should have the
part near the edge interposed between the magnet and the core,

in which situation it was first rotated rapidly, and then held quiescent alternately, for periods according with that required for the swinging of the needle; but not the least effect upon the galvanometer was produced.

1716. A plate of shell-lac 0·6 of an inch in thickness was applied in the same manner, but whether rotating or not it produced no effect.

1717. Occasionally the plane of rotaton was directly across the magnetic curve : at other times it was made as oblique as possible; the direction of the rotation being also changed in different experiments, but not the least effect was produced.

1718. I now removed the helices with their soft iron cores, and replaced them by two *flat helices* wound upon cardboard, each containing forty-two feet of silked copper wire, and having no associated iron. Otherwise the arrangement was as before, and exceedingly sensible; for a very slight motion of the magnet between the helices produced an abundant vibration of the galvanometer needle.

1719. The introduction of plates of shell-lac, sulphur, or copper into the intervals between the magnet and these helices (1713.), produced not the least effect, whether the former were quiescent or in rapid revolution (1715.). So here no evidence of the influence of the intermediate particles could be obtained (1710.).

1720. The magnet was then removed and replaced by a flat helix, corresponding to the two former, the three being parallel to each other. The middle helix was so arranged that a voltaic current could be sent through it at pleasure. The former galvanometer was removed, and one with a double coil employed, one of the lateral helices being connected with one coil, and the other helix with the other coil, in such manner that when a voltaic current was sent through the middle helix its inductive action (26.) on the lateral helices should cause currents in them, having contrary directions in the coils of the galvanometer. By a little adjustment of the distances these induced currents were rendered exactly equal, and the galvanometer needle remained stationary notwithstanding their frequent production in the instrument. I will call the middle coil C, and the external coils A and B.

1721. A plate of copper 0·7 of an inch thick and six inches square, was placed between coils C and B, their respective distances remaining unchanged; and then a voltaic current from twenty pairs of 4-inch plates was sent through the coil C, and intermitted, in periods fitted to produce an effect on the galvanometer (1712.), if any difference had been produced in the effect of C on A and B. But notwithstanding the presence of air in one interval and copper in the other, the inductive effect was exactly alike on the two coils, and as if air had occupied both intervals. So that notwithstanding the facility with which any induced currents might form in the thick copper plate, the coil outside of it was just as much affected by the central helix C as if no such conductor as the copper had been there (65.).

1722. Then, for the copper plate was substituted one of sulphur 0·9 of an inch thick; still the results were exactly the same, *i. e.* there was no action at the galvanometer.

1723. Thus it appears that when a voltaic current in one wire is exerting its inductive action to produce a contrary or a similar current in a neighbouring wire, according as the primary current is commencing or ceasing, it makes not the least difference whether the intervening space is occupied by such insulating bodies as air, sulphur, and shell-lac, or such conducting bodies as copper, and the other non-magnetic metals.

1724. A correspondent effect was obtained with the like forces when resident in a magnet thus. A single flat helix (1718.) was connected with a galvanometer, and a magnetic pole placed near to it; then by moving the magnet to and from the helix, or the helix to and from the magnet, currents were produced indicated by the galvanometer.

1725. The thick copper plate (1721.) was afterwards interposed between the magnetic pole and the helix; nevertheless on moving these two and fro, effects, exactly the same in direction and amount, were obtained as if the copper had not been there. So also on introducing a plate of sulphur into the interval, not the least influence on the currents produced by motion of the magnet or coils could be obtained.

1726. These results, with many others which I have not thought it needful to describe, would lead to the conclusion that (judging by the *amount* of effect produced at a distance by forces transverse to the electric current, *i. e.* magnetic forces), the intervening matter, and therefore the intervening particles, have nothing to do with the phenomena; or in other words, that though the inductive force of static electricity is transmitted to a distance by the action of the intermediate particles (1164. 1666.), the transverse inductive force of currents, which can also act at a distance, is not transmitted by the intermediate particles in a similar way.

1727. It is however very evident that such a conclusion cannot be considered as proved. Thus when the metal copper is between the pole and the helix (1715. 1719. 1725.) or between the two helices (1721.) we know that its particles are affected, and can by proper arrangements make their peculiar state for the time very evident by the production of either electrical or magnetical effects. It seems impossible to consider this effect on the particles of the intervening matter as independent of that produced by the inductric coil or magnet C, on the inducteous coil or core A (1715. 1721.) ; for since the inducteous body is equally affected by the inductric body whether these intervening and affected particles of copper are present or not (1723. 1725.), such a supposition would imply that the particles so affected had no reaction back on the original inductric forces. The more reasonable conclusion, as it appears to me, is, to consider these affected particles as efficient in continuing the action onwards from the inductric to the inducteous body, and by this very communication producing the effect of *no loss* of induced power at the latter.

1728. But then it may be asked what is the relation of the particles of insulating bodies, such as air, sulphur, or lac, when *they* intervene in the line of magnetic action ? The answer to this is at present merely conjectural. I have long thought there must be a particular condition of such bodies corresponding to the state which causes currents in metals and other conductors (26. 53. 191. 201. 213.) ; and considering that the bodies are insulators one would expect that state to be one of tension. I have by rotating non-conducting bodies near magnetic poles and poles near them, and also by causing powerful electric currents to be suddenly formed and to cease around and about insulators in various directions, endeavoured to make some such state sensible, but have not succeeded. Nevertheless, as any such state must be of exceedingly low intensity, because of the feeble intensity of the currents which are used to induce it, it may well be that the state may exist, and may be discoverable by some more expert experimentalist, though I have not been able to make it sensible.

1729. It appears to me possible, therefore, and even probable, that magnetic action may be communicated to a distance
by the action of the intervening particles, in a manner having
a relation to the way in which the inductive forces of static
electricity are transferred to a distance (1677.) ; the intervening
particles assuming for the time more or less of a peculiar condition, which (though with a very imperfect idea) I have several
times expressed by the term *electro-tonic state* (60. 242. 1114.
1661.). I hope it will not be understood that I hold the settled
opinion that such is the case. I would rather in fact have
proved the contrary, namely, that magnetic forces are quite independent of the matter intervening between the inductric and
the inducteous bodies ; but I cannot get over the difficulty
presented by such substances as copper, silver, lead, gold,
carbon, and even aqueous solutions (201. 213.), which though
they are known to assume a peculiar state whilst intervening
between the bodies acting and acted upon (1727.), no more interfere with the final result than those which have as yet had
no peculiarity of condition discovered in them.

1730. A remark important to the whole of this investigation
ought to be made here. Although I think the galvanometer
used as I have described it (1711. 1720.) is quite sufficient to
prove that the final amount of action on each of the two coils
or the two cores A and B (1713. 1719.) is equal, yet there is
an effect which *may* be consequent on the difference of action
of two interposed bodies which it would not show. As time
enters as an element into these actions* (125.), it is very possible that the induced actions on the helices or cores A, B,
though they rise to the same degree when air and copper, or
air and lac are contrasted as intervening substances, do not do
so in the same time; and yet, because of the length of time
occupied by a vibration of the needle, this difference may not
be visible, both effects rising to their maximum in periods so
short as to make no sensible portion of that required for a vibration of the needle, and so exert no visible influence upon it.

---

1731. If the lateral or transverse force of electrical currents,
or what appears to be the same thing, magnetic power, could
be proved to be influential at a distance independently of the

* See Annales de Chemie, 1833, tom. li. pp. 422, 428.

intervening contiguous particles, then, as it appears to me, a real distinction, of a high and important kind, would be established between the natures of these two forces (1654. 1664.). I do not mean that the powers are independent of each other and might be rendered separatively active, on the contrary they are probably essentially associated (1654.), but it by no means follows that they are of the same nature. In common statical induction, in conduction, and in electrolyzation, the forces at the opposite extremities of the particles which coincide with the lines of action, and have commonly been distinguished by the term electric, are polar, and in the cases of contiguous particles act only to insensible distances; whilst those which are transverse to the direction of these lines, and are called magnetic, are circumferential, act at a distance, and if not through the mediation of the intervening particles, have their relations to ordinary matter entirely unlike those of the electrical forces with which they are associated.

1732. To decide this question of the identity or distinction of the two kinds of power, and establish their true relation, would be exceedingly important. The question seems fully within the reach of experiment, and offers a high reward to him who will attempt its settlement.

1733. I have already expressed a hope of finding an effect or condition which shall be to statical electricity what magnetic force is to current electricity (1658.). If I could have proved to my own satisfaction that magnetic forces extended their influence to a distance by the conjoined action of the intervening particles in a manner analogous to that of electrical forces, then I should have thought that the lateral tension of the lines of inductive action (1659.), or that state so often hinted at as the electro-tonic state (1661. 1662.), was this related condition of statical electricity.

1734. It may be said that the state of *no lateral action* is to static or inductive force the equivalent of *magnetism* to current force; but that can only be upon the view that electric and magnetic action are in their nature essentially different (1664.). If they are the same power, the whole difference in the results being the consequence of the difference of *direction*, then the normal or *undeveloped* state of electric force will correspond with the state of *no lateral action* of the magnetic state of the force; the electric current will correspond with the lateral ef-

fects commonly called magnetism : but the state of static induction which is between the normal condition and the current
will still require a corresponding lateral condition in the magnetic series, presenting its own peculiar phenomena ; for it can
hardly be supposed that the normal electric, and the inductive
or polarized electric condition, can both have the same lateral
relation.   If magnetism be a separate and a higher relation of
the powers developed, then perhaps the argument which presses
for this third condition of that force would not be so strong.

1735. I cannot conclude these general remarks upon the relation of the electric and magnetic forces without expressing
my surprise at the results obtained with the copper plate (1721.
1725.).   The experiments with the flat helices represent one
of the simplest cases of the induction of electrical currents
(1720.) ; the effect, as is well known, consisting in the production of a momentary current in a wire at the instant when a
current in the contrary direction begins to pass through a
neighbouring parallel wire, and the production of an equally
brief current in the reverse direction when the determining
current is stopped (26.).   Such being the case, it seems very
extraordinary that this induced current which takes place in
the helix A when there is only air between A and C (1720.)
should be equally strong when that air is replaced by an enormous mass of that excellently conducting metal copper (1721.).
It might have been supposed that this mass would have allowed
of the formation and discharge of almost any quantity of currents in it, which the helix C was competent to induce, and so
in some degree have diminished if not altogether prevented
the effect in A : instead of which, though we can hardly doubt
that an infinity of currents are formed at the moment in the
copper plate, still not the smallest diminution or alteration of
the effect in A appears (65.).   Almost the only way of reconciling this effect with generally received notions is, as it appears
to me, to admit that magnetic action is communicated by the
action of the intervening particles (1729. 1733.).

1736. This condition of things, which is very remarkable,
accords perfectly with the effects observed in solid helices
where wires are coiled over wires to the amount of five or six
or more layers in succession, no diminution of effect on the
outer ones being occasioned by those within.

## § 22.  *Note on electrical excitation.*

1737. That the different modes in which electrical excitement takes place will some day or other be reduced under one
common law can hardly be doubted, though for the present we
are bound to admit distinctions.   It will be a great point gained
when these distinctions are, not removed, but understood.

1738. The strict relation of the electrical and chemical
powers renders the chemical mode of excitement the most instructive of all, and the case of two isolated combining particles is probably the simplest that we possess.   Here however
the action is local, and we still want such a test of electricity as
shall apply to it, to cases of current electricity, and also to those
of static induction.   Whenever by virtue of the previously
combined condition of some of the acting particles (923.) we are
enabled, as in the voltaic pile, to expand or convert the local
action into a current, then chemical action can be traced through
its variations to the production of *all* the phenomena of tension
and the static state, these being in every respect the same as
if the electric forces producing them had been developed by
friction.

1739. It was Berzelius, I believe, who first spoke of the aptness
of certain particles to assume opposite states when in presence
of each other (959.).   Hypothetically we may suppose these
states to increase in intensity by increased approximation, or
by heat, &c. until at a certain point combination occurs, accompanied by such an arrangement of the forces of the two
particles between themselves as is equivalent to a discharge,
producing at the same time a particle which is throughout a
conductor (1700.).

1740. This aptness to assume an excited electrical state
(which is probably polar in those forming non-conducting matter) appears to be a primary fact, and to partake of the nature
of induction (1162.), for the particles do not seem capable of
retaining their particular state independently of each other
(1177.) or of matter in the opposite state.   What appears to be
definite about the particles of matter is their assumption of a
*particular* state, as the positive or negative, in relation to each
other, and not of either one or other indifferently; and also
the acquirement of force up to a certain amount.

1741. It is easily conceivable that the same force which causes local action between two free particles shall produce current force if one of the particles is previously in combination, forming part of an electrolyte (923. 1738.). Thus a particle of zinc, and one of oxygen, when in presence of each other, exert their inductive forces (1740.), and these at last rise up to the point of combination. If the oxygen be previously in union with hydrogen, it is held so combined by an analogous exertion and arrangement of the forces; and as the forces of the oxygen and hydrogen are for the time of combination mutually engaged and related, so when the superior relation of the forces between the oxygen and zinc come into play, the induction of the former or oxygen towards the metal cannot be brought on and increased without a corresponding deficiency in its induction towards the hydrogen with which it is in combination (for the amount of force in a particle is considered as definite), and the latter therefore has its force turned towards the oxygen of the next particle of water; thus the effect may be considered as extended to sensible distances, and thrown into the condition of static induction, which being discharged and then removed by the action of other particles produces currents.

1742. In the common voltaic battery, the current is occasioned by the tendency of the zinc to take the oxygen of the water from the hydrogen, the effective action being at the place where the oxygen leaves the previously existing electrolyte. But Schœnbein has arranged a battery in which the effective action is at the other extremity of this essential part of the arrangement, namely, where oxygen goes to the electrolyte*. The first may be considered as a case where the current is put into motion by the abstraction of oxygen from hydrogen, the latter by that of hydrogen from oxygen. The direction of the electric current is in both cases the same, when referred to the direction in which the elementary particles of the electrolyte are moving (923. 962.), and both are equally in accordance with the hypothetical view of the inductive action of the particles just described (1740.).

1743. In such a view of voltaic excitement, the action of the particles may be divided into two parts, that which occurs whilst the force in a particle of oxygen is rising towards a par-

* Philosophical Magazine, 1838, xii. 225, 315. See also De la Rive's results with peroxide of manganese. Annales de Chimie, 1836, lxi. p. 40.—*Dec.* 1838.

ticle of zinc acting on it, and falling towards the particle of hydrogen with which it is associated (this being the progressive period of the inductive action), and that which occurs when the change of association takes place, and the particle of oxygen leaves the hydrogen and combines with the zinc. The former appears to be that which produces the current, or if there be no current, produces the state of tension at the termination of the battery; whilst the latter, by terminating for the time the influence of the particles which have been active, allows of others coming into play, and so the effect of current is continued.

1744. It seems highly probable, that excitement by friction may very frequently be of the same character. Wollaston endeavoured to refer such excitement to chemical action\*; but if by chemical action ultimate union of the acting particles is intended, then there are plenty of cases which are opposed to such a view. Davy mentions some such, and for my own part I feel no difficulty in admitting other means of electrical excitement than chemical action, especially if by chemical action is meant a final combination of the particles.

1745. Davy refers experimentally to the opposite states which two particles having opposite chemical relations can assume when they are brought into the close vicinity of each other, but *not* allowed to combine†. This, I think, is the first part of the action already described (1743.); but in my opinion it cannot give rise to a continuous current unless combination take place, so as to allow other particles to act successively in the same manner, and not even then unless one set of the particles be present as an element of an electrolyte (923. 963.); *i. e.* mere quiescent contact alone without chemical action does not in such cases produce a *current*.

1746. Still it seems very possible that such a relation may produce a high charge, and thus give rise to excitement by friction. When two bodies are rubbed together to produce electricity in the usual way, one at least must be an insulator. During the act of rubbing, the particles of opposite kinds must be brought more or less closely together, the few which are most favourably circumstanced being in such close contact as to be short only of that which is consequent upon chemical combination. At such moments they may acquire by their

\* Philosophical Transactions, 1801, p. 427.        † Ibid. 1807, p. 34.

mutual induction (1740.) and partial discharge to each other, very exalted opposite states, and when, the moment after, they are by the progress of the rub removed from each other's vicinity, they will retain this state if both bodies be insulators, and exhibit them upon their complete separation.

1747. All the circumstances attending friction seem to me to favour such a view. The irregularities of form and pressure will cause that the particles of the two rubbing surfaces will be at very variable distances, only a few at once being in that very close relation which is probably necessary for the development of the forces; further, those which are nearest at one time will be further removed at another, and others will become the nearest, and so by continuing the friction many will in succession be excited. Finally, the lateral direction of the separation in rubbing seems to me the best fitted to bring many pairs of particles, first of all into that close vicinity necessary for their assuming the opposite states by relation to each other, and then to remove them from each other's influence whilst they retain that state.

1748. It would be easy, on the same view, to explain hypothetically, how, if one of the rubbing bodies be a conductor, as the amalgam of an electrical machine, the state of the other when it comes from under the friction is (as a mass) exalted; but it would be folly to go far into such speculation before that already advanced has been confirmed or corrected by fit experimental evidence. I do not wish it to be supposed that I think all excitement by friction is of this kind; on the contrary, certain experiments lead me to believe, that in many cases, and perhaps in all, effects of a thermo-electric nature conduce to the ultimate effect; and there are very probably other causes of electric disturbance influential at the same time, which we have not as yet distinguished.

*Royal Institution,*
   *June* 1838.

# INDEX TO VOLUME I

N.B. A dash rule represents the *italics* immediately preceding it. The references are sometimes to the individual paragraph, and sometimes to that in conjunction with those which follow.

*Insulation dependent on the* distance in air, 1303, 1364, 1371.

—— —— density of air, 1365, 1375.

—— —— induction, 1368.

—— —— form of conductors, 1302, 1374.

——, as affected by temperature of air, 1367, 1380.

—— *in different gases,* 1381, 1388.

—— —— differs, 1395.

—— in liquids and solids, 1403.

—— in metals, 1328, 1331, 1332.

—— and conduction not essentially different, 1320, 1326, 1336, 1338, 1561.

——, its relation to induction, 1324, 1362, 1368, 1678.

*Insulators,* liquid, good, 1172.

——, solid, good, 1254.

——, the best conduct, 1233, 1241, 1245, 1247, 1254.

—— tested as to conduction, 1255.

—— and conductors, relation of, 1328, 1334, 1338.

*Intensity,* its influence in conduction, 419.

——, inductive, how represented, 1370.

——, relative, of magneto-electric currents, 183, 193, 211, 213.

—— of disruptive discharge constant, 1410.

——, electrolytic, 912, 966, 983, 1354.

—— necessary for electrolyzation, 911, 966.

—— *of the current of single circles,* 904.

—— —— increased, 906.

—— of electricity in the voltaic battery, 990, 993.

—— of voltaic current increased, 906, 990.

*Interference with combining power of platina,* 638, 655.

—— by olefiant gas, 640.

—— carbonic oxide, 645.

—— sulphuret of carbon, 650.

—— ether, 651.

Interpositions, their retarding effects, 1018.

*Iodides in* solution, their electrolysis, 769.

—— fusion, their electrolysis, 802, 813.

*Iodide* of lead, electrolysed, 802, 818.

—— of potassium, test of chemical action, 316.

*Ions,* what, 665, 824, 833, 834, 849.

—— not transferable alone, 542, 547, 826.

——, table of, 847.

*Iron,* both magnetic and magneto-electric at once, 138, 254.

——, copper and sulphur circles, 943.

Jenkin, his shock by one pair of plates, 1049.

Kemp, his amalgam of zinc, 999.

Knight, Dr. Gowin, his magnet, 44.

*Lac,* charge removed from, 1203.

——, induction through, 1255.

——, specific inductive capacity of, 1256, 1269.

*Lac,* effects of its conducting power, 1234.

——, its relation to conduction and insulation, 1324.

*Lateral* direction of inductive forces of currents, 26, 1108.

—— forces of the current, 1653, 1709.

*Law of conduction, new,* 380, 394, 410.

—— magneto-electric induction, 114.

—— volta-electric induction, 26.

*Lead,* chloride of, electrolysed, 794, 815.

——, fluoride of, conducts well when heated, 1340.

——, iodide of, electrolysed, 802, 818.

——, oxide of, electrolysed, 797.

*Leyden jar,* condition of its charge, 1682.

——, its charge, nature of, 1300.

——, its discharge, 1300.

——, its residual charge, 1249.

*Light,* polarized, passed across electrolytes, 951.

——, *electric,* 1405, 1445, 1560, *note.*

——, ——, spark, 1406, 1553.

——, ——, brush, 1425, 1444, 1445.

——, ——, glow, 1526.

Lightning, 1420, 1464, 1641.

*Lines of inductive force,* 1231, 1304.

—— often curved, 1219, 1224, 1230.

——, as shown by the brush, 1449.

——, their lateral relation, 1231, 1297, 1304.

——, their relation to magnetism, 1411, 1658, 1709.

Liquefaction, conduction consequent upon, 380, 394, 410.

Liquid bodies which are non-conductors, 405.

Local chemical affinity, 947, 959, 961, 1739,

*Machine,* electric, evolution of electricity by, 1748.

——, magneto-electric, 135, 154, 158, 1118.

*Magnelectric* induction, 58.

——, collectors or conductors, 86.

*Magnesia,* sulphate, decomposed against water, 494, 533.

——, transference of, 495.

*Magnet,* a measure of conducting power, 216.

—— *and* current, their relation remembered, 38, *note.*

—— —— plate revolved together, 218.

—— —— cylinder revolved together, 219.

—— revolved alone, 220, 223.

—— and moving conductors, their general relation, 256.

—— made by induced current, 13, 14.

——, electricity from, 36, 220, 223.

*Magnetic* bodies, but few, 255.

——, curves, their inductive relation, 217, 232.

—— *effects of* voltaic electricity, 277.

# Plates to Volume I

PLATE I (Vol. I, Series I)

Fig. 1.

Fig. 2.

Fig. 3.

Fig. 4.

Fig. 5.

Fig. 6.

Fig. 7.

PLATE I (continued)

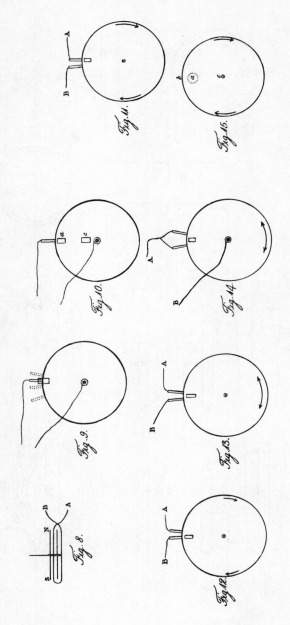

Fig. 8.

Fig. 9.

Fig. 10.

Fig. 11.

Fig. 12.

Fig. 13.

Fig. 14.

Fig. 15.

PLATE I (concluded)

Fig. 16.

Fig. 17.

Fig. 18.

Fig. 19.

Fig. 20.

Fig. 21.

Fig. 22.

Fig. 23.

Fig. 24.

Fig. 25.

Fig. 26.

Fig. 27.

Fig. 28.

Fig. 29.

PLATE II (Vol. I, Series II)

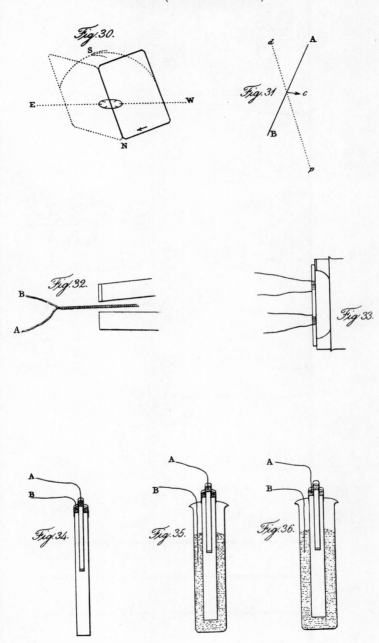

# PLATE II (concluded)

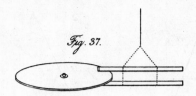

*Fig. 37.*

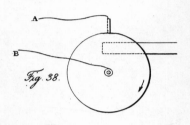

*Fig. 38.*

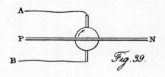

*Fig. 39.*

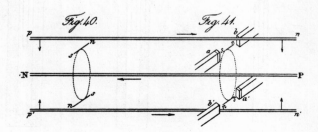

*Fig. 40.*   *Fig. 41.*

PLATE III (Vol. I, Series III)

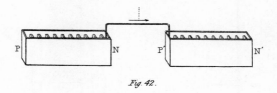

Fig. 42.

Fig. 43.

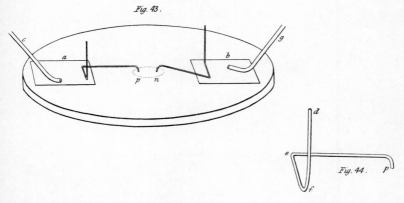

Fig. 44.

Fig. 45.

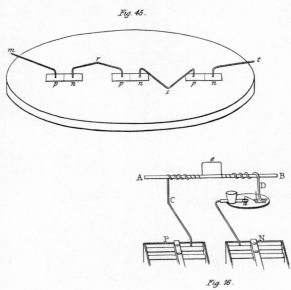

Fig. 16.

PLATE IV (Vol. I, Series V)

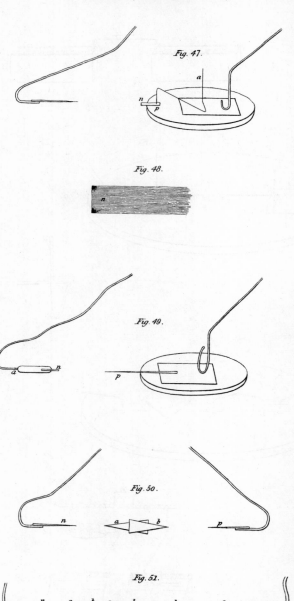

Fig. 47.

Fig. 48.

Fig. 49.

Fig. 50.

Fig. 51.

# PLATE IV (concluded)

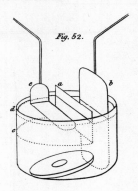

Fig. 52.

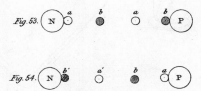

Fig. 53.

Fig. 54.

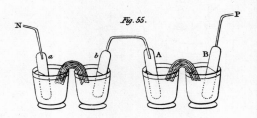

Fig. 55.

# PLATE V (Vol. I, Series VI and VII)

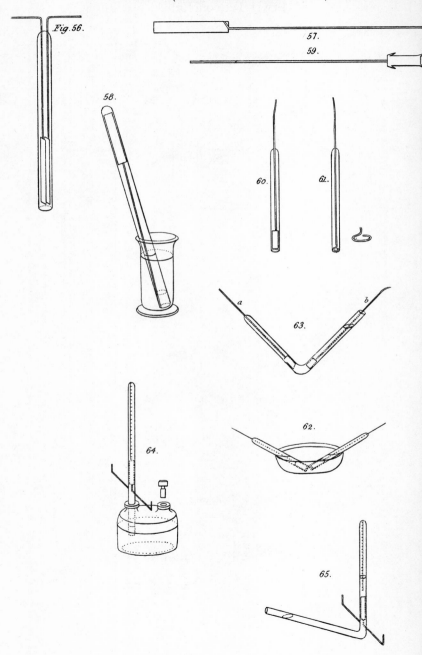

*Fig. 56.*

57.

59.

58.

60.

61.

63.

*a*  *b*

64.

62.

65.

PLATE V (concluded)

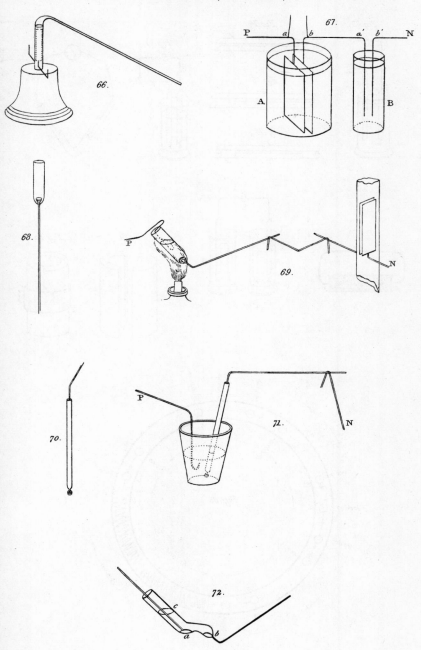

## PLATE VI (Vol. I, Series VIII)

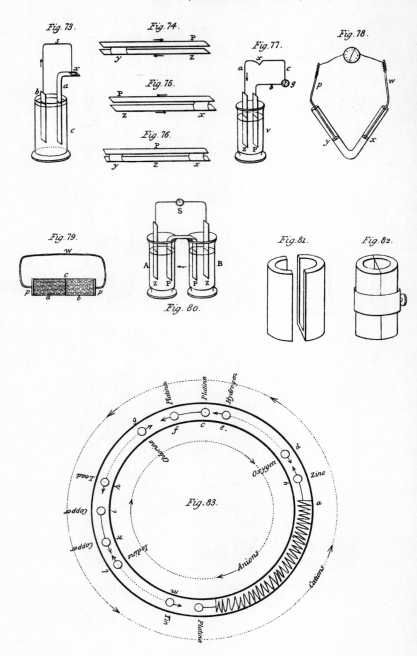

Fig. 73.

Fig. 74.

Fig. 75.

Fig. 76.

Fig. 77.

Fig. 78.

Fig. 79.

Fig. 80.

Fig. 81.

Fig. 82.

Fig. 83.

PLATE VI (continued)

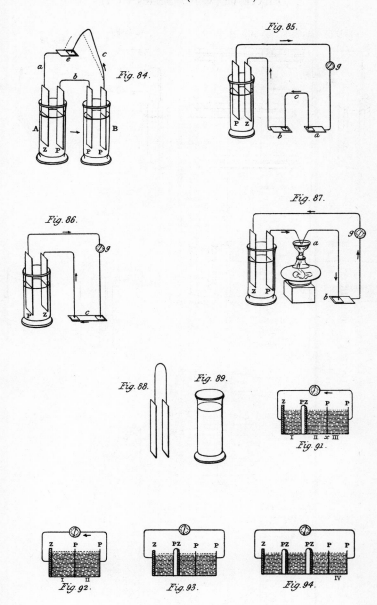

PLATE VI (concluded)

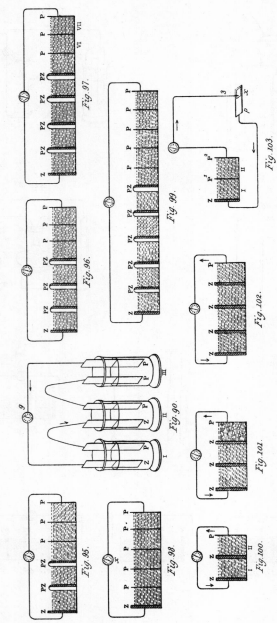

Fig. 97.

Fig. 96.

Fig. 99.

Fig. 103.

Fig. 95.

Fig. 90.

Fig. 102.

Fig. 98.

Fig. 101.

Fig. 100.

PLATE VII (Vol. I, Series XI)

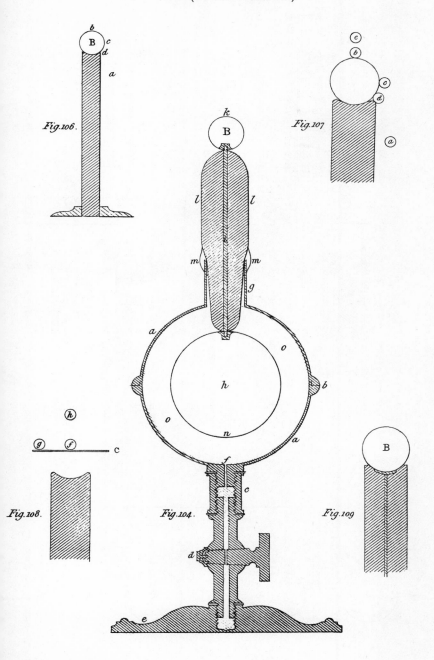

Fig.106.

Fig.107.

Fig.108.

Fig.104.

Fig.109

PLATE VII (concluded)

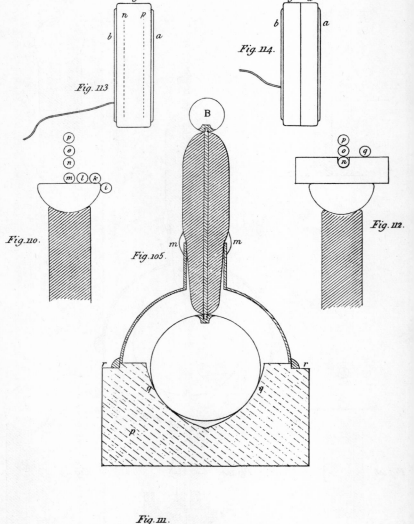

*Fig. 113*

*Fig. 114.*

*Fig. 110.*

*Fig. 105.*

*Fig. 112.*

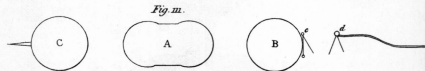

*Fig. 111.*

PLATE VIII (Vol. I, Series XII and XIII)

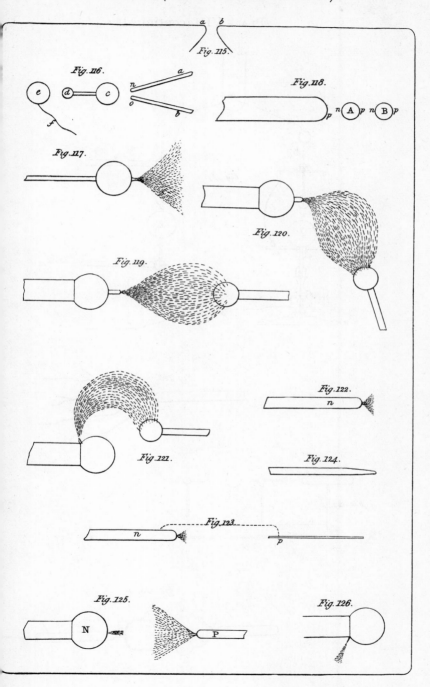

# PLATE VIII (continued)

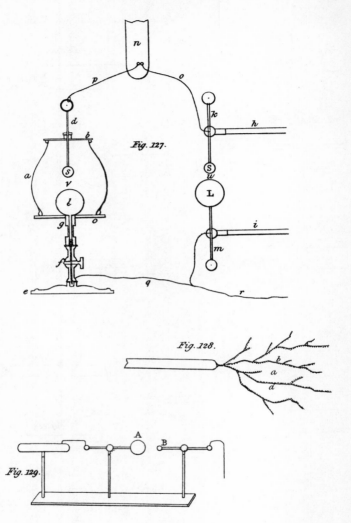

Fig. 127.

Fig. 128.

Fig. 129.

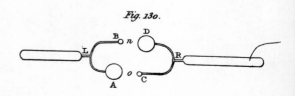

Fig. 130.

# PLATE VIII (concluded)

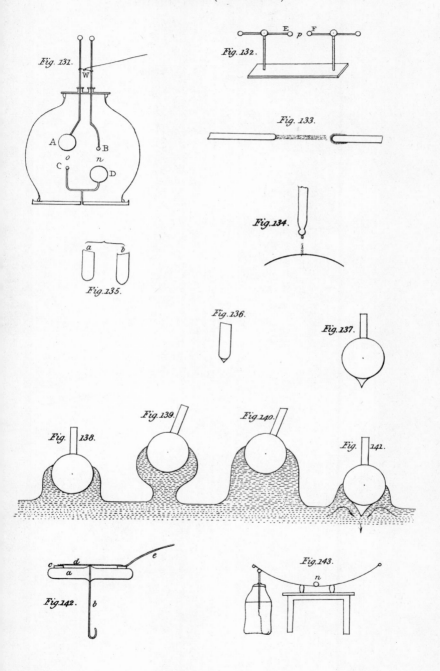

*Fig. 131.*

*Fig. 132.*

*Fig. 133.*

*Fig. 134.*

*Fig. 135.*

*Fig. 136.*

*Fig. 137.*

*Fig. 138.*

*Fig. 139.*

*Fig. 140.*

*Fig. 141.*

*Fig. 142.*

*Fig. 143.*

# EXPERIMENTAL RESEARCHES IN ELECTRICITY

## by MICHAEL FARADAY

*Volume II*

# PREFACE.

For reasons stated in the former volume of Experimental Researches in Electricity, I have been induced to gather the remaining Series together, and to add to them certain other papers devoted to Electrical research.

To the prefatory remarks containing these reasons, I would recall the recollection of those who may honour these Researches with any further attention. I have printed the papers in this volume, as before, with little or no alteration, except that I have placed the fair and just date of each at the top of the pages.

I regret the presence of those papers which partake of a controversial character, but could not help it ; some of them contain much new, important and explanatory matter. The introduction of matter due to other parties than myself, as Nobili and Antinori, or Hare, was essential to the comprehension of the further development given in the replies.

I owe many thanks to the Royal Society, to Mr. Murray, and to Mr. Taylor, for the great kindness I have received in the loan of plates, &c., and in other facilities granted to me for the printing of the volume.

As the Index belongs both to the Experimental Researches and to the miscellaneous papers, its references are of necessity made in two ways ; those to the Researches are, as before, to the numbers of the Paragraphs, and are easily recognised by the greatness of the numbers : the other references are to the pages, and being always preceded by *p.* or *pp.*, are known by that mark.

MICHAEL FARADAY.

# CONTENTS.

# EXPERIMENTAL RESEARCHES

## IN

# ELECTRICITY.

---

## FIFTEENTH SERIES.

§ 23. *Notice of the character and direction of the electric force of the Gymnotus.*

Received November 15,—Read December 6, 1838.

1749. WONDERFUL as are the laws and phenomena of electricity when made evident to us in inorganic or dead matter, their interest can bear scarcely any comparison with that which attaches to the same force when connected with the nervous system and with life; and though the obscurity which for the present surrounds the subject may for the time also veil its importance, every advance in our knowledge of this mighty power in relation to inert things, helps to dissipate that obscurity, and to set forth more prominently the surpassing interest of this very high branch of Physical Philosophy. We are indeed but upon the threshold of what we may, without presumption, believe man is permitted to know of this matter; and the many eminent philosophers who have assisted in making this subject known have, as is very evident in their writings, felt up to the latest moment that such is the case.

1750. The existence of animals able to give the same concussion to the living system as the electrical machine, the voltaic battery, and the thunder storm, being with their habits made known to us by Richer, S'Gravesende, Firmin, Walsh, Humboldt, &c. &c., it became of growing importance to identify the living power which they possess, with that which man can call into action from inert matter, and by him named electricity (265. 351.). With the *Torpedo* this has been done to perfection, and the direction of the current of force determined by the united and successive labours of Walsh[1], Cavendish[2], Galvani[3], Gardini[4], Humboldt and Gay-Lussac[5], Todd[6], Sir Humphry Davy[7], Dr. Davy[8], Becquerel[9], and Matteucci[10].

1751. The Gymnotus has also been experimented with for the same purpose, and the investigations of Williamson[11], Garden[12], Humboldt[13], Fahlberg[14], and Guisan[15], have gone very far in showing the identity of the electric force in this animal with the electricity excited by ordinary means; and the two latter philosophers have even obtained the spark.

1752. As an animal fitted for the further investigation of this refined branch of science, the Gymnotus seems, in certain respects, better adapted than the Torpedo, especially (as Humboldt has remarked) in its power of bearing confinement, and capability of being preserved alive and in health for a long period. A Gymnotus has been kept for several months in activity, whereas Dr. Davy could not preserve Torpedos above twelve or fifteen days; and Matteucci was not able out of 116 such fish to keep one living above three days, though every circumstance favourable to their preservation was attended to[16]. To obtain Gymnoti has therefore been a matter of consequence; and being stimulated, as much as I was honoured, by very kind communications from Baron Humboldt, I in the year 1835 applied to the Colonial Office, where I was promised

---

[1] Philosophical Transactions, 1773, p. 461.          [2] Ibid. 1776, p. 196.
[3] Aldini's Essai sur la Galvanism, ii. 61.
[4] De Electrici ignis Natura, §. 71.    Mantua, 1792.
[5] Annales de Chimie, xiv. 15.
[6] Philosophical Transactions, 1816, p. 120.          [7] Ibid. 1829, p. 15.
[8] Ibid. 1832, p. 259; and 1834, p. 531.
[9] Traité de l'Electricité, iv. 264.
[10] Bibliothèque Universelle, 1837, tom. xii. 163.
[11] Philosophical Transactions, 1775, p. 94.          [12] Ibid. 1775, p. 102.
[13] Personal Narrative, chap. xvii.
[14] Swedish Transactions, 1801, pp. 122. 156.
[15] De Gymnoto Electrico.   Tubingen, 1819.
[16] Bibliothèque Universelle, 1837, xii. p. 174.

every assistance in procuring some of these fishes, and continually expect to receive either news of them or the animals themselves.

1753. Since that time Sir Everard Home has also moved a friend to send some Gymnoti over, which are to be consigned to His Royal Highness our late President; and other gentlemen are also engaged in the same work. This spirit induces me to insert in the present communication that part of the letter from Baron Humboldt which I received as an answer to my inquiry of how they were best to be conveyed across the Atlantic. He says, "The Gymnotus, which is common in the Llanos de Caracas (near Calabozo), in all the small rivers which flow into the Orinoco, in English, French or Dutch Guiana, is not of difficult transportation. We lost them so soon at Paris because they were too much fatigued (by experiments) immediately after their arrival. MM. Norderling and Fahlberg retained them alive at Paris above four months. I would advise that they be transported from Surinam (from Essequibo, Demerara, Cayenne) in summer, for the Gymnotus in its native country lives in water of 25° centigrade (or 77° Fahr.). Some are five feet in height, but I would advise that such as are about twenty-seven or twenty-eight inches in length be chosen. Their power varies with their food, and their state of rest. Having but a small stomach they eat little and often, their food being cooked meat, *not salted*, small fish, or even bread. Trial should be made of their strength and the fit kind of nourishment before they are shipped, and those fish only selected already accustomed to their prison. I retained them in a box or trough about four feet long, and sixteen inches wide and deep. The water must be *fresh*, and be changed every three or four days: the fish must not be prevented from coming to the surface, for they like to swallow air. A net should be put over and round the trough, for the Gymnotus often springs out of the water. These are all the directions that I can give you. It is, however, *important* that the animal should not be tormented or fatigued, for it becomes exhausted by frequent electric explosions. Several Gymnoti may be retained in the same trough."

1754. A Gymnotus has lately been brought to this country by Mr. Porter, and purchased by the proprietors of the Gallery in Adelaide Street: they immediately most liberally offered me the liberty of experimenting with the fish for scientific purposes; they placed it for the time exclusively at my disposal, that (in accordance with Humboldt's directions (1753.)) its powers might not be impaired; only desiring me to have a regard for its life and health.   I was not slow to take advantage of their wish to forward the interests of science, and with many thanks accepted their offer.   With this Gymnotus, having the kind assistance of Mr. Bradley of the Gallery, Mr. Gassiot, and occasionally other gentlemen, as Professors Daniell, Owen and Wheatstone, I have obtained every proof of the identity of its power with common electricity (265. 351, &c.).  All of these had been obtained before with the Torpedo (1750.), and some, as the shock, circuit, and spark (1751.), with the Gymnotus; but still I think a brief account of the results will be acceptable to the Royal Society, and I give them as necessary preliminary experiments to the investigations which we may hope to institute when the expected supply of animals arrives (1752.).

1755. The fish is forty inches long.   It was caught about March 1838; was brought to the Gallery on the 15th of August, but did not feed from the time of its capture up to the 19th of October.  From the 24th of August Mr. Bradley nightly put some blood into the water, which was changed for fresh water next morning, and in this way the animal perhaps obtained some nourishment.   On the 19th of October it killed and eat four small fish; since then the blood has been discontinued, and the animal has been improving ever since, consuming upon an average one fish daily[1].

1756. I first experimented with it on the 3rd of September, when it was apparently languid, but gave strong shocks when the hands were favourably disposed on the body (1760. 1773, &c.). The experiments were made on four different days, allowing periods of rest from a month to a week between each.   His health seemed to improve continually, and it was during this period, between the third and fourth days of experiment, that he began to eat.

1757. Beside the hands two kinds of collectors were used. The one sort consisted each of a copper rod fifteen inches long, having a copper disc one inch and a half in diameter brazed to

---

[1] The fish eaten were gudgeons, carp, and perch.

one extremity, and a copper cylinder to serve as a handle, with large contact to the hand, fixed to the other, the rod from the disc upwards being well covered with a thick caoutchouc tube to insulate that part from the water. By these the states of particular parts of the fish whilst in the water could be ascertained.

1758. The other kind of collectors were intended to meet the difficulty presented by the complete immersion of the fish in water ; for even when obtaining the spark itself I did not think myself justified in asking for the removal of the animal into air. A plate of copper eight inches long by two inches and a half wide, was bent into a saddle shape, that it might pass over the fish, and inclose a certain extent of the back and sides, and a thick copper wire was brazed to it, to convey the electric force to the experimental apparatus ; a jacket of sheet caoutchouc was put over the saddle, the edges projecting at the bottom and the ends ; the ends were made to converge so as to fit in some degree the body of the fish, and the bottom edges were made to spring against any horizontal surface on which the saddles were placed. The part of the wire liable to be in the water was covered with caoutchouc.

1759. These conductors being put over the fish, collected power sufficient to produce many electric effects ; but when, as in obtaining the spark, every possible advantage was needful, then glass plates were placed at the bottom of the water, and the fish being over them, the conductors were put over it until the lower caoutchouc edges rested on the glass, so that the part of the animal within the caoutchouc was thus almost as well insulated as if the Gymnotus had been in the air.

1760. *Shock.*—The shock of this animal was very powerful when the hands were placed in a favourable position, i. e. one on the body near the head, and the other near the tail; the nearer the hands were together within certain limits the less powerful was the shock. The disc conductors (1757.) conveyed the shock very well when the hands were wetted and applied in close contact with the cylindrical handles ; but scarcely at all if the handles were held in the dry hands in an ordinary way.

1761. *Galvanometer.*—Using the saddle conductors (1758.) applied to the anterior and posterior parts of the Gymnotus, a galvanometer was readily affected. It was not particularly delicate; for zinc and platina plates on the upper and lower surface of the tongue did not cause a permanent deflection of more than 25°; yet when the fish gave a powerful discharge the deflection was as much as 30°, and in one case even 40°. The deflection was constantly in a given direction, the electric current being always from the anterior parts of the animal through the galvanometer wire to the posterior parts. The former were therefore for the time externally positive, and the latter negative.

1762. *Making a magnet.*—When a little helix containing twenty-two feet of silked wire wound on a quill was put into the circuit, and an annealed steel needle placed in the helix, the needle became a magnet, and the direction of its polarity in every case indicated a current from the anterior to the posterior parts of the Gymnotus through the conductors used.

1763. *Chemical decomposition.*—Polar decomposition of a solution of iodide of potassium was easily obtained. Three or four folds of paper moistened in the solution (322.) were placed between a platina plate and the end of a wire also of platina, these being respectively connected with the two saddle conductors (1758.). Whenever the wire was in conjunction with the conductor at the fore part of the Gymnotus, iodine appeared at its extremity; but when connected with the other conductor, none was evolved at the place on the paper where it before appeared. So that here again the direction of the current proved to be the same as that given by the former tests.

1764. By this test I compared the middle part of the fish with other portions before and behind it, and found that the conductor A, which being applied to the middle was negative to the conductor B applied to the anterior parts, was, on the contrary, positive to it when B was applied to places near the tail. So that within certain limits the condition of the fish externally at the time of the shock appears to be such, that any given part is negative to other parts anterior to it, and positive to such as are behind it.

1765. *Evolution of heat.*—Using a Harris's thermo-electrometer belonging to Mr. Gassiot, we thought we were able in one case, namely, that when the deflection of the galvanometer was

40° (1761.), to observe a feeble elevation of temperature. I was not observing the instrument myself, and one of those who at first believed they saw the effect now doubts the result[1].

1766. *Spark.*—The electric spark was obtained thus. A good magneto-electric coil, with a core of soft iron wire, had one extremity made fast to the end of one of the saddle collectors (1758.), and the other fixed to a new steel file; another file was made fast to the end of the other collector. One person then rubbed the point of one of these files over the face of the other, whilst another person put the collectors over the fish, and endeavoured to excite it to action. By the friction of the files contact was made and broken very frequently; and the object was to catch the moment of the current through the wire and helix, and by breaking contact *during the current* to make the electricity sensible as a spark.

1767. The spark was obtained four times, and nearly all who were present saw it. That it was not due to the mere attrition of the two piles was shown by its not occurring when the files were rubbed together, independently of the animal. Since then I have substituted for the lower file a revolving steel plate, cut file fashion on its face, and for the upper file wires of iron, copper and silver, with all of which the spark was obtained[2].

1768. Such were the general electric phenomena obtained from this Gymnotus whilst living and active in his native element. On several occasions many of them were obtained together; thus a magnet was made, the galvanometer deflected, and perhaps a wire heated, by one single discharge of the electric force of the animal.

1769. I think a few further but brief details of experiments relating to the quantity and disposition of the electricity in and about this wonderful animal will not be out of place in this short account of its powers.

1770. When the shock is strong, it is like that of a large

[1] In more recent experiments of the same kind we could not obtain the effect.

[2] At a later meeting, at which attempts were made to cause the attraction of gold leaves, the spark was obtained directly between fixed surfaces, the inductive coil (1766.) being removed, and only short wires (by comparison) employed.

Leyden battery charged to a low degree, or that of a good
voltaic battery of perhaps one hundred or more pair of plates,
of which the circuit is completed for a moment only.  I endeavoured to form some idea of the *quantity* of electricity by connecting a large Leyden battery (291.) with two brass balls,
above three inches in diameter, placed seven inches apart in a
tub of water, so that they might represent the parts of the
Gymnotus to which the collectors had been applied; but to
lower the intensity of the discharge, eight inches in length of
six-fold thick wetted string were interposed elsewhere in the
circuit, this being found necessary to prevent the easy occurrence of the spark at the ends of the collectors (1758.), when
they were applied in the water near to the balls, as they had
been before to the fish.  Being thus arranged, when the battery
was strongly charged and discharged, and the hands put into
the water near the balls, a shock was felt, much resembling
that from the fish; and though the experiments have no pre-
tension to accuracy, yet as the tension could be in some degree
imitated by reference to the more or less ready production of a
spark, and after that the shock be used to indicate whether the
quantity was about the same, I think we may conclude that a
single medium discharge of the fish is at least equal to the
electricity of a Leyden battery of fifteen jars, containing 3500
square inches of glass coated on both sides, charged to its
highest degree (291.).   This conclusion respecting the great
quantity of electricity in a single Gymnotus shock, is in perfect
accordance with the degree of deflection which it can produce
in a galvanometer needle (367. 860. 1761.), and also with the
amount of chemical decomposition produced (374. 860. 1763.)
in the electrolyzing experiments.

1771. Great as is the force in a single discharge, the Gymnotus, as Humboldt describes, and as I have frequently experienced, gives a double and even a triple shock; and this capability of immediately repeating the effect with scarcely a
sensible interval of time, is very important in the considerations
which must arise hereafter respecting the origin and excitement of the power in the animal.  Walsh, Humboldt, Gay-
Lussac, and Matteucci have remarked the same thing of the
Torpedo, but in a far more striking degree.

1772. As, at the moment when the fish wills the shock, the

anterior parts are positive and the posterior parts negative, it may be concluded that there is a current from the former to the latter through every part of the water which surrounds the animal, to a considerable distance from its body. The shock which is felt, therefore, when the hands are in the most favourable position, is the effect of a very small portion only of the electricity which the animal discharges at the moment, by far the largest portion passing through the surrounding water. This enormous external current must be accompanied by some effect within the fish *equivalent* to a current, the direction of which is from the tail towards the head, and equal to the sum of *all these external forces*. Whether the process of evolving or exciting the electricity within the fish includes the production of this internal current (which need not of necessity be as quick and momentary as the external one), we cannot at present say; but at the time of the shock the animal does not apparently feel the electric sensation which he causes in those around him.

1773. By the help of the accompanying diagram I will state a few experimental results which illustrate the current around the fish, and show the cause of the difference in character of the shock occasioned by the various ways in which the person is connected with the animal, or his position altered with respect to it. The large circle represents the tub in which the animal is confined; its diameter is forty-six inches, and the depth of water in it three inches and a half; it is supported on dry wooden legs. The figures represent the places where the hands or the disc conductors (1757.) were applied, and where they are close to the figure of the animal, it implies that contact with the fish was made. I will designate different persons by A, B, C, &c., A being the person who excited the fish to action.

1774. When one hand was in the water the shock was felt in that hand only, whatever part of the fish it was applied to; it was not very strong, and was only in the part immersed in the water. When the hand and part of the arm was in, the shock was felt in all the parts immersed.

1775. When *both* hands were in the water at the *same* part of the fish, still the shock was comparatively weak, and only in the parts immersed. If the hands were on opposite sides, as at 1, 2, or at 3, 4, or 5, 6, or if one was above and the other below at the same part, the effect was the same. When the disc collectors were used in these positions no effect was felt by the

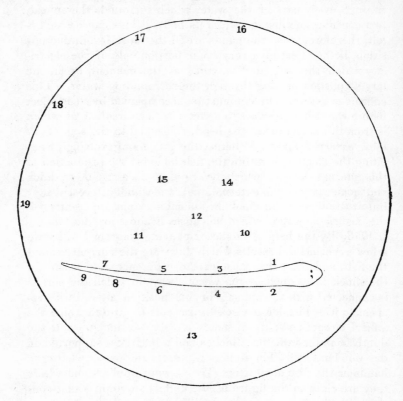

person holding them (and this corresponds with the observation of Gay-Lussac on Torpedos[1]), whilst other persons, with both hands in at a distance from the fish, felt considerable shocks.

1776. When both hands or the disc collectors were applied at places separated by a part of the length of the animal, as at 1, 3, or 4, 6, or 3, 6, then strong shocks extending up the arms, and even to the breast of the experimenter, occurred, though another person with a single hand in at any of these places, felt comparatively little. The shock could be obtained at parts very near

[1] Annales de Chimie, xiv. p. 18.

the tail, as at 8, 9. I think it was strongest at about 1 and 8. As the hands were brought nearer together the effect diminished, until being in the same cross plane, it was, as before described, only sensible in the parts immersed (1775.).

1777. B placed his hands at 10, 11, at least four inches from the fish, whilst A touched the animal with a glass rod to excite it to action; B quickly received a powerful shock. In another experiment of a similar kind, as respects the non-necessity of touching the fish, several persons received shocks independently of each other; thus A was at 4, 6; B at 10, 11; C at 16, 17; and D at 18, 19; all were shocked at once, A and B very strongly, C and D feebly. It is very useful, whilst experimenting with the galvanometer or other instrumental arrangements, for one person to keep his hands in the water at a moderate distance from the animal, that he may know and give information when a discharge has taken place.

1778. When B had both hands at 10, 11, or at 14, 15, whilst A had but one hand at 1, or 3, or 6, the former felt a strong shock, whilst the latter had but a weak one, though in contact with the fish. Or if A had both hands in at 1, 2, or 3, 4, or 5, 6, the effect was the same.

1779. If A had the hands at 3, 5, B at 14, 15, and C at 16, 17, A received the most powerful shock, B the next powerful, and C the feeblest.

1780. When A excited the Gymnotus by his hands at 8, 9, whilst B was at 10, 11, the latter had a much stronger shock than the former, though the former touched and excited the animal.

1781. A excited the fish by one hand at 3, whilst B had both hands at 10, 11 (or along), and C had the hands at 12, 13 (or across); A had the pricking shock in the immersed hand only (1774.); B had a strong shock up the arms; C felt but a slight effect in the immersed parts.

1782. The experiments I have just described are of such a nature as to require many repetitions before the general results drawn from them can be considered as established; nor do I pretend to say that they are anything more than indications of the direction of the force. It is not at all impossible that the fish may have the power of throwing each of its four electric organs separately into action, and so to a certain degree direct the shock, i. e. he may have the capability of causing the electric current to emanate from one side, and at the same time bring the other side of his body into such a condition, that it shall be as a non-conductor in that direction.    But I think the appearances and results are such as to forbid the supposition, that he has any control over the direction of the currents after they have entered the fluid and substances around him.

1783. The statements also have reference to the fish when in a straight form ; if it assume a bent shape, then the lines of force around it vary in their intensity in a manner that may be anticipated theoretically.    Thus if the hands were applied at 1, 7, a feebler shock in the arms would be expected if the animal were curved with that side inwards, than if it were straight, because the distance between the parts would be diminished, and the intervening water therefore conduct more of the force. But with respect to the parts *immersed*, or to animals, as fish *in the water* between 1 and 7, they would be more powerfully, instead of less powerfully, shocked.

1784. It is evident from all the experiments, as well as from simple considerations, that all the water and all the conducting matter around the fish through which a discharge circuit can in any way be completed, is filled at the moment with circulating electric power ; and this state might be easily represented generally in a diagram by drawing the lines of inductive action (1231. 1304. 1338.) upon it : in the case of a Gymnotus, surrounded equally in all directions by water, these would resemble generally, in disposition, the magnetic curves of a magnet, having the same straight or curved shape as the animal, i. e. provided he, in such cases, employed, as may be expected, his four electric organs at once.

1785. This Gymnotus can stun and kill fish which are in very various positions to its own body ; but on one day when I saw it eat, its action seemed to me to be peculiar.    A live fish about five inches in length, caught not half a minute before, was dropped into the tub.    The Gymnotus instantly turned round in such a manner as to form a coil inclosing the fish, the latter representing a diameter across it ; a shock passed, and there in an instant was the fish struck motionless, as if by lightning, in the midst of the waters, its side floating to the light. The Gymnotus made a turn or two to look for its prey, which having found he bolted, and then went searching about for more. A second smaller fish was given him, which being hurt in the conveyance, showed but little signs of life, and this he swallowed at once, apparently without shocking it. The coiling of the Gymnotus round its prey had, in this case, every appearance of being intentional on its part, to increase the force of the shock, and the action is evidently exceedingly well suited for that purpose (1783.), being in full accordance with the well-known laws of the discharge of currents in masses of conducting matter; and though the fish may not always put this artifice in practice, it is very probable he is aware of its advantage, and may resort to it in cases of need.

1786. Living as this animal does in the midst of such a good conductor as water, the first thoughts are thoughts of surprise that it can sensibly electrify anything, but a little consideration soon makes one conscious of many points of great beauty, illustrating the wisdom of the whole arrangement. Thus the very conducting power which the water has ; that which it gives to the moistened skin of the fish or animal to be struck ; the extent of surface by which the fish and the water conducting the charge to it are in contact ; all conduce to favour and increase the shock upon the doomed animal, and are in the most perfect contrast with the inefficient state of things which would exist if the Gymnotus and the fish were surrounded by air; and at the same time that the power is one of low intensity, so that a dry skin wards it off, though a moist one conducts it (1760.) ; so is it one of great quantity (1770.), that though the surrounding water does conduct away much, enough to produce a full effect may take its course through the body of the fish that is to be caught for food, or the enemy that is to be conquered.

1787. Another remarkable result of the relation of the Gymnotus and its prey to the medium around them is, that the larger the fish to be killed or stunned, the greater will be the shock to which it is subject, though the Gymnotus may exert only an equal power ; for the large fish has passing through its body those currents of electricity, which, in the case of a smaller one, would have been conveyed harmless by the water at its sides.

1788. The Gymnotus appears to be sensible when he has

shocked an animal, being made conscious of it, probably, by the *mechanical impulse* he receives, caused by the spasms into which it is thrown.  When I touched him with my hands, he gave me shock after shock ; but when I touched him with glass rods, or the insulated conductors, he gave one or two shocks, felt by others having their hands in at a distance, but then ceased to exert the influence, as if made aware it had not the desired effect.  Again, when he has been touched with the conductors several times, for experiments on the galvanometer or other apparatus, and appears to be languid or indifferent, and not willing to give shocks, yet being touched by the hands, they, by convulsive motion, have informed him that a sensitive thing was present, and he has quickly shown his power and his willingness to astonish the experimenter.

1789. It has been remarked by Geoffroy St. Hilaire, that the electric organs of the Torpedo, Gymnotus, and similar fishes, cannot be considered as essentially connected with those which are of high and direct importance to the life of the animal, but to belong rather to the common teguments ; and it has also been found that such Torpedos as have been deprived of the use of their peculiar organs, have continued the functions of life quite as well as those in which they were allowed to remain.  These, with other considerations, lead me to look at these parts with a hope that they may upon close investigation prove to be a species of natural apparatus, by means of which we may apply the principles of *action and reaction* in the investigation of the nature of the *nervous influence*.

1790. The anatomical relation of the nervous system to the electric organ; the evident exhaustion of the nervous energy during the production of electricity in that organ; the apparently equivalent production of electricity in proportion to the quantity of nervous force consumed ; the constant direction of the current produced, with its relation to what we may believe to be an equally constant direction of the nervous energy thrown into action at the same time; all induce me to believe, that it is not impossible but that, on passing electricity per force through the organ, a reaction back upon the nervous system belonging to it might take place, and that a restoration, to a greater or smaller degree, of that which the animal expends in the act of exciting a current, might perhaps be effected. We have the analogy in relation to heat and magnetism. Seebeck taught us how to commute heat into electricity; and Peltier has more lately given us the strict converse of this, and shown us how to convert the electricity into heat, including both its relation of hot and cold. Oersted showed how we were to convert electric into magnetic forces, and I had the delight of adding the other member of the full relation, by reacting back again and converting magnetic into electric forces. So perhaps in these organs, where nature has provided the apparatus by means of which the animal can exert and convert nervous into electric force, we may be able, possessing in that point of view a power far beyond that of the fish itself, to reconvert the electric into the nervous force.

1791. This may seem to some a very wild notion, as assuming that the nervous power is in some degree analogous to such powers as heat, electricity, and magnetism. I am only assuming it, however, as a reason for making certain experiments, which, according as they give positive or negative results, will regulate further expectation. And with respect to the nature of nervous power, that exertion of it which is conveyed along the nerves to the various organs which they excite into action, is not the direct principle of *life*; and therefore I see no natural reason why we should not be allowed in certain cases to *determine* as well as observe its course. Many philosophers think the power is electricity. Priestley put forth this view in 1774 in a very striking and distinct form, both as regards ordinary animals and those which are electric, like the Torpedo[1]. Dr. Wilson Philip considers that the agent in certain nerves is electricity modified by vital action[2]. Mat-

[1] Priestley on Air, vol. i. p. 277. Edition of 1774.

[2] Dr. Wilson Philip is of opinion, that the nerves which excite the muscles and effect the chemical changes of the vital functions, operate by the electric power supplied by the brain and spinal marrow, in its effects, modified by the vital powers of the living animal; because he found, as he informs me, as early as 1815, that while the vital powers remain, all these functions can be as well performed by voltaic electricity after the removal of the nervous influence, as by that influence itself; and in the end of that year he presented a paper to the Royal Society, which was read at one of their meetings, giving an account of the experiments on which this position was founded.

teucci thinks that the nervous fluid or energy, in the nerves belonging to the electric organ at least, is electricity[1]. MM. Prevost and Dumas are of opinion that electricity moves in the nerves belonging to the muscles; and M. Prevost adduces a beautiful experiment, in which steel was magnetized, in proof of this view; which, if it should be confirmed by further observation and by other philosophers, is of the utmost consequence to the progress of this high branch of knowledge[2]. Now though I am not as yet convinced by the facts that the nervous fluid is only electricity, still I think that the agent in the nervous system may be an inorganic force; and if there be reasons for supposing that magnetism is a higher relation of force than electricity (1664. 1731. 1734.), so it may well be imagined that the nervous power may be of a still more exalted character, and yet within the reach of experiment.

1792. The kind of experiment I am bold enough to suggest is as follows. If a Gymnotus or Torpedo has been fatigued by frequent exertion of the electric organs, would the sending of currents of similar force to those he emits, or of other degrees of force, either continuously or intermittingly in the same direction as those he sends forth, restore him his powers and strength more rapidly than if he were left to his natural repose?

1793. Would sending currents through in the contrary direction exhaust the animal rapidly? There is, I think, reason to believe the Torpedo (and perhaps the Gymnotus) is not much disturbed or excited by electric currents sent only through the electric organ; so that these experiments do not appear very difficult to make.

1794. The disposition of the organs in the Torpedo suggest still further experiments on the same principle. Thus when a current is sent in the natural direction, i. e. from below upwards through the organ on one side of the fish, will it excite the organ on the other side into action? or if sent through in the contrary direction, will it produce the same or any effect on that organ? Will it do so if the nerves proceeding to the organ or organs be tied? and will it do so after the animal has been so far exhausted by previous shocks as to be unable to

[1] Bibliothèque Universelle, 1837, tom. xii. 192.
[2] Ibid, 1837, xii. 202; xiv. 200.

throw the organ into action in any, or in a similar, degree of his own will?

1795. Such are some of the experiments which the conformation and relation of the electric organs of these fishes suggest, as being rational in their performance, and promising in anticipation. Others may not think of them as I do; but I can only say for myself, that were the means in my power, they are the very first that I would make.

*Royal Institution,*
*November 9th,* 1838.

## SIXTEENTH SERIES.

§ 24. *On the source of power in the voltaic pile.* ¶ i. *Exciting electrolytes, &c. being conductors of thermo and feeble currents.* ¶ ii. *Inactive conducting circles containing an electrolytic fluid.* ¶ iii. *Active circles excited by solution of sulphuret of potassium, &c.*

Received January 23,—Read February 6, 1840.

§ 24. *On the source of power in the voltaic pile.*

1796. WHAT is the source of power in a voltaic pile? This question is at present of the utmost importance in the theory and to the development of electrical science. The opinions held respecting it are various; but by far the most important are the two which respectively find the source of power in contact, and in chemical force. The question between them touches the first principles of electrical action; for the opinions are in such contrast, that two men respectively adopting them are thenceforward constrained to differ, in every point, respecting the probable and intimate nature of the agent or force on which all the phenomena of the voltaic pile depend.

1797. The theory of contact is the theory of Volta, the great discoverer of the voltaic pile itself, and it has been sustained since his day by a host of philosophers, amongst whom, in recent times, rank such men as Pfaff, Marianini, Fechner, Zamboni, Matteucci, Karsten, Bouchardat, and as to the excitement of the power, even Davy; all bright stars in the exalted regions of science. The theory of chemical action was first advanced by Fabroni[1], Wollaston[2], and Parrot[3], and has been more or less developed since by Œrsted, Becquerel, De la Rive, Ritchie, Pouillet, Schœnbein, and many others, amongst whom Becquerel ought to be distinguished as having contri-

---

[1] A.D. 1792, 1799. Becquerel's Traité de l'Électricité, i. pp. 81—91, and Nicholson's Quarto Journal, iii. 308. iv. 120, or Journal de Physique, vi. 348.

[2] A.D. 1801. Philosophical Transactions, 1801, p. 427.

[3] A.D. 1801. Annales de Chimie, 1829, xlii. 45; 1831, xlvi. 361.

buted, from the first, a continually increasing mass of the strongest experimental evidence in proof that chemical action always evolves electricity[1]; and De la Rive should be named as most clear and constant in his views, and most zealous in his production of facts and arguments, from the year 1827 to the present time[2].

1798. Examining this question by the results of definite electro-chemical action, I felt constrained to take part with those who believed the origin of voltaic power to consist in chemical action alone (875. 965.), and ventured a paper on it in April 1834[3] (875, &c.), which obtained the especial notice of Marianini[4]. The rank of this philosopher, the observation of Fechner[5], and the consciousness that over the greater part of Italy and Germany the contact theory still prevailed, have induced me to re-examine the question most carefully. I wished not merely to escape from error, but was anxious to convince myself of the truth of the contact theory; for it was evident that if contact electromotive force had any existence, it must be a power not merely unlike every other natural power as to the phenomena it could produce, but also in the far higher points of limitation, definite force, and finite production (2065.).

1799. I venture to hope that the experimental results and arguments which have been thus gathered may be useful to science. I fear the detail will be tedious, but that is a necessary consequence of the state of the subject. The contact theory has long had possession of men's minds, is sustained by a great weight of authority, and for years had almost undisputed sway in some parts of Europe. If it be an error, it can only be rooted out by a great amount of forcible experimental evidence; a fact sufficiently clear to my mind by the circumstance, that De la Rive's papers have not already convinced the workers upon

[1] A.D. 1824, &c. Annales de Chimie, 1824, xxv. 405; 1827, xxxv. 113; 1831, xlvi. 265, 276, 337; xlvii. 113; xlix. 131.

[2] Ibid. 1828, xxxvii. 225; xxxix. 297; 1836, lxii. 147: or Mémoires de Genève, 1829, iv. 285; 1832, vi. 149; 1835, vii.

[3] Philosophical Transactions, 1834, p. 425.

[4] Memorie della Società Italiana in Modena, 1837, xxi. p. 205.

[5] Philosophical Magazine, 1838, xiii. 205; or Poggendorf's Annalen, xlii. p. 481. Fechner refers also to Pfaff's reply to my paper. I never cease to regret that the German is a sealed language to me.

this subject. Hence the reason why I have thought it needful
to add my further testimony to his and that of others, entering
into detail and multiplying facts in a proportion far beyond any
which would have been required for the proof and promulga-
tion of a new scientific truth (2017.). In so doing I may occasionally be only enlarging, yet then I hope strengthening, what
others, and especially De la Rive, have done.

1800. It will tend to clear the question, if the various views
of contact are first stated. Volta's theory is, that the simple
contact of conducting bodies causes electricity to be developed
at the point of contact without any change in nature of the
bodies themselves ; and that though such conductors as water
and aqueous fluids have this property, yet the degree in which
they possess it is unworthy of consideration in comparison with
the degree to which it rises amongst the metals[1]. The present
views of the Italian and German contact philosophers are, I
believe, generally the same, except that occasionally more importance is attached to the contact of the imperfect conductors
with the metals. Thus Zamboni (in 1837) considers the metallic
contact as the most powerful source of electricity, and not that
of the metals with the fluids[2]; but Karsten, holding the contact theory, transfers the electromotive force to the contact of
the fluids with the solid conductors[3]. Marianini holds the same
view of the principle of contact, with this addition, that actual
contact is not required to the exertion of the exciting force,
but that the two approximated dissimilar conductors may affect
each other's state, when separated by sensible intervals of the
$\frac{1}{10000}$ dth of a line and more, air intervening[4].

1801. De la Rive, on the contrary, contends for simple and
strict chemical action, and, as far as I am aware, admits of no current in the voltaic pile that is not conjoined with and dependent
upon a complete chemical effect. That admirable electrician
Becquerel, though expressing himself with great caution, seems
to admit the possibility of chemical attractions being able to

[1] Annales de Chimie, 1802, xl. p. 225.
[2] Bibliothèque Universelle, 1836, v. 387; 1837, viii. 189.
[3] L'Institut, No. 150.
[4] Mem. della Soc. Ital. in Modena, 1837, xxi. 232—237.

produce electrical currents when they are not strong enough to overcome the force of cohesion, and so terminate in combination[1]. Schœnbein states that a current may be produced by a tendency to chemical action, i. e. that substances which have a tendency to unite chemically may produce a current, though that tendency is not followed up by the actual combination of the substances[2]. In these cases the assigned force becomes the same as the contact of Volta, inasmuch as the acting matters are not altered whilst producing the current. Davy's opinion was, that contact like that of Volta excited the current or was the cause of it, but that chemical changes supplied the current. For myself I am at present of the opinion which De la Rive holds, and do not think that, in the voltaic pile, mere contact does anything in the excitation of the current, except as it is preparatory to, and ends in, complete chemical action (1741. 1745.).

1802. Thus the views of contact vary, and it may be said that they pass gradually from one to another, even to the extent of including chemical action : but the two extremes appear to me irreconcilable in principle under any shape ; they are as follows. The contact theory assumes, that when two different bodies being conductors of electricity are in contact, there is a force at the point of contact by which one of the bodies gives a part of its natural portion of electricty to the other body, which the latter takes in addition to its own natural portion ; that, though the touching points have thus respectively given and taken electricity, they cannot retain the charge which their contact has caused, but discharge their electricities to the masses respectively behind them (2067.) : that the force which, at the point of contact, induces the particles to assume a new state, cannot enable them to keep that state (2069.) : that all this happens without any permanent alteration of the parts that are in contact, and has no reference to their chemical forces (2065. 2069.).

1803. The chemical theory assumes, that at the place of action, the particles which are in contact act chemically upon

[1] Annales de Chimie, 1835, lx. 171 ; and Traité de l'Electricité, i. pp. 253, 258.
[2] Philosophical Magazine, 1838, xii. 227, 311, 314 ; also Bibliothèque Universelle, 1838, xiv. 155, 395.

each other and are able, under the circumstances, to throw
more or less of the acting force into a dynamic form (947. 996.
1120.): that in the most favourable circumstances, the whole
is converted into dynamic force (1000.): that then the amount
of current force produced is an exact equivalent of the original
chemical force employed ; and that in no case (in the voltaic
pile) can any electric current be produced, without the active
exertion and consumption of an equal amount of chemical force,
ending in a given amount of chemical change.

─────────────

1804. Marianini's paper [1] was to me a great motive for re-
examining the subject ; but the course I have taken was not so
much for the purpose of answering particular objections, as for
the procuring evidence, whether relating to controverted points
or not, which should be satisfactory to my own mind, open to
receive either one theory or the other.   This paper, therefore,
is not controversial, but contains further facts and proofs of the
truth of De la Rive's views.   The cases Marianini puts are of
extreme interest, and all his objections must, one day, be answered, when numerical results, both as to intensity and
quantity of force, are obtained ; but they are all debateable,
and, to my mind, depend upon variations of quantity which do
not affect seriously the general question.   Thus, when that
philosopher quotes the numerical results obtained by considering two metals with fluids at their opposite extremities which
tend to form counter currents, the difference which he puts
down to the effect of metallic contact, either made or interrupted, I think accountable for, on the facts partly known
respecting opposed currents ; and with me differences quite
as great, and greater, have arisen, and are given in former
papers (1046.), when metallic contacts were in the circuit.   So
at page 213 of his memoir, I cannot admit that $e$ should give
an effect equal to the difference of $b$ and $d$ ; for in $b$ and $d$ the
opposition presented to the excited currents is merely that of
a bad conductor, but in the case of $e$ the opposition arises from
the power of an opposed acting source of a current.

1805. As to the part of his memoir respecting the action of

─────────────

[1] Memorie della Società Italiana in Modena, 1827, xxi. p. 205.

sulphuretted solutions[1], I hope to be allowed to refer to the investigations made further on. I do not find, as the Italian philosopher, that iron with gold or platina, in solution of the sulphuret of potassa, is positive to them[2], but, on the contrary, powerfully negative, and for reasons given in the sequel (2049.).

1806. With respect to the discussion of the cause of the spark before contact[3], Marianini admits the spark, but I give it up altogether. Jacobi's paper[4] convinces me I was in error as to *that proof* of the existence of a state of tension in the metals before contact (915. 956.). I need not therefore do more at present than withdraw my own observations.

1807. I now proceed to address myself to the general argument, rather than to particular controversy, or to the discussion of cases feeble in power and doubtful in nature ; for I have been impressed from the first with the feeling that it is no weak influence or feeble phenomenon that we have to account for, but such as indicates a force of extreme power, requiring, therefore, that the cause assigned should bear some proportion, both in intensity and quantity, to the effects produced.

1808. The investigations have all been made by aid of currents and the galvanometer, for it seemed that such an instrument and such a course were best suited to an examination of the electricity of the voltaic pile. The electrometer is no doubt a most important instrument, but the philosophers who do use it are not of accord in respect to the safety and delicacy of its results. And even if the few indications as yet given by the electrometer be accepted as correct, they are far too general to settle the question of, whether contact or chemical action is the exciting force in the voltaic battery. To apply that instrument closely and render it of any force in supplying affirmative arguments to either theory, it would be necessary to construct a table of contacts, or the effects of contacts, of the different metals and fluids concerned in the construction of the voltaic pile, taken in pairs (1868.), expressing in such table both the *direction* and the *amount* of the contact force.

1809. It is assumed by the supporters of the contact theory,

---

[1] Memorie della Società Italiana in Modena, 1827, xxi. p. 217.
[2] Ibid. p. 217.                     [3] Ibid. p. 225.
[4] Philosophical Magazine, 1838, xiii. 401.

that though the metals exert strong electromotive forces at their points of contact with each other, yet these are so balanced in a metallic circuit that no current is ever produced whatever their arrangement may be. So in Plate III. fig. 1. if the contact force of copper and zinc is 10 ——>, and a third metal be introduced at *m*, the effect of its contacts, whatever that metal may be, with the zinc and copper at *b* and *c*, will be an amount of force in the opposite direction = 10. Thus, if it were potassium, its contact force at *b* might be 5 ——> , but then its contact force at *c* would be <—— 15 : or if it were gold, its contact force at *b* might be <—— 19, but then its contact force at *c* would be 9 ——>. This is a very large assumption, and that the theory may agree with the facts is necessary : still it is, I believe, only an assumption, for I am not aware of any data, independent of the theory in question, which prove its truth.

1810. On the other hand, it is assumed that fluid conductors, and such bodies as contain water, or, in a word, those which I have called electrolytes (664. 823. 921.), either exert no contact force at their place of contact with the metals, or if they do exert such a power, then it is with this most important difference, that the forces are not subject to the same law of compensation or neutralization in the complete circuit, as holds with the metals (1809.). But this, I think I am justified in saying, is an assumption also, for it is supported not by any independent measurement or facts (1808.), but only by the theory which it is itself intended to support.

1811. Guided by this opinion, and with a view to ascertain what is, in an active circle, effected by contact and what by chemical action, I endeavoured to find some bodies in this latter class (1810.) which should be without chemical action on the metals employed, so as to exclude that cause of a current, and yet such good conductors of electricity as to show any currents due to the contact of these metals with each other or with the fluid : concluding that any electrolyte which would conduct the thermo current of a single pair of bismuth and antimony plates would serve the required purpose, I sought for such, and fortunately soon found them.

¶ i. *Exciting electrolytes, &c., being conductors of thermo
and feeble currents.*

1812. *Sulphuret of potassium.*—This substance and its solution were prepared as follows. Equal weights of caustic potash (potassa fusa) and sulphur were mixed with and heated
gradually in a Florence flask, till the whole had fused and
united, and the sulphur in excess began to sublime. It was
then cooled and dissolved in water, so as to form a strong solution, which by standing became quite clear.

1813. A portion of this solution was included in a circuit
containing a galvanometer and a pair of antimony and bismuth
plates; the connexion with the electrolyte was made by two
platinum plates, each about two inches long and half an inch
wide: nearly the whole of each was immersed, and they were
about half an inch apart. When the circuit was completed,
and all at the same temperature, there was no current; but the
moment the junction of the antimony and bismuth was either
heated or cooled, the corresponding thermo current was produced, causing the galvanometer-needle to be permanently deflected, occasionally as much as 80°. Even the small difference
of temperature occasioned by touching the Seebeck element
with the finger, produced a very sensible current through the
electrolyte. When in place of the antimony-bismuth combination mere wires of *copper and platinum,* or *iron and platinum*
were used, the application of the spirit-lamp to the junction of
these metals produced a thermo current which instantly travelled round the circuit.

1814. Thus this electrolyte will, as to high conducting power,
fully answer the condition required (1811.). It is so excellent
in this respect, that I was able to send the thermo current of a
single Seebeck's element across five successive portions connected with each other by platinum plates.

1815. *Nitrous acid.*—Yellow anhydrous nitrous acid, made
by distilling dry nitrate of lead, being put into a glass tube and
included in a circuit with the antimony-bismuth arrangement
and the galvanometer, gave no indication of the passage of the
thermo current, though the immersed electrodes consisted each
of about four inches in length of moderately thick platinum
wire, and were not above a quarter of an inch apart.

1816. A portion of this acid was mixed with nearly its volume of pure water; the resulting action caused depression of
temperature, the evolution of some nitrous gas, the formation
of some nitric acid, and a dark green fluid was produced. This
was now such an excellent conductor of electricity, that almost
the feeblest current could pass it. That produced by Seebeck's
circle was sensible when only one-eighth of an inch in length
of the platinum wires dipped in the acid. When a couple of
inches of each electrode was in the fluid, the conduction was
so good, that it made very little difference at the galvanometer
whether the platinum wires touched each other in the fluid, or
were a quarter of an inch apart [1].

1817. *Nitric acid.*—Some pure nitric acid was boiled to
drive off all the nitrous acid, and then cooled. Being included
in the circuit by platinum plates (1813.), it was found to conduct so badly that the effect of the antimony-bismuth pair,
when the difference of temperature was at the greatest, was
scarcely perceptible at the galvanometer.

1818. On using a pale yellow acid, otherwise pure, it was
found to possess rather more conducting power than the former.
On employing a red nitric acid, it was found to conduct the
thermo current very well. On adding some of the green nitrous acid (1816.) to the colourless nitric acid, the mixture acquired high conducting powers. Hence it is evident that nitric
acid is not a good conductor when pure, but that the presence
of nitrous acid in it (conjointly probably with water), gives it
this power in a very high degree amongst electrolytes [2]. A
very red strong nitric acid, and a weak green acid, (consisting
of one vol. strong nitric acid and two vols. of water, which had
been rendered green by the action of the negative platinum
electrode of a voltaic battery,) were both such excellent conductors that the thermo current could pass across five separate
portions of them connected by platinum plates, with so little
retardation, that I believe twenty interruptions would not have
stopped this feeble current.

[1] De la Rive has pointed out the facility with which an electric current passes
between platinum and nitrous acid.   Annales de Chimie, 1828, xxxvii. 278.
[2] Schœnbein's experiments on a compound of nitric and nitrous acids will
probably bear upon and illustrate this subject.   Bibliothèque Universelle, 1817,
x. 406.

1819. *Sulphuric acid.*—Strong oil of vitriol, when between platinum electrodes (1813.), conducted the antimony-bismuth thermo current sensibly, but feebly. A mixture of two volumes acid and one volume water conducted much better, but not nearly so well as the two former electrolytes (1814. 1816.). A mixture of one volume of oil of vitriol and two volumes saturated solution of sulphate of copper conducted this feeble current very fairly.

*Potassa.*—A strong solution of caustic potassa, between platinum plates, conducted the thermo current sensibly, but very feebly.

1820. I will take the liberty of describing here, as the most convenient place, other results relating to the conducting power of bodies, which will be required hereafter in these investigations. Galena, yellow sulphuret of iron, arsenical pyrites, native sulphuret of copper and iron, native gray artificial sulphuret of copper, sulphurets of bismuth, iron, and copper, globules of oxide of burnt iron, oxide of iron by heat or scale oxide, conducted the thermo current very well. Native peroxide of manganese and peroxide of lead conducted it moderately well.

1821. The following are bodies, in some respect analogous in nature and composition, which did not sensibly conduct this weak current when the contact surfaces were small :—artificial gray sulphuret of tin, blende, cinnabar, hæmatite, Elba iron-ore, native magnetic oxide of iron, native peroxide of tin or tinstone, wolfram, fused and cooled protoxide of copper, peroxide of mercury.

1822. Some of the foregoing substances are very remarkable in their conducting power. This is the case with the solution of sulphuret of potassium (1813.) and the nitrous acid (1816.), for the great amount of this power. The peroxide of manganese and lead are still more remarkable for possessing this power, because the *protoxides* of these metals do not conduct either the feeble thermo current or a far more powerful one from a voltaic battery. This circumstance made me especially anxious to verify the point with the peroxide of lead. I therefore prepared some from red-lead by the action of successive portions of nitric acid, then boiled the brown oxide, so obtained, in several portions of distilled water, for days together, until every trace of nitric acid and nitrate of lead had been removed; after which it was well and perfectly dried. Still, when a heap of it in powder, and consequently in very imperfect contact throughout its own mass, was pressed between two plates of platinum and so brought into the thermo-electric circuit (1813.), the current was found to pass readily.

¶ ii. *Inactive conducting circles containing a fluid or electrolyte.*

1823. De la Rive has already quoted the case of potash, iron and platina[1], to show that where there was no chemical action there was no current. My object is to increase the number of such cases; to use other fluids than potash, and such as have good conducting power for weak currents; to use also strong and weak solutions; and thus to accumulate the conjoint experimental and argumentative evidence by which the great question must finally be decided.

1824. I first used the sulphuret of potassium as an electrolyte of good conducting power, but chemically inactive (1811.) when associated with iron and platinum in a circuit. The arrangement is given in fig. 2, where D, E represent two testglasses containing the strong solution of sulphuret of potassium (1812.); and also four metallic plates, about 0·5 of an inch wide and two inches long in the immersed part, of which the three marked P, P, P were platinum, and that marked I, of clean iron: these were connected by iron and platinum wires, as in fig. 2, a galvanometer being introduced at G. In this arrangement there were three metallic contacts of platinum and iron, *a b* and *x*: the first two, being opposed to each other, may be considered as neutralizing each other's forces; but the third, being unopposed by any other metallic contact, can be compared with either the difference of *a* and *b* when one is warmer than the other, or with itself when in a heated or cooled state (1830.), or with the force of chemical action when any body capable of such action is introduced there (1831.).

1825. When this arrangement is completed and in order, there is absolutely no current circulating through it, and the galvanometer-needle rests at 0°; yet is the whole circuit open

[1] Philosophical Magazine, 1837, xi. 275.

to a very feeble current, for a difference of temperature at any one of the junctions *a*, *b*, or *x*, causes a corresponding thermo current, which is instantly detected by the galvanometer, the needle standing permanently at 30° or 40°, or even 50°.

1826. But to obtain this proper and normal state, it is necessary that certain precautions be attended to. In the first place, if the circuit be complete in every part except for the immersion of the iron and platinum plates into the cup D, then, upon their introduction, a current will be produced directed from the platinum (which appears to be positive) through the solution to the iron; this will continue perhaps five or ten minutes, or if the iron has been carelessly cleaned, for several hours; it is due to an action of the sulphuretted solution on *oxide of iron*, and not to any effect on the metallic iron; and when it has ceased, the disturbing cause may be considered as exhausted. The experimental proofs of the truth of this explanation, I will quote hereafter (2049.).

1827. Another precaution relates to the effect of accidental movements of the plates in the solution. If two platinum plates be put into a solution of this sulphuret of potassium, and the circuit be then completed, including a galvanometer, the arrangement, if perfect, will show no current; but if one of the plates be lifted up into the air for a few seconds and then replaced, it will be negative to the other, and produce a current lasting for a short time [1]. If the two plates be iron and platinum, or of any other metal or substance not acted on by the sulphuret, the same effect will be produced. In these cases, the current is due to the change wrought by the air on the film of sulphuretted solution adhering to the removed plate [2]; but a far less cause than this will produce a current, for if one of the platinum plates be removed, washed well, dried, and even heated, it will, on its re-introduction, almost certainly exhibit the negative state for a second or two.

1828. These or other disturbing causes appear the greater in these experiments in consequence of the excellent conduct-

[1] Marianini observed effects of this kind produced by exposure to the air, of one of two plates dipped in nitric acid. Annales de Chimie, 1830, xlv. p. 42.

[2] Becquerel long since referred to the effect of such exposure of a plate, dipped in certain solutions, to the air. Generally the plate so exposed became positive on re-immersion. Annales de Chimie, 1824, xxv. 405.

ing power of the solution used; but they do not occur if care
be taken to avoid any disturbance of the plates or the solution,
and then, as before said, the whole acquires a normal and perfectly inactive state.

1829. Here then is an arrangement in which the contact of
platinum and iron at *x* is at liberty to produce any effect which
such a contact may have the power of producing; and yet what
is the consequence? absolutely nothing. This is not because
the electrolyte is so bad a conductor that a current of contact
cannot pass, for currents far feebler than this is assumed to be,
pass readily (1813.); and the electrolyte employed is vastly
superior in conducting power to those which are commonly
used in voltaic batteries or circles, in which the current is still
assumed to be dependent upon contact. The simple conclusion to which the experiment should lead is, in my opinion,
that the contact of iron and platinum is absolutely without any
electromotive force (1835. 1859. 1889.).

1830. If the contact be made really active and effective,
according to the beautiful discovery of Seebeck, by making its
temperature different to that of the other parts of the circuit,
then its power of generating a current is shown (1824.). This
enables us to compare the supposed power of the mere contact
with that of a thermo contact; and we find that the latter
comes out as infinitely greater than the former, for the former
is nothing. The same comparison of mere contact and thermo
contact may be made by contrasting the effect of the contact *c*
at common temperatures, with either the contact at *a* or at *b*,
either heated or cooled. Very moderate changes of temperature at these places produce instantly the corresponding current, but the mere contact at *x* does nothing.

1831. So also I believe that a true and philosophic and even
rigid comparison may be made at *x*, between the assumed effect
of mere contact and that of chemical action. For if the metals
at *x* be separated, and a piece of paper moistened in dilute
acid, or a solution of salt, or if only the tongue or a wet finger
be applied there, then a current is caused, stronger by far than
the thermo currents before produced (1830.), passing from the
iron through the introduced acid or other active fluid to the
platinum. This is a case of current from chemical action without any metallic contact in the circuit on which the effect

can for a moment be supposed to depend (879.); it is even a
case where metallic contact is changed for chemical action,
with the result, that where contact is found to be quite ineffectual, chemical action is very energetic in producing a current.

1832. It is of course quite unnecessary to say that the same
experimental comparisons may be made at either of the other
contacts, *a* or *b*.

1833. Admitting for the moment that the arrangement proves
that the contact of platinum and iron at *x* has no electromotive force (1835. 1859.), then it follows also that the contact
of either platinum or iron with any other metal has no such
force. For if another metal, as zinc, be interposed between
the iron and platinum at *x*, fig 2, no current is produced; and
yet the test application of a little heat at *a* or *b*, will show by
the corresponding current, that the circuit being complete will
conduct any current that may tend to pass. Now that the
contacts of zinc with iron and with platinum are of equal electromotive force, is not for a moment admitted by those who
support the theory of contact activity; we ought therefore to
have a resulting action equal to the differences of the two
forces, producing a certain current. No such current is produced, and I conceive, with the admission above, that such a
result proves that the contacts *iron-zinc* and *platinum-zinc* are
entirely without electromotive force.

1834. Gold, silver, potassium, and copper were introduced
at *x* with the like negative effect; and so no doubt might every
other metal, even according to the relation admitted amongst
the metals by the supporters of the contact theory (1809.).
The same negative result followed upon the introduction of
many other conducting bodies at the same place; as, for instance, those already mentioned as easily conducting the thermo
current (1820.); and the effect proves, I think, that the contact of any of these with either iron or platinum is utterly ineffective as a source of electromotive force.

1835. The only answer which, as it appears to me, the contact theory can set up in opposition to the foregoing facts and
conclusions is, to say that the solution of sulphuret of potassium
in the cup D, fig. 2, acts as a metal would do (1809.), and so
the effects of all the contacts in the circuit are exactly balanced.

I will not stop at this moment to show that the departure with respect to electrolytes, or the fluid bodies in the voltaic pile, *from the law* which is supposed to hold good with the metals and solid conductors, though only an assumption, is still essential to the contact theory of the voltaic pile (1810. 1861.)[1]; nor to prove that the electrolyte is no otherwise like the metals than in having no contact electromotive force whatever. But believing that this will be very evident shortly, I will go on with the experimental results, and resume these points hereafter (1859. 1889.).

1836. The experiment was now repeated with the substitution of a bar of *nickel* for that of iron, fig. 2 (1824.), all other things remaining the same[2]. The circuit was again found to be a good conductor of a feeble thermo current, but utterly inefficient as a voltaic circuit when all was at the same temperature, and due precautions taken (2051.). The introduction of metals at the contact $x$ was as ineffective as before (1834.); the introduction of chemical action at $x$ was as striking in its influence as in the former case (1831.); all the results were, in fact, parallel to those already obtained; and if the reasoning then urged was good, it will now follow that the contact of platinum and nickel with each other, or of either with any of the different metals or solid conductors introduced at $x$, is entirely without electromotive force[3].

1837. Many other pairs of metals were compared together in the same manner; the solution of sulphuret of potassium connecting them together at one place, and their mutual contact

[1] See Fechner's words. Philosophical Magazine, 1838, xiii. 377.

[2] There is another form of this experiment which I sometimes adopted, in which the cup E, fig. 2, with its contents, was dismissed, and the platinum plates in it connected together. The arrangement may then be considered as presenting three contacts of iron and platinum, two acting in one direction, and one in the other. The arrangement and the results are virtually the same as those already given. A still simpler but equally conclusive arrangement for many of the arguments, is to dismiss the iron between $a$ and $b$ altogether, and so have but one contact, that at $x$, to consider.

[3] One specimen of nickel was, on its immersion, positive to platinum for seven or eight minutes, and then became neutral. On taking it out it seemed to have a yellowish tint on it, as if invested by a coat of sulphuret; and I suspected this piece had acted like lead (1885.) and bismuth (1895.). It is difficult to get pure and also perfectly compact nickel; and if porous, then the matter retained in the pores produces currents.

doing that office at another. The following are cases of this kind : iron and gold ; iron and palladium ; nickel and gold ; nickel and palladium ; platina and gold ; platina and palladium. In all these cases the results were the same as those already given with the combinations of platinum and iron.

1838. It is necessary that due precaution be taken to have the arrangements in an unexceptionable state. It often happened that the first immersion of the plates gave deflections ; it is, in fact, almost impossible to put two plates of the *same metal* into the solution without causing a deflection ; but this generally goes off very quickly, and then the arrangement may be used for the investigation (1826.). Sometimes there is a feeble but rather permanent deflection of the needle ; thus when platinum and palladium were the metals, the first effect fell and left a current able to deflect the galvanometer-needle 3°, indicating the platinum to be positive to the palladium. This effect of 3°, however, is almost nothing compared to what a mere thermo current can cause, the latter producing a deflection of 60° or more ; besides which, even supposing it an essential effect of the arrangement, it is in the wrong direction for the contact theory. I rather incline to refer it to that power which platinum and other substances have of effecting combination and decomposition without themselves entering into union ; and I have occasionally found that when a platinum plate has been left for some hours in a strong solution of sulphuret of potassium (1812.) a small quantity of sulphur has been deposited upon it. Whatever the cause of the final feeble current may be, the effect is too small to be of any service in support of the contact theory ; while, on the other hand, it affords delicate, and, therefore, strong indications in favour of the chemical theory.

1839. A change was made in the form and arrangement of the cup D, fig. 2, so as to allow of experiments with other bodies than the metals. The solution of sulphuret of potassium was placed in a shallow vessel, the platinum plate was bent so that the immersed extremity corresponded to the bottom of the vessel ; on this a piece of loosely folded cloth was laid in the solution, and on that again the mineral or other substance to be compared with the platinum ; the fluid being of such depth that only part of that substance was in it, the rest being clean and dry ; on this portion the platinum wire, which completed the circuit, rested. The arrangement of this part of the circuit is given in section at fig. 3, where H represents a piece of galena to be compared with the platinum P.

1840. In this way galena, compact yellow copper pyrites, yellow iron pyrites, and globules of oxide of burnt iron, were compared with platinum, (the solution of sulphuret of potassium being the electrolyte used in the circuit,) and with the same results as were before obtained with metals (1829. 1833.).

1841. Experiments hereafter to be described gave arrangements in which, with the same electrolyte, sulphuret of lead was compared with gold, palladium, iron, nickel, and bismuth (1885. 1886.); also sulphuret of bismuth with platinum, gold, palladium, iron, nickel, lead, and sulphuret of lead (1894.), and always with the same result. Where no chemical action occurred there no current was formed; although the circuit remained an excellent conductor, and the contact existed by which, it is assumed in the contact theory, such a current should be produced.

1842. Instead of the strong solution, a dilute solution of the yellow sulphuret of potassium, consisting of one volume of strong solution (1812.) and ten volumes of water, was used. Plates of platinum and iron were arranged in this fluid as before (1824.): at first the iron was negative (2049.), but in ten minutes it was neutral, and the needle at $0°$[1]. Then a weak chemical current excited at $x$ (1831.) easily passed: and even a thermo current (1830.) was able to show its effects at the needle. Thus a strong or a weak solution of this electrolyte showed the same phenomena. By diluting the solution still further, a fluid could be obtained in which the iron was, after the first effect, permanently but feebly positive. On allowing time, however, it was found that in all such cases black sulphuret formed here and there on the iron. Rusted iron was negative to platinum (2049.) in this very weak solution, which by direct chemical action could render metallic iron positive.

---

[1] Care was taken in these and the former similar cases to discharge the platinum surface of any reacting force it might acquire from the action of the previous current, by separating it from the other metals, and touching it in the liquid for an instant with another platinum plate.

1843. In all the preceding experiments the electrolyte used has been the sulphuret of potassium solution; but I now changed this for another, very different in its nature, namely, the *green nitrous acid* (1816.), which has already been shown to be an excellent conductor of electricity. Iron and platinum were the metals employed, both being in the form of wires. The vessel in which they were immersed was a tube like that formerly described (1815.); in other respects the arrangement was the same in principle as those already used (1824. 1836.). The first effect was the production of a current, the iron being positive in the acid to the platina; but this *quickly ceased*, and the galvanometer-needle came to 0°. In this state, however, the circuit could not in all things be compared with the one having the solution of sulphuret of potassium for its electrolyte (1824.); for although it could conduct the thermo current of antimony and bismuth in a certain degree, yet that degree was very small compared to the power possessed by the former arrangement, or to that of a circle in which the nitrous acid was between two platinum plates (1816.). This remarkable retardation is consequent upon the assumption by the iron of that peculiar state which Schœnbein has so well described and illustrated by his numerous experiments and investigations. But though it must be admitted that the iron in contact with the acid is in a peculiar state (1951. 2001. 2033.), yet it is also evident that a circuit consisting of platinum, iron, peculiar iron, and nitrous acid, does not cause a current though it have sufficient conducting power to carry a thermo current.

1844. But if the contact of platinum and iron has an electromotive force, why does it not produce a current? The application of heat (1830.), or of a little chemical action (1831.) at the place of contact, does produce a current, and in the latter case a strong one. Or if any other of the contacts in the arrangement can produce a current, why is not that shown by some corresponding effect? The only answers are, to say, that the peculiar iron has the same electromotive properties and relations as platinum, or that the nitrous acid is included under the same law with the metals (1809. 1835.); and so the sum of the effects of all the contacts in the circuit is nought, or an exact balance of forces. That the iron is like the platinum in having no electromotive force at its contacts without chemical

action, I believe; but that it is unlike it in its electrical relations, is evident from the difference between the two in strong
nitric acid, as well as in weak acid; from their difference in the
power of transmitting electric currents to either nitric acid or
sulphuret of potassium, which is very great; and also by other
differences. That the nitrous acid is, as to the power of its
contacts, to be separated from other electrolytes and classed
with the metals in what is, with them, only an assumption, is a
gratuitous mode of explaining the difficulty, which will come
into consideration, with the case of sulphuret of potassium,
hereafter (1835. 1859. 1889. 2060.).

1845. To the electro-chemical philosopher, the case is only
another of the many strong instances, showing that where chemical action is absent in the voltaic circuit, there no current can
be formed; and that whether solution of sulphuret of potassium or nitrous acid be the electrolyte or connecting fluid
used, still the results are the same, and contact is shown to be
inefficacious as an active electromotive condition.

1846. I need not say that the introduction of different metals
between the iron and platinum at their point of contact, produced no difference in the results (1833. 1834.) and caused no
current; and I have said that heat and chemical action applied
there produced their corresponding effects. But these paral-
lels in action and non-action show the identity in nature of this
circuit, (notwithstanding the production of the surface of peculiar iron on that metal,) and that with solution of sulphuret
of potassium: so that all the conclusions drawn from it apply
here; and if that case ultimately stand firm as a proof against
the theory of contact force, this will stand also.

1847. I now used oxide of iron and platinum as the extremes
of the solid part of the circuit, and the nitrous acid as the fluid;
i. e. I heated the iron wire in the flame of a spirit-lamp, covering it with a coat of oxide in the manner recommended by
Schœnbein in his investigations, and then used it instead of
the clean iron (1843.). The oxide of iron was at first in the
least degree positive, and then immediately neutral. This circuit, then, like the former, gave no current at common temperatures; but it differed much from it in conducting power,
being a very excellent conductor of a thermo current, the oxide
of iron not offering that obstruction to the passage of the cur-

rent which the peculiar iron did (1843. 1844.).   Hence scale oxide of iron and platinum produce no current by contact, the third substance in the proof circuit being nitrous acid; and so the result agrees with that obtained in the former case, where that third substance was solution of sulphuret of potassium.

1848. In using nitrous acid it is necessary that certain precautions be taken, founded on the following effect.   If a circuit be made with the green nitrous acid, platinum wires, and a galvanometer, in a few seconds all traces of a current due to first disturbances will disappear; but if one wire be raised into the air and instantly returned to its first position, a current is formed, and that wire is negative, across the electrolyte, to the other.   If one wire be dipped only a small distance into the acid, as for instance one fourth of an inch, then the raising that wire not more than one eighth of an inch and instantly restoring it, will produce the same effect as before.   The effect is due to the evaporation of the nitrous acid from the exposed wire (1937.).   I may perhaps return to it hereafter, but wish at present only to give notice of the precaution that is required in consequence, namely, to retain the immersed wires undisturbed during the experiment.

---

1849. Proceeding on the facts made known by Schœnbein respecting the relation of iron and nitric acid, I used that acid as the fluid in a voltaic circuit formed with iron and platinum. Pure nitric acid is so deficient in conducting power (1817.) that it may be supposed capable of stopping any current due to the effect of contact between the platinum and iron; and it is further objectionable in these experiments, because, acting feebly on the iron, it produces a chemically excited current, which may be considered as mingling its effect with that of contact: whereas the object at present is, by excluding such chemical action, to lay bare the influence of contact alone. Still the results with it are consistent with the more perfect ones already described; for in a circuit of iron, platinum, and nitric acid, the joint effects of the chemical action on the iron and the contact of iron and platinum, being to produce a current of a certain constant force indicated by the galvanometer, a little chemical action, brought into play where the iron and platinum were in contact as before (1831.), produced a current far stronger than that previously existing. If then, from the weaker current, the part of the effect due to chemical action be abstracted, how little room is there to suppose that any effect is due to the contact of the metals!

1850. But a *red nitric acid* with platinum plates conducts a thermo current well, and will do so even when considerably diluted (1818.). When such red acid is used between iron and platinum, the conducting power is such, that one half of the permanent current can be overcome by a counter thermo current of bismuth and antimony. Thus a sort of comparison is established between a thermo current on the one hand, and a current due to the joint effects of chemical action on iron and contact of iron and platinum on the other. Now considering the admitted weakness of a thermo current, it may be judged what the strength of that part of the second current due to contact can, at the utmost, be; and how little it is able to account for the strong currents produced by ordinary voltaic combinations.

1851. If for a clean iron wire one oxidized in the flame of a spirit-lamp be used, being associated with platinum in pure strong nitric acid, there is a feeble current, the oxide of iron being positive to the platinum, and the facts mainly as with iron. But the further advantage is obtained of comparing the contact of strong and weak acid with this oxidized wire. If one volume of the strong acid and four volumes of water be mixed, this solution may be used, and there is even less deflection than with the strong acid: the iron side is now not sensibly active, except the most delicate means be used to observe the current. Yet in both cases if a chemical action be introduced in place of the contact, the resulting current passes well, and even a thermo current can be made to show itself as more powerful than any due to contact.

1852. In these cases it is safest to put the whole of the oxidized iron under the surface and connect it in the circle by touching it with a platinum wire; for if the oxidized iron be continued through from the acid to the air, it is almost certain to suffer from the joint action of the acid and air at their surface of contact.

1853. I proceeded to use a fluid differing from any of the

former : this was solution of *potassa*, which has already been employed by De la Rive (1823.) with iron and platina, and which when strong has been found to be a substance conducting so well, that even a thermo current could pass it (1819.), and therefore fully sufficient to show a contact current, if any such exists.

1854. Yet when a strong solution of this substance was arranged with silver and platinum, (bodies differing sufficiently from each other when connected by nitric or muriatic acid,) as in the former cases, a very feeble current was produced, and the galvanometer-needle stood nearly at zero. The contact of these metals therefore did not appear to produce a sensible current; and, as I fully believe, because no electromotive power exists in such contact. When that contact was exchanged for a very feeble chemical action, namely, that produced by interposing a little piece of paper moistened in dilute nitric acid (1831.), a current was the result. So here, as in the many former cases, the arrangement with a little chemical action and no metallic contact produces a current, but that without the chemical action and with the metallic contact produces none.

1855. Iron or nickel associated with platinum in this strong solution of potassa was positive. The force of the produced current soon fell, and after an hour or so was very small. Then annulling the metallic contact at *x*, fig. 2, and substituting a feeble chemical action there, as of dilute nitric acid, the current established by the latter would pass and show itself. Thus the cases are parallel to those before mentioned (1849, &c.), and show how little contact alone could do, since the effect of the conjoint contact of iron and platinum and chemical action of potash and iron were very small as compared with the contrasted chemical action of the dilute nitric acid.

1856. Instead of a strong solution of potassa, a much weaker one consisting of one volume of strong solution and six volumes of water was used, but the results with the silver and platinum were the same : no current was produced by the metallic contact as long as that only was left for exciting cause, but on substituting a little chemical action in its place (1831.), the current was immediately produced.

1857. Iron and nickel with platinum in the weak solution also produced similar results, except that the positive state of these metals was rather more permanent than with the strong solution. Still it was so small as to be out of all proportion to what was to be expected according to the contact theory.

───────────

1858. Thus these different contacts of metals and other well-conducting solid bodies prove utterly inefficient in producing a current, as well when solution of potassa is the third or fluid body in the circuit, as when that third body is either solution of sulphuret of potassium, or hydrated nitrous acid, or nitric acid, or mixed nitric and nitrous acids. Further, all the argu- -ments respecting the inefficacy of the contacts of bodies interposed at the junction of the two principal solid substances, which were advanced in the case of the sulphuret of potassium solution (1833.), apply here with potassa; as they do indeed in every case of a conducting circuit where the interposed fluid is without chemical action and no current is produced. If a case could be brought forward in which the interposed fluid is without action, is yet a sufficiently good conductor, and a current *is* produced; then, indeed, the theory of contact would find evidence in its favour, which, as far as I can perceive, could not be overcome. I have most anxiously sought for such a case, but cannot find one (1798.).

───────────

1859. The argument is now in a fit state for the resumption of that important point before adverted to (1835. 1844.), which, if truly advanced by an advocate for the contact theory, would utterly annihilate the force of the previous experimental results, though it would not enable that theory to give a reason for the activity of, and the existence of a current in, the pile; but which, if in error, would leave the contact theory utterly defenceless and without foundation.

1860. A supporter of the contact theory may say that the various conducting electrolytes used in the previous experiments are like the metals; i. e. that they have an electromotive force at their points of contact with the metals and other solid conductors employed to complete the circuit; but that this is of such consistent strength at each place of contact, that, in a complete circle, the sum of the forces is 0 (1809.). The actions at the contacts are tense electromotive actions, but balanced, and so no current is produced. But what experiment is there to support this statement? where are the measured electromotive results proving it (1808.)? I believe there are none.

1861. The contact theory, after assuming that mere contacts of dissimilar substances have electromotive powers, further assumes a difference between metals and liquid conductors (1810.) without which it is impossible that the theory can explain the current in the voltaic pile : for whilst the contact effects in a metallic circuit are assumed to be always perfectly balanced, it is also assumed that the contact effects of the electrolytes or interposed fluid with the metals are not balanced, but are so far removed from anything like an equilibrium, as to produce most powerful currents, even the strongest that a voltaic pile can produce. If so, then why should the solution of sulphuret of potassium be an exception? it is quite unlike the metals : it does not appear to conduct without decomposition; it is an excellent electrolyte, and an excellent *exciting* electrolyte in proper cases (1880.), producing most powerful currents when it acts chemically ; it is in all these points quite unlike the metals, and, in its action, like any of the acid or saline exciting electrolytes commonly used. How then can it be allowed that, without a single direct experiment, and solely for the purpose of avoiding the force of those which are placed in opposition, we should suppose it to leave its own station amongst the electrolytes, and class with the metals; and that too, in a point of character, which, even with them, is as yet a mere assumption (1809.)?

1862. But it is not with the sulphuret of potassium alone that this freedom must be allowed ; it must be extended to the nitrous acid (1843. 1847.), to the nitric acid (1849, &c.), and even to the solution of potash (1854.) ; all these being of the class of electrolytes, and yet exhibiting no current in circuits where they do not occasion chemical action. Further, this exception must be made for *weak solutions* of sulphuret of potassium (1842.) and of potassa (1856.), for they exhibit the same phenomena as the stronger solutions. And if the contact theorists claim it for these weak solutions, then how will they meet the case of weak nitric acid which is not similar in its action on iron to strong nitric acid (1977.), but can produce a powerful current?

1863. The chemical philosopher is embarrassed by none of these difficulties; for he first, by a simple direct experiment, ascertains whether any of the two given substances in the circuit are active chemically on each other. If they are, he expects and finds the corresponding current; if they are not, he expects and he finds no current, though the circuit be a good conductor and he look carefully for it (1829.).

1864. Again; taking the case of iron, platina, and solution of sulphuret of potassium, there is no current; but for iron substitute zinc, and there is a powerful current. I might for zinc substitute copper, silver, tin, cadmium, bismuth, lead, and other metals; but I take zinc, because its sulphuret dissolves and is carried off by the solution, and so leaves the case in a very simple state; the fact, however, is as strong with any of the other metals. Now if the contact theory be true, and if the iron, platina, and solution of sulphuret of potassium give contacts which are in perfect equilibrium as to their electromotive force, then why does changing the iron for zinc destroy the equilibrium? Changing one metal for another in a metallic circuit causes no alteration of this kind: nor does changing one substance for another among the great number of bodies which, as solid conductors, may be used to form conducting (but chemically inactive) circuits (1867, &c.). If the solution of sulphuret of potassium is to be classed with the metals as to its action in the experiments I have quoted (1825, &c.), then, how comes it to act quite unlike them, and with a power equal to the *best* of the other class, in the new cases of zinc, copper, silver, &c. (1882. 1885, &c.)?

1865. This difficulty, as I conceive, must be met, on the part of the contact theorists, by a new assumption, namely, that this fluid sometimes acts as the best of the metals, or first class of conductors, and sometimes as the best of the electrolytes or second class. But surely this would be far too loose a method of philosophizing in an experimental science (1889.); and further, it is most unfortunate for such an assumption, that this second condition or relation of it never comes on by itself, so as to give us a pure case of a current from contact alone; it never comes on *without* that chemical action to which the chemist so simply refers all the current which is then produced.

1866. It is unnecessary for me to say that the same argument

applies with equal force to the cases where nitrous acid, nitric
acid, and solution of potash are used; and it is supported with
equal strength by the results which they have given (1843.
1849. 1853.).

1867. It may be thought that it was quite unnecessary, but
in my desire to establish contact electromotive force, to do
which I was at one time very anxious, I made many circuits of
three substances, including a galvanometer, all being conductors, with the hope of finding an arrangement, which, without
chemical action, should produce a current. The number and
variety of these experiments may be understood from the following summary; in which metals, plumbago, sulphurets and
oxides, all being conductors even of a thermo current, were thus
combined in various ways:

      1. Platinum.
      2. Iron.
      3. Zinc.
      4. Copper.
      5. Plumbago.
      6. Scale oxide of iron.
      7. Native peroxide of manganese.
      8. Native gray sulphuret of copper.
      9. Native iron pyrites.
     10. Native copper pyrites.
     11. Galena.
     12. Artificial sulphuret of copper.
     13. Artificial sulphuret of iron.
     14. Artificial sulphuret of bismuth.

1 and 2 with 5, 6, 7, 8, 9, 10, 11, 12, 13, 14, in turn.
1 and 3 with 5, 6, 7, 8, 9, 10, 11, 12, 13, 14.
1 and 5 with 6, 7, 8, 9, 10, 11, 12, 13, 14.
3 and 6 with 7, 8, 9, 10, 11, 12, 13, 14.
4 and 5 with 6, 7, 8, 9, 10, 11, 12, 13, 14.
4 and 6 with 7, 8, 9, 10, 11, 12, 13, 14.
4 and 7 with 8, 9, 10, 11, 12, 13, 14.
4 and 8 with 9, 10, 11, 12, 13, 14.
4 and 9 with 10, 11, 12, 13, 14.
4 and 10 with 11, 12, 13, 14.

4 and 11 with 12, 13, 14.
4 and 12 with 13, 14.
4 and 13 with 14.
1 and 4 with 12.

1868. Marianini states from experiment that copper is positive to sulphuret of copper[1]: with the Voltaists, according to the same philosopher, sulphuret of copper is positive to iron (1878.), and with them also iron is positive to copper. These three bodies therefore ought to give a most powerful circle: but on the contrary, whatever sulphuret of copper I have used, I have found not the slightest effect from such an arrangement.

1869. As peroxide of lead is a body causing a powerful current in solution of sulphuret of potassium, and indeed in every case of a circuit where it can give up part of its oxygen, I thought it reasonable to expect that its contact with metals would produce a current, if contact ever could. A part of that which had been prepared (1822.), was therefore well dried, which is quite essential in these cases, and formed into the following combinations:

| Platinum. | Zinc.    | Peroxide of lead. |
| Platinum. | Lead.    | Peroxide of lead. |
| Platinum. | Cadmium. | Peroxide of lead. |
| Platinum. | Iron.    | Peroxide of lead. |

Of these varied combinations, not one gave the least signs of a current, provided differences of temperature were excluded; though in every case the circle formed was, as to conducting power, perfect for the purpose, i. e. able to conduct even a very weak thermo current.

---

1870. In the contact theory it is not therefore the metals alone that must be assumed to have their contact forces so balanced as to produce, in any circle of them, an effect amounting to nothing (1809.); but all solid bodies that are able to conduct, whether they be forms of carbon, or oxides, or sulphurets, must be included in the same category. So also must the electrolytes already referred to, namely, the solutions of sulphuret of potassium and potash, and nitrous and nitric acids, in every case where they do not act chemically. In fact *all*

[1] Memoria della Società Italiana in Modena, 1827, xxi. 224.

*conductors* that do not act chemically in the circuit must be assumed, by the contact theory, to be in this condition, until a case of voltaic current without chemical action is produced (1858.).

1871. Then, even admitting that the results obtained by Volta and his followers with the electrometer prove that mere contact has an electromotive force and can produce an effect, surely all experience with contact alone goes to show that the electromotive forces in a circuit are always balanced. How else is it likely that the above-named most varied substances should be found to agree in this respect? unless indeed it be, as I believe, that all substances agree in this, of having no such power at all. If so, then where is the source of power which can account by the theory of contact for the current in the voltaic pile? If they are not balanced, then where is the sufficient case of contact alone producing a current? or where are the numerical data which indicate that such a case can be (1808. 1868.)? The contact philosophers are bound to produce, not a case where the current is infinitesimally small, for such cannot account for the current of the voltaic pile, and will always come within the debatable ground which De la Rive has so well defended, but a case and data of such distinctness and importance as may be worthy of opposition to the numerous cases produced by the chemical philosopher (1892.); for without them the contact theory as applied to the pile appears to me to have *no* support, and, as it asserts contact electromotive force even *with* the balanced condition, to be almost without foundation.

1872. To avoid these and similar conclusions, the contact theory must bend about in the most particular and irregular way. Thus the contact of solution of sulphuret of potassium with iron must be considered as balanced by the joint force of its contact with platinum, and the contact of iron and platinum with each other; but changing the iron for lead, then the contact of the sulphuret with the latter metal is no longer balanced by the other two contacts, it has all of a sudden changed its relation: after a few seconds, when a film of sulphuret has been formed by the chemical action, then the current ceases, though the circuit be a good conductor (1885.); and now it must be assumed that the solution has acquired its first relation to the metals and to the sulphuret of lead, and gives an equilibrium condition of the contacts in the circle.

1873. So also with this sulphuretted solution and with potassa, dilution must, by the theory, be admitted as producing *no change* in the character of the contact force; but with nitric acid, it, on the contrary, must be allowed to change the character of the force greatly (1977.). So again acids and alkalies (as potassa) in the cases where the currents are produced by them, as with zinc and platinum for instance, must be assumed as giving the preponderance of electromotive force on the same side, though these are bodies which might have been expected to give opposite currents, since they differ so much in their nature.

1874. Every case of a current is obliged to be met, on the part of the contact advocates, by assuming powers at the points of contact, in *the particular case*, of such proportionate strengths as will consist with the results obtained, and the theory is made to bend about (1956. 1992. 2006. 2014. 2063.), having no general relation for the acids or alkalies, or other electrolytic solution used. The result therefore comes to this: The theory can predict nothing regarding the results; it is accompanied by no case of a voltaic current produced without chemical action, and in those associated with chemical action, it bends about to suit the real results, these contortions being exactly parallel to the variations which the pure chemical force, by experiment, indicates.

1875. In the midst of all this, how simply does the chemical theory meet, include, combine, and even predict, the numerous experimental results! When there is a current there is also chemical action; when the action ceases, the current stops (1882. 1885. 1894.); the action is determined either at the anode or the cathode, according to circumstances (2039. 2041.), and the direction of the current is invariably associated with the direction in which the active chemical forces oblige the anions and cations to move in the circle (962. 2052.).

1876. Now when in conjunction with these circumstances it is considered, that the many arrangements without chemical action (1825, &c.) produce no current; that those with chemical action almost always produce a current; that hundreds occur in which chemical action without contact produces a current (2017, &c.) ; and that as many with contact but without chemical action (1867.) are known and are inactive; how can we resist the conclusion, that the powers of the voltaic battery originate in the exertion of chemical force ?

¶ iii. *Active circles excited by solution of sulphuret of potassium.*

1877. In 1812 Davy gave an experiment to show, that of two different metals, copper and iron, that having the strongest attraction for oxygen was positive in oxidizing solutions, and that having the strongest attraction for sulphur was positive in sulphuretting solutions[1]. In 1827 De la Rive quoted several such inversions of the states of two metals, produced by using different solutions, and reasoned from them, that the mere contact of the metals could not be the cause of their respective states, but that the chemical action of the liquid produced these states[2].

1878. In a former paper I quoted Sir Humphry Davy's experiment (943.), and gave its result as a proof that the contact of the iron and copper could not originate the current produced ; since when a dilute acid was used in place of the sulphuret, the current was reverse in direction, and yet the contact of the metals remained the same.  M. Marianini[3] adds, that copper will produce the same effect with tin, lead, and even zinc ; and also that silver will produce the same results as copper.  In the case of copper he accounts for the effect by referring it to the relation of the iron and the new body formed on the copper, the latter being, according to Volta, positive to the former[4].  By his own experiment the same substance was negative to the iron across the same solution[5].

1879. I desire at present to resume the class of cases where a solution of sulphuret of potassium is the liquid in a voltaic circuit; for I think they give most powerful proof that the current in the voltaic battery cannot be produced by contact, but is due altogether to chemical action.

1880. The solution of sulphuret of potassium (1812.) is a

[1] Elements of Chemical Philosophy, p. 148.
[2] Annales de Chimie, 1828, xxxvii. 231–237 ; xxxix. 299.
[3] Memorie della Società Italiana in Modena, 1837, xxi. p. 224.
[4] Ibid. p. 219.                              [5] Ibid. p. 224.

most excellent conductor of electricity (1814.). When subjected between platinum electrodes to the decomposing power
of a small voltaic battery, it readily gave pure sulphur at the
anode, and a little gas, which was probably hydrogen, at the
cathode. When arranged with platinum surfaces so as to form
a Ritter's secondary pile, the passage of a feeble primary current, for a few seconds only, makes this secondary battery effective in causing a counter current; so that, in accordance
with electrolytic conduction (923. 1343.), it probably does not
conduct without decomposition, or if at all, its point of electrolytic intensity (966. 983.) must be very low. Its exciting
action (speaking on the chemical theory) is either the giving an
anion (sulphur) to such metallic and other bodies as it can act
upon, or, in some cases, as with the peroxides of lead and
manganese, and the protoxide of iron (2046.), the abstraction
of an anion *from* the body in contact with it, the current produced being in the one or the other direction accordingly. Its
chemical affinities are such, that in many cases its anion goes
to that metal, of a pair of metals, which is left untouched when
the usual exciting electrolytes are employed; and so a beautiful inversion of the current in relation to the metals is obtained;
thus, when copper and nickel are used with it, the anion goes
to the copper; but when the same metals are used with the
ordinary electrolytic fluids, the anion goes to the nickel. Its
excellent conducting power renders the currents it can excite
very evident and strong; and it should be remembered that the
strength of the resulting currents, as indicated by the galvanometer, depends jointly upon the energy (not the mere quantity)
of the exciting action called into play, and the conductive ability
of the circuit through which the current has to run. The
value of this exciting electrolyte is increased for the present
investigation, by the circumstance of its giving, by its action on
the metals, resulting compounds, some of which are insoluble,
whilst others are soluble; and, of the insoluble results, some
are excellent conductors, whilst others have no conducting
power at all.

1881. The experiments to be described were made generally
in the following manner. Wires of platinum, gold, palladium,
iron, lead, tin, and the other malleable metals, about one twentieth of an inch in diameter and six inches long, were prepared.

Two of these being connected with the ends of the galvano-meter-wires, were plunged at the same instant into the solution of sulphuret of potassium in a test-glass, and kept there without agitation (1919.), the effects at the same time being observed. The wires were in every case carefully cleansed with fresh fine sand-paper and a clean cloth ; and were sometimes even burnished by a glass rod, to give them a smooth surface. Precautions were taken to avoid any difference of temperature at the junctions of the different metals with the galvanometer-wires.

1882. *Tin and platinum.*—When tin was associated with platinum, gold, or, I may say, any other metal which is chemically inactive in the solution of the sulphuret, a strong electric current was produced, the tin being positive to the platinum through the solution, or, in other words, the current being from the tin through the solution to the platinum. In a very short time this current fell greatly in power, and in ten minutes the galvanometer-needle was nearly at 0°. On then endeavouring to transmit the antimony-bismuth thermo current (1825.) through the circuit, it was found that it could not pass, the circle having lost its conducting power. This was the consequence of the formation on the tin of an insoluble, investing, non-conducting sulphuret of that metal; the non-conducting power of the body formed is not only evident from the present result, but also from a former experiment (1821.).

1883. Marianini thinks it is possible that (in the case of copper, at least (1878.), and, so I presume, for all similar cases, for surely one law or principle should govern them,) the current is due to the contact force of the sulphuret formed. But that application is here entirely excluded ; for how can a *non-conducting* body form a current, either by contact or in any other way? No such case has ever been shown, nor is it in the nature of things ; so that it cannot be the contact of the sulphuret that here causes the current; and if not in the present, why in any case? for nothing happens here that does not happen in any other instance of a current produced by the same exciting electrolyte.

1884. On the other hand, how beautiful a proof the result gives in confirmation of the chemical theory! Tin can take sulphur from the electrolyte to form a sulphuret; and whilst it is doing so, and in proportion to the degree in which it is doing so, it produces a current; but when the sulphuret which is formed, by investing the metal, shuts off the fluid and prevents further chemical action, then the current ceases also. Nor is it *necessary* that it should be a non-conductor for this purpose, for conducting sulphurets will perform the same office (1885. 1894.), and bring about the same result. What, then, can be more clear, than that whilst the sulphuret is *being formed* a current is produced, but that when formed its mere contact can do nothing towards such an effect?

1885. *Lead.*—This metal presents a fine result in the solution of sulphuret of potassium. Lead and platinum being the metals used, the lead was at first highly positive, but in a few seconds the current fell, and in two minutes the galvanometer-needle was at 0°. Still the arrangement conducted a feeble thermo current extremely well, the conducting power not having disappeared, as in the case of tin; for the investing sulphuret of lead is a conductor (1820.). Nevertheless, though a conductor, it could stop the further chemical action; and that ceasing, the current ceased also.

1886. Lead and gold produced the same effect. Lead and palladium the same. Lead and iron the same, except that the circumstances respecting the tendency of the latter metal under common circumstances to produce a current from the electrolyte to itself, have to be considered and guarded against (1826. 2049.). Lead and nickel also the same. In all these cases, when the lead was taken out and washed, it was found beautifully invested with a thin polished pellicle of sulphuret of lead.

1887. With lead, then, we have a *conducting* sulphuret formed, but still there is no sign that its contact can produce a current, any more than in the case of the *non-conducting* sulphuret of tin (1882.). There is no new or additional action produced by this *conducting* body; there was no deficiency of action with the former *non-conducting* product; both are alike in their results, being, in fact, essentially alike in their relation to that on which the current really depends, namely, an active chemical force. A piece of lead put *alone* into the solution of sulphuret of potassium, has its surface converted into sulphuret of lead, the proof thus being obtained, even when the current cannot be formed, that there is a force (chemical) present and active under such circumstances ; and such force can produce a current of chemical force when the circuit form is given to the arrangement.   The force at the place of excitement shows itself, both by the formation of sulphuret of lead and the production of a current.   In proportion as the formation of the one decreases the production of the other diminishes, though all the bodies produced are conductors, and contact still remains to perform any work or cause any effect to which it is competent.

1888. It may perhaps be said that the current is due to the contact between the solution of sulphuret and the lead, (or tin, as the case may be,) which occurs at the beginning of the experiment; and that when the action ceases, it is because a new body, the sulphuret of lead, is introduced into the circuit, the various contacts being then balanced in their force.   This would be to fall back upon the assumption before resisted (1861. 1865. 1872.), namely, that the solution may class with metals and such like bodies, giving balanced effects of contact in relation to *some* of these bodies, as in this case, to the sulphuret of lead produced, but not with *others*, as the lead itself; both the lead and its sulphuret being in the same category as the metals generally (1809. 1870.).

1889. The utter improbability of this as a natural effect, and the absence of all experimental proof in support of it, have been already stated (1861. 1871.), but one or two additional reasons against it now arise.   The state of things may perhaps be made clearer by a diagram or two, in which assumed contact forces may be assigned, in the absence of all experimental expression, without injury to the reasoning.   Let fig. 4, Plate III. represent the electromotive forces of a circle of platinum, iron, and solution of sulphuret of potassium; or platinum, nickel, and solution of sulphuret; cases in which the forces are, according to the contact theory, balanced (1860.).   Then fig. 5 may represent the circle of platinum, lead, and solution of sulphuret, which does produce a current, and, as I have assumed, with a resulting force of 11 ——➤.   This in a few minutes becomes quiescent, i. e. the current ceases, and fig. 6 may represent this new case according to the contact theory.   Now is it at all likely that by the intervention of sulphuret of lead at the contact *c*, fig. 5, and the production of two contacts *d* and *e*, fig. 6, such an enormous change of the contact force suffering alteration should be made as from 10 to 21? the intervention of the same sulphuret either at *a* or *b* (1834. 1840.) being able to do nothing of the kind, for the sum of the force of the two new contacts is in that case exactly equal to the force of the contact which they replace, as is proved by such interposition making no change in the effects of the circle (1867. 1840.). If therefore the intervention of this body between *lead* and platinum at *a*, or between solution of *sulphuret of potassium* and platinum at *b* (fig. 5) causes no change, these cases including its contact with both lead and the solution of sulphuret, is it at all probable that its intervention between these two bodies at *c* should make a difference equal to double the amount of force previously existing, or indeed any difference at all?

1890. Such an alteration as this in the sum assigned as the amount of the forces belonging to the sulphuret of lead by virtue of its two places of contact, is equivalent I think to saying that it partakes of the anomalous character already supposed to belong to certain fluids, namely, of sometimes giving balanced forces in circles of good conductors, and at other times not (1865.).

1891. Even the metals themselves must in fact be forced into this constrained condition; for the effect at a point of contact, if there be *any at all*, must be the result of the *joint* and *mutual actions* of the bodies in contact. If therefore in the circuit, fig. 5, the contact forces are not balanced, it must be because of the deficient *joint* action of the lead and solution at *c*[1]. If the metal and fluid were to act in their proper character, and as iron or nickel would do in the place of the lead, then the force there would be ◄—— 21, whereas it is less, or according to the assumed numbers only ◄—— 10. Now as there is no reason why the lead should have any superiority assigned to it over the solution, since the latter can give a balanced condition amongst good conductors in its proper situation as well as the former; how can this be, unless lead possess that strange cha-

[1] My numbers are assumed, and if other numbers were taken, the reasoning might be removed to contact *b*, or even to contact *a*, but the end of the argument would in every case be the same.

racter of sometimes giving equipoised contacts, and at other times not (1865.)?

1892. If that be true of lead, it must be true of all the metals which, with this sulphuretted electrolyte, give circles producing currents; and this would include bismuth, copper, antimony, silver, cadmium, zinc, tin, &c. &c. With other electrolytic fluids iron and nickel would be included, and even gold, platinum, palladium; in fact all the bodies that can be made to yield in any way active voltaic circuits. Then is it possible that this can be true, and yet not a single combination of this extensive class of bodies be producible that can give the current without chemical action (1867.), considered not as a result, but as a known and pre-existing force?

1893. I will endeavour to avoid further statement of the arguments, but think myself bound to produce (1799.) a small proportion of the enormous body of facts which appear to me to bear evidence all in one direction.

1894. *Bismuth.*—This metal, when associated with platinum, gold, or palladium in solution of the sulphuret of potassium, gives active circles, the bismuth being positive. In the course of less than half an hour the current ceases; but the circuit is still an excellent conductor of thermo currents. Bismuth with iron or nickel produces the same final result with the reservation before made (1826.). Bismuth and lead give an active circle; at first the bismuth is positive; in a minute or two the current ceases, but the circuit still conducts the thermo current well.

1895. Thus whilst sulphuret of bismuth is in the act of formation the current is produced; when the chemical action ceases the current ceases also; though contact continues and the sulphuret be a good conductor. In the case of bismuth and lead the chemical action occurs at both sides, but is most energetic at the bismuth, and the current is determined accordingly. Even in that instance the cessation of chemical action causes the cessation of the current.

1896. In these experiments with *lead* and *bismuth* I have given their associations with platinum, gold, palladium, iron, and nickel; because, believing in the first place that the results prove all current to depend on chemical action, then, the quiescent state of the resulting or final circles shows that the contacts of these metals in their respective pairs are *without force* (1829.): and upon that again follows the passive condition of all those contacts which can be produced by interposing other conducting bodies between them (1833.); an argument that need not again be urged.

1897. *Copper.*—This substance being associated with platinum, gold, iron, or any metal chemically inactive in the solution of sulphuret, gives an active circle, in which the copper is positive through the electrolyte to the other metal. The action, though it falls, does not come to a close as in the former cases, and for these simple reasons; that the sulphuret formed is not compact but porous, and does not adhere to the copper, but separates from it in scales. Hence results a continued renewal of the chemical action between the metal and electrolyte, and a continuance of the current. If after a while the copper plate be taken out and washed, and dried, even the wiping will remove part of the sulphuret in scales, and the nail separates the rest with facility. Or if a copper plate be left in abundance of the solution of sulphuret, the chemical action *continues*, and the coat of sulphuret of copper becomes thicker and thicker.

1898. If, as Marianini has shown[1], a copper plate which has been dipped in the solution of sulphuret, be removed before the coat formed is so thick as to break up from the metal beneath, and be washed and dried, and then replaced, in association with platinum or iron, in the solution, it will at first be neutral, or, as is often the case, negative (1827. 1838.) to the other metal, a result quite in opposition to the idea, that the mere presence of the sulphuret on it could have caused the former powerful current and positive state of the copper (1897. 1878.). A further proof that it is not the mere *presence*, but the *formation*, of the sulphuret which causes the current, is, that, if the plate be left long enough for the solution to penetrate the investing crust of sulphuret of copper and come into activity on the metal beneath, then the plate becomes active, and a current is produced.

1899. I made some sulphuret of copper, by igniting thick copper wire in a Florence flask or crucible in abundance of vapour of sulphur. The body produced is in an excellent

[1] Memorie della Società Italiana in Modena, 1837, xxi. 224.

form for these experiments, and a good conductor; but it is not without action on the sulphuretted solution, from which it can take more sulphur, and the consequence is, that it is positive to platinum or iron in such a solution. If such sulphuret of copper be left long in the solution, and then be washed and dried, it will generally acquire the final state of sulphuration, either in parts or altogether, and also be inactive, as the sulphuret formed on the copper was before (1898.); i. e. when its chemical action is exhausted, it ceases to produce a current.

1900. *Native gray sulphuret of copper* has the same relation to the electrolyte: it takes sulphur from it and is raised to a higher state of combination; and, as it is also a conductor (1820.), it produces a current, being itself positive so long as the action continues.

1901. But when the copper is *fully sulphuretted,* then all these actions cease; though the sulphuret be a conductor, the contacts still remain, and the circle can carry with facility a feeble thermo current. This is not only shown by the quiescent cases just mentioned (1898.), but also by the utter inactivity of platinum and *compact yellow copper pyrites,* when conjoined by this electrolyte, as shown in a former part of this paper (1840.).

1902. *Antimony.*—This metal, being put alone into a solution of sulphuret of potassium, is acted on, and a sulphuret of antimony formed which does not adhere strongly to the metal, but wipes off. Accordingly, if a circle be formed of antimony, platinum, and the solution, the antimony is positive in the electrolyte, and a powerful current is formed, which continues. Here then is another beautiful variation of the conditions under which the chemical theory can so easily account for the effects, whilst the theory of contacts cannot. The sulphuret produced in this case is a non-conductor whilst in the solid state (402.); it cannot therefore be that any contact of this sulphuret can produce the current; in that respect it is like the sulphuret of tin (1882.). But that circumstance does not stop the occurrence of the chemical current; for; as the sulphuret forms a porous instead of a continuous crust, the electrolyte has access to the metal and the action goes on.

1903. *Silver.*—This metal, associated with platinum, iron, or other metals inactive in this electrolyte, is strongly positive, and gives a powerful continuous current. Accordingly, if a plate of silver, coated with sulphuret by the simple action of the solution, be examined, it will be found that the crust is brittle and broken, and separates almost spontaneously from the metal. In this respect, therefore, silver and copper are alike, and the action consequently continues in both cases; but they differ in the sulphuret of silver being a non-conductor (434.) for these feeble currents, and, in that respect, this metal is analogous to antimony (1902.).

1904. *Cadmium.*—Cadmium with platinum, gold, iron, &c., gives a powerful current in the solution of sulphuret, and the cadmium is positive. On several occasions this current continued for two or three hours or more; and at such times, the cadmium being taken out, washed and wiped, the sulphuret was found to separate easily in scales on the cloth used.

1905. Sometimes the current would soon cease; and then the circle was found not to conduct the thermo current (1813.). In these cases, also, on examining the cadmium, the coat of sulphuret was strongly adherent, and this was more especially the case when prior to the experiment the cadmium, after having been cleaned, was burnished by a glass rod (1881.). Hence it appears that the sulphuret of this metal is a non-conductor, and that its contact could not have caused the current (1883.) in the manner Marianini supposes. All the results it supplies are in perfect harmony with the chemical theory and adverse to contact theory.

1906. *Zinc.*—This metal, with platinum, gold, iron, &c., and the solution of sulphuret, produces a very powerful current, and is positive through the solution to the other metal. The current was permanent. Here another beautiful change in the circumstances of the general experiment occurs. Sulphuret of zinc is a non-conductor of electricity (1821.), like the sulphurets of tin, cadmium, and antimony; but then it is soluble in the solution of sulphuret of potassium; a property easily ascertainable by putting a drop of solution of zinc into a portion of the electrolytic solution, and first stirring them a little, by which abundance of sulphuret of zinc will be formed; and then stirring the whole well together, when it will be redissolved. The consequence of this solubility is, that the zinc when taken out of the solution is perfectly free from investing sulphuret of zinc. Hence, therefore, a very sufficient reason, on the chemical theory, why the action should go on. But how can the theory of contact refer the current to any contact of the metallic sulphuret, when that sulphuret is, in the first place, a non-conductor, and, in the next, is dissolved and carried off into the solution at the moment of its formation?

1907. Thus all the phenomena with this admirable electrolyte (1880.), whether they be those which are related to it as an active (1879.) or as a passive (1825, &c.) body, confirm the chemical theory, and oppose that of contact. With tin and cadmium it gives an impermeable non-conducting body; with lead and bismuth it gives an impermeable conducting body; with antimony and silver it produces a permeable non-conducting body; with copper a permeable conducting body; and with zinc a soluble non-conducting body. The chemical action and its resulting current are perfectly consistent with all these variations. But try to explain them by the theory of contact, and, as far as I can perceive, that can only be done by twisting the theory about and making it still more tortuous than before (1861. 1865. 1872. 1874. 1889.); special assumptions being necessary to account for the effects which, under it, become so many special cases.

1908. *Solution of protosulphuret of potassium, or bihydrosulphuret of potassa.*—I used a solution of this kind as the electrolyte in a few cases. The results generally were in accordance with those already given, but I did not think it necessary to pursue them at length. The solution was made by passing sulphuretted hydrogen gas for twenty-four hours through a strong solution of pure caustic potassa.

1909. Iron and platinum with this solution formed a circle in which the iron was first negative, then gradually became neutral, and finally acquired a positive state. The solution first acted as the yellow sulphuret in reducing the investing oxide (2049.), and then, apparently, directly on the iron, dissolving the sulphuret formed. Nickel was positive to platinum from the first, and continued so though producing only a weak current. When weak chemical action was substituted for metallic contact at *x*, fig. 2 (1831.), a powerful current passed. Copper was highly positive to iron and nickel; as also to platinum, gold, and the other metals which were unacted upon by the solution. Silver was positive to iron, nickel, and even lead ; as well as to platinum, gold, &c. Lead is positive to platinum, then the current falls, but does not cease. Bismuth is also positive at first, but after a while the current almost entirely ceases, as with the yellow sulphuret of potassium (1894.).

1910. Native gray sulphuret of copper and artificial sulphuret of copper (1899.) were positive to platinum and the inactive metals : but yellow copper pyrites, yellow iron pyrites, and galena, were inactive with these metals in this solution ; as before they had been with the solution of yellow or bisulphuret of potassium. This solution, as might be expected from its composition, has more of alkaline characters in it than the yellow sulphuret of potassium.

1911. Before concluding this account of results with the sulphuretted solutions, as exciting electrolytes, I will mention the varying and beautiful phenomena which occur when copper and silver, or two pieces of copper, or two pieces of silver, form a circle with the yellow solution. If the metals be copper and silver, the copper is at first positive and the silver remains untarnished ; in a short time this action ceases, and the silver becomes positive ; at the same instant it begins to combine with sulphur and becomes covered with sulphuret of silver ; in the course of a few moments the copper again becomes positive ; and thus the action will change from side to side several times, and the current with it, according as the circumstances become in turn more favourable at one side or the other.

1912. But how can it be thought that the current first produced is due in any way to the *contact* of the sulphuret of copper formed, since its presence there becomes at last the reason why that first current diminishes, and enables the silver, which is originally the weaker in exciting force, and has no sulphuret as yet formed on it, to assume for a time the predominance, and produce a current which can overcome that excited at the copper (1911.) ? What can account for these changes, but chemical action ? which, as it appears to me, accounts, as far as we have yet gone, with the utmost simplicity, for *all* the effects produced, however varied the mode of action and their circumstances may be.

*Royal Institution,*
*December* 12, 1839.

# SEVENTEENTH SERIES.

§ 24. *On the source of power in the voltaic pile.*—(Continued.)
¶ iv. *The exciting chemical force affected by temperature.*
¶ v. *The exciting chemical force affected by dilution.*
¶ vi. *Differences in the order of the metallic elements of
voltaic circles.* ¶ vii. *Active voltaic circles and batteries
without metallic contact.* ¶ viii. *Considerations of the sufficiency of chemical action.* ¶ ix. *Thermo-electric evidence.*
¶ x. *Improbable nature of the assumed contact force.*

Received January 30,—Read March 19, 1840.

¶ iv. *The exciting chemical force affected by temperature.*

1913. ON the view that chemical force is the origin of the
electric current in the voltaic circuit, it is important that we
have the power of causing by ordinary chemical means, a variation of that force within certain limits, without involving any
alteration of the metallic or even the other contacts in the circuit.    Such variations should produce corresponding voltaic
effects, and it appeared not improbable that these differences
alone might be made effective enough to produce currents
without any metallic contact at all.

1914. De la Rive has shown that the increased action of a
pair of metals, when put into hot fluid instead of cold, is in a
great measure due to the exaltation of the chemical affinity on
that metal which was acted upon[1].    My object was to add to
the argument by using but one metal and one fluid, so that the
fluid might be alike at both contacts, but to exalt the chemical force at one only of the contacts by the action of heat.
If such difference produced a current with circles which either
did not generate a thermo current themselves, or could not
conduct that of an antimony and bismuth element, it seemed
probable that the effect would prove to be a result of pure chemical force, contact doing nothing.

[1] Annales de Chimie, 1828, xxxvii. p. 242.

1915. The apparatus used was a glass tube (Plate III. fig. 7.) about five inches long and 0·4 of an inch internal diameter, open at both ends, bent, and supported on a retort-stand. In this the liquid was placed, and the portion in the upper part of one limb could then easily be heated and retained so, whilst that in the other limb was cold. In the experiments I will call the left-hand side A, and the right-hand side B, taking care to make no change of these designations. C and D are the wires of metal (1881.) to be compared; they were formed into a circuit by means of the galvanometer, and, often also, a Seebeck's thermo-element of antimony and bismuth; both these, of course, caused no disturbing effect so long as the temperature of their various junctions was alike. The wires were carefully prepared (1881.), and when two of the same metal were used, they consisted of the successive portions of the same piece of wire.

1916. The precautions which are necessary for the elimination of a correct result are rather numerous, but simple in their nature.

1917. *Effect of first immersion.*—It is hardly possible to have the two wires of the same metal, even platinum, so exactly alike that they shall not produce a current in consequence of their difference; hence it is necessary to alternate the wires and repeat the experiment several times, until an undoubted result independent of such disturbing influences is obtained.

1918. *Effect of the investing fluid or substance.*—The fluid produced by the action of the liquid upon the metal exerts, as is well known, a most important influence on the production of a current. Thus when two wires of cadmium were used with the apparatus, fig. 7, (1915.) containing dilute sulphuric acid, hot on one side and cold on the other, the hot cadmium was at first positive, producing a deflection of about 10°; but in a short time this effect disappeared, and a current in the reverse direction equal to 10° or more would appear, the hot cadmium being now negative. This I refer to the quicker exhaustion of the chemical forces of the film of acid on the heated metallic surface (1003. 1036. 1037.), and the consequent final superiority of the colder side at which the action was thus necessarily more powerful (1953, &c. 1966. 2015. 2031, &c.). Marianini has described many cases of the effects of investing solutions, showing that if two pieces of the same metal (iron, tin, lead, zinc, &c.) be used, the one first immersed is negative to the other, and has given his views of the cause[1]. The precaution against this effect was not to put the metals into the acid until the proper temperature had been given to both parts of it, and then to observe the *first effect* produced, accounting that as the true indication, but repeating the experiment until the result was certain.

1919. *Effect of motion.*—This investing fluid (1918.) made it necessary to guard against the effect of successive rest and motion of the metal in the fluid. As an illustration, if two tin wires (1881.) be put into dilute nitric acid, there will probably be a little motion at the galvanometer, and then the needle will settle at 0°. If either wire be then moved, the other remaining quiet, that in motion will become positive. Again, tin and cadmium in dilute sulphuric acid gave a strong current, the cadmium being positive, and the needle was deflected 80°. When left, the force of the current fell to 35°. If the cadmium were then moved it produced very little alteration; but if the tin were moved it produced a great change, not showing, as before, an increase of its force, but the reverse, for it became more negative, and the current force rose up again to 80°[2]. The precaution adopted to avoid the interference of these actions, was not only to observe the first effect of the introduced wires, but to keep them moving from the moment of the introduction.

1920. The above effect was another reason for heating the acids, &c. (1918.) before the wires were immersed; for in the experiment just described, if the cadmium side were heated to boiling, the moment the fluid was agitated on the tin side by

[1] Annales de Chimie, 1830, xlv. p. 40.

[2] Tin has some remarkable actions in this respect. If two tins be immersed in succession into dilute nitric acid, the one last in is positive to the other at the moment: if, both being in, one be moved, that is for the time positive to the other. But if dilute sulphuric acid be employed, the last tin is always negative: if one be taken out, cleaned, and reimmersed, it is negative: if, both being in and neutral, one be moved, it becomes negative to the other. The effects with muriatic acid are the same in kind as those with sulphuric acid, but not so strong. This effect perhaps depends upon the compound of tin first produced in the sulphuric and muriatic acids tending to acquire some other and more advanced state, either in relation to the oxygen, chlorine or acid concerned, and so adding a force to that which at the first moment, when only metallic tin and acid are present, tends to determine a current.

the boiling on the cadmium side, there was more effect by far produced by the motion than the heat: for the heat at the cadmium alone did little or nothing, but the jumping of the acid over the tin made a difference in the current of 20° or 30°.

1921. *Effect of air.*—Two platinum wires were put into cold strong solution of sulphuret of potassium (1812.), fig. 7 ; and the galvanometer was soon at 0°. On heating and boiling the fluid on the side A (1915.) the platinum in it became negative ; cooling that side, by pouring a little water over it from a jug, and heating the side B, the platinum there in turn became negative ; and, though the action was irregular, the same general result occurred however the temperatures of the parts were altered. This was not due to the chemical effect of the electrolyte on the heated platinum. Nor do I believe it was a true thermo current (1933.) ; but if it were the latter, then the heated platinum was *negative* through the electrolyte to the cold platinum. I believe it was altogether the increased effect of the air upon the electrolyte at the heated side ; and it is evident that the application of the heat, by causing currents in the fluid and also in the air, facilitates their mutual action at that place. It has been already shown, that lifting up a platinum wire in this solution, so as to expose it for a moment to the air (1827.), renders it negative when reimmersed, an effect which is in perfect accordance with the assumed action of the heated air and fluid in the present case. The interference of this effect is obviated by raising the temperature of the electrolyte quietly before the wires are immersed (1918.), and observing only the first effect.

1922. *Effect of heat.*—In certain cases where two different metals are used, there is a very remarkable effect produced on heating the negative metal. This will require too much detail to be described fully here ; but I will briefly point it out and illustrate it by an example or two.

1923. When two platinum wires were compared in hot and cold dilute sulphuric acid (1935.), they gave scarcely a sensible trace of any electric current. If any real effect of heat occurred, it was that the hot metal was the least degree positive. When silver and silver were compared, hot and cold, there was also no sensible effect. But when platinum and silver were compared in the same acid, different effects occurred. Both

being cold, the silver in the A side fig. 7 (1915.) was positive about 4°, by the galvanometer; moving the platina on
the other side B did not alter this effect, but on heating
the acid and platinum there, the current became very powerful, deflecting the needle 30°, and the silver was positive.
Whilst the heat continued, the effect continued; but on cooling
the acid and platinum it went down to the first degree. No
such effect took place at the silver; for on heating that side,
instead of becoming negative, it became more positive, but only
to the degree of deflecting the needle 16°. Then, *motion* of
the platinum (1919.) facilitated the passing of the current and
the deflection increased, but *heating* the platinum side did far
more.

1924. *Silver and copper* in dilute sulphuric acid produced
very little effect; the copper was positive about 1° by the galvanometer; moving the copper or the silver did nothing;
heating the copper side caused no change; but on heating the
silver side it became negative 20°. On cooling the silver side
this effect went down, and then, either moving the silver or
copper, or heating the copper side, caused very little change :
but heating the silver side made it negative as before.

1925. All this resolves itself into an effect of the following
kind; that where two metals are in the relation of positive and
negative to each other in such an electrolyte as dilute acids,
(and perhaps others,) heating the negative metal at its contact with the electrolyte enables the current, which tends to
form, to pass with such facility, as to give a result sometimes
tenfold more powerful than would occur without it. It is not
displacement of the investing fluid, for motion will in these
cases do nothing : it is not chemical action, for the effect occurs at that electrode where the chemical action is not active;
it is not a thermo-electric phenomenon of the ordinary kind,
because it depends upon a voltaic relation; i. e. the metal
showing the effect must be negative to the other metal in the
electrolyte; so silver heated does nothing with silver cold,
though it shows a great effect with copper either hot or cold
(1924.); and platinum hot is as nothing to platina cold, but
much to silver either hot or cold.

1926. Whatever may be the intimate action of heat in these
cases, there is no doubt that it is dependent on the current
which tends to pass round the circuit. It is essential to re-

member that the increased effect on the galvanometer is not
due to any increase in the electromotive force, but solely to the
removal of obstruction to the current by an increase probably
of discharge. M. de la Rive has described an effect of heat,
on the passage of the electric current, through dilute acid
placed in the circuit, by platinum electrodes. Heat applied to
the negative electrode increased the deflection of a galvanometer needle in the circuit, from 12° to 30° or 45°; whilst heat
applied to the positive electrode caused no change[1]. I have
not been able to obtain this nullity of effect at the positive electrode when a voltaic battery was used (1639.); but I have no
doubt the present phenomena will prove to be virtually the same
as those which that philosopher has described.

1927. The effect interferes frequently in the ensuing experiments when *two* metals, hot and cold, are compared with
each other; and the more so as the negative metal approxi-
mates in inactivity of character to platinum or rhodium. Thus
in the comparison of cold copper, with hot silver, gold, or
platinum, in dilute nitric acid, this effect tends to make the
copper appear more positive than it otherwise would do.

1928. *Place of the wire terminations.*—It is requisite that
the *end* of the wire on the hot side should be *in* the heated
fluid. Two copper wires were put into diluted solution of
sulphuret of potassium, fig. 8; that portion of the liquid extending from C to D was heated, but the part between D and
E remained cold. Whilst both ends of the wires were in the
cold fluid, as in the figure, there were irregular movements of
the galvanometer, small in degree, leaving the B wire positive.
Moving the wires about, but retaining them as in the figure,
made no difference; but on raising the wire in A, so that its
termination should be in the hot fluid between C and D, then
it became positive and continued so. On lowering the end
into the cold part, the former state recurred; on raising it into
the hot part, the wire again became positive. The same is the
case with two silver wires in dilute nitric acid; and though it
appears very curious that the current should increase in strength
as the extent of bad conductor increases, yet such is often the
case under these circumstances. There can be no reason to
doubt that the part of the wire which is in the hot fluid at the
A side, is at all times equally positive or nearly so; but at one

time the whole of the current it produces is passing through the entire circuit by the wire in B, and at another, a part, or the whole, of it is circulating to the cold end of its own wire, only by the fluid in tube A.

1929. *Cleaning the wires.*—That this should be carefully done has been already mentioned (1881.); but it is especially necessary to attend to the very extremities of the wires, for if these circular spaces, which occur in the most effective part of the circle, be left covered with the body produced on them in a preceding trial, an experimental result will often be very much deranged, or even entirely falsified.

1930. Thus the best mode of experimenting (1915.) is to heat the liquid in the limb A or B, fig. 8, first; and, having the wires well cleaned and connected, to plunge both in at once, and, retaining the *end* of the heated wire in the hot part of the fluid, to keep both wires in motion, and observe, especially, the first effects: then to take out the wires, reclean them, change them side for side and repeat the experiment, doing this so often as to obtain from the several results a decided and satisfactory conclusion.

1931. It next becomes necessary to ascertain whether any true thermo current can be produced by electrolytes and metals, which can interfere with any electro-chemical effects dependent upon the action of heat. For this purpose different combinations of electrolytes and metals not acted on chemically by them, were tried, with the following results.

1932. Platinum and a very *strong solution of potassa* gave, as the result of many experiments, the hot platinum positive across the electrolyte to the cold platinum, producing a current that could deflect the galvanometer needle about 5°, when the temperatures at the two junctures were 60° and 240°. Gold and the same solution gave a similar result. Silver and a moderately strong solution, of specific gravity 1070, like that used in the ensuing experiments (1948.) gave the hot silver positive, but now the deflection was scarcely sensible, and not more than 1°. Iron was tried in the same solution, and there was a constant current and deflection of 50° or more, but there was also chemical action (1948.).

1933. I then used *solution of the sulphuret of potassium* (1812.). As already said, hot platinum is negative in it to the cold metal (1921.) ; but I do not think the action was thermo-electric. Palladium with a weaker solution gave no indication of a current.

1934. Employing dilute nitric acid, consisting of one volume strong acid and fifty volumes water, platinum gave no certain indication : the hot metal was sometimes in the least degree positive, and at others an equally small degree negative. Gold in the same acid gave a scarcely sensible result ; the hot metal was negative. Palladium was as gold.

1935. With dilute sulphuric acid, consisting of one by weight of oil of vitriol and eighty of water, neither platinum nor gold produced any sensible current to my galvanometer by the mere action of heat.

1936. *Muriatic acid* and platinum being conjoined, and heated as before, the hot platinum was very slightly negative in strong acid : in dilute acid there was no sensible current.

1937. *Strong nitric acid* at first seemed to give decided results. Platinum and pure strong nitric acid being heated at one of the junctions, the hot platinum became constantly negative across the electrolyte to the cold metal, the deflection being about 2°. When a yellow acid was used, the deflection was greater ; and when a very orange-coloured acid was employed, the galvanometer needle stood at 70°, the hot platinum being still negative. This effect, however, is not a pure thermo current, but a peculiar result due to the presence of nitrous acid (1848.). It disappears almost entirely when a dilute acid is used (1934.) ; and what effect does remain indicates that the hot metal is negative to the cold.

1938. Thus the *potash solution* seems to be the fluid giving the most probable indications of a thermo current. Yet there the deflection is only 5°, though the fluid, being very strong, is a good conductor (1819.). When the fluid was diluted, and of specific gravity 1070, like that before used (1932.), the effect was only 1°, and cannot therefore be confounded with the results I have to quote.

1939. The dilute *sulphuric* (1935.) and *nitric* acids used (1934.) gave only doubtful indications in some cases of a thermo current. On trial it was found that the thermo current of an antimony-bismuth pair could not pass these solutions, as arranged in these and other experiments (1949. 1950.) ; that, therefore, if the little current obtained in the experiments be of a thermo-electric nature, this combination of platinum and acid is far more powerful than the antimony-bismuth pair of Seebeck; and yet that (with the interposed acid) it is scarcely sensible by this delicate galvanometer. Further, when there is a current, the hot metal is generally negative to the cold, and it is therefore impossible to confound these results with those to be described where the current has a contrary direction.

1940. In strong nitric acid, again, the hot metal is negative.

1941. If, after I show that heat applied to metals in acids or electrolytes which *can act on them* produces considerable currents, it be then said that though the metals which are inactive in the acids produce no thermo currents, those which, like copper, silver, &c. act chemically, may; then, I say, that such would be a mere supposition, and a supposition at variance with what we know of thermo-electricity; for amongst the solid conductors, metallic or non-metallic (1867.), there are none, I believe, which are able to produce thermo currents with some of the metals, and not with others. Further, these metals, copper, silver, &c., do not always show effects which can be mistaken or pass for thermo-electric, for silver in hot dilute nitric acid is scarcely different from silver in the same acid cold (1950.); and in other cases, again, the hot metals become negative instead of positive (1953.).

### *Cases of one metal and one electrolyte ; one junction being heated.*

1942. The cases I have to adduce are far too numerous to be given in detail; I will therefore describe one or two, and sum up the rest as briefly as possible.

1943. *Iron in diluted sulphuret of potassium.*—The hot iron is well positive to the cold metal. The negative and cold wire continues quite clean, but from the hot iron a dark sulphuret separates, which becoming diffused through the solution discolours it. When the cold iron is taken out, washed and wiped, it leaves the cloth clean; but that which has been heated leaves a black sulphuret upon the cloth when similarly treated.

1944. *Copper and the sulphuretted solution.*—The hot copper is well positive to the cold on the first immersion, but the effect quickly falls, from the general causes already referred to (1918.).

1945. *Tin and solution of potassa.*—The hot tin is strongly and constantly positive to the cold.

1946. *Iron and dilute sulphuric acid* (1935.).—The hot iron was constantly positive to the cold, 60° or more. *Iron and diluted nitric acid gave* even a still more striking result.

I must now enumerate merely, not that the cases to be mentioned are less decided than those already given, but to economize time.

1947. *Dilute solution of yellow sulphuret of potassium,* consisting of one volume of the strong solution (1812.), and eighteen volumes of water.—Iron, silver, and copper, with this solution, gave good results. The hot metal was positive to the cold.

1948. *Dilute solution of caustic potassa* (1932.).—Iron, copper, tin, zinc, and cadmium gave striking results in this electrolyte. The hot metal was always positive to the cold. Lead produced the same effect, but there was a momentary jerk at the galvanometer at the instant of immersion, as if the hot lead was negative at that moment. In the case of iron it was necessary to continue the application of heat, and then the formation of oxide at it could easily be observed; the alkali gradually became turbid, for the protoxide first formed was dissolved, and becoming peroxide by degrees, was deposited, and rendered the liquid dull and yellow.

1949. *Dilute sulphuric acid* (1935.).—Iron, tin, lead, and zinc, in this electrolyte, showed the power of heat to produce a current by exalting the chemical affinity, for the hot side was in each case positive.

1950. *Dilute nitric acid* is remarkable for presenting only one case of a metal hot and cold exhibiting a striking difference, and that metal is iron. With silver, copper, and zinc, the hot side is at the first moment positive to the cold, but only in the smallest degree.

1951. *Strong nitric acid.*—Hot iron is positive to cold. Both in the hot and cold acid the iron is in its peculiar state (1844. 2001.).

1952. *Dilute muriatic acid :* 1 *volume strong muriatic acid, and* 29 *volumes water.*—This acid was as remarkable for the number of cases it supplied as the dilute nitric acid was for the contrary (1950.). Iron, copper, tin, lead, zinc, and cadmium gave active circles with it, the hot metal being positive to the cold; all the results were very striking in the strength and permanency of the electric current produced.

1953. Several cases occur in which the hot metal becomes *negative* instead of positive, as above; and the principal cause of such an effect I have already adverted to (1918.). Thus with the solution of the *sulphuret of potassium* and zinc, on the first immersion of the wires into the hot and cold solution there was a pause, i. e. the galvanometer needle did not move at once, as in the former cases; afterwards a current gradually came into existence, rising in strength until the needle was deflected 70° or 80°, the hot metal being *negative* through the electrolyte to the cold metal. *Cadmium* in the same solution gave also the first pause and then a current, the hot metal being negative; but the effect was very small. Lead, hot, was negative, producing also only a feeble current. Tin gave the same result, but the current was scarcely sensible.

1954. *In dilute sulphuric acid.*—Copper and zinc, after having produced a first positive effect at the hot metal, had that reversed, and a feeble current was produced, the hot metal being negative. Cadmium gave the same phenomena, but stronger (1918.).

1955. *In dilute nitric acid.*—Lead produced no effect at the first moment; but afterwards an electric current, gradually increasing in strength, appeared, which was able to deflect the needle 20° or more, the hot metal being negative. Cadmium gave the same results as lead. Tin gave an uncertain result: at first the hot metal appeared to be a very little negative, it then became positive, and then again the current diminished, and went down almost entirely.

1956. I cannot but view in these results of the action of heat, the strongest proofs of the dependence of the electric current in voltaic circuits on the chemical action of the substances constituting these circuits: the results perfectly accord with the known influence of heat on chemical action. On the other hand, I cannot see how the theory of contact can take cognizance of them, except by adding new assumptions to those already composing it (1874.). How, for instance, can it explain the powerful effects of iron in sulphuret of potassium, or in potassa, or in dilute nitric acid; or of tin in potassa or sulphuric acid; or of iron, copper, tin, &c. in muriatic acid; or indeed of any of the effects quoted? That they cannot be due to thermo contact has been already shown by the results with inactive metals (1931. 1941.); and to these may now be added those of the active metals, silver and copper in dilute nitric acid, for heat produces scarcely a sensible effect in these cases. It seems to me that no other cause than chemical force (a very sufficient one), remains, or is needed to account for them.

1957. If it be said that, on the theory of chemical excitement, the experiments prove either too much or not enough, that, in fact, heat ought to produce the same effect with *all* the metals that are acted on by the electrolytes used, then, I say, that that does not follow. The force and other circumstances of chemical affinity vary almost infinitely with the bodies exhibiting its action, and the added effect of heat upon the chemical affinity would, necessarily, partake of these variations. Chemical action often goes on without any current being produced; and it is well known that, in almost every voltaic circuit, the chemical force has to be considered as divided into that which is local and that which is current (1120.). Now heat frequently assists the local action much, and, sometimes, without appearing to be accompanied by any great increase in the *intensity* of chemical affinity; whilst at other times we are sure, from the chemical phenomena, that it does affect the intensity of the force. The electric current, however, is not determined by the amount of action which takes place, but by the intensity of the affinities concerned; and so cases may easily be produced, in which that metal exerting the least amount of action is nevertheless the positive metal in a voltaic circuit; as with copper in weak nitric acid associated with other copper in strong acid (1975.), or iron or silver in the same weak acid against copper in the strong acid (1996.). Many of those instances where the hot side ultimately becomes negative, as of zinc in dilute solution of sulphuret of potassium (1953.), or cadmium and lead in dilute nitric acid (1955.), are of this nature; and yet the conditions and result are in perfect agreement with the chemical theory of voltaic excitement (1918.).

1958. The distinction between currents founded upon that difference of intensity which is due to the difference in force of the chemical action which is their exciting cause, is, I think, a necessary consequence of the chemical theory, and in 1834 I adopted that opinion[1] (891. 908. 916. 988.). De la Rive in 1836 gave a still more precise enunciation of such a principle[2], by saying, that the intensity of currents is exactly proportional to the degree of affinity which reigns between the particles, the combination or separation of which produces the currents.

1959. I look upon the question of the origin of the power in the voltaic battery as abundantly decided by the experimental results not connected with the action of heat (1824, &c. 1878, &c.). I further view the results with heat as adding very strong confirmatory evidence to the chemical theory; and the numerous questions which arise as to the varied results produced, only tend to show how important the voltaic circuit is as a means of investigation into the nature and principles of chemical affinity (1967.). This truth has already been most strikingly illustrated by the researches of De la Rive made by means of the galvanometer, and the investigations of my friend Professor Daniell into the real nature of acid and other compound electrolytes[3].

## Cases of two metals and one electrolyte; one junction being heated.

1960. Since heat produced such striking results with single metals, I thought it probable that it might be able to affect the mutual relation of the metals in some cases, and even invert their order : on making circuits with two metals and electrolytes, I found the following cases.

1961. In the solution of *sulphuret of potassium*, hot tin is well positive to cold silver : cold tin is very slightly positive to hot silver, and the silver then rapidly tarnishes.

1962. In the solution of *potassa*, cold tin is fairly positive to hot lead, but hot tin is much more positive to cold lead. Also

---

[1] Philosophical Transactions, 1834, p. 428.
[2] Annales de Chimie, 1836, lxi. p. 44. &c.
[3] Philosophical Transactions, 1839, p. 97.

cold cadmium is positive to hot lead, but hot cadmium is far more positive to cold lead. In these cases, therefore, there are great differences produced by heat, but the metals still keep their order.

1963. In *dilute sulphuric acid,* hot iron is *well positive* to cold tin, but hot tin is *still more positive* to cold iron. Hot iron is a little positive to cold lead, and hot lead is very positive to cold iron. These are cases of the actual inversion of order ; and tin and lead may have their states reversed exactly in the same manner.

1964. *In dilute nitric acid,* tin and iron, and iron and lead may have their states reversed, whichever is the hot metal being rendered positive to the other. If, when the iron is to be plunged into the heated side (1930.) the acid is only moderately warm, it seems at first as if the tin would almost overpower the iron, so beautifully can the forces be either balanced or rendered predominant on either side at pleasure. Lead is positive to tin in both cases ; but far more so when hot than when cold.

1965. These effects show beautifully that, in many cases, when two different metals are taken, either can be made positive to the other at pleasure, by acting on their chemical affinities ; though the contacts of the metals with each other (supposed to be an electromotive cause,) remain *entirely unchanged.* They show the effect of heat in reversing or strengthening the natural differences of the metals, according as its action is made to oppose or combine with their natural chemical forces, and thus add further confirmation to the mass of evidence already adduced.

---

1966. There are here, as in the cases of one metal, some instances where the heat renders the metal more negative than it would be if cold. They occur, principally, in the solution of sulphuret of potassium. Thus, with zinc and cadmium, or zinc and tin, the coldest metal is positive. With lead and tin, the hot tin is a little positive, cold tin very positive. With lead and zinc, hot zinc is a little positive, cold zinc much more so. With silver and lead, the hot silver is a little positive to the lead, the cold silver is more, and well positive. In these cases the current is preceded by a moment of quiescence (1953.), during which the chemical action at the hot metal reduces the efficacy of the electrolyte against it more than at the cold metal, and the latter afterwards shows its advantage.

---

1967. Before concluding these observations on the effects of heat, and in reference to the probable utility of the voltaic circuit in investigations of the intimate nature of chemical affinity (1959.), I will describe a result which, if confirmed, may lead to very important investigations. Tin and lead were conjoined and plunged into cold dilute sulphuric acid ; the tin was positive a little. The same acid was heated, and the tin and lead, having been perfectly cleaned, were reintroduced, then the lead was a little positive to the tin. So that a difference of temperature not limited to one contact, for the two electrolytic contacts were always at the same temperature, caused a difference in the relation of these metals the one to the other. Tin and iron in dilute sulphuric acid appeared to give a similar result; i. e. in the cold acid the tin was always positive, but with hot acid the iron was sometimes positive. The effects were but small, and I had not time to enter further into the investigation.

1968. I trust it is understood that, in every case, the precautions as to very careful cleansing of the wires, the places of the ends, simultaneous immersion, observation of the first effects, &c., were attended to.

¶ v. *The exciting chemical force affected by dilution.*

1969. Another mode of affecting the chemical affinity of these elements of voltaic circuits, the metals and acids, and also applicable to the cases of such circuits, is to vary the proportion of water present. Such variation is known, by the simplest chemical experiments, to affect very importantly the resulting action, and, upon the chemical theory, it was natural to expect that it would also produce some corresponding change in the voltaic pile. The effects observed by Avogadro and Œrsted in 1823 are in accordance with such an expectation, for they found that when the same pair of metals was plunged in succession into a strong and a dilute acid, in certain cases an inversion of the current took place[1]. In 1828 De la Rive carried these and similar cases much further, especially in voltaic com-

[1] Annales de Chimie, 1823, xxii. p. 361.

binations of copper and iron with lead[1]. In 1827 Becquerel[2] experimented with one metal, copper, plunged at its two extremities into a solution of the same substance (salt) of *different strengths*; and in 1828 De la Rive[3] made many such experiments with one metal and a fluid in different states of dilution, which I think of very great importance.

1970. The argument derivable from effects of this kind appeared to me so strong that I worked out the facts to some extent, and think the general results well worthy of statement. Dilution is the circumstance which most generally exalts the existing action, but how such a circumstance should increase the electromotive force of *mere contact* did not seem evident to me, without *assuming*, as before (1874.), exactly those influences at the points of contact in the various cases, which the prior results, ascertained by experiments, would require.

1971. The form of apparatus used was the bent tube already described (1915.) fig. 7. The precautions before directed with the wires, tube, &c., were here likewise needful. But there were others also requisite, consequent upon the current produced by combination of water with acid, an effect which has been described long since by Becquerel[4], but whose influence in the present researches requires explanation.

1972. Figs. 9 and 10 represent the two arrangements of fluids used, the part below *m* in the tubes being strong acid, and that above diluted. If the fluid was nitric acid and the platinum wires as in the figures, drawing the end of the wire D upwards above *m*, or depressing it from above *m* downwards, caused great changes at the galvanometer; but if they were preserved quiet at any place, then the electro-current ceased, or very nearly so. Whenever the current existed it was from the weak to the strong acid through the liquid.

1973. When the tube was arranged, as in fig. 9, with water or dilute acid on one side only, and the wires were immersed not more than one third of an inch, the effects were greatly diminished; and more especially, if, by a little motion with a platinum wire, the acids had been mixed at *m*, so that the transition from weak to strong was gradual instead of sudden. In such cases, even when the wires were moved, horizontally, in

[1] Annales de Chimie, 1828, xxxvii. p. 234.    [2] Ibid. 1827, xxxv. p. 120.
[3] Ibid. 1828, xxxvii. p. 240, 241.    [4] Traité de l'Electricité, ii. p. 81.

the acid, the effect was so small as to be scarcely sensible, and not likely to be confounded with the chemical effects to be described hereafter. Still more surely to avoid such interference, an acid moderately diluted was used instead of water. The precaution was taken of emptying, washing, and re-arranging the tubes with fresh acid after each experiment, lest any of the metal dissolved in one experiment should interfere with the results of the next.

1974. I occasionally used the tube with dilute acid on one side only, fig. 9, and sometimes that with dilute acid on both sides, fig. 10. I will call the first No. 1. and the second No. 2.

1975. In illustration of the general results I will describe a particular case. Employing tube No. 1. with strong and dilute nitric acid[1], and two copper wires, the wire in the dilute acid was powerfully positive to the one in the strong acid at the first moment, and continued so. By using tube No. 2. the galvanometer-needle could be held stiffly in either direction, simply by simultaneously raising one wire and depressing the other, so that the first should be in weak and the second in strong acid; the former was always the positive piece of metal.

1976. On repeating the experiments with the substitution of platinum, gold, or even palladium for the copper, scarcely a sensible effect was produced (1973.).

1977. *Strong and dilute nitric acid*[1].—The following single metals being compared with themselves in these acids, gave most powerful results of the kind just described with copper (1975.); silver, iron, lead, tin, cadmium, zinc. The metal in the weaker acid was positive to that in the stronger. Silver is very changeable, and after some time the current is often suddenly reversed, the metal in the strong acid becoming positive: this again will change back, the metal in the weaker acid returning to its positive state. With tin, cadmium, and zinc, violent action in the acid quickly supervenes and mixes all up together. Iron and lead show the alternations of state in the tube No. 2. as beautifully as copper (1975.).

1978. *Strong and dilute sulphuric acid.*—I prepared an acid

[1] The dilute acid consisted of three volumes of strong nitric acid and two volumes of water.

of 49 by weight, strong oil of vitriol, and 9 of water, giving a sulphuric acid with two proportions of water, and arranged the tube No. 1. (1974.) with this and the strongest acid. But as this degree of dilution produced very little effect with the iron, as compared with what a much greater dilution effected, I adopted the plan of putting strong acid into the tube, and then adding a little water at the top at one of the sides, with the precaution of stirring and cooling it previous to the experiment (1973.).

1979. With *iron*, the part of the metal in the weaker acid was powerfully positive to that in the stronger acid. With copper, the same result, as to direction of the current, was produced; but the amount of the effect was small. With silver, cadmium, and zinc, the difference was either very small or unsteady, or nothing; so that, in comparison with the former cases, the electromotive action of the strong and weak acid appeared balanced. With lead and tin, the part of the metal in the *strong* acid was *positive* to that in the weak acid; so that they present an effect the reverse of that produced by iron or copper.

1980. *Strong and dilute muriatic acid.*—I used the strongest pure muriatic acid in tube No. 1, and added water on the top of one side for the dilute extremity (1973.), stirring it a little as before. With silver, copper, lead, tin, cadmium, and zinc, the metal in the *strongest acid* was positive, and the current in most cases powerful. With iron, the end in the strongest acid was first positive: but shortly after the weak acid side became positive and continued so. With palladium, gold, and platinum, nearly insensible effects were the results.

1981. *Strong and dilute solution of caustic potassa.*—With iron, copper, lead, tin, cadmium, and zinc, the metal in the strong solution was positive: in the case of iron slightly, in the case of copper more powerfully, deflecting the needle 30° or 38°, and in the cases of the other metals very strongly. Silver, palladium, gold, and platinum, gave the merest indications (1973.).

Thus potash and muriatic acid are, in several respects, contrasted with nitric and sulphuric acids. As respects muriatic acid, however, and perhaps even the potash, it may be admitted that, even in their strongest states, they are not fairly comparable to the very strong nitric and sulphuric acids, but rather to those acids when somewhat diluted (1985.).

———————

1982. I know it may be said in reference to the numerous changes with strong and dilute acids, that the results are the consequence of corresponding alterations in the contact force; but this is to change about the theory with the phenomena and with chemical force (1874. 1956. 1985. 2006. 2014. 2063.); or it may be alleged that it is the contact force of the solutions produced at the metallic surfaces which, differing, causes difference of effect; but this is to put the effect before the cause in the order of *time.* If the liberty of shifting the point of efficacy from metals to fluids, or from one place to another, be claimed, it is at all events quite time that some definite statement and data respecting the active points (1808.) should be given. At present it is difficult to lay hold of the contact theory by any argument derived from experiment, because of these uncertainties or variations, and it is in that respect in singular contrast with the definite expression as to the place of action which the chemical theory supplies.

1983. All the variations which have been given are consistent with the extreme variety which chemical action under different circumstances possesses, but, as it still appears to me, are utterly incompatible with, what should be, the simplicity of mere contact action; further they admit of even greater variation, which renders the reasons for the one view and against the other, still more conclusive.

1984. Thus if a contact philosopher say that it is only the very strongest acids that can render the part of the metals in it negative, and therefore the effect does not happen with muriatic acid or potash (1980. 1981.), though it does with nitric and sulphuric acids (1977. 1978.); then, the following result is an answer to such an assumption. Iron in *dilute nitric acid,* consisting of one volume of strong acid and twenty of water, is positive to iron in strong acid, or in a mixture of one volume of strong acid with one of water, or with three, or even with five volumes of water. Silver also, in the weakest of these acids, is positive to silver in any of the other four states of it.

1985. Or if, modifying the statement upon these results, it

should be said that diluting the acid at one contact *always* tends to give it a certain *proportionate* electromotive force, and therefore diluting one side more than the other will still allow this force to come into play; then, how is it that with muriatic acid and potassa the effect of dilution is the reverse of that which has been quoted in the cases with nitric acid and iron or silver? (1977. 1984.)   Or if, to avoid *difficulty*, it be assumed that each electrolyte must be considered apart, the nitric acid by itself, and the muriatic acid by itself, for that one may differ from another in the *direction* of the change induced by dilution, then how can the following results with a single acid be accounted for?

1986. I prepared four nitric acids:

A was very strong pure nitric acid;
B was one volume of A and one volume of water;
C was one volume of A and three volumes of water;
D was one volume of A and twenty volumes of water.

Experimenting with these acids and a metal, I found that copper in C acid was positive to copper in A or D acid. Nor was it the *first* addition of water to the strong acid that brought about this curious relation, for copper in the B acid was positive to copper in the strong acid A, but negative to the copper in the weak acid D: the negative effect of the stronger nitric acid with this metal does not therefore depend upon a very high degree of concentration.

1987. Lead presents the same beautiful phenomena. In the C acid it is positive to lead either in A or D acid: in B acid it is positive to lead in the strongest, and negative to lead in the weakest acid.

1988. I prepared also three sulphuric acids:

E was strong oil of vitriol;
F one volume of E and two volumes of water;
G one volume of E and twenty volumes of water.

Lead in F was well *negative* to lead either in E or G. Copper in F was also negative to copper in E or G, but in a smaller degree.   So here are two cases in which metals in an acid of a certain strength are *negative* to the same metals in the same acid, either stronger or weaker.   I used platinum wires ultimately in all these cases with the same acids to check the interference of the combination of acid and water (1973.); but the results were then almost nothing, and showed that the phenomena could not be so accounted for.

1989. To render this complexity for the contact theory still more complicated, we have further variations, in which, with the same acid strong and diluted, some metals are positive in the strong acid and others in the weak. Thus, tin in the strongest sulphuric acid E (1988.) was positive to tin in the moderate or the weak acids F and G ; and tin in the moderate acid F was positive to the same metal in G. Iron, on the contrary, being in the strong acid E was negative to the weaker acids F and G ; and iron in the medium acid F was negative to the same metal in G.

1990. For the purpose of understanding more distinctly what the contact theory has to do here, I will illustrate the case by a diagram. Let fig. 11 represent a circle of metal and sulphuric acid. If A be an arc of iron or copper, and B C strong oil of vitriol, there will be no determinate current: or if B C be weak acid, there will be no such current: but let it be strong acid at B, and diluted at C, and an electric current will run round A C B. If the metal A be silver, it is equally indifferent with the strong and also with the weak acid, as iron has been found to be as to the production of a current; but, besides that, it is indifferent with the strong acid at B and the weak acid at C. Now if the dilution of the electrolyte at one part, as C, had so far increased the contact electromotive force there, when iron or copper was present, as to produce the current found by experiment; surely it ought (consistently with any reasonable limitations of the assumptions in the contact theory,) to have produced the same effect with silver: but there was none. Making the metal A lead or tin, the difficulty becomes far greater ; for though with the strong or the weak acid alone any effect of a determinate current is nothing, yet one occurs upon dilution at C, but now dilution must be supposed to *weaken* instead of *strengthen* the contact force, for the current is in the reverse direction.

1991. Neither can these successive changes be referred to a gradual progression in the effect of dilution, dependent upon the *order of the metals*. For supposing dilution more favourable to the electromotive force of the contact of an acid and a metal, *in proportion* as the metals were in a certain order, as for instance that of their efficacy in the voltaic battery; though such an assumption might seem to account for the gradual diminution of effect from iron to copper, and from copper to silver, one would not expect the reverse effects, or those on the other side of zero, to appear by a return back to such metals as lead and tin (1979. 1989.), but rather look for them in platinum or gold, which, however, produce no results of the kind (1976. 1988.). To increase still further this complexity, it appears, from what has been before stated, that on changing the *acids* the order must again be changed (1981.); nay, more, that with the same acid, and merely by changing the proportion of dilution, such alteration of the order must take place (1986. 1988.).

1992. Thus it appears, as before remarked (1982.), that to apply the theory of contact electromotive force to the facts, that theory must twist and bend about with every variation of chemical action; and after all, with every variety of contact, active and inactive, in no case presents phenomena independent of the active exertion of chemical force.

1993. As the influence of dilution and concentration was so strong in affecting the relation of different parts of the same metal to an acid, making one part either positive or negative to another, I thought it probable that, by mere variation in the strength of the interposed electrolyte, the order of metals when in acids or other solutions of uniform strength, might be changed. I therefore proceeded to experiment on that point, by combining together two metals, tin and lead, through the galvanometer (1915.); arranging the electrolytic solution in tube No. 1, strong on one side and weak on the other: immersing the wires simultaneously, tin into the strong, and lead into the weak solution, and after observing the effect, re-cleaning the wires, re-arranging the fluid, and re-immersing the wires, the tin into the weak, and the lead into the strong portion. De la Rive has already stated[1] that inversions take place when dilute and strong sulphuric acid is used; these I could not obtain when care was taken to avoid the effect of the investing fluid (1918.): the general statement is correct, however, when applied to another acid, and I think the evidence very important to the consideration of the great question of contact or chemical action.

1994. *Two metals in strong and weak solution of potash.*— Zinc was positive to tin, cadmium, or lead, whether in the weak or strong solution. Tin was positive to cadmium, either in weak or strong alkali. Cadmium was positive to lead both ways, but most when in the strong alkali. Thus, though there were *differences in degree* dependent on the strength of the solution, there was *no inversion* of the order of the metals.

1995. *Two metals in strong and weak sulphuric acid.*— Cadmium was positive to iron and tin both ways: tin was also positive to iron, copper, and silver; and iron was positive to copper and silver, whichever side the respective metals were in. Thus none of the metals tried could be made to pass the others, and so take a different order from that which they have in acid uniform in strength. Still there were great variations in degree; thus iron in strong acid was only a little positive to silver in weak acid, but iron in weak acid was very positive to silver in strong acid. Generally the metal, usually called positive, was most positive in the weak acid; but that was not the case with lead, tin, and zinc.

1996. *Two metals in strong and weak nitric acid.*—Here the degree of change produced by difference in the strength of the acid was so great, as to cause not merely difference in degree, but inversions of the order of the metals, of the most striking nature. Thus iron and silver being in tube No. 2 (1974.), whichever metal was in the weak acid was positive to the other in the strong acid. It was merely requisite to raise the one and lower the other metal to make either positive at pleasure (1975.). Copper in weak acid was positive to silver, lead, or tin, in strong acid. Iron in weak acid was positive to silver, copper, lead, zinc, or tin, in strong acid. Lead in weak acid was positive to copper, silver, tin, cadmium, zinc, and iron in strong acid. Silver in weak acid was positive to iron, lead, copper, and, though slightly, even to tin, in strong acid. Tin in weak acid was positive to copper, lead, iron, zinc, and silver, and either neutral or a little positive to cadmium in strong acid. Cadmium in weak acid is very positive, as might be expected, to silver, copper, lead, iron, and tin, and, moderately so, to zinc in the strong acid. When cadmium is in the strong acid it is slightly positive to silver, copper, and iron, in weak acid. Zinc in weak acid is very positive to silver, copper, lead, iron, tin, and cadmium in strong acid : when in the strong acid it is a little positive to silver and copper in weak acid.

1997. Thus wonderful changes occur amongst the metals in circuits containing this acid, merely by the effect of dilution ; so that of the five metals, silver, copper, iron, lead, and tin, any one of them can be made either positive or negative to any other, with the exception of silver positive to copper. The order of these five metals only may therefore be varied about one hundred different ways in the same acid, merely by the effect of dilution.

1998. So also zinc, tin, cadmium, and lead ; and likewise zinc, tin, iron, and lead, being groups each of four metals ; any one of these metals may be made either positive or negative to any other metal of the same group, by dilution of this acid.

---

1999. But the case of variation by dilution may, as regards the opposed theories, be made even still stronger than any yet stated ; for the *same metals* in the *same acid* of the *same strength at the two sides* may be made to change their order, as the chemical action of the acid on each particular metal is affected, by dilution, in a smaller or greater degree.

2000. A voltaic association of iron and silver was dipped, both metals at once, into the same strong nitric acid ; for the first instant, the iron was positive ; the moment after, the silver became positive, and continued so. A similar association of iron and silver was put into weak nitric acid, and the iron was immediately positive, and continued so. With iron and copper the same results were obtained.

2001. These, therefore, are *finally* cases of such an inversion (1999.) ; but as the iron in the strong nitric acid acquires a state the moment after its immersion, which is probably not assumed by it in the weak acid (1843. 1951. 2033.), and as the action on the iron in its *ordinary* state may be said to be, to render it positive to the silver or copper, both in the strong or weak acid, we will not endeavour to force the fact, but look to other metals.

2002. *Silver and nickel* being associated in weak nitric acid, the nickel was positive ; being associated in strong nitric acid, the nickel was still positive at the first moment, but the silver was finally positive.   The nickel lost its superiority through the influence of an investing film (1918.) ; and though the effect might easily pass unobserved, the case cannot be allowed to stand, as fulfilling the statement made (1999.).

2003.  *Copper and nickel* were put into strong nitric acid ; the copper was positive from the first moment.   Copper and nickel being in dilute nitric acid, the nickel was slightly but clearly positive to the copper.   Again, *zinc and cadmium* in strong nitric acid ; the cadmium was positive strongly to the zinc ; the same metals being in dilute nitric acid, the zinc was very positive to the cadmium.   These I consider beautiful and unexceptionable cases (1999.).

2004.  Thus the nitric acid furnishes a most wonderful variety of effects when used as the electrolytic conductor in voltaic circles ; and its difference from sulphuric acid (1995.) or from potassa (1994.) in the phenomena consequent upon dilution, tend, in conjunction with many preceding facts and arguments, to show that the electromotive force in a circle is not the consequence of any power in bodies generally, belonging to them in classes rather than as individuals, and having that simplicity of character which contact force has been assumed to have ; but one that has all the variations which chemical force is *known* to exhibit.

2005.  The changes occurring where any one of four or five metals, differing from each other as far as silver and tin, can be made positive or negative to the others (1997. 1998.), appears to me to shut out the probability that the contact of these metals with each other can produce the smallest portion of the effect in these voltaic arrangements ; and then, if not there, neither can they be effective in any other arrangements ; so that what has been deduced in that respect from former experiments (1829. 1833.) is confirmed by the present.

2006.  Or if the scene be shifted, and it be said that it is the *contact* of the acids or solutions which, by dilution at one side, produce these varied changes (1874. 1982. 1991. 2014. 2060.), then how *utterly unlike* such contact must be to that of the

numerous class of conducting solid bodies (1809. 1867.)! and
where, to give the assumption any show of support, is the case
of such contact (apart from chemical action) producing such
currents ?

2007. That it cannot be an alteration of contact force by
mere dilution at one side (2006.) is also shown by making such
a change, but using metals that are chemically inactive in the
electrolyte employed. Thus when nitric or sulphuric ăcids
were diluted at one side, and then the strong and the weak
parts connected by platinum or gold (1976.), there was no
sensible current, or only one so small as to be unimportant.

2008. A still stronger proof is afforded by the following result. I arranged the tube, fig. 9 (1972.), with strong solution
of yellow sulphuret of potassium (1812.) from A to *m*, and a
solution consisting of one volume of the strong solution, with
six of water from *m* to B. The extremities were then connected by platinum and iron in various ways ; and when the
first effect of immersion was guarded against, including the first
brief negative state of the iron (2049.), the effects were as follows. Platinum being in A and in B, that in A, or the strong
solution, was very slightly positive, causing a permanent deflection of $2^{\circ}$. Iron being in A and in B, the same result was
obtained. Iron being in A and platinum in B, the iron was
positive about $2^{\circ}$ to the platinum. Platinum being in A and
iron in B, the platinum was now positive to the iron by about
$2^{\circ}$. So that not only the contact of the iron and platinum
passes for nothing, but the contact of strong and weak solution of this electrolyte with either iron or platinum, is ineffectual in producing a current. The current which is constant is
very feeble, and evidently related to the mutual position of the
strong and weak solutions, and is probably due to their gradual
mixture.

2009. The results obtained by dilution of an electrolyte
capable of acting on the metals employed to form with it a
voltaic circuit, may in some cases depend on making the acid a
better electrolyte. It would appear, and would be expected
from the chemical theory, that whatever circumstance tends to
make the fluid a more powerful chemical agent and a better
electrolyte, (the latter being a relation purely chemical and not
one of contact,) favours the production of a determinate cur-

rent.   Whatever the cause of the effect of dilution may be, the results still tend to show how valuable the voltaic circle will become as an investigator of the nature of chemical affinity (1959.).

¶ vi. *Differences in the order of the metallic elements of voltaic circles.*

2010. Another class of experimental arguments, bearing upon the great question of the origin of force in the voltaic battery, is supplied by a consideration of the different order in which the metals appear as electromotors when associated with different exciting electrolytes.   The metals are usually arranged in a certain order ; and it has been the habit to say, that a metal in the list so arranged is negative to any one above it, and positive to any one beneath it, as if (and indeed upon the conviction that) they possessed a certain direct power one with another.   But in 1812 Davy showed inversions of this order in the case of iron and copper[1] (943.) ; and in 1828 De la Rive showed many inversions in different cases[2] (1877.) ; gave a strong contrast in the order of certain metals in strong and dilute nitric acid[3] ; and in objecting to Marianini's result most clearly says, that any order must be considered in relation only to that liquid employed in the experiments from which the order is derived[4].

2011. I have pursued this subject in relation to several solutions, taking the precautions before referred to (1917, &c.), and find that no such single order as that just referred to can be maintained.   Thus nickel is negative to antimony and bismuth in strong nitric acid ; it is positive to antimony and bismuth in dilute nitric acid ; it is positive to antimony and negative to bismuth in strong muriatic acid ; it is positive to antimony and bismuth in dilute sulphuric acid ; it is negative to bismuth and antimony in potash ; and it is very negative to bismuth and antimony, either in the colourless or the yellow solution of sulphuret of potassium.

2012. In further illustration of this subject I will take ten metals, and give their order in seven different solutions.

[1] Elements of Chemical Philosophy, p. 149.
[2] Annales de Chimie, 1828, xxxvii. p. 232.
[3] Ibid., p. 235.                                         Ibid., p. 243.

| Dilute nitric acid. | Dilute sulphuric acid. | Muriatic acid. | Strong nitric acid. | Solution of caustic potassa. | Colourless bihydrosulphuret of potassium. | Yellow hydrosulphuret of potassium. |
|---|---|---|---|---|---|---|
| 1. Silver. | 1. Silver. | 3. Antimony. | 5. Nickel. | 1. Silver. | 6. Iron. | 6. Iron. |
| 2. Copper. | 2. Copper. | 1. Silver. | 1. Silver. | 5. Nickel. | 5. Nickel. | 5. Nickel. |
| 3. Antimony. | 3. Antimony. | 5. Nickel. | 3. Antimony. | 2. Copper. | 4. Bismuth. | 4. Bismuth. |
| 4. Bismuth. | 4. Bismuth. | 4. Bismuth. | 2. Copper. | 6. Iron. | 8. Lead. | 3. Antimony. |
| 5. Nickel. | 5. Nickel. | 2. Copper. | 4. Bismuth. | 4. Bismuth. | 1. Silver. | 8. Lead. |
| 6. Iron. | 6. Iron. | 6. Iron. | 6. Iron. | 8. Lead. | 3. Antimony. | 1. Silver. |
| 7. Tin. | 8. Lead. | 8. Lead. | 7. Tin. | 3. Antimony. | 7. Tin. | 7. Tin. |
| 8. Lead. | 7. Tin. | 7. Tin. | 8. Lead. | 9. Cadmium. | 2. Copper. | 9. Cadmium. |
| 9. Cadmium. | 9. Cadmium. | 9. Cadmium. | 10. Zinc. | 7. Tin. | 10. Zinc. | 2. Copper. |
| 10. Zinc. | 10. Zinc. | 10. Zinc. | 9. Cadmium. | 10. Zinc. | 9. Cadmium. | 10. Zinc. |

2013. The dilute nitric acid consisted of one volume strong acid and seven volumes of water; the dilute sulphuric acid, of one volume strong acid and thirteen of water; the muriatic acid, of one volume strong solution and one volume water. The strong nitric acid was pure, and of specific gravity 1·48. Both strong and weak solution of potassa gave the same order. The yellow sulphuret of potassium consisted of one volume of strong solution (1812.) and five volumes of water. The metals are numbered in the order which they presented in the dilute acids (the negative above), for the purpose of showing, by the comparison of these numbers in the other columns, the striking departures there, from this, the most generally assumed order. Iron is included, but only in its ordinary state: its place in nitric acid being given as that which it possesses on its first immersion, not that which it afterwards acquires.

2014. The displacements appear to be most extraordinary, as extraordinary as those consequent on dilution (2005.); and thus show that there is no general ruling influence of fluid conductors, or even of acids, alkalies, &c. as distinct classes of such conductors, apart from their pure chemical relations. But how can the contact theory account for these results? To meet such facts it must be bent about in the most extraordinary manner, following all the contortions of the string of facts (1874. 1956. 1992. 2006. 2063.), and yet never showing a case of the production of a current by contact alone, i. e. unaccompanied by chemical action.

2015. On the other hand, how simply does the chemical theory of excitement of the current represent the facts! as far as we can yet follow them they go hand in hand. Without chemical action, no current; with the changes of chemical action, changes of current; whilst the influence of the strongest cases of *contact*, as of silver and tin (1997.) with each other, pass for nothing in the result.   In further confirmation, the exciting power does not rise, but fall, by the contact of the bodies produced, as the chemical actions producing these decay or are exhausted; the consequent result being well seen in the effect of the investing fluids produced (1918. 1953. 1966.).

2016. Thus, as De la Rive has said, any list of metals in their order should be constructed in reference to the exciting fluid selected.   Further, a zero point should be expressed in the series; for as the electromotive power may be either at the anode or cathode (2040. 2052.), or jointly at both, that substance (if there be one) which is absolutely without any exciting action should form the zero point.   The following may be given, by way of illustration, as the order of a few metals, and other substances in relation to muriatic acid:

> *Peroxide of lead,*
> *Peroxide of manganese,*
> *Oxide of iron,*
> PLUMBAGO,
> Rhodium,
> Platinum,
> Gold,
> Antimony,
> Silver,
> Copper,
> Zinc:

in which plumbago is the neutral substance; those in italics are active at the cathode, and those in Roman characters at the anode.   The upper are of course negative to the lower.   To make such lists as complete as they will shortly require to be, numbers expressive of the relative exciting force, counting from the zero point, should be attached to each substance.

¶ vii. *Active voltaic circles and batteries without metallic contact.*

2017. There are cases in abundance of electric currents produced by pure chemical action, but not one undoubted instance

of the production of a current by pure contact.   As I conceive the great question must now be settled by the weight of
evidence, rather than by simple philosophic conclusions (1799.),
I propose adding a few observations and facts to show the
number of these cases, and their force.   In the Eighth Series
of these Researches[1] (April, 1834) I gave the first experiment,
that I am aware of, in which chemical action was made to produce an electric current and chemical decomposition at a
distance, in a simple circuit, without any contact of metals
(880, &c.).   It was further shown, that when a pair of zinc and
platinum plates were excited at one end of the dilute nitro-
sulphuric acid (880.), or solution of potash (884.), or even in
some cases a solution of common salt (885.), decompositions
might be produced at the other end, of solutions of iodide of
potassium (900.), protochloride of tin (901.), sulphate of soda,
muriatic acid, and nitrate of silver (906.); or of the following
bodies in a state of fusion; nitre, chlorides of silver and lead,
and iodide of lead (902. 906.); no metallic contact being allowed in any of the experiments.

2018.  I will proceed to mention new cases; and first, those
already referred to, where the action of a little dilute acid produced a current passing through the solution of the sulphuret
of potassium (1831.), or green nitrous acid (1844.), or the solution of potassa (1854.); for here no metallic contact was allowed,
and chemical action was the evident and only cause of the currents produced.

2019.  The following is a table of cases of similar excitement
and volatic action, produced by chemical action without
metallic contact.   Each horizontal line contains the four substances forming a circuit, and they are so arranged as to give
the direction of the current, which was in all cases from left to
right through the bodies as they now stand.   All the combinations set down were able to effect decomposition, and they
are but a few of those which occurred in the course of the investigation.

[1] Philosophical Transactions, 1834, p. 426.

2020.

| | | | | |
|---|---|---|---|---|
| Iron. | Dilute nitric acid. | Platinum. | Sulph. of Potassium (1812.) | Full current. |
| Iron. | Dilute nitric acid. | Platinum. | Red nitric acid. | Full current. |
| Iron. | Dilute nitric acid. | Platinum. | Pale nitric acid, strong. | Good. |
| Iron. | Dilute nitric acid. | Platinum. | Green nitrous acid. | Very powerful. |
| Iron. | Dilute nitric acid. | Platinum. | Iodide of potassium. | Full current. |
| Iron. | Dilute sulphuric acid. | Platinum. | Sulphuret of potassium. | Full. |
| Iron. | Dilute sulphuric acid. | Platinum. | Red nitric acid. | Good. |
| Iron. | Muriatic acid. | Platinum. | Green nitrous acid. | Most powerful. |
| Iron. | Dilute muriatic acid. | Platinum. | Red nitric acid. | Good. |
| Iron. | Dilute muriatic acid. | Platinum. | Sulphuret of potassium. | Good. |
| Iron. | Solution of salt. | Platinum. | Green nitrous acid. | Most powerful. |
| Iron. | Common water. | Platinum. | Green nitrous acid. | Good. |
| Zinc. | Dilute nitric acid. | Platinum. | Iodide of potassium. | Good. |
| Zinc. | Muriatic acid. | Platinum. | Iodide of potassium. | Good. |
| Cadmium. | Dilute nitric acid. | Platinum. | Iodide of potassium. | Good. |
| Cadmium. | Muriatic acid. | Platinum. | Iodide of potassium. | Good. |
| Lead. | Dilute nitric acid. | Platinum. | Iodide of potassium. | Good. |
| Lead. | Muriatic acid. | Platinum. | Iodide of potassium. | Good. |
| Copper. | Dilute nitric acid. | Platinum. | Iodide of potassium. | |
| Copper. | Muriatic acid. | Platinum. | Iodide of potassium. | |
| Lead. | Strong sulphuric acid. | Iron. | Dilute sulphuric acid. | Strong. |
| Tin. | Strong sulphuric acid. | Iron. | Dilute sulphuric acid. | Strong. |
| Copper. | Sulphuret of potassium. | Iron. | Dilute nitric acid. | Powerful. |
| Copper. | Sulphuret of potassium. | Iron. | Iodide of potassium. | |
| Copper. | Strong nitric acid. | Iron. | Dilute nitric acid. | Very powerful. |
| Copper. | Strong nitric acid. | Iron. | Iodide of potassium. | |
| Silver. | Strong nitric acid. | Iron. | Dilute nitric acid. | Strong. |
| Silver. | Strong nitric acid. | Iron. | Iodide of potassium. | Good. |
| Silver. | Sulphuret of potassium. | Iron. | Dilute nitric acid. | Strong. |
| Tin. | Strong sulphuric acid. | Copper. | Dilute sulphuric acid. | |

2021. It appears to me probable that any one of the very numerous combinations which can be made out of the following Table, by taking one substance from each column and arranging them in the order in which the columns stand, would produce a current without metallic contact, and that some of these currents would be very powerful.

Rhodium
Gold
Platinum
Palladium
Silver
Nickel
Copper
Lead
Tin
Zinc
Cadmium
} Strong nitrous acid, or strong solution of sulphuret of potassium.

Iron {
Dilute nitric acid
Dilute sulphuric acid
Muriatic acid
Solution of vegetable acids
Iodide of potassium
Iodide of zinc
Solution of salt
Many metallic solutions.

2022. To these cases must be added the many in which one metal in a uniform acid gave currents when one side was heated (1942, &c.). Also those in which one metal with an acid strong and diluted gave a current (1977, &c.).

2023. In the cases where by dilution of the acid one metal can be made either positive or negative to another (1996, &c.), one half of the results should be added to the above, except that they are too strong; for instead of proving that chemical action can produce a current without contact, they go to the extent of showing a total disregard of it, and production of the current against the force of contact, as easily as with it.

2024. That it is easy to construct batteries without metallic contact was shown by Sir Humphry Davy in 1801[1], when he described various effective arrangements including only one metal. At a later period Zamboni constructed a pile in which but one metal and one fluid was used[2], the only difference being extent of contact at the two surfaces. The following forms, which are dependent upon the mere effect of dilution, may be added to these.

2025. Let *a b*, *a b*, *a b*, fig. 12, Plate III., represent tubes or other vessels, the parts at *a* containing strong nitric or sulphuric acid, and the parts at *b* dilute acid of the same kind; then connect these by wires, rods, or plates of one metal only, being copper, iron, silver, tin, lead, or any of those metals which become positive and negative by difference of dilution in the acid (1979, &c.). Such an arrangement will give an effective battery.

2026. If the acid used be the sulphuric, and the metal employed be iron, the current produced will be in one direction, thus ⟵ , through the part figured; but if the metal be tin, the resulting current will be in the contrary direction, thus ⟶ .

2027. Strong and weak solutions of potassa being employed in the tubes, then the single metals zinc, lead, copper, tin, and cadmium (1981.), will produce a similar battery.

2028. If the arrangements be as in fig. 13, in which the vessels 1, 3, 5, &c. contain strong sulphuric acid, and the vessels 2, 4, 6, &c. dilute sulphuric acid; and if the metals *a*, *a*, *a*, are tin, and *b*, *b*, *b*, are iron (1979.), a battery electric current will be produced in the direction of the arrow. If the metals

[1] Philosophical Transactions, 1801, p. 397. Also Journals of the Royal Institution, 1802, p. 51; and Nicholson's Journal, 8vo, 1802, vol. i. p. 144.

[2] Quarterly Journal of Science, viii. 177; or Annales de Chimie, xi. 190. (1819.).

be changed for each other, the acids remaining; or the acids be changed, the metals remaining; the direction of the current will be reversed.

¶ viii. *Considerations of the sufficiency of chemical action.*

2029. Thus there is no want of cases in which chemical action alone produces voltaic currents (2017.); and if we proceed to look more closely to the correspondence which ought to exist between the chemical action and the current produced, we find that the further we trace it the more exact it becomes; in illustration of which the following cases will suffice.

2030. *Chemical action does evolve electricity.*—This has been abundantly proved by Becquerel and De la Rive. Becquerel's beautiful voltaic arrangement of acid and alkali[1] is a most satisfatory proof that chemical action is abundantly sufficient to produce electric phenomena. A great number of the results described in the present papers prove the same statement.

2031. *Where chemical action has been, but diminishes or ceases, the electric current diminishes or ceases also.*—The cases of tin (1882. 1884.), lead (1885.), bismuth (1895.), and cadmium (1905.), in the solution of sulphuret of potassium, are excellent instances of the truth of this proposition.

2032. If a piece of grain tin be put into strong nitric acid, it will generally exert no action, in consequence of the film of oxide which is formed upon it by the heat employed in the process of breaking it up. Then two platinum wires, connected by a galvanometer, may be put into the acid, and one of them pressed against the piece of tin, yet without producing an electric current. If, whilst matters are in this position, the tin be scraped under the acid by a glass rod, or other non-conducting substance capable of breaking the surface, the acid acts on the metal newly exposed, and produces a current; but the action ceases in a moment or two from the formation of oxide of tin and an exhausted investing solution (1918.), and the current ceases with it. Each scratch upon the surface of the tin reproduces the series of phenomena.

[1] Annales de Chimie, 1827, xxxv. p. 122. Bibliothèque Universelle, 1838; xiv. 129, 171.

2033. The case of iron in strong nitric acid, which acts and produces a current at the first moment (1843. 1951. 2001.), but is by that action deprived of so much of its activity, both chemical and electrical, is also a case in point.

2034. If lead and tin be associated in muriatic acid, the lead is positive at the first moment to the tin. The tin then becomes positive, and continues so. This change I attribute to the circumstance, that the chloride of lead formed partly invests that metal, and prevents the continuance of the action there; but the chloride of tin, being far more soluble than that of lead, passes more readily into the solution; so that action goes on there, and the metal exhibits a permanent positive state.

2035. The effect of the investing fluid already referred to in the cases of tin (1919.) and cadmium (1918.), some of the results with two metals in hot and cold acid (1966.), and those cases where metal in a heated acid became negative to the same metal in cold acid (1953, &c.), are of the same kind. The latter can be beautifully illustrated by two pieces of lead in dilute nitric acid: if left a short time, the needle stands nearly at $0°$, but on heating either side, the metal there becomes negative $20°$ or more, and continues so as long as the heat is continued. On cooling that side and heating the other, that piece of lead which before was positive now becomes negative in turn, and so on for any number of times.

2036. *When the chemical action changes the current changes also.*—This is shown by the cases of two pieces of the same active metal in the same fluid. Thus if two pieces of silver be associated in strong muriatic acid, first the one will be positive and then the other; and the changes in the direction of the current will not be slow as if by a gradual action, but exceedingly sharp and sudden. So if silver and copper be associated in a dilute solution of sulphuret of potassium, the copper will be chemically active and positive, and the silver will remain clean; until of a sudden the copper will cease to act, the silver will become instantly covered with sulphuret, showing by that the commencement of chemical action there, and the needle of the galvanometer will jump through $180°$. Two pieces of silver or of copper in solution of sulphuret of potassium produce the same effect.

2037. If metals be used which are inactive in the fluids employed, and the latter undergo no change during the time, from other circumstances, as heat, &c. (1838. 1937.), then no currents, and of course no such alterations in direction, are produced.

2038. *Where no chemical action occurs no current is produced.*—This in regard to ordinary solid conductors, is well known to be the case, as with metals and other bodies (1867.). It has also been shown to be true when fluid conductors (electrolytes) are used, in every case where they exert no chemical action, though such different substances as acid, alkalies and sulphurets have been employed (1843. 1853. 1825. 1829.). These are very striking facts.

2039. *But a current will occur the moment chemical action commences.*—This proposition may be well illustrated by the following experiment. Make an arrangement like that in fig. 14: the two tubes being charged with the same pure, pale, strong nitric acid, the two platinum wires $p$ $p$ being connected by a galvanometer, and the wire $i$, of iron. The apparatus is only another form of the simple arrangement fig. 15, where, in imitation of a former experiment (889.), two plates of iron and platinum are placed parallel, but separated by a drop of strong nitric acid at each extremity. Whilst in this state no current is produced in either apparatus; but if a drop of water be added at $b$ fig. 15, chemical action commences, and a powerful current is produced, though without metallic or any additional contact. To observe this with the apparatus, fig. 14, a drop of water was put in at $b$. At first there was no chemical action and no electric current, though the water was there, so that contact with the water did nothing: the water and acid were moved and mixed together by means of the end of the wire $i$; in a few moments proper chemical action came on, the iron evolving nitrous gas at the place of its action, and at the same time acquiring a positive condition at that part, and producing a powerful electric current.

2040. *When the chemical action which either has or could have produced a current in one direction is reversed or undone, the current is reversed (or undone) also.*

2041. This is a principle or result which most strikingly confirms the chemical theory of voltaic excitement, and is illustrated by many important facts. Volta in the year 1802[1], showed that crystallized *oxide of manganese* was highly negative to zinc and similar metals, giving, according to his theory, electricity to the zinc at the point of contact. Becquerel worked carefully at this subject in 1835[2], and came to the conclusion, but reservedly expressed, that the facts were favourable to the theory of contact. In the following year De la Rive examined the subject[3], and shows, to my satisfaction at least, that the peroxide is at the time undergoing chemical change and losing oxygen, a change perfectly in accordance with the direction of the current it produces.

2042. The peroxide associated with platinum in the green nitrous acid originates a current, and is negative to the platinum, at the same time giving up oxygen and converting the nitrous acid into nitric acid, a change easily shown by a common chemical experiment. In nitric acid the oxide is negative to platinum, but its negative state is much increased if a little alcohol be added to the acid, that body assisting in the reduction of the oxide. When associated with platinum in solution of potash, the addition of a little alcohol singularly favours the increase of the current for the same reason. When the peroxide and platinum are associated with solution of sulphuret of potassium, the peroxide, as might have been expected, is strongly negative.

2043. In 1835 M. Muncke[4] observed the striking power of peroxide of lead to produce phenomena like those of the peroxide of manganese, and these M. de la Rive in 1836 immediately referred to corresponding chemical changes[5]. M. Schœnbein does not admit this inference, and bases his view of "currents of tendency" on the phenomena presented by this body and its non-action with nitric acid[6]. My own results confirm those of M. de la Rive, for by direct experiment I find that the peroxide is acted upon by such bodies as nitric acid. Potash and pure strong nitric acid boiled on peroxide of lead readily dissolved it, forming protonitrate of lead. A dilute

---

[1] Annales de Chimie, 1802, xl. 224.       [2] Ibid. 1835, lx. 164, 171.
[3] Ibid. 1836, lxi. 40 ; and Bibliothèque Universelle, 1836, i. 152, 158.
[4] Bibliothèque Universelle, 1836, i. 160.       [5] Ibid. 1836, i. 162, 154.
[6] Philosophical Magazine, 1838, xii. 226, 311 ; and Bibliothèque Universelle, 1838, xiv. 155.

nitric acid was made and divided into two portions; one was tested by a solution of sulphuretted hydrogen, and showed no signs of lead: the other was mingled with a little peroxide of lead (1822.) at common temperatures, and after an hour filtered and tested in the same manner, and found to contain plenty of lead.

2044. The peroxide of lead is negative to platinum in solutions of common salt and potash, bodies which might be supposed to exert no chemical action on it. But direct experiments show that they do exert sufficient action to produce all the effects. A circumstance in further proof that the current in the voltaic circuit formed by these bodies is chemical in its origin, is the rapid depression in the force of the current produced, after the first moment of immersion.

2045. The most powerful arrangement with peroxide of lead, platinum, and one fluid, was obtained by using a solution of the yellow sulphuret of potassium as the connecting fluid. A convenient mode of making such experiments was to form the peroxide into a fine soft paste with a little distilled water, to cover the lower extremity of a platinum plate uniformly with this paste, using a glass rod for the purpose, and making the coat only thick enough to hide the platinum well, then to dry it well, and finally, to compare that plate with a clean platinum plate in the electrolyte employed. Unless the platinum plate were perfectly covered, local electrical currents (1120.) took place which interfered with the result. In this way, the peroxide is easily shown to be negative to platinum either in the solution of the sulphuret of potassium or in nitric acid. Red-lead gave the same results in both these fluids.

2046. But using this sulphuretted solution, the same kind of proof in support of the chemical theory could be obtained from protoxides as before from the peroxides. Thus, some pure protoxide of lead, obtained from the nitrate by heat and fusion, was applied on the platinum plate (2045.), and found to be strongly negative to metallic platinum in the solution of sulphuret of potassium. White lead applied in the same manner was also found to acquire the same state. Either of these bodies when compared with platinum in dilute nitric acid was, on the contrary, very positive.

2047. The same effect is well shown by the action of oxidized iron. If a plate of iron be oxidized by heat so as to give an oxide of such aggregation and condition as to be acted on scarcely or not at all by the solution of sulphuret, then there is little or no current, such an oxide being as platinum in the solution (1840.). But if it be oxidized by exposure to air, or by being wetted and dried; or by being moistened by a little dilute nitric or sulphuric acid and then washed, first in solution of ammonia or potassa, and afterwards in distilled water and dried; or if it be moistened in solution of potassa, heated in the air, and then washed well in distilled water and dried; such iron associated with platinum and put into a solution of the sulphuret will produce a powerful current until all the oxide is reduced, the iron during the whole time being negative.

2048. A piece of rusty iron in the same solution is powerfully negative. So also is a platinum plate with a coat of protoxide, or peroxide, or native carbonate of iron on it (2045.).

2049. This result is one of those effects which has to be guarded against in the experiments formerly described (1826. 1886.). If what appears to be a clean plate of iron is put into a dilute solution of the sulphuret of potassium, it is first negative to platinum, then neutral, and at last generally feebly positive; if it be put into a strong solution, it is first negative, and then becomes neutral, continuing so. It cannot be cleansed so perfectly with sand-paper, but that when immersed it will be negative, but the more recently and well the plate has been cleansed, the shorter time does this state continue. This effect is due to the instantaneous oxidation of the surface of the iron during its momentary exposure to the atmosphere, and the after reduction of this oxide by the solution. Nor can this be considered an unnatural result to those who consider the characters of iron. Pure iron in the form of a sponge takes fire spontaneously in the air; and a plate recently cleansed, if dipped into water, or breathed upon, or only exposed to the atmosphere, produces an instant smell of hydrogen. The thin film of oxide which can form during a momentary exposure is, therefore, quite enough to account for the electric current produced.

2050. As a further proof of the truth of these explanations, I placed a plate of iron under the surface of a solution of the sulphuret of potassium, and rubbed it there with a piece of

wood which had been soaking for some time in the same sulphuret. The iron was then neutral or very slightly positive
to platinum connected with it. Whilst in connection with the
platinum it was again rubbed with the wood so as to acquire a
fresh surface of contact; it did not become negative, but continued in the least degree positive, showing that the former
negative current was only a temporary result of the coat of
oxide which the iron had acquired in the air.

2051. Nickel appears to be subject to the same action as
iron, though in a much slighter degree. All the circumstances
were parallel, and the proof applied to iron (2050.) was applied
to it also, with the same result.

2052. So all these phenomena with protoxides and peroxides
agree in referring the current produced to chemical action;
not merely by showing that the current depends upon the action, but also that the *direction* of the current depends upon
the direction which the chemical affinity determines the exciting or electromotive anion to take. And it is I think, a most
striking circumstance, that these bodies, which when they can
and do act chemically produce currents, have not the least
power of the kind when *mere contact only* is allowed (1869.),
though they are excellent conductors of electricity, and can
readily carry the currents formed by other and more effectual
means.

2053. With such a mass of evidence for the efficacy and
sufficiency of chemical action as that which has been given
(1878. 2052.); with so many current circuits without metallic
contact (2017.) and so many non-current circuits with (1867.);
what reason can there be for referring the effect in the joint
cases where both chemical action and contact occur, to contact,
or to anything but the chemical force alone? Such a reference
appears to me most unphilosophical: it is dismissing a proved
and active cause to receive in its place one which is merely
hypothetical.

¶ ix. *Thermo-electric evidence.*

2054. The phenomena presented by that most beautiful discovery of Seebeck, thermo-electricity, has occasionally and,

also, recently been adduced in proof of the electromotive influence of contact amongst the metals, and such like solid conductors[1] (1809. 1867.). A very brief consideration is, I think, sufficient to show how little support these phenomena give to the theory in question.

2055. If the contact of metals exert any exciting influence in the voltaic circuit, then we can hardly doubt that thermo-electric currents are due to the same force; i. e. to disturbance, by local temperature, of the balanced forces of the different contacts in a metallic or similar circuit. Those who quote thermo effects as proofs of the effect of contact must, of course, admit this opinion.

2056. Admitting contact force, we may then assume that heat either increases or diminishes the electromotive force of contact. For if in fig. 16. A be antimony and B bismuth, heat applied at $x$ causes a current to pass in the direction of the arrow; if it be assumed that bismuth in contact with antimony tends to become positive and the antimony negative, then heat diminishes the effect; but if it be supposed that the tendency of bismuth is to become negative, and of antimony positive, then heat increases the effect. How we are to decide which of these two views is the one to be adopted, does not seem to me clear; for nothing in the thermo-electric phenomena alone can settle the point by the galvanometer.

2057. If for that purpose we go to the voltaic circuit, there the situation of antimony and bismuth varies according as one or another fluid conductor is used (2012.). Antimony, being negative to bismuth with the acids, is positive to it with an alkali or sulphuret of potassium; still we find they come *nearly together* in the midst of the metallic series. In the thermo series, on the contrary, their position is at the *extremes*, being as different or as much opposed to each other as they can be. This difference was long ago pointed out by Professor Cumming[2]: how is it consistent with the contact theory of the voltaic pile?

2058. Again, if silver and antimony form a thermo circle (fig.17.), and the junction $x$ be heated, the current there is

---

[1] See Fechner's words. Philosophical Magazine, 1838, xiii. p. 206.
[2] Annals of Philosophy, 1823, vi. 177.

from the silver to the antimony. If silver and bismuth form a
thermo series (fig. 18.), and the junction *x* be heated, the current is from the bismuth to the silver; and assuming that heat
increases the force of contact (2056.), these results will give
the direction of contact force between these metals, *antimony*
◄——*silver*, and *bismuth*——►*silver*. But in the voltaic series
the current is *from the silver* to both the antimony and bismuth
at their points of contact, whenever dilute sulphuric or nitric
acid, or strong nitric acid, or solution of potassa (2012.) are
used; so that metallic contact, like that in the thermo circle,
can at all events have *very little* to do here. In the yellow sulphuret of potassium the current is from both antimony and bismuth *to the silver* at their contacts, a result equally inconsistent
with the thermo effect as the former. When the colourless
hydrosulphuret of potassium is used to complete the voltaic
circle, the current is from bismuth to silver, and from silver to
antimony at their points of contact; whilst, with strong muriatic acid, precisely the reverse direction occurs, for it is from
silver to bismuth, and from antimony to silver at the junctions.

2059. Again;—by the heat series copper gives a current to
gold; tin and lead give currents to copper, rhodium, or gold;
zinc gives one to antimony, or iron, or even plumbago; and
bismuth gives one to nickel, cobalt, mercury, silver, palladium,
gold, platinum, rhodium, and plumbago; at the *point of contact* between the metals:—currents which are just the reverse
of those produced by the same metals, when formed into voltaic circuits and excited by the ordinary acid solutions (2012.).

2060. These, and a great number of other discrepancies,
appear by a comparison, according to theory, of thermo contact and voltaic contact action, which can only be accounted
for by assuming a specific effect of the contact of water, acids,
alkalies, sulphurets, and other exciting electrolytes, for each
metal; this assumed contact force being not only unlike ther-
mo-metallic contact, in not possessing a balanced state in the
complete circuit at uniform temperatures, but, also, having no
relation to it as to the *order* of the metals employed. So bismuth and antimony, which are far apart in thermo-electric
order, must have this extra character of acid contact very
greatly developed in an opposite direction as to its result, to

render them only a feeble voltaic combination with each other: and with respect to silver, which stands between tin and zinc thermo-electrically, not only must the same departure be required, but how great must the effect of this, its incongruous contact, be, to overcome so completely as it does, and even powerfully reverse the differences which the metals (according to the contact theory) tend to produce!

2061. In further contrast with such an assumption, it must be remembered that, though the series of thermo-electric bodies is different from the usual voltaic order (2012.), it is perfectly consistent with itself, i. e. that if iron and antimony be weak with each other, and bismuth be strong with iron, it will also be strong with antimony. Also that if the electric current pass from bismuth to rhodium at the hot junction, and also from rhodium to antimony at the hot junction, it will pass far more powerfully from bismuth to antimony at the heated junction. To be at all consistent with this simple and true relation, sulphuric acid should not be strongly energetic with iron or tin and weakly so with silver, as it is in the voltaic circuit, since these metals are not far apart in the thermo series : nor should it be nearly alike to platinum and gold voltaically, since they are far apart in the thermo series.

2062. Finally, in the thermo circuit there is that relation to heat which shows that for every portion of electric force evolved, there is a corresponding change in another force, or form of force, namely heat, able to account for it; this, the united experiments of Seebeck and Peltier have shown. But contact force is a force which has to produce something from nothing, a result of the contact theory which can be better stated a little further on (2069. 2071. 2073.).

2063. What evidence then for mere contact excitement, derivable from the facts of thermo-electricity, remains, since the power must thus be referred to the acid or other electrolyte used (2060.) and made, not only to vary uncertainly for each metal, but to vary also in direct conformity with the variation of chemical action (1874. 1956. 1992. 2006. 2014.) ?

2064. The contact theorist seems to consider that the advocate of the chemical theory is called upon to account for the phenomena of thermo-electricity. I cannot perceive that Seebeck's circle has any relation to the voltaic pile, and think that

the researches of Becquerel[1] are quite sufficient to authorize
that conclusion.

¶ x. *Improbable nature of the assumed contact force.*

2065. I have thus given a certain body of experimental evidence and consequent conclusions, which seem to me fitted to
assist in the elucidation of the disputed point, in addition to
the statements and arguments of the great men who have already advanced their results and opinions in favour of the
chemical theory of excitement in the voltaic pile, and against
that of contact. I will conclude by adducing a further argument founded upon the, to me, unphilosophical nature of the
force to which the phenomena are, by the contact theory, referred.

2066. It is assumed by the theory (1802.) that where two
dissimilar metals (or rather bodies) touch, the dissimilar particles act on each other, and induce opposite states. I do not
deny this, but on the contrary think, that in many cases such
an effect takes place between contiguous particles; as for instance, preparatory to action in common chemical phenomena,
and also preparatory to that act of chemical combination which,
in the voltaic circuit, causes the current (1738. 1743.).

2067. But the contact theory assumes that these particles,
which have thus by their mutual action acquired opposite electrical states, can discharge these states one to the other, and
yet remain in the state they were first in, being *in every point*
entirely unchanged by what has previously taken place. It assumes also that the particles, being by their mutual action rendered plus and minus, can, whilst under this inductive action,
discharge to particles of like matter with themselves and so
produce a current.

2068. This is in no respect consistent with known actions.
If in relation to chemical phenomena we take two substances,
as oxygen and hydrogen, we may conceive that two particles,
one of each, being placed together and heat applied, they induce contrary states in their opposed surfaces, according, perhaps, to the view of Berzelius (1739.), and that these states
becoming more and more exalted end at last in a mutual dis-

---

[1] Annales de Chimie, 1829, xli. 355. xlvi. 275.

charge of the forces, the particles being ultimately found combined, and unable to repeat the effect.   Whilst they are under
induction and before the final action comes on, they cannot
spontaneously lose that state; but by removing the *cause* of
the increased inductive effect, namely the heat, the effect itself
can be lowered to its first condition.   If the acting particles
are involved in the constitution of an electrolyte, then they
can produce current force (921. 924.) proportionate to the
amount of chemical force consumed (868.).

2069. But the contact theory, which is obliged, according
to the facts, to admit that the acting particles are not changed
(1802. 2067.) (for otherwise it would be the chemical theory),
is constrained to admit also, that the force which is able to
make two particles assume a certain state in respect to each
other, is unable to make them *retain* that state; and so it virtually denies the great principle in natural philosophy, that
cause and effect are equal (2071.).   If a particle of platinum
by contact with a particle of zinc willingly gives of its own
electricity to the zinc, because this by its presence tends to
make the platinum assume a negative state, why should the
particle of platinum take electricity from any other particle of
platinum behind it, since that would only tend to destroy the
very state which the zinc has just forced it into?   Such is not
the case in common induction; (and Marianini admits that the
effect of contact may take place through air and measurable
distances[1]); for there a ball rendered negative by induction,
will not take electricity from surrounding bodies, however thoroughly we may uninsulate it; and if we force electricity into
it, it will, as it were, be spurned back again with a power equivalent to that of the inducing body.

2070. Or if it be supposed rather, that the zinc particle, by
its inductive action, tends to make the platinum particle positive, and the latter, being in connection with the earth by other
platinum particles, calls upon them for electricity, and so acquires a positive state; why should it discharge that state to
the zinc, the very substance, which, making the platinum assume
that condition, ought of course to be able to sustain it?   Or

---

[1] Memorie della Società Italiana in Modena, 1837, xxi. 232, 233, &c.

again, if the zinc tends to make the platinum particle positive, why should not electricity go to the platinum *from the zinc*, which is as much in contact with it as its neighbouring platinum particles are? Or if the zinc particle in contact with the platinum tends to become positive, why does not electricity flow to it from the zinc particles behind, as well as from the platinum[1]? There is no sufficient probable or philosophic cause assigned for the assumed action; or reason given why one or other of the consequent effects above mentioned should not take place: and, as I have again and again said, I do not know of a single fact, or case of contact current, on which, in the absence of such probable cause, the theory can rest.

2071. The contact theory assumes, in fact, that a force which is able to overcome powerful resistance, as for instance that of the conductors, good or bad, through which the current passes, and that again of the electrolytic action where bodies are decomposed by it, can arise out of nothing ; that, without any change in the acting matter or the consumption of any generating force, a current can be produced which shall go on for ever against a constant resistance, or only be stopped, as in the voltaic trough, by the ruins which its exertion has heaped up in its own course. This would indeed be *a creation of power*, and is like no other force in nature. We have many processes by which the form of the power may be so changed that an apparent *conversion* of one into another takes place. So we can change chemical force into the electric current, or the current into chemical force. The beautiful experiments of Seebeck and Peltier show the convertibility of heat and electricity ; and others by Œrsted and myself show the convertibility of electricity and magnetism. But in no cases, not even those of the Gymnotus and Torpedo (1790.), is there a pure creation of force ; a production of power without a corresponding exhaustion of something to supply it[2].

[1] I have spoken, for simplicity of expression, as if one metal were active and the other passive in bringing about these induced states, and not, as the theory implies, as if each were mutually subject to the other. But this makes no difference in the force of the argument; whilst an endeavour to state fully the joint changes on both sides, would rather have obscured the objections which arise, and which yet are equally strong in either view.

[2] (*Note*, March 29, 1840.)—I regret that I was not before aware of most

2072. It should ever be remembered that the chemical theory sets out with a power the existence of which is pre-proved, and then follows its variations, rarely assuming anything which is not supported by some corresponding simple chemical fact. The contact theory sets out with an assumption, to which it adds others as the cases require, until at last the contact force, instead of being the firm unchangeable thing at first supposed by Volta, is as variable as chemical force itself.

2073. Were it otherwise than it is, and were the contact theory true, then, as it appears to me, the equality of cause and effect must be denied (2069.). Then would the perpetual motion also be true; and it would not be at all difficult, upon the first given case of an electric current by contact alone, to produce an electro-magnetic arrangement, which, as to its principle, would go on producing mechanical effects for ever.

*Royal Institution,*
*December 26, 1839.*

NOTE.

2074. In a former series (925, &c.) I have said that I do not think any part of the electricty of the voltaic pile is due to the

important evidence for this philosophical argument, consisting of the opinion of Dr. Roget, given in his Treatise on Galvanism in the Library of Useful Knowledge, the date of which is January 1829. Dr. Roget is, upon the facts of the science, a supporter of the chemical theory of excitation; but the striking passage I desire now to refer to, is the following, at § 113. of the article Galvanism. Speaking of the voltaic theory of contact, he says, "Were any further reasoning necessary to overthrow it, a forcible argument might be drawn from the following consideration. If there could exist a power having the property ascribed to it by the hypothesis, namely, that of giving continual impulse to a fluid in one constant direction, without being exhausted by its own action, it would differ essentially from all the other known powers in nature. All the powers and sources of motion, with the operation of which we are acquainted, when producing their peculiar effects, are expended in the same proportion as those effects are produced; and hence arises the impossibility of obtaining by their agency a perpetual effect; or, in other words, a perpetual motion. But the electromotive force ascribed by Volta to the metals when in contact is a force which, as long as a free course is allowed to the electricity it sets in motion, is never expended, and continues to be excited with undiminished power, in the production of a never-ceasing effect. Against the truth of such a supposition, the probabilities are all but infinite."—*Roget.*

combination of the oxide of zinc with the sulphuric acid used, and that I agreed so far with Sir Humphry Davy in thinking that acids and alkalies did not in combining evolve electricity in large quantity when they were not parts of electrolytes.

This I would correct; for I think that Becquerel's pile is a perfect proof that when acid and alkali combine an electric current is produced[1].

I perceive that Dr. Mohr of Coblentz appears to have shown that it is only nitric acid which amongst acids can in combining with alkalies produce an electric current[2].

For myself, I had made exception of the hydracids (929.) on theoretical grounds. I had also admitted that oxyacids when in solution might in such cases produce small currents of electricity (928. and *Note.*); and Jacobi says that in Becquerel's improved acid and alkaline pile, it is not above a thirtieth part of the whole power which appears as current. But I now wish to say, that though in the voltaic battery, dependent for its power on the oxidizement of zinc, I do not think that the *quantity* of electricity is at all increased or affected by the combination of the oxide with the acid (933. 945.), still the latter circumstance cannot go altogether for nothing. The researches of Mr. Daniell on the nature of compound electrolytes[3] ties together the electrolyzation of a salt and the water in which it is dissolved, in such a manner as to make it almost certain that, in the corresponding cases of the *formation* of a salt at the place of excitement in the voltaic circuit, a similar connection between the water and the salt formed must exist: and I have little doubt that the joint action of water, acids, and bases, in Becquerel's battery, in Daniell's electrolyzations, and at the zinc in the ordinary active pile, are, in principle, closely connected together.

[1] Bibliothèque Universelle, 1838, xiv. 129. 171. Comptes Rendus, i. p. 455. Annales de Chimie, 1827, xxxv. 122.

[2] Philosophical Magazine, 1838, xiii. p. 382; or Poggendorf's Annalen, xlii. p. 76.

[3] Philosophical Transactions, 1839, p. 97.

## EIGHTEENTH SERIES.

Received January 26,—Read February 2, 1843.

§ 25. *On the electricity evolved by the friction of water and steam against other bodies.*

2075. TWO years ago an experiment was described by Mr. Armstrong and others [1], in which the issue of a stream of high pressure steam into the air produced abundance of electricity. The source of the electricity was not ascertained, but was supposed to be the evaporation or change of state of the water, and to have a direct relation to atmospheric electricity. I have at various times since May of last year been working upon the subject, and though I perceive Mr. Armstrong has, in recent communications, anticipated by publication some of the facts which I also have obtained, the Royal Society may still perhaps think a compressed account of my results and conclusions, which include many other important points, worthy its attention.

2076. The apparatus I have used was not competent to furnish me with much steam or a high pressure, but I found it sufficient for my purpose, which was the investigation of the effect and its cause, and not necessarily an increase of the electric development. Mr. Armstrong, as is shown by a recent paper, has well effected the latter [2]. The boiler I used, belonging to the London Institution, would hold about ten gallons of water, and allow the evaporation of five gallons. A pipe $4\frac{1}{2}$ feet long was attached to it, at the end of which was a large stop-cock and a metal globe, of the capacity of thirty-two cubic inches, which I will call the *steam-globe*, and to this globe, by its mouth-piece, could be attached various forms of apparatus,

---

[1] Philosophical Magazine, 1840, vol. xvii. pp. 370, 452, &c.
[2] Ibid. 1843, vol. xxii. p. 1.

serving as vents for the issuing steam[1]. Thus a cock could be connected with the steam-globe, and this cock be used as the experimental steam-passage; or a wooden tube could be screwed in; or a small metal or glass tube put through a good cork, and the cork screwed in; and in these cases the steam way of the globe and tube leading to the boiler was so large, that they might be considered as part of the boiler, and these terminal passages as the obstacles which, restraining the issue of steam, produced any important degree of friction.

2077. Another issue piece consisted of a metal tube terminated by a metal funnel, and of a cone advancing by a screw more or less into the funnel, so that the steam as it rushed forth beat against the cone (Plate I. fig. 2.); and this cone could either be electrically connected with the funnel and boiler, or be insulated.

2078. Another terminal piece consisted of a tube, with a stop-cock and feeder attached to the top part of it, by which any fluid could be admitted into the passage, and carried on with the steam (fig. 3.).

2079. In another terminal piece, a small cylindrical chamber was constructed (fig. 4.) into which different fluids could be introduced, so that, when the cocks were opened, the steam passing on from the steam-globe (2076.) should then enter this chamber and take up anything that was there, and so proceed with it into the final passage, or out against the cone (2077.), according as the apparatus had been combined together. This little chamber I will always call C.

2080. The pressure at which I worked with the steam was from eight to thirteen inches of mercury, never higher than thirteen inches, or about two-fifths of an atmosphere.

2081. The boiler was insulated on three small blocks of lac, the chimney being connected by a piece of funnel-pipe removable at pleasure. Coke and charcoal were burnt, and the insulation was so good, that when the boiler was attached to a gold-leaf electrometer and charged purposely, the divergence of the leaves did not alter either by the presence of a large fire, or the abundant escape of the results of the combustion.

[1] This globe and the pieces of apparatus are represented upon a scale of one-fourth in the Plate belonging to this paper.

2082. When the issuing steam produces electricity, there are two ways of examining the effect: either the insulated boiler may be observed, or the steam may be examined, but these states are always contrary one to the other. I attached to the boiler both a gold-leaf and a discharging electrometer, the first showed any charge short of a spark, and the second by the number of sparks in a given time carried on the measurement of the electricity evolved. The state of the steam may be observed either by sending it through an insulated wide tube in which are some diaphragms of wire gauze, which serves as a discharger to the steam, or by sending a puff of it near an electrometer when it acts by induction; or by putting wires and plates of conducting matter in its course, and so discharging it. To examine the state of the boiler or substance against which the steam is excited, is far more convenient, as Mr. Armstrong has observed, than to go for the electricity to the steam itself; and in this paper I shall give the state of the former, unless it be otherwise expressed.

2083. Proceeding to the cause of the excitation, I may state first that I have satisfied myself it is not due to evaporation or condensation, nor is it affected by either the one or the other. When the steam was at its full pressure, if the valve were suddenly raised and taken out, no electricity was produced in the boiler, though the evaporation was for the time very great. Again, if the boiler were charged by excited resin before the valve was opened, the opening of the valve and consequent evaporation did not affect this charge. Again, having obtained the power of constructing steam passages which should give either the positive or the negative, or the neutral state (2102. 2110. 2117.), I could attach these to the steam way, so as to make the boiler either positive, or negative, or neutral at pleasure with the same steam, and whilst the evaporation for the whole time continued the same. So that the excitation of electricity is clearly independent of the evaporation or of the change of state.

2084. The issue of *steam alone* is not sufficient to evolve electricity[1]. To illustrate this point I may say that the cone apparatus (2077.) is an excellent exciter: so also is a box-wood tube (2102. fig. 5.) soaked in water, and screwed into the steam-globe. If with either of these arrangements, the steam-globe (fig. 1.) be empty of water, so as to catch and retain that which is condensed from the steam, then after the first moment (2089.), and when the apparatus is hot, the issuing steam excites no electricity; but when the steam-globe is filled up so far that the rest of the condensed water is swept forward with the steam, abundance of electricity appears. If then the globe be emptied of its water, the electricity ceases; but upon filling it up to the proper height, it immediately reappears in full force. So when the feeder apparatus (2078.) was used, whilst there was no water in the passage-tube, there was no electricity; but on letting in water from the feeder, electricity was immediately evolved.

2085. The electricity is due entirely to the friction of the particles of water which the steam carries forward against the surrounding solid matter of the passage, or that which, as with the cone (2077.), is purposely opposed to it, and is in its nature like any other ordinary case of excitement by friction. As will be shown hereafter (2130. 2132.), a very small quantity of water properly rubbed against the obstructing or interposed body, will produce a very sensible proportion of electricity.

2086. Of the many circumstances affecting this evolution of electricity, there are one or two which I ought to refer to here. Increase of pressure (as is well illustrated by Mr. Armstrong's experiments) greatly increases the effect, simply by rubbing the two exciting substances more powerfully together. Increase of pressure will sometimes change the positive power of a passage to negative; not that it has power of itself to change the quality of the passage, but as will be seen presently (2108.), by carrying off that which gave the positive power; no increase of pressure, as far as I can find, can change the negative power of a given passage to positive. In other phenomena hereafter to be described (2090. 2105.), increase of pressure will no doubt have its influence; and an effect which has

---

[1] Mr. Armstrong has also ascertained that water is essential to a high development.   Phil. Mag. 1843, vol. xxii. p. 2.

been decreased, or even annihilated (as by the addition of substances to the water in the steam-globe, or to the issuing current of water and steam), may, no doubt, by increase of pressure be again developed and exalted.

2087. The shape and form of the exciting passage has great influence, by favouring more or less the contact and subsequent separation of the particles of water and the solid substance against which they rub.

2088. When the mixed steam and water pass through a tube or stop-cock (2076.), they may issue, producing either a hissing smooth sound, or a rattling rough sound[1]; and with the cone apparatus (2077. fig. 2.), or certain lengths of tube, these conditions alternate suddenly. With the smooth sound little or no electricity is produced; with the rattling sound plenty. The rattling sound accompanies that irregular rough vibration, which casts the water more violently and effectually against the substance of the passage, and which again causes the better excitation. I converted the end of the passage into a steam-whistle, but this did no good.

2089. If there be no water in the steam-globe (2076.), upon opening the steam-cock the *first effect* is very striking; a good excitement of electricity takes place, but it very soon ceases. This is due to water condensed in the cold passages, producing excitement by rubbing against them. Thus, if the passage be a stop-cock, whilst cold it excites electricity with what is supposed to be steam only; but as soon as it is hot, the electricity ceases to be evolved. If, then, whilst the steam is issuing, the cock be cooled by an insulated jet of water, it resumes its power. If, on the other hand, it be made hot by a spirit-lamp before the steam be let on, then there is *no* first effect. On this principle, I have made an exciting passage by surrounding one part of an exit tube with a little cistern, and putting spirits of wine or water into it.

---

2090. We find then that particles of water rubbed against other bodies by a current of steam evolve electricity. For this

---

[1] Messrs. Armstrong and Schafhaeutl have both observed the coincidence of certain sounds or noises with the evolution of the electricity.

purpose, however, it is not merely water but *pure* water which must be used. On employing the feeding apparatus (2078.), which supplied the rubbing water to the interior of the steam passage, I found, as before said, that with steam only I obtained no electricity (2084.). On letting in distilled water, abundance of electricity was evolved; on putting a small crystal of sulphate of soda, or of common salt into the water, the evolution ceased entirely. Re-employing distilled water, the electricity appeared again; on using the common water supplied to London, it was unable to produce it.

2091. Again, using the steam-globe (2076.), and a box-wood tube (2102.) which excites well if the water distilling over from the boiler be allowed to pass with the steam, when I put a small crystal of sulphate of soda, of common salt, or of nitre, or the smallest drop of sulphuric acid, into the steam-globe with the water, the apparatus was utterly ineffective, and no electricity could be produced. On withdrawing such water and replacing it by distilled water, the excitement was again excellent: on adding a very small portion of any of these substances, it ceased; but upon again introducing pure water it was renewed.

2092. Common water in the steam-globe was powerless to excite. A little potash added to distilled water took away all its power; so also did the addition of *any* of those saline or other substances which give conducting power to water.

2093. The effect is evidently due to the water becoming so good a conductor, that upon its friction against the metal or other body, the electricity evolved can be immediately discharged again, just as if we tried to excite lac or sulphur by flannel which was damp instead of dry. It shows very clearly that the exciting effect, when it occurs, is due to water and not to the passing steam.

2094. As ammonia increases the conducting power of water only in a small degree (554.), I concluded that it would not take away the power of excitement in the present case; accordingly on introducing some to the pure water in the globe, electricity was still evolved though the steam of vapour and water was able to redden moist turmeric paper. But the addition of a very small portion of dilute sulphuric acid, by forming sulphate of ammonia, took away all power.

2095. When in any of these cases, the steam-globe contained water which could not excite electricity, it was beautiful to observe how, on opening the cock which was inserted into the steam-pipe before the steam-globe, fig. 1. (the use of which was to draw off the water condensed in the pipe before it entered the steam-globe), electricity was instantly evolved; yet a few inches further on the steam was quite powerless, because of the small change in the quality of the water over which it passed, and which it took with it.

2096. When a wooden or metallic tube (2076.) was used as the exciting passage, the application of solution of salts to the outside and end of the tube in no way affected the evolution. But when a wooden cone (2077.) was used, and that cone moistened with the solutions, there was no excitement on first letting out the steam, and it was only as the solution was washed away that the power appeared; soon rising, however, to its full degree.

---

2097. Having ascertained these points respecting the necessity of water and its purity, the next for examination was the influence of the substance against which the stream of steam and water rubbed. For this purpose I first used cones (2077.) of various substances, either insulated or not, and the following, namely, brass, box-wood, beech-wood, ivory, linen, kerseymere, white silk, sulphur, caoutchouc, oiled silk, japanned leather, melted caoutchouc and resin, all became negative, causing the stream of steam and water to become positive. The fabrics were applied stretched over wooden cones. The melted caoutchouc was spread over the surface of a box-wood or a linen cone, and the resin cone was a linen cone dipped in a strong solution of resin in alcohol, and then dried. A cone of wood dipped in oil of turpentine, another cone soaked in olive oil, and a brass cone covered with the alcholic solution of resin and dried, were at first inactive, and then gradually became negative, at which time the oil of turpentine, olive-oil and resin were found cleared off from the parts struck by the stream of steam and water. A cone of kerseymere, which had been dipped in alcoholic solution of resin and dried two or three times in succession, was very irregular, becoming positive and negative by turns, in a manner difficult to comprehend at first, but easy to be understood hereafter (2113.).

2098. The end of a rod of shell-lac was held a moment in the stream of steam and then brought near a gold-leaf electrometer: it was found excited negatively, exactly as if it had been rubbed with a piece of flannel. The corner of a plate of sulphur showed the same effect and state when examined in the same way.

2099. Another mode of examining the substance rubbed was to use it in the shape of wires, threads or fragments, holding them by an insulating handle in the jet, whilst they were connected with a gold-leaf electrometer. In this way the following substances were tried:—

| | | |
|---|---|---|
| Platinum, | Horse-hair, | Charcoal, |
| Copper, | Bear's hair, | Asbestus, |
| Iron, | Flint glass, | Cyanite, |
| Zinc, | Green glass, | Hæmatite, |
| Sulphuret of copper, | Quill, | Rock-crystal, |
| Linen, | Ivory, | Orpiment, |
| Cotton, | Shell-lac on silk, | Sulphate of baryta, |
| Silk, | Sulphur on silk, | Sulphate of lime, |
| Worsted, | Sulphur in piece, | Carbonate of lime, |
| Wood, | Plumbago, | Fluor-spar. |

*All* these substances were rendered negative, though not in the same degree. This apparent difference in degree did not depend *only* upon the specific tendency to become negative, but also upon the conducting power of the body itself, whereby it gave its charge to the electrometer; upon its tendency to become wet (which is very different, for instance in shell-lac or quill, to that of glass or linen), by which its conducting quality was affected; and upon its size or shape. Nevertheless I could distinguish that bear's hair, quill and ivory had very feeble powers of exciting electricity as compared to the other bodies.

2100. I may make here a remark or two upon the introduction of bodies into the jet. For the purpose of preventing condensation on the substance, I made a platinum wire white-hot by an insulated voltaic battery, and introduced it into the jet: it was quickly lowered in temperature by the stream of steam

and water to 212°, but of course could never be below the boiling-point.   No difference was visible between the effect at the
first instant of introduction or any other time.   It was always
instantly electrified and negative.

2101. The threads I used were stretched across a fork of
stiff wire, and the middle part of the thread was held in the jet
of vapour.   In this case, the string or thread, if held exactly
in the middle of the jet and looked at end-ways to the thread,
was seen to be still, but if removed the least degree to the
right or left of the axis of the stream it (very naturally) vibrated, or rather rotated, describing a beautiful circle, of which
the axis of the stream was the tangent: the interesting point
was to observe, that when the thread rotated, travelling as it
were with the current, there was little or no electricity evolved,
but that when it was nearly or quite stationary there was abundance of electricity, thus illustrating the effect of friction.

2102. The difference in the quality of the substances above
described (2099.) gives a valuable power of arrangement at the
jet.   Thus if a metal, glass, or wood tube[1] (2076.) be used for
the steam issue, the boiler is rendered well negative and the
steam highly positive; but if a quill tube or, better still, an
ivory tube be used, the boiler receives scarcely any charge,
and the stream of steam is also in a neutral state.   This result
not only assists in proving that the electricity is not due to
evaporation, but is also very valuable in the experimental inquiry.   It was in such a neutral jet of steam and water that
the excitation of the bodies already described (2099.) was obtained.

2103. Substances, therefore, may be held either in the neutral jet from an ivory tube, or in the positive jet from a wooden
or metal tube; and in the latter case effects occurred which,
if not understood, would lead to great confusion.   Thus an
insulated wire was held in the stream issuing from a glass or
metal tube, about half an inch from the mouth of the tube,
and was found to be unexcited: on moving it in one direction a little further off, it was rendered positive; on moving

---

[1] A box-wood tube, 3 inches long and $\frac{1}{8}$th of an inch inner diameter, well
soaked in distilled water and screwed into the steam-globe, is an admirable exciter.

it in the other direction, nearer to the tube, it was negative. This was simply because, when near the tube in the forcible part of the current, it was excited and rendered negative, rendering the steam and water more positive than before, but that when further off, in a quieter part of the current, it served merely as a discharger to the electricity previously excited in the exit tube, and so showed the same state with it. Platinum, copper, string, silk, wood, plumbago, or any of the substances mentioned above (2099.), excepting quill, ivory and bear's hair, could, in this way, be made to assume either one state or the other, according as they were used as exciters or dischargers, the difference being determined by their place in the stream. A piece of fine wire gauze held across the issuing jet shows the above effect very beautifully; the difference of an eighth of an inch either way from the neutral place will change the state of the wire gauze.

2104. If, instead of an excited jet of steam and water (2103.), one issuing from an ivory tube (2102.), and in the neutral state be used, then the wires, &c. can no longer be made to assume both states. They may be excited and rendered negative (2099.), but at no distance can they become dischargers, or show the positive state.

2105. We have already seen that the presence of a very minute quantity of matter able to give conducting power to the water took away all power of excitation (2090, &c.) up to the highest degree of pressure, i. e. of mechanical friction that I used (2086.); and the next point was to ascertain whether it would be so for all the bodies rubbed by the stream, or whether differences in degree would begin to manifest themselves. I therefore tried all these bodies again, at one time adding about two grains of sulphate of soda to the four ounces of water which the steam-globe retained as a constant quantity when in regular action, and at another time adding not a fourth of this quantity of sulphuric acid (2091.). In both cases all the substances (2099.) remained entirely unexcited and neutral. Very probably, great increase of pressure might have developed some effect (2086.).

2106. With dilute sulphuric acid in the steam-globe, varying from extreme weakness to considerable sourness, I used tubes and cones of zinc, but could obtain *no trace* of electricity.

Chemical action, therefore, appears to have nothing to do with the excitement of electricity by a current of steam.

2107. Having thus given the result of the friction of the steam and water against so many bodies, I may here point out the remarkable circumstance of water being *positive* to them all. It very probably will find its place above all other substances, even cat's hair and oxalate of lime (2131.). We shall find hereafter, that we have power, not merely to prevent the jet of steam and water from becoming positive, as by using an ivory tube (2102.), but also of reducing its own power when passing through or against such substances as wood, metal, glass, &c. Whether, with a jet so reduced, we shall still find amongst the bodies above mentioned (2099.) some that can render the stream positive and others that can make it negative, is a question yet to be answered.

2108. Advancing in the investigation, a new point was to ascertain what other bodies, than water, would do if their particles were carried forward by the current of steam. For this purpose the feeding apparatus (2078.) was mounted and charged with oil of turpentine, to be let in at pleasure to the steam-exit passage. At first the feeder stop-cock was shut, and the issuing steam and water made the boiler negative. On letting down the oil of turpentine, this state was instantly changed, the boiler became powerfully positive, and the jet of steam, &c. as strongly negative. Shutting off the oil of turpentine, this state gradually fell, and in half a minute the boiler was negative, as at first. The introduction of more oil of turpentine instantly changed this to positive, and so on with perfect command of the phenomena.

2109. Removing the feeder apparatus and using only the steam-globe and a wooden exit tube (2076.), the same beautiful result was obtained. With pure water in the globe the boiler was negative, and the issuing steam, &c. positive; but a drop or two of oil of turpentine, introduced into the steam-globe with the water, instantly made the boiler positive and the issuing stream negative. On using the little interposed chamber C (2079.), the effects were equally decided. A piece of clean new sail-cloth was formed into a ring, moistened with oil of turpentine and placed in the box; as long as a trace of the fluid remained in the box the boiler was positive and the issuing stream negative.

2110. Thus the positive or negative state can be given at pleasure, either to the substance rubbed or to the rubbing stream; and with respect to this body, oil of turpentine, its perfect and ready dissipation by the continuance of the passage of the steam soon causes the new effect to cease, yet with the power of renewing it in an instant.

2111. With olive oil the same general phenomena were observed, i. e. it made the stream of steam, &c. *negative*, and the substance rubbed by it *positive*. But from the comparative fixedness of oil, the state was much more permanent, and a very little oil introduced into the steam-globe (2076.), or into the chamber C (2079.), or into the exit tube, would make the boiler positive for a long time. It required, however, that this oil should be in such a place that the steam stream, after passing by it, should rub against other matter. Thus, on using a wooden tube (2076. 2102.) as the exciter, if a little oil were applied to the inner termination, or that at which the steam entered it, the tube was made positive and the issuing steam negative; but if the oil were applied to the outer termination of the tube, the tube had its ordinary negative state, as with pure water, and the issuing steam was positive.

2112. Water is essential to this excitation by fixed oil, for when the steam-globe was emptied of water, and yet oil left in it and in the passages, there was no excitement. The first effect (2089.) it is true was one of excitement, and it rendered the boiler positive, but that was an effect due to the water condensed in the passage, combined with the action of the oil. Afterwards when all was hot, there was no evolution of electricity.

2113. I tried many other substances with the chamber C and other forms of apparatus, using the wet wooden tube (2102.) as the place and substance by which to excite the steam stream. Hog's-lard, spermaceti, bees'-wax, castor-oil, resin applied dissolved in alcohol; these, with olive-oil, oil of turpentine, and oil of laurel, all rendered the boiler positive, and the issuing steam negative. Of substances which seemed to have the reverse power, it is doubtful if there are any above water.

Sulphuret of carbon, naphthaline, sulphur, camphor, and melted caoutchouc, occasionally seemed in strong contrast to the former bodies, making the boiler very negative, but on trying pure water immediately after, it appeared to do so quite as powerfully. Some of the latter bodies with oil-gas liquid, naphtha and caoutchoucine, gave occasionally variable results, as if they were the consequence of irregular and complicated effects. Indeed, it is easy to comprehend, that according as a substance may adhere to the body rubbed, or be carried off by the passing stream, exchanging its mechanical action from rubbed to rubber, it should give rise to variable effects; this, I think, was the case with the cone and resin before referred to (2097.).

2114. The action of salts, acids, &c., when present in the water to destroy its effect, I have already referred to (2090, &c.). In addition, I may note that sulphuric ether, pyroxylic spirit, and boracic acid did the same.

2115. Alcohol seemed at the first moment to render the boiler positive. Half alcohol and half water rendered the boiler negative, but much less so than pure water.

2116. It must be considered that a substance having the reverse power of water, but only in a small degree, may be able to indicate that property merely by diminishing the power of water. This diminution of power is very different in its cause to that dependent on increasing the conducting power of the water, as by saline matter (2090.), and yet the apparent effect will be the same.

2117. When it is required to render the issuing steam permanently negative, the object is very easily obtained. A little oil or wax put into the steam-globe (2076.), or a thick ring of string or canvas soaked in wax, or solution of resin in alcohol, and introduced into the box C (2079.), supplies all that is required. By adjusting the application it is easy to neutralize the power of the water, so that the issuing stream shall neither become electric, nor cause that to be electrified against which it rubs.

2118. We have arrived, therefore, at three modes of rendering the jet of steam and water neutral, namely, the use of an ivory or quill tube (2102.), the presence of substances in the water (2090, &c.), and the neutralization of its natural power by the contrary force of oil, resin, &c. &c.

2119. In experiments of the kind just described an ivory tube cannot be used safely with acid or alkalies in the steam-globe, for they, by their chemical action on the substance of the tube, in the evolution or solution of the oily matter for instance, change its state and make its particular power of excitement very variable. Other circumstances also powerfully affect it occasionally (2144.).

2120. A very little oil in the rubbing passages produces a great effect, and this at first was a source of considerable annoyance, by the continual occurrence of unexpected results; a portion may lie concealed for a week together in the thread of an unsuspected screw, and yet be sufficient to mar the effect of every arrangement. Digesting and washing with a little solution of alkali, and avoiding all oiled washers, is the best way in delicate experiments of evading the evil. Occasionally I have found that a passage, which was in some degree persistently negative, from a little melted caoutchouc, or positive from oil, resin, &c., might be cleared out thoroughly by letting oil of turpentine be blown through it; it assumed for a while the positive state, but when the continuance of steam had removed that (2110.), the passage appeared to be perfectly clear and good and in its normal condition.

2121. I now tried the effect of oil, &c. when a little saline matter or acid was added to the water in the steam-globe (2090, &c.), and found that when the water was in such a state as to have no power of itself, still oil of turpentine, or oil, or resin in the box C, showed their power, in conjunction with such water, of rendering the boiler positive, but their power appeared to be reduced: increase of the force of steam, as in all other cases, would, there is little doubt, have exalted it again. When alkali was in the steam-globe, oil and resin lost very much of their power, and oil of turpentine very little. This fact will be important hereafter (2126.).

2122. We have seen that the action of such bodies as oil introduced into the jet of steam changed its power (2108.), but it was only by experiment we could tell whether this change was to such an extent as to alter the electricity for few or many of the bodies against which the steam stream rubbed. With olive oil in the box C, *all* the insulated cones before enumerated (2097.) were made positive. With acetic acid in the steam-

globe all were made neutral (2091.).   With resin in the box C
(2113.), all the substances in the former list (2099.) were made
positive, there was not one exception.

2123. The remarkable power of oil, oil of turpentine, resin,
&c., when in very small quantity, to change the exciting power
of water, though as regards some of them (2112.) they are inactive without it, will excuse a few theoretical observations upon
their mode of action.   In the first place it appears that steam
alone cannot by friction excite the electricity, but that the minute globules of water which it carries with it being swept over,
rubbed upon and torn from the rubbed body (2085.) excite it
and are excited, just as when the hand is passed over a rod of
shell-lac.   When olive oil or oil of turpentine is present, these
globules are, I believe, virtually converted into globules of these
bodies, and it is no longer water, but the new fluids which are
rubbing the rubbed bodies.

2124. The reasons for this view are the following. If a splinter
of wood dipped in olive oil or oil of turpentine touch the surface
of water, a pellicle of the former instantly darts and spreads
over the surface of the latter.   Hence it is pretty certain that
every globule of water passing through the box C, containing
olive oil or oil of turpentine, will have a pellicle over it.   Again,
if a metal, wooden, or other balance-pan be *well cleaned* and
*wetted* with water, and then put on the surface of clean water
in a dish, and the other pan be loaded until almost, but not
quite able to pull the first pan from the water, it will give a
rough measure of the cohesive force of the water.   If now the
oily splinter of wood touch any part of the clean surface of the
water in the dish, not only will it spread over the whole surface,
but cause the pan to separate from the water, and if the pan
be put down again, the water in the dish will no longer be able
to retain it.   Hence it is evident that the oil facilitates the separation of the water into parts by a mechanical force not otherwise sufficient, and invests these parts with a film of its own
substance.

2125. All this must take place to a great extent in the steam
passage: the particles of water there must be covered each
with a film of oil.   The tenuity of this film is no objection to
the supposition, for the action of excitement is without doubt

at that surface where the film is believed to exist, and such a globule, though almost entirely water, may well act as an oil globule, and by its friction render the wood, &c. positive, itself becoming negative.

2126. That water which is rendered ineffective by a little saline or acid matter should still be able to show the effect of the film of oil (2121.) attached to it, is perfectly consistent with this view. So also is the still more striking fact that alkalized water (2092.) having no power of itself should deeply injure the power of olive oil or resin, and hardly touch that of oil of turpentine (2121.), for the olive oil or resin would no longer form a film over it but dissolve in it, on the contrary the oil of turpentine would form its film.

2127. That resin should produce a strong effect and sulphur not is also satisfactory, for I find resin in boiling hot water melts, and has the same effect on the balance (2124.) as oil, though more slowly; but sulphur has not this power, its point of fusion being too high.

2128. It is very probable that when wood, glass or even metal is rubbed by these oily currents, the oil may be considered as rubbing not merely against wood, &c., but water also, the water being now on the side of the thing rubbed. Under the circumstances water has much more attraction for the wood rubbed than oil has, for in the steam-current, canvas, wood, &c. which has been well soaked in oil for a long time are quickly dispossessed of it, and found saturated with water. In such case the effect would still be to increase the positive state of the substance rubbed, and the negative state of the issuing stream.

---

2129. Having carried the experiments thus far with steam, and having been led to consider the steam as ineffectual by itself, and merely the mechanical agent by which the rubbing particles were driven onwards, I proceeded to experiment with compressed air[1]. For this purpose I used a strong copper box of the capacity of forty-six cubic inches, having two stop-cocks, by one of which the air was always forced in, and the other

[1] Mr. Armstrong has also employed air in much larger quantities. Philosophical Magazine, 1841, vol. xviii. pp. 133, 328.

retained for the exit aperture. The box was very carefully cleaned out by caustic potash. Extreme care was taken (and required) to remove and avoid oil, wax, or resin about the exit apertures. The air was forced into it by a condensing syringe, and in certain cases when I required dry air, four or five ounces of cylinder potassa fusa were put into the box, and the condensed air left in contact with the substance ten or fifteen minutes. The average quantity of air which issued and was used in each blast was 150 cubic inches. It was very difficult to deprive this air of the smell of oil which it acquired in being pumped through the condensing syringe.

2130. I will speak first of undried common air: when such compressed air was let suddenly out against the brass or the wood cone (2077.), it rendered the cone negative, exactly as the steam and water had done (2097.). This I attributed to the particles of water suddenly condensed from the expanding and cooled air rubbing against the metal or wood : such particles were very visible in the mist that appeared, and also by their effect of moistening the surface of the wood and metal. The electricity here excited is quite consistent with that evolved by steam and water : but the idea of that being due to evaporation (2083.) is in striking contrast with the actual condensation here.

2131. When however common air was let out against ice it rendered the ice *positive*, again and again, and that in alternation with the negative effect upon wood and metal. This is strongly in accordance with the high positive position which has already been assigned to water (2107.).

2132. I proceeded to experiment with dry air (2129.), and found that it was in all cases quite *incapable* of exciting electricity against wood or sulphur, or brass, in the form of cones (2077. 2097.) ; yet if, in the midst of these experiments, I let out a portion of air immediately after its compression, allowing it no time to dry, then it rendered the rubbed wood or brass negative (2130.). This is to me a satisfactory proof that in the former case the effect was due to the condensed water, and that neither *air alone* nor *steam alone* can excite these bodies, wood, brass, &c., so as to produce the effect now under investigation.

2133. In the next place the box C was attached to this air apparatus and experiments made with different substances introduced into it (2108.), using common air as the carrying vehicle.

2134. With distilled water in C, the metal cone was every now and then rendered negative, but more frequently no effect was produced. The want of a continuous jet of air sadly interfered with the proper adjustment of the proportion of water to the issuing stream.

2135. With common water (2090.), or a very dilute saline solution, or very dilute sulphuric acid (2091.) or ammonia, I never could obtain any traces of electricity.

2136. With oil of turpentine only in box C, the metal cone was rendered positive ; but when both distilled water and oil of turpentine were introduced, the cone was very *positive*, indeed far more so than before. When sent against ice, the ice was made positive.

2137. In the same manner olive oil and water in C, or resin in alcohol and water in C, rendered the cone positive, exactly as if these substances had been carried forward in their course by steam.

---

2138. Although the investigation as respects the steam stream may here be considered as finished, I was induced in connection with the subject to try a few experiments with the air current and dry powders. *Sulphur* in powder (sublimed) rendered both metal and wood, and even the sulphur cone negative, only once did it render metal positive. *Powdered resin* generally rendered metal negative, and wood positive, but presented irregularities, and often gave *two states in the same experiment*, first diverging the electrometer leaves, and yet at the end leaving them uncharged. *Gum* gave unsteady and double results like the resin. *Starch* made wood negative. *Silica*, being either very finely powdered rock-crystal or that precipitated from fluo-silicic acid by water, gave very constant and powerful results, but both metal and wood were made strongly positive by it, and the silica when caught on a wet insulated board and examined was found to be negative.

2139. These experiments with powders give rise to two or three observations. In the first place the high degree of friction occurring between particles carried forward by steam or air was well illustrated by what happened with sulphur; it was found driven into the dry box-wood cone opposed to it with such force that it could not be washed or wiped away, but had to be removed by scraping. In the next place, the *double* excitements were very remarkable. In a single experiment, the gold leaves would open out very wide at first, and then in an instant as suddenly fall, whilst the jet still continued, and remains at last either neutral or a very little positive or negative : this was particularly the case with gum and resin. The fixation upon the wood of some of the particles issuing at the begining of the blast and the condensation of moisture by the expanding air, are circumstances which, with others present, tend to cause these variable results.

2140. Sulphur is nearly constant in its results, and silica very constant, yet their states are the reverse of those that might have been expected. Sulphur in the lump is rendered negative whether rubbed against wood or any of the metals which I have tried, and renders them *positive* (2141.), yet in the above experiments it almost always made both negative. Silica, in the form of a crystal, by friction with wood and metals renders them *negative*, but applied as above, it constantly made them strongly positive. There must be some natural cause for these changes, which at present can only be considered as imperfect results, for I have not had time to investigate the subject.

2141. In illustration of the effect produced by steam and water striking against other bodies, I rubbed these other substances (2099.) together in pairs to ascertain their order, which was as follows :—

| | |
|---|---|
| 1. Catskin or bearskin. | 8. Linen, canvas. |
| 2. Flannel. | 9. White silk. |
| 3. Ivory. | 10. The hand. ⎧ Iron. |
| 4. Quill. | 11. Wood. ⎪ Copper. |
| 5. Rock-crystal. | 12. Lac. ⎪ Brass. |
| 6. Flint glass. | 13. Metals . . . ⎨ Tin. |
| 7. Cotton. | 14. Sulphur ⎪ Silver. |
| | ⎩ Platinum. |

Any one of these became negative with the substances above, and positive with those beneath it. There are however many exceptions to this general statement: thus one part of a catskin is very negative to another part, and even to rock-crystal: different pieces of flannel also differ very much from each other.

2142. The mode of rubbing also makes in some cases a great difference, although it is not easy to say why, since the particles that actually rub ought to present the same constant difference; a feather struck lightly against dry canvas will become strongly negative, and yet the same feather drawn with a little pressure between the folds of the same canvas will be strongly positive, and these effects alternate, so that it is easy to take away the one state in a moment by the degree of friction which produces the other state. When a piece of flannel is halved and the two pieces drawn across each other, the two pieces will have different states irregularly, or the same piece will have both states in different parts, or sometimes both pieces will be negative, in which case, doubtless, air must have been rendered positive, and then dissipated.

2143. Ivory is remarkable in its condition. It is very difficult of excitement by friction with the metals, much more so than linen, cotton, wood, &c., which are lower in the scale than it (2141.), and withal are much better conductors, yet both circumstances would have led to the expectation that it would excite better than them when rubbed with metals. This property is probably very influential in giving character to it as a non-exciting steam passage (2102.).

2144. Before concluding this paper, I will mention, that having used a thin ivory tube fixed in a cork (2076.) for many experiments with oil, resin, &c., it at last took up such a state as to give not merely a non-exciting passage for the steam, but to exert upon it a nullifying effect, for the jet of steam and water passing through it produced no excitation against any of the bodies opposed, as on the former occasion, to it (2099.). The tube was apparently quite clean, and was afterwards soaked in alcohol to remove any resin, but it retained this peculiar state.

2145. Finally, I may say that the cause of the evolution of electricity by the liberation of confined steam is not evaporation; and further, being, I believe, friction, it has no effect in producing, and is not connected with, the general electricity of the atmosphere: also, that as far as I have been able to proceed, pure gases, *i. e.* gases not mingled with solid or liquid particles, do not excite electricity by friction against solid or liquid substances[1].

## PLATE I.

*Description of the Apparatus* represented in section, and to a
scale of one-fourth.

Fig. 1. The steam-globe (2076.), principal steam-cock, and drainage-cock to remove the water condensed in the pipe. The current of steam, &c. travelled in the direction of the arrow-heads.

Fig. 2. The cone apparatus (2077.) in one of its forms. The cone could be advanced and withdrawn by means of the milled head and screw.

Fig. 3. The feeding apparatus (2078.). The feeder was a glass tube or retort neck fitted by a cork into the cap of the feeding stop-cock. Other apparatus, as that figured 2, 5, 6, could be attached by a connecting piece to this apparatus.

Fig. 4. The chamber C (2079.) fitted by a cork on to a metal pipe previously screwed into the steam-globe; and having a metallic tube and adjusting piece screwed into its mouth. Other parts, as the cone fig. 2, or the wooden or glass tubes 5, 6, could be conjoined with this chamber.

Fig. 5. The box-wood tube (2102.).

Fig. 6. A glass or thin metal tube (2076.) attached by a cork to a mouth-piece fitting into the steam-globe.

[1] References to papers in the Philosophical Magazine, 1840–1843. Armstrong, Phil. Mag. vol. xvii. pp. 370, 452; vol. xviii. pp. 50, 133, 328; vol. xix. p. 25; vol. xx. p. 5; vol. xxii. p. 1. Pattinson, Phil. Mag. vol. xvii. pp. 375, 457. Schafhaeutl, Phil. Mag. vol. xvii. p. 449; vol. xviii. pp. 14, 95, 265. See also Philosophical Magazine, 1843, xxiii. p. 194, for Armstrong's account of the *Hydro-electric Machine.*

Papers on Electricity from the Quarterly Journal of
Science, Philosophical Magazine, &c.

## On some new Electro-Magnetical Motions, and on the Theory of Magnetism[1].

In making an experiment the beginning of last week, to ascertain the position of the magnetic needle to the connecting
wire of a voltaic apparatus, I was led into a series which appear
to me to give some new views of electro-magnetic action, and
of magnetism altogether; and to render more distinct and clear
those already taken. After the great men who have already
experimented on the subject, I should have felt doubtful that
anything I could do could be new or possess an interest, but
that the experiments seem to me to reconcile considerably the
opposite opinions that are entertained on it. I am induced in
consequence to publish this account of them, in the hope they
will assist in making this important branch of knowledge more
perfect.

The apparatus used was that invented by Dr. Hare of Philadelphia, and called by him a calorimotor; it is in fact a single
pair of large plates, each having its power heightened by the
induction of others, consequently all the positions and motions
of the needles, poles, &c., are opposite to those produced by
an apparatus of several plates; for, if a current be supposed
to exist in the connecting wire of a battery from the zinc to
the copper, it will be in each connected pair of plates from
the copper to the zinc; and the wire I have used is that connection between the two plates of one pair. In the diagrams
I may have occasion to subjoin, the ends of a connecting wire,
marked Z and C, are connected with the zinc and copper-
plates respectively; the sections are all horizontal and seen
from above, and the arrow-heads have been used sometimes to
mark the pole of a needle or magnet which points to the north,
and sometimes to mark the direction of motion; no difficulty

[1] Quarterly Journal of Science, xii. 74.

can occur in ascertaining to which of those uses any particular head is applied.

On placing the wire perpendicularly, and bringing a needle towards it to ascertain the attractive and repulsive positions with regard to the wire; instead of finding these to be four, one attractive and one repulsive for each pole, I found them to be eight, two attractive and two repulsive for each pole; thus allowing the needle to take its natural position across the wire, which is exactly opposite to that pointed out by Œrsted for the reason before mentioned, and then drawing the support away from the wire slowly, so as to bring the north pole, for instance, nearer to it, there is attraction, as is to be expected ; but on continuing to make the end of the needle come nearer to the wire, repulsion takes place, though the wire still be on the same side of the needle. If the wire be on the other side of the same pole of the needle, it will repel it when opposite to most parts between the centre of motion and the end; but there is a small portion at the end where it attracts it. Fig. 1, plate II., shows the positions of attraction for the north and south poles, fig. 2 the positions of repulsion.

If the wire be made to approach perpendicularly towards one pole of the needle, the pole will pass off on one side, in that direction which the attraction and repulsion at the extreme point of the pole would give; but, if the wire be continually made to approach the centre of motion, by either the one or other side of the needle, the tendency to move in the former direction diminishes; it then becomes null, and the needle is quite indifferent to the wire, and ultimately the motion is reversed, and the needle powerfully endeavours to pass the opposite way.

It is evident from this that the centre of the active portion of either limb of the needle, or the true pole, as it may be called, is not at the extremity of the needle, but may be represented by a point generally in the axis of the needle, at some little distance from the end. It was evident, also, that this point had a tendency to revolve round the wire, and necessarily, therefore, the wire round the point; and as the same effects in the opposite direction took place with the other pole, it was evident that each pole had the power of acting on the wire by itself, and not as any part of the needle, or as connected with the opposite pole.

By attending to fig. 3, which represents sections of the wire in its different positions to the needle, all this will be plain; the active poles are represented by two dots, and the arrow-heads show the tendency of the wire in its positions to go round these poles.

Several important conclusions flow from these facts; such as that there is no attraction between the wire and either pole of a magnet; that the wire ought to revolve round a magnetic pole and a magnetic pole round the wire; that both attraction and repulsion of connecting wires, and probably magnets, are compound actions; that true magnetic poles are centres of action induced by the whole bar, &c. &c. Such of these as I have been able to confirm by experiment, shall be stated, with their proofs.

The revolution of the wire and the pole round each other being the first important thing required to prove the nature of the force mutually exerted by them, various means were tried to succeed in producing it. The difficulty consisted in making a suspension of part of the wire sufficiently delicate for the motion, and yet affording sufficient mass of matter for contact. This was overcome in the following manner:—A piece of brass wire had a small button of silver soldered on to its end, a little cup was hollowed in the silver, and the metal being amalgamated, it would then retain a drop of mercury in it, though placed upside down for an upper centre of motion; for a lower centre, a similar cup was made of copper, into which a little mercury was put; this was placed in a jar of water under the former centre. A piece of copper wire was then bent into the form of a crank, its ends amalgamated, and the distances being arranged, they were placed in the cups. To prevent too much friction from the weight of the wire on the lower cup, it had been passed through a cork duly adjusted in size, and that being pushed down on the wire till immersed in the water, the friction became very little, and the wire very mobile, yet with good contacts. The plates being then connected with the two cups, the apparatus was completed. In this state, a magnetic pole being brought to the centre of motion of the crank, the wire immediately made an effort to revolve until it struck the magnet, and that being rapidly brought round to the other side, the wire again made a revolution, giving evidence that it would have gone round continually but for the extension of the magnet on the outside. To do away with this impediment, the wire and lower metal cup were removed, and a deep basin of mercury placed beneath; at the bottom of this was a piece of wax, and a small round bar magnet was stuck upright in it, so that one pole was about half or three-fourths of an inch above the surface of the mercury, and directly under the silver cup. A straight piece of copper wire, long enough to reach from the cup, and dip about half an inch into the mercury, had its ends amalgamated, and a small round piece of cork fixed on to one of them to make it more buoyant; this being dipped in the mercury close beside the magnet, and the other end placed under the little cup, the wire remained upright, for the adhesion of the cork to the magnet was sufficient for that purpose, and yet at its lower end had freedom of motion round the pole. The connection being now made from the plates to the upper cup, and to the mercury below, the wire immediately began to revolve round the pole of the magnet, and continued to do so as long as the connexion was continued.

When it was wished to give a large diameter to the circle described by the wire, the cork was moved from the magnet, and a little loop of platinum passed round the magnet and wire, to prevent them from separating too far. Revolution again took place on making the connexion, but more slowly as the distance increased.

The direction in which the wire moved was according to the way in which the connexions were made, and to the magnetic pole brought into action. When the upper part of the wire was connected with the zinc, and the lower with the copper plate, the motion round the north and south poles of a magnet were as in figs. 4 and 5, looking from above; when the connexions were reversed, the motions were in the opposite direction.

On bringing the magnetic pole from the centre of motion to the side of the wire, there was neither attraction nor repulsion; but the wire endeavoured to pass off in a circle, still having the pole for its centre, and that either to the one side or the other, according to the above law.

When the pole was on the outside of the wire, the wire moved in a direction directly contrary to that taken when the pole was in the inside; but it did not move far, the endeavour was

still to go round the pole as a centre, and it only moved till
that power and the power which retained it in a circle about
its own axis were equipoised.

The next object was to make the magnet revolve round the
wire. This was done by so loading one pole of the small magnet with platinum that the magnet would float upright in a basin of mercury, with the other pole above its surface; then
connecting the mercury with one plate and bringing a wire
from the other perpendicularly into it in another part near the
floating magnet; the upper pole immediately began to revolve
round the wire, whilst the lower pole being removed away
caused no interference or counteracting effect.

The motions were again according to the pole and the connexions. When the upper part of the wire was in contact with
the zinc plate, and the lower with the copper, the direction of
the curve described by the north and south poles were as in
figs. 6 and 7. When the connexions were reversed, the motions
were in the opposite directions.

Having succeeded thus far, I endeavoured to make a wire
and a magnet revolve on their own axis by preventing the rotation in a circle round them, but have not been able to get the
slightest indications that such can be the case; nor does it, on
consideration, appear probable. The motions evidently belong
to the current, or whatever else it be, that is passing through
the wire, and not to the wire itself, except as the vehicle of the
current. When that current is made a curve by the form of
the wire, it is easy to conceive how, in revolving, it should take
the wire with it; but when the wire is straight, the current
may revolve without any motion being communicated to the
wire through which it passes.

M. Ampère has shown that two similar connecting wires, by
which is meant, having currents in the same direction through
them, attract each other, and that two wires having currents in
opposite directions through them, repel each other, the attraction and repulsion taking place in right lines between them.
From the attraction of the north pole of a needle on one side
the wire, and of the south on the other, and the repulsion of
the poles on the opposite sides, Dr. Wollaston called this magnetism vertiginous, and conceived that the phenomena might
be explained upon the supposition of an electro-magnetic cur-

rent passing round the axis of the conjunctive wire, its direction depending upon that of the electric current, and exhibiting north and south powers on the opposite sides. It is, indeed, an ascertained fact, that the connecting wire has different powers at its opposite sides; or rather, each power continues all round the wire, the direction being the same, and hence it is evident that the attractions and repulsions of M. Ampère's wires are not simple, but complicated results.

A simple case which may be taken of magnetic motion, is the circle described by the wire or the pole round each other. If a wire be made into a helix, as M. Ampère describes, the arrangement is such that all the vertiginous magnetism, as Dr. Wollaston has named it, of the one kind, or one side of the wire, is concentrated in the axis of the helix, whilst the contrary kind is very much diffused, *i. e.* the power exerted by a great length of wire to make a pole pass one way round it, all tends to carry that pole to a particular spot, whilst the opposite power is diffused and much weakened in its action on any one pole. Hence the power on one side of the wire is very much concentrated, and its particular effects brought out strongly, whilst that on the other is rendered insensible. A means is thus obtained of separating, as it were, the one power from the other; but when this is done, and we examine the end of the helix, it is found very much to resemble a magnetic pole; the power is concentrated at the extremity of the helix; it attracts or repels one pole in all directions; and I find that it causes the revolution of the connecting wire round it, just as a magnetic pole does. Hence it may, for the present, be considered identical with a magnetic pole; and I think that the experimental evidence of the ensuing pages will much strengthen that opinion.

Assuming, then, that the pole of a magnetic needle presents us with the properties of one side of the wire, the phenomena it presents with the wire itself, offers us a means of analysis, which, probably, if well pursued, will give us a much more intimate knowledge of the state of the powers active in magnets. When it is placed near the wire, always assuming the latter to be connected with the battery, it is made to revolve round it, passing towards that side by which it is attracted, and from that side by which it is repelled, *i. e.* the pole is at once attracted and repelled by equal powers, and therefore neither recedes nor approaches; but the powers being from opposite sides of the wire, the pole in its double effort to recede from one side and approach the other revolves in the circle, that circle being evidently decided by the particular pole and state of the wire, and deducible from the law before mentioned.

The phenomena presented by the approximation of one pole to two or more wires, or two poles to one or more wires, offer many illustrations of this double action, and will lead to more correct views of the magnet. These experiments are easily made by loading a needle with platinum at one pole, that the other may float above mercury, or by almost floating a small magnetic needle by cork in a basin of water, at the bottom of which is some mercury with which to connect the wires. In describing them I shall refrain from entering into all their variations, or pursuing them to such conclusions as are not directly important.

Two similar wires, Ampère has shown, attract each other; and Sir H. Davy has shown that the filings adhering to them attract from one to another on the same side. They are in that position in which the north and south influence of the different wires attract each other. They seem also to neutralize each other in the parts that face, for the magnetic pole is quite inactive between them, but if put close together, it moves round the outside of both, circulating round them as round one wire, and their influences being in the same direction, the greatest effect is found to be at the further outside surfaces of the wires. If several similar wires be put together, side by side like a ribbon, the result is the same, and the needle revolves round them all; the internal wires appear to lose part of their force, which is carried on towards the extreme wire in opposite directions, so that the floating pole is accelerated in its motion as it passes by the edges that they form. If, in place of a ribbon of parallel wires, a slip of metal be used, the effect is the same, and the edges act as if they contained in a concentrated state the power that belonged to the inner portion of the slip. In this way we procure the means of removing, as it were, in that direction, the two sides of the wire from each other.

If two wires in opposite states be arranged parallel to each other, and the pole be brought near them, it will circulate round either of them in obedience to the law laid down; but

as the wires have opposite currents, it moves in opposite directions round the two, so that when equidistant from them,
the pole is propelled in a right line perpendicular to the line
which joins them, either receding or approaching; and if it
approaches, passing between and then receding; hence it exhibits the curious appearance of first being attracted by the
two wires, and afterwards repelled (fig. 8.). If the connexion
with both wires be inverted, or if the pole be changed, the line
it describes is in the opposite direction. If these two opposite
currents be made by bending a piece of silked wire parallel to
itself, fig. 9, it, when connected with the apparatus, becomes
a curious magnet; with the north pole, for instance, it attracts
powerfully on one side at the line between the two currents,
but repels strongly to the right or left; whilst on the other
side the line repels the north pole, but attracts it strongly to
the right or left. With the south pole the attractions and repulsions are reversed.

When both poles of the needle were allowed to come into
action on the wire or wires, the effects were in accordance
with those described. When a magnetic needle was floated
on water, and the perpendicular wire brought towards it, the
needle turned round more or less, until it took a direction perpendicular to, and across the wire, the poles being in such positions that either of them alone would revolve round the wire
in a circle proceeding by the side to which it had gone, according to the law before stated. The needle then approaches to
the wire, its centre (not either pole) going in a direct line
towards it. If the wire be then lifted up and put down the
other side of the needle, the needle passes on in the same line
receding from the wire, so that the wire seems here to be both
attractive and repulsive of the needle. This effect will be
readily understood from fig. 10, where the poles and direction
of the wire are not marked, because they are the same as before.
If either be reversed, the others reverse themselves. The
experiment is analogous to the one described above; there the
pole passed between two dissimilar wires, here the wire between two dissimilar poles.

If two dissimilar wires be used, and the magnet have both
poles active, it is repelled, turned round, or is attracted in various ways, until it settles across between the two wires; all

its motions being easily reducible to those impressed on the
poles by the wires, both wires and both poles being active in
giving that position.    Then if it happens not to be midway between the two, or they are not of equal power, it goes slowly
towards one of them, and acts with it just as the single wire of
the last paragraph.

Figs. 11 and 12 exhibit more distinctly the direction of the
forces which influence the poles in passing between two dissimilar wires: fig. 11, when the pole draws up between the
wires; fig. 12, the pole thrown out from between them.    The
poles and state of the wire are not marked, because the diagrams illustrate the attraction and repulsion of both poles; for
any particular pole, the connexion of the wires must be accordingly.

If one of the poles be brought purposely near either wire in
the position in which it appears to attract most strongly, still
if freedom of motion be given by a little tapping, the needle
will slip along till it stands midway across the wire.

A beautiful little apparatus has been made by M. de la Rive
to whom I am indebted for one of them, consisting of a small
voltaic combination floating by a cork; the ends of the little
zinc and copper slips come through the cork, and are connected
above by a piece of silked wire which has been wrapped
four or five times round a cylinder, and the wires tied together with a silk thread so as to form a close helix about one
inch in diameter.    When placed on acidulated water it is very
obedient to the magnet and serves admirably to transform, as
it were, the experiments with straight wires that have been
mentioned, to the similar ones made with helices.    Thus, if a
magnet be brought near it and level with its axis, the apparatus will recede or turn round until that side of the curve next
to the nearest pole is the side attracted by it.    It will then
approach the pole, pass it, recede from it until it gains the
middle of the magnet, where it will rest like an equator round
it, its motions and position being still the same as those before
pointed out (fig. 13.).    If brought near either pole it will still
return to the centre; and if purposely placed in the opposite
direction at the centre of the magnet, it will pass off by either
pole to which it happens to be nearest, being apparently first
attracted by the pole and afterwards repelled, as is actually the
case; will, if any circumstance disturbs its perpendicularity to

the magnet, turn half way round ; and will then pass on to the magnet again, into the position first described. If, instead of passing the magnet through the curve, it be held over it, it stands in a plane perpendicular to the magnet, but in an opposite direction to the former one. So that a magnet, both within and without this curve, causes it to direct.

When the poles of the magnet are brought over this floating curve, there are some movements and positions which at first appear anomalous, but are by a little attention easily reducible to the circular movement of the wire about the pole. I do not think it necessary to state them particularly.

The attractive and repulsive positions of this curve may be seen by fig. 13, the curve in the two dotted positions is attracted by the poles near them. If the positions be reversed, repulsion takes place.

From the central situation of the magnet in these experiments, it may be concluded that a strong and powerful curve or helix would suspend a powerful needle in its centre. By making a needle almost float on water and putting the helix over a glass tube, this result has in part been obtained.

In all these magnetic movements between wires and poles, those which resemble attraction and repulsion, that is to say, those which took place in right lines, required at least either two poles and a wire, or two wires and a pole ; for such as appear to exist between the wire and either pole of the battery, are deceptive and may be resolved into the circular motion. It has been allowed, I believe, by all who have experimented on these phenomena, that the similar powers repel and the dissimilar powers attract each other; and that, whether they exist in the poles of the magnets or in the opposite sides of conducting wires. This being admitted, the simplest cases of magnetic action will be those exerted by the poles of helices, for, as they offer the magnetic states of the opposite sides of the wire independent, or nearly so, one of the other, we are enabled by them to bring into action two of those powers only, to the exclusion of the rest; and, from experiment it appears that when the powers are similar, repulsion takes place, and when dissimilar, attraction ; so that two cases of repulsion and one of attraction are produced by the combination of these magnetic powers[1].

[1] This is perhaps not strictly true, because, though the opposite powers are weakened, they still remain in action.

The next cases of magnetic motion, in the order of simplicity, are those where three powers are concerned, or those produced by a pole and a wire. These are the circular motions described in the early part of this paper. They resolve themselves into two; a north pole and the wire round each other, and a south pole and the wire round each other. The law which governs these motions has been stated.

Then follow the actions between two wires: these when similarly electrified attract as M. Ampère has shown; for then the opposite sides are towards each other, and the four powers all combine to draw the currents together, forming a double attraction; but when the wires are dissimilar they repel, because, then on both sides of the wire the same powers are opposed, and cause a double repulsion.

The motions that result from the action of two dissimilar poles and a wire next follow: the wire endeavours to describe opposite circles round the poles; consequently it is carried in a line passing through the central part of the needle in which they are situated. If the wire is on the side on which the circles close together, it is attracted; if on the opposite side, from whence the circles open, it is repelled, fig. 10.

The motions of a pole with two wires are almost the same as the last; when the wires are dissimilar, the pole endeavours to form two opposite circles about the wires; when it is on that side of the wires on which the circles meet, it is attracted; when on the side on which they open, it is repelled, figs. 8, 11, 12.

Finally, the motion between two poles and two dissimilar wires, is an instance where several powers combine to produce an effect.

M. Ampère, whilst reasoning on the discovery of M. Oersted, was led to the adoption of a theory, by which he endeavoured to account for the properties of magnets, by the existence of concentric currents of electricity in them, arranged round the axis of the magnet. In support of this theory, he first formed the spiral or helix wire, in which currents could be made to pass nearly perpendicular to, and round the axis of a cylinder. The ends of such helices were found when connected with the voltaic apparatus to be in opposite magnetic states, and to present the appearance of poles. Whilst pursuing the mutual

action of poles and wires, and tracing out the circular movements, it seemed to me that much information respecting the
competency of this theory might be gained from an attempt to
trace the action of the helix, and compare it with that of the
magnet more rigorously than had yet been done; and to form
artificial electro-magnets, and analyse natural ones. In doing
this, I think I have so far succeeded as to trace the action of
an electro-magnetic pole, either in attracting or repelling, to the
circulating motion before described.

If three inches of connecting wire be taken, and a magnetic
pole be allowed to circulate round the middle of it, describing
a circle of a little less than one inch in diameter, it will be moved
with equal force in all parts of the circle, fig. 14; bend then
the wire into a circle, leaving that part round which the pole
revolves perpendicularly undisturbed, as seen by the dotted
lines, and make it a condition that the pole be restrained from
moving out of the circle by a radius. It will immediately be
evident that the wire now acts very differently on the pole in
the different parts of the circle it describes. Every part of it
will be active at the same time on the pole, to make it move
through the centre of the wire ring, whilst as it passes away
from that position the powers diverge from it, and it is either
removed from their action or submitted to opposing ones, until
on its arriving at the opposite part of the circle it is urged by
a very small portion indeed of those which moved it before.
As it continues to go round, its motion is accelerated, the
forces rapidly gather together on it, until it again reaches the
centre of the wire ring where they are at their highest, and
afterwards diminish as before. Thus the pole is perpetually
urged in a circle, but with powers constantly changing.

If the wire ring be conceived to be occupied by a plane, then
the centre of that plane is the spot where the powers are most
active on the pole, and move it with most force. Now this spot
is actually the pole of this magnetic apparatus. It seems to
have powers over the circulating pole, making it approach or
attracting it on the one side, and making it recede or repelling
it on the other, with powers varying as the distance; but its
powers are only apparent, for the force is in the ring, and this
spot is merely the place where they are most accumulated; and
though it seems to have opposite powers, namely, those of at-

tracting and repelling; yet this is merely a consequence of its
situation in the circle, the motion being uniform in its direction,
and really and truly impressed on the pole by its motor, the
wire.

At page 133 it was shown that two or more similar wires put
together in a line, acted as one; the power being, as it were,
accumulated towards the extreme wires, by a species of induction taking place among them all; and at the same time was
noticed the similar case of a plate of metal connecting the ends
of the apparatus, its powers being apparently strongest at the
edges. If, then, a series of concentric rings be placed one inside the other, they having the electric current sent through
them in the same direction; or if, which is the same thing, a
flat spiral of silked wire passing from the centre to the circumference be formed, and its ends be in connexion with the battery, fig. 15, then the circle of revolution would still be as in
fig. 14, passing through the centre of the rings or spiral, but
the power would be very much increased. Such a spiral, when
made, beautifully illustrates this fact; it takes up an enormous
quantity of iron filings, which approach to the form of cones,
so strong is the action at the centre; and its action on the
needle by the different sides, is eminently powerful.

If in place of putting ring within ring, they be placed side
by side, so as to form a cylinder, or if a helix be made, then
the same kind of neutralization takes place in the intermediate
wires, and accumulated effect in the extreme ones, as before.
The line which the pole would now travel, supposing the inner
end of the radius to move over the inner and outer surface of
the cylinder, would be through the axis of the cylinder round
the edge to one side, back up that side, and round to the axis,
down which it would go, as before. In this case the force
would probably be greatest at the two extremes of the
axis of the cylinder, and least at the middle distance on the
outside.

Now consider the internal space of the cylinder filled up by
rings or spirals, all having the currents in the same direction;
the direction and kind of force would be the same, but very
much strengthened: it would exist in the strongest degree
down the axis of the mass, because of the circular form, and
it would have the two sides of the point in the centre of the

simple ring, which *seemed* to possess attractive and repulsive powers on the pole, removed to the ends of the cylinder; giving rise to two points, apparently distinct in their action, one being attractive, and the other repulsive, of the poles of a magnet. Now conceive that the pole is not confined to a motion about the sides of the ring, or the flat spiral, or cylinder; it is evident that if placed in the axis of any of them at a proper distance for action, it, being impelled by two or more powers in equal circles, would move in a right line in the intersection of those circles, and approach directly to or recede from, the points before spoken of, giving the appearance of a direct attraction and repulsion; and if placed out of that axis, it would move towards or from the same spot in a curve line, its direction and force being determined by the curve lines representing the active forces from the portions of wire forming the ends of the cylinder, spiral, or ring, and the strength of those forces.

Thus the phenomena of a helix, or a solid cylinder of spiral silked wire, are reduced to the simple revolution of the magnetic pole round the connecting wire of the battery, and its resemblance to a magnet is so great, that the strongest presumption arises in the mind, that they both owe their powers, as M. Ampère has stated, to the same cause. Filings of iron sprinkled on paper held over this cylinder, arranged themselves in curved lines passing from one end to the other, showing the path the pole would follow, and so they do over a magnet; the ends attract and repel as do those of a magnet; and in almost every point do they agree. The following experiments will illustrate and confirm the truth of these remarks on the action of the ring, helix, or cylinder; and will show in what their actions agree with, and differ (for there are differences) from, the action of a magnet.

A small magnet being nearly floated in water by cork, a ring of silked copper wire, fig. 16, having its ends connected with the battery, was brought near its poles in different positions; sometimes the pole was repelled from, sometimes attracted into, the ring, according to the position of the pole, and the connexions with the battery. If the wire happened to be opposite to the pole, the pole passed sideways and outwards when it was repelled, and sideways and inwards when it was attracted; and on entering within the ring and passing through, it moved sideways in the opposite direction, endeavouring to go round the wire. The actions also presented by M. de la Rive's ring are actions of this kind, and indeed are those which best illustrate the relations between the ring and the pole ; some of them have been mentioned, and if referred to, will be found to accord with the statement given.

With a flat spiral the magnetic power was very much increased ; and when the rings were not continued to the centre, the power of the inner edge over the outer was well shown either by the pole of a needle, or iron filings. With the latter the appearance was extremely beautiful and instructive ; when laid flat upon a heap of them, they arranged themselves in lines, passing through the ring parallel to its axis, and then folding up on either side as radii round to the edge, where they met ; so that they represented, exactly, the lines which a pole would have described round the sides of the rings ; and those filings which were in the axis of the rings, stood up in perpendicular filaments, half an inch long and so as to form an actual axis to the ring, tending neither one way nor the other, but according in their form and arrangement with what has been described ; whilst the intermediate portion also formed long threads, bending this way and that from the centre, more or less, according as they were further from, or nearer to it.

With a helix the phenomena were interesting, because according to the view given of the attractions and repulsions, that is of the motions toward and from the ends, some conclusions should follow, that if found to be true in fact, and to hold also with magnets, would go far to prove the identity of the two. Thus the end which seems to attract a certain pole on the outside, ought to repel it as it were on the inside, and that which seems to repel it on the outside, ought to appear to attract it on the inside ; *i. e.* that as the motions on the inside and outside are in different directions for the same pole, it would move in the one case to and in the other case from the same end of the helix. Some phenomena of this kind have been described in explaining figs. 8, 11, 12, and 13 ; others are as follows.

A helix of silked copper wire was made round a glass tube, the tube being about an inch in diameter ; the helix was about three inches long. A magnetic needle nearly as long was floated with cork, so as to move about in water with the slightest im-

pulse. The helix being connected with the apparatus and put
into the water in which the needle lay, its ends appeared to
attract and repel the poles of the needle according to the laws
before mentioned. But, if that end which attracted one of the
poles of the needle was brought near that pole, it entered the
glass tube, but did not stop just within side in the neighbourhood of this pole (as we may call it for the moment) of the helix,
but passed up the tube, drawing the whole needle in, and went
to the opposite pole of the helix, or the one which on the outside would have repelled it; on trying the other pole of the
magnet with its corresponding end or pole of the helix the same
effect took place; the needle pole entered the tube and passed
to the other end, taking the whole needle into the same position it was in before.

Thus each end of the helix seemed to attract and repel both
poles of the needle; but this is only a natural consequence of
the circulating motion before experimentally demonstrated, and
each pole would have gone through the helix and round on the
outside, but for the counteraction of the opposite pole. It has
been stated that the poles circulate in opposite directions
round the wires, and they would consequently circulate in opposite directions through and round the helix; when, therefore,
one end of the helix was near that pole, which would, according to the law stated, enter it and endeavour to go through, it
would enter, and it would continue its course until the other
pole, at first at a distance, would be brought within action of
the helix; and, when they were both equally within the helix
and consequently equally acted on, their tendency to go in different directions would counterbalance each other, and the
needle would remain motionless. If it were possible to separate
the two poles from each other, they would dart out of each end
of the helix, being apparently repelled by those parts that before seemed to attract them, as is evident from the first and
many other experiments.

By reversing the needle and placing it purposely in the helix
in that position, the poles of the needle and the corresponding
poles of the helix as they attract on the outside, are brought
together on the inside, but both pairs now seem to repel; and,
whichever end of the helix the needle happens to be nearest to,
it will be thrown out at. This motion may be seen to exhibit

in its passing state, attraction between similar poles, since the inner and active pole is drawn towards that end on the inside, by which it is thrown off on the outside [1].

These experiments may be made with the single curve of M. de la Rive, in which case it is the wire that moves and not the magnet; but as the motions are reciprocal, they may be readily anticipated.

A plate of copper was bent nearly into a cylinder, and its edges made to dip into two portions of mercury; when placed in a current it acted exactly as a helix.

A solid cylinder of silked wire was made exactly in fashion like a helix, but that one length of the wire served as the axis, and the folds were repeated over and over again. This as well as the former helix, had poles the same in every respect as to kind as the north and south poles of a magnet; they took up filings, they made the connecting wire revolve, they attracted and re-pelled in four parallel positions as is described of common magnets in the first pages of this paper, and filings sprinkled on paper over them, formed curves from one to the other as with magnets; these lines indicating the direction in which a north or south pole would move about them.

Now with respect to the accordance which is found between the appearances of a helix or cylinder when in the voltaic circuit, and a cylindrical common magnet, or even a regular square bar magnet; it is so great, as at first to leave little doubt, that whatever it is that causes the properties of the one, also causes the properties of the other, for the one may be substi-tuted for the other in, I believe, every magnetical experiment; and, in the bar magnet, all the effects on a single pole or filings, &c., agree with the notion of a circulation, which if the magnet were not solid would pass through its centre, and back on the outside.

The following, however, are differences between the appear-ances of a magnet and those of a helix or cylinder: one pole of a magnet attracts the opposite pole of a magnetic needle in all directions and positions; but when the helix is held along-side the needle nearly parallel to it, and with opposite poles together, so that attraction should take place, and then the helix is moved

---

[1] The magnetizing power of the helix is so strong that if the experiment be made slowly, the needle will have its mangetism changed and the result will be fallacious.

on so that the pole of the needle gradually comes nearer to the middle of the helix, repulsion generally takes place before the pole gets to the middle of the helix, and in a situation where with the magnet it would be attracted. This is probably occasioned by the want of continuity in the sides of the curves or elements of the helix, in consequence of which the unity of action which takes place in the rings into which a magnet may be considered to be divided is interfered with and disturbed.

Another difference is that the poles, or those spots to which the needle points when perpendicular to the ends or sides of a magnet or helix, and where the motive power may be considered perhaps as most concentrated, are in the helix at the extremity of its axis, and not any distance in from the end; whilst in the most regular magnets they are almost always situate in the axis at some distance in from the end; a needle pointing perpendicularly towards the end of a magnet is in a line with its axis, but perpendicularly to the side it points to a spot some distance from the end, whilst in the helix, or cylinder, it still points to the end. This variation is, probably, to be attributed to the distribution of the exciting cause of magnetism in the magnet and helix. In the latter, it is necessarily uniform everywhere, inasmuch as the current of electricity is uniform. In the magnet it is probably more active in the middle than elsewhere; for as the north pole of a magnet brought near a south one increases its activity, and that the more as it is nearer, it is fair to infer that the similar parts which are actually united in the inner part of the bar, have the same power. Thus a piece of soft iron put to one end of a horse-shoe magnet, immediately moves the pole towards that end; but if it be then made to touch the other end also, the pole moves in the opposite direction, and is weakened; and it moves the further, and is made weaker as the contact is more perfect. The presumption is, that if it were complete, the two poles of the magnet would be diffused over the whole of its mass, the instrument there exhibiting no attractive or repulsive powers. Hence it is not improbable that, caused by some induction, a greater accumulation of power may take place in the middle of the magnet than at the end, and may cause the poles to be inwards, rather than at the extremities.

A third difference is, that the similar poles of magnets, though they repel at most distances, yet when brought very near together, attract each other. This power is not strong, but I do not believe it is occasioned by the superior strength of one pole over the other, since the most equal magnets exert it, and since the poles as to their magnetism remain the same, and are able to take up as much, if not more, iron filings when together, as when separated, whereas opposite poles, when in contact, do not take up so much. With similar helix poles, this attraction does not take place.

The attempts to make magnets resembling the helix and the flat spirals, have been very unsuccessful. A plate of steel was formed into a cylinder and magnetized, one end was north all round, the other south ; but the outside and the inside had the same properties, and no pole of a needle would have gone up the axis and down the sides, as with the helix, but would have stopped at the dissimilar pole of the needle. Hence it is certain, that the rings of which the cylinder may be supposed to be formed, are not in the same state as those of which the helix was composed. All attempts to magnetize a flat circular plate of steel, so as to have one pole in the centre of one side, and the other pole in the centre of the opposite side, for the purpose of imitating the flat spiral, fig. 15, failed ; nothing but an irregular distribution of the magnetism could be obtained.

M. Ampère is, I believe, undecided with regard to the size of the currents of electricity that are assumed to exist in magnets, perpendicular to their axis. In one part of his memoirs they are said, I think, to be concentric, but this cannot be the case with those of the cylinder magnet, except two be supposed in opposite directions, the one on the inside, the other on the outside surface. In another part, I believe, the opinion is advanced that they may be exceedingly small; and it is, perhaps, possible to explain the cause of the most irregular magnet by theoretically bending such small currents in the direction required.

In the previous attempt to explain some of the electro-magnetic motions, and to show the relation between electro and other magnets, I have not intended to adopt any theory of the cause of magnetism, nor to oppose any. It appears very probable that in the regular bar magnet, the steel, or iron, is in the same state as the copper wire of the helix magnet; and perhaps, as M. Ampère supports in his theory, by the same means, namely, currents of electricity; but still other proofs are wanting of the presence of a power like electricity than the magnetic effects only. With regard to the opposite sides of the connecting wire, and the powers emanating from them, I have merely spoken of them as two, to distinguish the one set of effects from the other. The high authority of Dr. Wollaston is attached to the opinion that a single electro-magnetic current passing round the axis of the wire in a direction determined by the position of the voltaic poles, is sufficient to explain all the phenomena.

M. Ampère, who has been engaged so actively in this branch of natural philosophy, drew from his theory, the conclusion that a circular wire forming part of the connexion between the poles of the battery, should be directed by the earth's magnetism, and stand in a plane perpendicular to the magnetic meridian and the dipping needle. This result was said to be actually obtained, but its accuracy has been questioned, both on theoretical and experimental grounds. As the magnet directs the wire when in form of a curve, and the curve a needle, I endeavoured to repeat the experiment, and succeeded in the following manner. A voltaic combination of two plates was formed, which were connected by a copper wire, bent into a circular form; the plates were put into a small glass jar with dilute acid, and the jar floated on the surface of water; being then left to itself in a quiet atmosphere, the instrument so arranged itself that the curve was in a plane perpendicular to the magnetic meridian; when moved from this position, either one way or the other, it returned again; and on examining the side of the curve towards the north, it was found to be that, which, according to the law already stated, would be attracted by a south pole. A voltaic circle made in a silver capsule, and mounted with a curve, also produced the same effect; as did likewise, very readily, M. de la Rive's small ring apparatus [1]. When placed on acidulated water, the gas liberated from the plates prevented its taking up a steady position; but when put into a little floating cell, made out of the neck of a Florence flask, the whole readily took the position mentioned above, and even vibrated slowly about it.

As the straight connecting wire is directed by a magnet,

[1] Quarterly Journal of Science, xii. 186.

there is every reason to believe that it will act in the same way with the earth, and take a direction perpendicular to the magnetic meridian.  It also should act with the magnetic pole of the earth, as with the pole of a magnet, and endeavour to circulate round it.  Theoretically, therefore, a horizontal wire perpendicular to the magnetic meridian, if connected first in one way with a voltaic battery, and then in the opposite way, should have its weight altered ; for in the one case it would tend to pass in a circle downwards, and in the other upwards.  This alteration should take place differently in different parts of the world.  The effect is actually produced by the pole of a magnet, but I have not succeeded in obtaining it, employing only the polarity of the earth.—September 11, 1821.

---

### *Electro-magnetic Rotation Apparatus*[1].

Since the paper in the preceding pages has been printed, I have had an apparatus made by Mr. Newman, of Lisle-street, for the revolutions of the wire round the pole, and a pole round the wire.  When Hare's calorimoter was connected with it, the wire revolved so rapidly round the pole, that the eye could scarcely follow the motion, and a single galvanic trough, containing ten pair of plates, of Dr. Wollaston's construction, had power enough to move the wire and the pole with considerable rapidity.  It consists of a stand, about 3 inches by 6, from one end of which a brass pillar rises about 6 inches high, and is then continued horizontally by a copper rod over the stand ; at the other end of the stand a copper plate is fixed with a wire for communication, brought out to one side ; in the middle is a similar plate and a wire ; these are both fixed.  A small shallow glass cup, supported on a hollow foot of glass has a plate of metal cemented to the bottom, so as to close the aperture and form a connexion with the plate on the stand ; the hollow foot is a socket, into which a small cylindrical bar magnet can be placed, so that the upper pole shall be a little above the edge of the glass ; mercury is then poured in until the glass is nearly full ; a rod of metal descends from the horizontal arm perpendicularly over this cup ; a little cavity is hollowed at the end and amalgamated, and a piece of stiff copper wire is also

[1] Quarterly Journal of Science, xii. 186.

amalgamated, and placed in it as described in the paper, except that it is attached by a piece of thread in the manner of a ligament, passing from the end of the wire to the inner surface of the cup; the lower end of the wire is amalgamated, and furnished with a small roller, which dips so as to be under the surface of the mercury in the cup beneath it.

The other plate on the stand has also its cup, which is nearly cylindrical, a metal pin passes through the bottom of it, to connect by contact with the plate below, and to the inner end of the pin a small round bar magnet is attached at one pole by thread, so as to allow the other to be above the surface of the mercury when the cup is filled, and have freedom of motion there; a thick wire descends from the rod above perpendicularly, so as to dip a little way into the mercury of the cup; it forms the connecting wire, and the pole can move in any direction round it.    When the connexions are made with the pillar, and either of the wires from the stand plates, the revolution of the wire, or pole above, takes place; or if the wires be connected with the two coming from the plates, motion takes place in both cups at once, and in accordance with the law stated in the paper.    This apparatus may be much reduced in size, and made very much more delicate and sensible.

---

### Description of an Electro-Magnetical Apparatus for the Exhibition of Rotatory Motion[1].

The account given in the Miscellanea of the last Journal (p. 147.), of the apparatus invented in illustration of the paper in the body of that Number, being short and imperfect; a plate is given in the present Number, presenting a section of that apparatus, and a view of a smaller apparatus, illustrative of the motions of the wire and the pole round each other. The larger apparatus is delineated, fig. 1. Plate iv., on a scale of one half. It consists of two glass vessels, placed side by side with their appendages.    In that on the left of the plate the motion of a magnetic pole round the connecting wire of the voltaic battery is produced.    That a current of voltaic electricity may be established through this cup, a hole is drilled at the bottom, and into this a copper pin is ground tight, which projects up-

[1] Quarterly Journal of Science, xii. 283.

wards a little way into the cup, and below is riveted to a small round plate of copper, forming part of the foot of the vessel. A similar plate of copper is fixed to the turned wooden base on which the cup is intended to stand, and a piece of strong copper wire, which is attached to it beneath, after proceeding downwards a little way, turns horizontally to the left hand, and forms one of the connexions. The surfaces of these two plates intended to come together, are tinned and amalgamated, that they may remain longer clean and bright, and afford better contact. A small cylindrical and powerful magnet has one of its poles fastened to a piece of thread, which, at the other end, is attached to the copper pin at the bottom of the cup; and the height of the magnet and length of the thread is so adjusted, that when the cup is nearly filled with clean mercury, the free pole shall float almost upright on its surface.

A small brass pillar rises from the stand behind the glass vessels: an arm comes forward from the top of it, supporting at its extremity a cross wire, which at the place on the left hand, where it is perpendicularly over the cup just described, bends downwards, and is continued till it just dips into the centre of the mercurial surface. The wire is diminished in size for a short distance above the surface of the mercury, and its lower extremity amalgamated, for the purpose of ensuring good contact; and so also is the copper pin at the bottom of the cup. When the poles of a voltaic apparatus are connected with the brass pillar, and with the lateral copper wire, the upper pole of the magnet immediately rotates round the wire which dips into the mercury; and in one direction or the other, according as the connexions are made.

The other vessel is of the form delineated in the plate. The stem is hollow and tubular; but, instead of being filled by a plug, as is the aperture in the first vessel, a small copper socket is placed in it, and retained there by being fastened to a circular plate below, which is cemented to the glass foot, so that no mercury shall pass out by it. This plate is tinned and amalgamated on its lower surface, and stands on another plate and wire, just as in the former instance. A small circular bar magnet is placed in the socket, at any convenient height, and then mercury poured in until it rises so high that nothing but the projecting pole of the magnet is left above its surface at the centre. The forms and relative positions of the magnet, socket, plate, &c., are seen in fig. 2.

The cross wire supported by the brass pillar is also prolonged on the right hand, until over the centre of the vessel just described; it then turns downwards and descends about half an inch: it has its lower extremity hollowed out into a cup, the inner surface of which is well amalgamated. A smaller piece of copper wire has a spherical head fixed on to it, of such a size that it may play in the cup in the manner of a ball and socket-joint, and being well amalgamated, it, when in the cup, retains sufficient fluid mercury by capillary attraction to form an excellent contact with freedom of motion. The ball is prevented from falling out of the socket by a piece of fine thread, which, being fastened to it at the top, passes through a small hole at the summit of the cup, and is made fast on the outside of the thick wire. This is more minutely explained by figs. 3 and 4. The small wire is of such a length that it may dip a little way into the mercury, and its lower end is amalgamated. When the connexions are so made with the pillar and right-hand wire, that the current of electricity shall pass through this moveable wire, it immediately revolves round the pole of the magnet, in a direction dependent on the pole used, and the manner in which the connexions are made.

Fig. 5 is the delineation of a small apparatus, the wire in which revolves rapidly, with very little voltaic power. It consists of a piece of glass tube, the bottom part of which is closed by a cork, through which a small piece of soft iron wire passes, so as to project above and below the cork. A little mercury is then poured in, to form a channel between the iron wire and the glass tube. The upper orifice is also closed by a cork, through which a piece of platinum wire passes which is terminated within by a loop; another piece of wire hangs from this by a loop, and its lower end, which dips a very little way into the mercury, being amalgamated, it is preserved from adhering either to the iron wire or the glass. When a very minute voltaic combination is connected with the upper and lower ends of this apparatus, and the pole of a magnet is placed in contact with the external end of the iron wire, the moveable wire within rapidly rotates round the magnet thus formed at the moment; and by changing either the connexion, or the pole of the magnet in contact with the iron, the direction of the motion itself is changed.

The small apparatus in the plate is not drawn to any scale. It has been made so small as to produce rapid revolutions, by the action of two plates of zinc and copper, containing not more than a square inch of surface each.

In place of the ball and socket-joint (fig. 3 and 4) loops may be used : or the fixed wire may terminate in a small cup containing mercury, with its aperture upwards, and the moveable wire may be bent into the form of a hook, of which the extremity should be sharpened, and rest in the mercury on the bottom of the cup.

---

### *Note on New Electro-Magnetical Motions* [1].

At page 147 of this volume, I mentioned the expectation I entertained of making a wire through which a current of voltaic electricity was passing, obey the magnetic poles of the earth in the way it does the poles of a bar magnet. In the latter case it rotates, in the former I expected it would vary in weight ; but the attempts I then made, to prove the existence of this action, failed. Since then I have been more successful, and the object of the present note is so far to complete that paper, as to show in what manner the rotative force of the wire round the terrestrial magnetic pole, is exerted, and what the effects produced by it, are.

Considering the magnetic pole as a mere centre of action, the existence and position of which may be determined by well-known means, it was shown by many experiments, in the paper, page 127, that the electro-magnetic wire would rotate round the pole, without any reference to the position of the axis joining it with the opposite pole in the same bar; for sometimes the axis was horizontal, at other times vertical, whilst the rotation continued the same. It was also shown that the wire, when influenced by the pole, moved laterally, its parts describing circles in planes perpendicular nearly to the wire itself. Hence the wire, when straight and confined to one point above, described

[1] Quarterly Journal of Science, xii. 416.

a cone in its revolution, but when bent into a crank, it described a cylinder; and the effect was evidently in all cases for each point of the wire to describe a circle round the pole, in a plane perpendicular to the current of electricity through the wire. In dispensing with the magnet, used to give these motions, and operating with the terrestrial magnetic pole, it was easy, by applying the information gained above, to deduce before-hand the direction the motions would probably take; for, assuming that the dipping-needle, if it does not point to the pole of the earth, points at least in the direction in which that pole is active, it is evident that a straight electro-magnetic wire, affected by the terrestrial as by an artificial pole, would move laterally at right angles to the needle; that is to say, it would endeavour to describe a cylinder round the pole, the radius of which may be represented by the line of the needle prolonged to the pole itself. As these cylinders, or circles, would be of immense magnitude, it was evident that only a very minute portion of them could be brought within the reach of the experiment; still, however, that portion would be sufficient to indicate their existence, inasmuch as the motions taking place in the part under consideration, must be of the same kind, and in the same direction, as in every other part.

Reasoning thus, I presumed that an electro-magnetic wire should move laterally, or in a line perpendicular to the current of electricity passing through it, in a plane perpendicular to the dipping-needle; and the dip being here 72° 30', that plane would form an angle with the horizon of 17° 30', measured on the magnetic meridian. This is not so far removed from the horizontal plane, but that I expected to get motions in the latter, and succeeded in the following manner :—A piece of copper wire, about ·045 of an inch thick, and fourteen inches long, had an inch at each extremity bent at right angles, in the same direction, and the ends amalgamated; the wire was then suspended horizontally, by a long silk thread from the ceiling. A basin of clean pure mercury was placed under each extremity of the wire and raised until the ends just dipped into the metal. The mercury in both basins was covered by a stratum of diluted pure nitric acid, which dissolving any film, allowed free motion. Then connecting the mercury in one basin with one pole of Hare's calorimotor, the instrument mentioned page 127, the moment the other pole was connected with the other basin, the suspended wire moved laterally across the basins till it touched the sides : on breaking the connexion, the wire resumed its first position; on restoring it, the motion was again produced. On changing the position of the wire, the effect still took place; and the direction of the motion was always the same relative to the wire, or rather to the current passing through it being at right angles to it.   Thus when the wire was east and west, the east end to the zinc, the west end to the copper plate, the motion was towards the north ; when the connexions were reversed, the motion was towards the south.   When the wire hung north and south, the north end to the zinc plate, the south end to the copper plate, the motion was towards the west; when the connexions were reversed, towards the east ; and the intermediate positions had their motions in intermediate directions.

The tendency, therefore, of the wire to revolve in a circle round the pole of the earth, is evident, and the direction of the motion is precisely the same as that pointed out in the former experiments.   The experiment also points out the power which causes Ampère's curve to traverse, and the way in which that power is exerted.   The well-known experiment, made by M. Ampère, proves, that a wire ring, made to conduct a current of electricity, if it be allowed to turn on a vertical axis, moves into a plane east and west of the magnetic meridian ; if on an east and west horizontal axis, it moves into a plane perpendicular to the dipping-needle.   Now if the curve be considered as a polygon of an infinite number of sides, and each of these sides be compared in succession to the straight wire just described, it will be seen that the motions given to them by the terrestrial pole, or poles, are such as would necessarily bring the polygon they form into a plane perpendicular to the dipping-needle; so that the traversing of the ring may be reduced to the simple rotation of the wire round a pole.   It is true the whole magnetism of the earth is concerned in producing the effect, and not merely that portion which I have, for the moment, supposed to respect the north pole of the earth as its centre of action; but the effect is the same, and produced in the same manner; and the introduction of the influence of the southern hemisphere, only renders the result analogous to the experiment at page 134, where two poles are concerned, instead of that at page 129, &c., where one pole only is active.

Besides the above proof of rotation round the terrestrial pole, I have made an experiment still more striking. As in the experiment of rotation round the pole of a magnet, the pole is perpendicular to but a small portion of the wire, and more or less oblique to the rest, I considered it probable, that a wire, very delicately hung, and connected, might be made to rotate round the dip of the needle by the earth's magnetism alone; the upper part being restrained to a point in the line of the dip, the lower being made to move in a circle surrounding it. This result was obtained in the following manner : a piece of copper wire, about 0·018 of an inch in diameter, and six inches long, was well amalgamated all over, and hung by a loop to another piece of the same wire, as described at page 151, so as to allow very free motion, and its lower end was thrust through a small piece of cork, to make it buoyant on mercury ; the upper piece was connected with a thick wire, that went away to one pole of the voltaic apparatus ; a glass basin, ten inches in diameter, was filled with pure clear mercury, and a little dilute acid put on its surface as before ; the thick wire was then hung over the centre of the glass basin, and depressed so low that the thin moveable wire having its lower end resting on the surface of the mercury, made an angle of about 40° with the horizon. Immediately the circuit through the mercury was completed, this wire began to move and rotate, and continued to describe a cone whilst the connexions were preserved, which though its axis was perpendicular, evidently, from the varying rapidity of its motion, regarded a line parallel to the dipping-needle as that in which the power acted that formed it. The direction of the motion was, as expected, the same as that given by the pole of a magnet pointing to the south. If the centre from which the wire hung was elevated until the inclination of the wire was equal to that of the dip, no motion took place when the wire was parallel to the dip; if the wire was not so much inclined as the dip, the motion in one part of the circle capable of being described by the lower end was reversed ; results that necessarily follow from the relation of the dip and the moving wire, and which may easily be extended.

I have described the effects above as produced by the north pole of the earth, assuming that pole as a centre of action, acting in a line represented by the dip of the needle. This has been done that the phenomena might more readily be compared with those produced by the pole of a magnet. M. Biot has shown by calculation that the magnetic poles of the earth may be considered as two points in the magnetic axis very near to each other in the centre of the globe. M. Ampère has in his theory advanced the opinion that the magnetism of the earth is caused by electric currents moving round its axis parallel to the equator. Of the consonance existing among the calculation, the theory and the facts, some idea may perhaps be gained from what was said, page 138, on the rotation of a pole through and round a wire ring. The different sides of the plane which pass through the ring, there described, and which may represent the equator in M. Ampère's theory, accord perfectly with the hemispheres of the globe; and the relative position of the supposed points of attraction and repulsion, coincide with those assigned by M. Biot for the poles of the earth itself. Whatever, however, may be the state and arrangement of terrestrial magnetism, the experiments I have described bear me out, I think, in presuming, that in every part of the terrestrial globe an electro-magnetic wire, if left to the free action of terrestrial magnetism, will move in a plane (for so the small part we can experiment on may be considered) perpendicular to the dip of the needle, and in a direction perpendicular to the current of electricity passing through it.

Reverting now to the expectation I entertained of altering the apparent weight of a wire, it was founded on the idea that the wire, moving towards the north round the pole, must rise, and moving towards the south, must descend; inasmuch as a plane perpendicular to the dipping-needle, ascends and descends in these directions. In order to ascertain the existence of this effect, I bent a wire twice at right angles, as in the first experiment described in this note, and fastened on to each extremity a short piece of thin wire amalgamated, and made the

connexion into the basins of mercury by these thin wires.
The wire was then suspended, not as before, from the ceiling,
but from a small and delicate lever, which would indicate any
apparent alteration in the weight of the wire; the connexions
were then made with a voltaic instrument, but I was surprised
to find that the wire seemed to become lighter in both directions, though not so much when its motion was towards the
south as towards the north. On further trial it was found to
ascend on the contacts being made, whatever its position to
the magnetic meridian, and I soon ascertained that it did
not depend on the earth's magnetism, nor on any local magnetic action of the conductors, or surrounding bodies on the
wire.

After some examination I discovered the cause of this unexpected phenomenon. An amalgamated piece of the thin copper wire was dipped into clean mercury, having a stratum of
water or dilute acid over it; this, however, was not necessary,
but it preserved the mercury clean and the wire cool. In this
position the cohesive attraction of the mercury raised a little
elevation of the metal round the wire of a certain magnitude,
which tended to depress the wire by adding to its weight.
When the mercury and the wire were connected with the
poles of the voltaic apparatus, this elevation visibly diminished
in magnitude by an apparent alteration in the cohesive attraction of the mercury, and a part of the force which before
tended to depress the wire was thus removed. This alteration
took place equally, whatever the direction in which the current
was passing through the wire and the mercury, and the effect
ceased the moment the connexions were broken.

Thus the cause which made the wire ascend in the former
case was evident, and by knowing it, it was easy to construct
an apparatus in which the ascent should be very considerable.
A piece of copper bell wire, about two inches long, had portions
of the amalgamated fine copper wire soldered on to its ends,
and those bent downwards till parallel to each other. This
was then hung by a silk thread from the lever, and the fine
wire ends dipped into two cups of clean mercury. When the
communications were completed from the voltaic instrument
through these two cups, the wires would rise nearly an inch

out of the mercury, and descend again on breaking the communication.

Thus it appears that, when a fine amalgamated copper wire dips into mercury, and a current of voltaic electricity passes through the combination, a peculiar effect is produced at the place where the wire first touches the mercury, equivalent to a diminution of the cohesive attraction of the mercury. The effect rapidly diminished by increasing the size of the wire, and 20 pair of plates of Dr. Wollaston's construction, and four inches square, would not produce it with the fine wire: on the contrary, two large plates are sufficient. Dr. Hare's calorimotor was the instrument used, and the charge was so weak that it would barely warm two inches of any sized wire. Whether the effect is an actual diminution of the attraction of the particles of the mercury, or depends on some other cause, remains as yet to be determined. But in any case its influence is so powerful, that it must always be estimated in experiments made to determine the force and direction of an electro-magnetic wire, acted on by a magnetic pole, if the direction is otherwise than horizontal, and if they are observed in the way described in this note. Thus, at the magnetic equator, for instance, where the apparent alteration of weight in an electro-magnetic wire may be expected to be greatest, the diminution of weight in its attempt to ascend would be increased by this effect, and the apparently increased gravity produced by its attempt to descend would be diminished, or perhaps entirely counteracted.

I have received an account by letter from Paris, of an ingenious apparatus[1] contrived by M. Ampère, to illustrate the rotatory motions described in my former paper. M. Ampère states that, if made of sufficient size, it will rotate by the magnetic action of the earth, and it is evident that will be the case in latitudes at some distance from the equator, if the rotatory wires, namely, those by which the ring of zinc is suspended, are in such a position as to form an angle with a vertical line, larger than that formed by the direction of the dip.

It is to be remarked that the motions mentioned in this note were produced by a single pair of plates, and therefore, as well

---

[1] See Quarterly Journal of Science, xii. 415.

as those described in the paper, page 127, are the reverse of
what would be produced by two or more pair of plates. It
should be remembered also, that the north pole of the earth is
opposite in its powers to what I have called the north poles of
needles or magnets, and similar to their south poles.

I may be allowed, in conclusion, to express a hope that the
law I have ventured to announce, respecting the directions of
the rotatory motions of an electro-magnetic wire, influenced by
terrestrial magnetism, will be put to the test in different latitudes; or, what is nearly the same thing, that the law laid
down by M. Ampère, as regulating the position taken by his
curve, namely, that it moves into a plane perpendicular to the
dipping-needle, will be experimentally ascertained by all those
having the opportunity.

### Historical Sketch, &c.

Prior to and just before September 1821, I had been engaged in writing an ' Historical Sketch of Electro-Magnetism,'
which may be found published in the Annals of Philosophy,
New Series, for September and October 1821, and February
1822, or in volumes ii. 195, 274, and iii. 107. The thoughts
which then arose led to the preceding papers and the discovery
of *Electro-Magnetic* rotation. As papers further on refer to
it for *dates*, I think it needful to indicate here where it may be
found, though I do not think it necessary to reprint the account,
as it describes the facts of others and not of myself.—Mar. 1844.

### Effect of Cold on Magnetic Needles[1].

Dr. De Sanctis has lately published some experiments on
the effect of cold in destroying the magnetic power of needles[2],
or at least in rendering them insensible to the action of iron
and other magnets. Mr. Ellis has claimed the merit of this
discovery, and the reasoning upon it, for the late Governor
Ellis. Conceiving it important to establish the fact, that cold as
well as heat injured or destroyed the magnetic power of iron
or steel, we wrapped a magnetic needle up in lint, dipped it in
sulphuret of carbon, placed it on its pivot under the receiver

---

[1] Quarterly Journal of Science, xiv. 435.          [2] Phil. Mag. lx. 199.

of an air-pump, and rapidly exhausted : in this way a cold, below the freezing of mercury, is readily obtained. When in this
state, the needle was readily affected by iron or a magnet, and
the number of vibrations performed in a given time by the influence of the earth upon it were observed. A fire was now
placed near the pump, and the whole warmed ; and when at
about 80° Fahr. the needle was again examined, it appeared
to be just in the same state as before as to obedience to iron
and a magnet, and the number of oscillations were very nearly
the same, though a little greater. The degree of exhaustion
remained uniform throughout the experiment.—ED.

---

*Historical Statement respecting Electro-Magnetic Rotation*[1].

In the xiith volume of the Quarterly Journal of Science, at
page 74, I published a paper on some new electro-magnetical
motions, and on the theory of magnetism (p. 127.). In consequence of some discussion, which arose immediately on the
publication of that paper, and also again within the last two
months, I think it right, both in justice to Dr. Wollaston and
myself, to make the following statement :—

Dr. Wollaston was, I believe, the person who first entertained the possibility of electro-magnetic rotation ; and if I now
understand aright, had that opinion very early after repeating
Professor Œrsted's experiments. It may have been about August 1820, that Dr. Wollaston first conceived the possibility of
making a wire in the voltaic circuit revolve on its own axis.
There are circumstances which lead me to believe that I did
not hear of this idea till November following ; and it was at
the beginning of the following year that Dr. Wollaston, provided with an apparatus he had made for the purpose, came
to the Institution with Sir Humphry Davy, to make an experiment of this kind. I was not present at the experiment, nor
did I see the apparatus, but I came in afterwards, and assisted
in making some further experiments on the rolling of wires on
edges[2]. I heard Dr. Wollaston's conversation at the time,
and his expectation of making a wire revolve on its own axis ;
and I suggested (hastily and uselessly) as a delicate method of

[1] Quarterly Journal of Science, xv. 288.
[2] See Sir Humphry Davy's Letter to Dr. Wollaston, Phil. Trans. 1821, p. 17

suspension, the hanging the needle from a magnet. I am not able to recollect, nor can I excite the memory of others to the recollection of the time when this took place. I believe it was in the beginning of 1821.

The paper which I first published was written, and the experiments all made, in the beginning of September, 1821. It was published on the first of October ; a second paper was published in the same volume on the last day of the same year. I have been asked, why in those papers I made no reference to Dr. Wollaston's opinions and intentions, inasmuch as I always acknowledged the relation between them and my own experiments. To this I answer, that upon obtaining the results described in the first paper, and which I showed very readily to all my friends, I went to Dr. Wollaston's house to communicate them also to him, and to ask permission to refer to his views and experiments. Dr. Wollaston was not in town, nor did he return whilst I remained in town; and, as I did not think I had any right to refer to views not published, and as far as I knew not pursued, my paper was printed and appeared without that reference whilst I remained in the country. I have regretted ever since I did not delay the publication, that I might have shown it first to Dr. Wollaston.

Pursuing the subject, I obtained some other results which seemed to me worthy of being known. Previous to their arrangement in the form in which they appear at page 416 of the same volume (p. 151.), I waited on Dr. Wollaston, who was so kind as to honour me with his presence two or three times, and witness the results. My object was then to ask him permission to refer to his views and experiments in the paper which I should immediately publish, in correction of the error of judgment of not having done so before. The impression that has remained on my mind ever since (one and twenty months) and which I have constantly expressed to every one when talking on the subject, is, that he wished me not to do so. Dr. Wollaston has lately told me that he cannot recollect the words he used at the time; that, as regarded himself, his feelings were it should not be done, as regarded me, that it should ; but that he did not tell me so. I can only say that my memory at this time holds most tenaciously the following words : " I would rather you should not ;" but I must, of course, have been mis-

taken. However, that is the only cause why the above statement was not made in December 1821; and that cause being
removed, I am glad to make it at this, the first opportunity.

It has been said I took my views from Dr. Wollaston. That
I deny; and refer to the following statement, as offering some
*proof* on that point. It has, also, been said, that I could never,
unprepared, have gained in the course of eight or ten days, the
facts described in my first paper. The following information
may elucidate that point also.

It cannot but be well known, (for Sir Humphry Davy himself
has done me the honour to mention it) that I assisted him in
the important series of experiments he made on this subject.
What is more important to me in the present case, however, is
not known; namely, that I am the author of the *Historical
Sketch of Electro-magnetism*, which appeared in the Annals
of Philosophy, New Series, vols. ii. and iii. Nearly the whole
of that sketch was written in the months of July, August, and
September of 1821; and the first parts, to which I shall particularly refer, were published in September and October of the
same year. Although very imperfect, I endeavoured, as I think
appears on the face of the papers, as far as in me lay, to make
them give an accurate account of the state of that branch of
science. I referred, with great labour and fatigue, to the different journals in which papers by various philosophers had
appeared, and repeated almost all the experiments described.

Now this sketch was written and published *after* I had heard
of Dr. Wollaston's expectations, and assisted at the experiments before referred to; and I may, therefore, refer to it as a
public testimony of the state of my knowledge on the subject
*before* I began my own experiments. I think any one, who
reads it attentively, will find, in every page of the first part of
it, proofs of my ignorance of Dr. Wollaston's views; but I will
refer more particularly to the paragraph which connects the
198th and 199th pages, and especially to the 18th and 19th
lines of it; and also to fig. 4 of the accompanying plate. There
is there an effect described in the most earnest and decided
manner (see the next paragraph but one to that referred to);
my accuracy, and even my ability, is pledged upon it; and yet
Dr. Wollaston's views and reasonings, which it is said I knew,
are founded, and were, from the first, as I now understand,

upon the knowledge of an effect quite the reverse of that I have stated. I describe a neutral position when the needle is opposite to the wire; Dr. Wollaston had observed, from the first, that there was no such thing as a neutral position, but that the needle passed by the wire: I, throughout the sketch, describe attractive and repulsive powers on each side of the wire; but what I thought to be attraction to, and repulsion from the wire in August 1821, Dr. Wollaston long before perceived to arise from a power not directed to or from the wire, but acting circumferentially round it as axis, and upon that knowledge founded his expectation.

I have before said, I repeated most of the experiments described in the papers referred to in the sketch; and it was in consequence of repeating and examining this particular experiment, that I was led into the investigation given in my first paper. He who will read that part of the sketch, above referred to[1], and then the first, second and third pages of my paper[2], will, I think, at once see the connexion between them; and from my difference of expression in the two, with regard to the attractive and repulsive powers, which I at first supposed to exist, will be able to judge of the new information which I had, at the period of writing the latter paper, then, for the first time acquired.

---

### Electro-magnetic Current (*under the Influence of a Magnet*[3]).

As the current of electricity, produced by a voltaic battery when passing through a metallic conductor, powerfully affects a magnet, tending to make its poles pass round the wire, and in this way moving considerable masses of matter, it was supposed that a reaction would be exerted upon the electric current capable of producing some visible effect; and the expectation being, for various reasons, that the approximation of a pole of a powerful magnet would diminish the current of electricity, the following experiment was made. The poles of a battery of from two to thirty 4-inch plates were connected by a

---

[1] Annals of Philosophy, N. S., ii. 198, 199.
[2] Quarterly Journal, xii. 74–76, or pp. 127–129 of this volume.
[3] Quarterly Journal of Science, xix. 338.

metallic wire formed in one part into a helix with numerous
convolutions, whilst into the circuit, at another part, was introduced a delicate galvanometer.  The magnet was then put, in
various positions, and to different extents, into the helix, and
the needle of the galvanometer noticed; no effect, however,
upon it could be observed.  The circuit was made very long,
short, of wires of different metals and different diameters down
to extreme fineness, but the results were always the same.  Magnets more and less powerful were used, some so strong as to
bend the wire in its endeavours to pass round it.  Hence it
appears, that however powerful the action of an electric current
may be upon a magnet, the latter has no tendency, by reaction,
to diminish or increase the intensity of the former;—a fact
which, though of a negative kind, appears to me to be of some
importance.—M. F. [See note at end of Series 1. of Exp. Res.
1843.]

---

### *Electric Powers (and place) of Oxalate of Lime*[1].

Some oxalate of lime, obtained by precipitation, when well-
washed, was dried in a Wedgewood's basin at a temperature
approaching 300°, until so dry as not to render a cold glass
plate, placed over it, dim.  Being then stirred with a platina
spatula, it, in a few moments, by friction against the metal,
became so strongly electrical, that it could not be collected
together, but flew about the dish whenever it was moved, and
over its sides into the sand-bath.  It required some little stirring before the particles of the powder were all of them sufficiently electrical to produce this effect.  It was found to take
place either in porcelain, glass, or metal basins, and with porcelain, glass, or metal stirrers; and when well excited, the
electrified particles were attracted on the approach of all bodies, and when shaken in small quantity on to the cap of a gold-
leaf electrometer, would make the leaves diverge two or three
inches.  The effect was not due to temperature, for when
cooled out of the contact of air, it equally took place when
stirred; being, however, very hygrometric, the effect soon went
off if the powder were exposed to air.  Excited in a silver cap-

---

[1] Quarterly Journal of Science, xix. 338.

sule, and then left out of contact of the air, the substance remained electrical a great length of time, proving its very bad
conducting power ; and in this respect surpassing, perhaps, all
other bodies. The effect may be produced any number of
times, and after any number of desiccations of the salt.

Platina rubbed against the powder became negative—the
powder positive ; all other metals tried, the same as platina.
When rubbed with glass, the glass became strongly negative, the oxalate positive, both being dry and warm; and indeed this body appears to stand at the head of the list of all
substances as yet tried, as to its power of becoming positively
electrical by friction.

Oxalates of zinc and lead produced none of these effects.—
M. F.

---

*On the Electro-motive Force of Magnetism. By Signori*
NOBILI *and* ANTINORI (*from the* Antologia, No. 131) : *with
Notes by* MICHAEL FARADAY, *F.R.S., &c*[1].

Mr. Faraday has recently discovered a new class of electro-
dynamic phenomena.   He has presented a memoir on this subject to the Royal Society of London, which is not yet published,
and of which we have received the simple notice, communicated by M. Hachette to the Academy of Sciences at Paris on
the 26th of December last, in consequence of a letter which he
had received from Mr. Faraday himself[2].   This relation in-

[1] Philosophical Magazine and Annals, 1832, xi. 402.
   In this paper the date on the right-hand page is that of my notes, that on
the left-hand is meant to be the one of Signori Nobili and Antinori's paper.
Of the latter however there is great doubt, for the date attached by the writer is
31st January, 1832, whilst the number of the Antologia in which it appears professes to have for date, November 1831.   The latter is probably the false date,
and so the real date of publication is unknown; it could not however be before
February 1832.

[2] I am glad of an opportunity of adding a few notes to a public version
of Sig. Nobili and Antinori's paper. My hasty letter to M. Hachette, in
consequence, probably, of my bad writing, has been translated with some
errors ; and has been, by Sig. Nobili at least, seriously misunderstood.   Had
it remained private, it would not have been of much consequence: but as it

duced Cav. Antinori and myself immediately to repeat the fundamental experiment, and to study it under its various aspects. As we flatter ourselves we have arrived at results of some importance, we hasten to publish them without any other preamble than the same notice which has served as the point of departure in our researches.

"The memoir of Mr. Faraday," so says the notice, " is divided into four parts. In the first, intitled ' Production of Voltaic Electricity [1],' is found the following important fact,— that a voltaic current which traverses a metallic wire produces another current in a neighbouring wire; that the second current is in a direction contrary to the first, and continues but for a moment; that if the producing current is removed, a second current is manifested in the wire submitted to its action contrary to that which was first formed in it, *i. e.* in the same direction as the producing current.

" The second part of the memoir treats of electric currents produced by the magnet. On causing helices to approach to magnets, Mr. Faraday has produced electric currents; on removing the spirals, currents in the contrary direction were formed. These currents act powerfully on the galvanometer; pass, though feebly, through brine and other solutions, and in a particular case Mr. Faraday *has obtained a spark*. Hence it follows that this philosopher has by using a magnet only produced the electric currents discovered [studied] by M. Ampère.

" The third part of the memoir is relative to a particular

has appeared in three or four languages, and forms the text of all subsequent papers on magnetic electricity, it is very requisite to correct certain errors which have arisen from it, especially that of Sig. Nobili relative to Arago's rotation.

My first paper was read to the Royal Society, November 24, 1831; and my letter to M. Hachette was dated the 17th of December, 1831; my second paper was read January 12th, 1832. Sig. Nobili's paper is dated January 31st, 1832. Signori Nobili and Antinori worked only from my letter to M. Hachette; but as I hope I may claim whatever is contained in my two papers, I have introduced into the present paper references, in figures included within parentheses, to paragraphs in my papers, wherever the experiments described are either altogether, or only to a partial extent, repetitions of my results.—M. F.]

[1 This should be *induction of voltaic electricity.*—M. F.]

electric state, which Mr. Faraday calls *electrotomo state*[1]. He intends to write of this another time.

"The fourth part speaks of the experiment not less curious than extraordinary of M. Arago, which consists, as is known, in making a magnetic needle revolve under the influence of a rotatory metallic disc, and *vice versâ.* Mr. Faraday considers this phenomenon as intimately connected with that of the magnetic rotation, which he had the fortune to discover about ten years ago. He has ascertained that by the rotation of the metallic disc under the influence of a magnet, there may be formed electric currents in the direction of the rays of the disc in sufficient number to render the disc a new electrical machine." —*Le Temps,* Dec. 28, 1831.

1. *Ordinary Magnetism* (Phil. Trans. 1832. Part I. *Experimental Researches in Electricity,* 27 *to* 59: 83 *to* 138 : 217 *to* 264).

We had no occasion to make trials before we succeeded in the experiment of Mr. Faraday. The first spirals which we brought near to the pole of a magnet quickly manifested their influence on the galvanometer. We observed three facts in succession (*Exp. Res.* 30. 37. 47.). Whilst approaching the magnet, the needle of the instrument is in the first place seen to deviate a certain number of degrees, which indicates a current excited by the magnetism, in the spirals previously made to communicate with the galvanometer. This current lasts but for a moment, and is then completely extinct, as is proved by the needle returning to its first position : this is the second observation. The third (finally) occurs when the spiral is taken from the magnet : the needle of the galvanometer then deviates on the other side, demonstrating the development of a current contrary to that excited in the first instance.

On experimenting with an annular spiral between the poles of a horse-shoe magnet, we observed that the action was much less than that produced with the same spiral when the lifter of the magnet was put to it or suddenly taken from it (*Exp. Res.* 34.). This fact suggested the idea of rolling a copper wire covered with silk round such a magnet, so as to have an ap-

[1 This should be *electrotonic state.* I said I should write to my friend about it another time.—M. F.]

paratus always mounted for the experiment in question. The spiral to be subjected to the magnetic influence is then always upon the magnet, and the immediate cause of the phenomena resides in the lifter, because of the property which that little piece of soft iron possesses of being magnetized and de-magnetized rapidly. When the lifter is detached, the spiral which before was in the presence of this piece of iron strongly magnetized, is suddenly removed from its action, and represents the case of a spiral which having been first approximated to a magnet is then removed. When the lifter is replaced, it is as if a magnet were caused to approach the spiral, for the lifter becomes magnetic on being attached to the poles of its own magnet.

This arrangement, besides being very active, has the advantage of supplying the philosopher with a *constant source* of voltaic electricity (*Exp. Res.* 46 note). The want of a constant current is often felt in such researches; and if thermo-magnetism offers a plausible means of satisfying such necessities, as I have indicated elsewhere [1], yet the new method offered us by a magnet covered with electro-dynamic spirals is not to be despised. Here the currents are always ready to be manifested. Suppose, as is usual, the lifter of the magnet is in its place, nothing more is required to obtain a current in the spiral than to detach the lifter, the current in the wire being, as it were, at first in a latent state.

There are two modes of using this arrangement; the one by attaching the lifter, the other by detaching it. When the two motions are made with the same rapidity, and with relation to the same points of the magnet, the deviations are in the inverse directions to each other, but precisely of the same value. The detachments are, however, always equally instantaneous, and for constancy of effect are preferable to approximations; for the latter to be always equally successful would require a mechanical arrangement, which it is not worth while either to imagine or to execute. By taking care that the lifter is constantly in its right place and position, there will always be produced the same deviation of the galvanometer when it is de-

---

[1] This means consists in having a thermo-electric elementary combination composed of two metals only, and heated at one juncture to 0° Fahr., at the other to 212° Fahr.—*Ann. de Chimie*, Feb. 1830, p. 130.

tached from the magnet.   This we repeat is a valuable result
applicable in numerous cases, and perhaps proper to measure
the force of large magnets in a more exact manner than by the
ordinary mode of ascertaining the weights sustained.

The arrangement described is highly advantageous; but
does it produce the maximum of electro-dynamic effects?
There is indeed another much better (*Exp. Res.* 46 note), which
consists in applying the electro-dynamic spiral to the central
part of the lifter, corresponding to the interval which separates
the poles of the horse-shoe magnet.   In this position a spiral
of a few turns is able to surpass the effects of a far greater number of spirals otherwise disposed.   Behold then the arrangement which it is convenient to make to obtain all the effects of
a magnet.   The central part of the lifter is to be entirely covered with wire, leaving exposed only the extremities, which are
to come in contact with the pole of the magnet.   The ordinary
form of the lifter is not the most convenient upon which to arrange this species of large electro-dynamic ring, but upon conveniently modifying its shape the wire may be applied with
facility, and thus the effect be obtained at its highest degree of
intensity.   The reason is evident; for two conditions in fact
require to be fulfilled : one, that the spiral should be subjected
to all the influence of the magnetic force; the other, that this
influence should be abstracted in the shortest possible time.
Now the wire round the lifter is exactly in the most favourable
position for the magnetic force to be concentrated upon it; and
this force vanishes the instant the lifter is detached, as is required by the second condition.

*Spirals of various Metals* (*Exp. Res.* 132. 139. 193. 208. &c.).

The metals with which we have experimented are four,—
copper, iron, bismuth, and antimony : iron is interesting as the
foremost amongst magnetic metals (*Exp. Res.* 8. 9. 211.); bismuth and antimony for the distinct position they hold in the
thermo-magnetic scale.   In experiments made under circumstances approximating to equality, it appeared that copper was
the most active in the present point of view; then at a little
distance iron (*Exp. Res.* 207. 212.); afterwards antimony; and
finally, bismuth.   But in truth the fragility of the two latter

only allowed us to give them the spiral figure by fusing them. For this method, which was long and difficult, we supplied another; which was, to make quadrangular spirals of a number of rods of these metals soldered at their extremities, or else merely held and pressed the one against the other, to ensure contact. It is scarcely necessary to say, that in order to obtain comparative results the same quadrangular form was given to the spirals of copper and iron.

### 2. *Electric Spark* (*Exp. Res.* 32. 57.[1]).

The relation placed at the head of this article says, " *that in a particular case Mr. Faraday had obtained a spark* " (*Exp. Res. 32.*). Although this expression gave no light on the subject, and rather rendered doubtful the constancy of so extra-

[1 Being much engaged in the investigation and confirmation of the laws of magneto-electric action, terrestrial magnetic induction, &c. &c. some of the results of which are contained in my second paper (The Bakerian Lecture), it will be seen that in the race which Sig. Nobili and Antinori (probably inadvertently) ran against me (see the last paragraph of their paper), they obtained the electric spark from the common magnet before me. I have great pleasure in bearing witness to the accuracy of their reasoning on this point, and also to the success of the result. Having made a variation of the experiment by obtaining the spark from the action of a common loadstone, in which their most perfect mode could not be applied, I will take the opportunity of describing the simple adjustment I have devised. A helix was fixed round the lifter, the wire ends were raised upwards; one, which may be called *a*, was bent into a hook as in the figure; the other, *b*, after rising was bent at a right angle, and had a thick small circular plate of copper fixed to it, which was made by the spring of the wire to press in the middle slightly against the rounded end of *a*; this plate and the end of *a* were amalgamated. On bringing the lifter down sud-

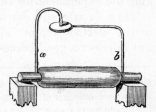

denly upon the poles in the position figured, the momentum of the plate caused it to separate from the end of *a*, and the spark passed. On lifting it up the concussion always separates the end of *a* from the plate, and a spark is again seen. When the plate and the point are well amalgamated, the spark will not fail once in a hundred times either at making or breaking contact. I have shown it brilliantly to two or three hundred persons at once, and over all parts of the theatre of the Royal Institution.

As Professor Ritchie expresses it, the spark has not yet been obtained except from a temporary magnet, *i. e.* from a magnet in the act of being made or ordinary a phenomenon, we nevertheless did not suspend our researches, and have been so fortunate as to succeed beyond our hopes. The following are the theoretical views which have conducted us to this important result, but which, we fairly say, at first gave us but very little confidence.

The voltaic pile gives a spark only when composed of a certain number of pairs of plates. A single Wollaston's voltaic element yields it; and when of a certain activity produces it constantly at the surface of mercury, to which the conjoining wires destined to close the circuit are conducted. In the voltaic pile having a certain degree of *electric tension*, the sparks pass between the zinc and copper poles, either in the case of opening or of closing the circuit. In a single Wollaston's element the tension is feeble, and the spark occurs only when the circuit is interrupted. At that moment the current which before was moving, accumulates as it were at the place of interruption, and acquires the intensity necessary to cause the spark. Such tension is wanting in the other case of closing the circuit, and the spark also is absent.

The currents developed in the electro-dynamic spirals by virtue of magnetism are also in motion, but circulate only for the moment during which they are approaching to or receding from the magnet. It was therefore, we concluded, in one of those two moments that we ought to open the circuit in making the experiment for the spark.

Thus we arranged our ideas relative to the best disposition of the electro-dynamic spirals; nothing therefore remained but to select a good horse-shoe magnet; to surround the lifter

---

destroyed. I obtained the first spark from a soft iron magnet made by the well-known influence of electric currents. Sig. Nobili and Antinori obtained the second spark from a soft iron magnet made so by the influence of a common artificial steel magnet; their result has been repeated by a great number of persons. Mr. Forbes of Edinburgh first obtained the spark from a soft iron magnet made so by the influence of the natural loadstone. The latter experiment is also that which I have made with Mr. Daniell's loadstone, lifting only about thirty pounds, and in the manner described. I was not aware of any other modes of performing the experiment except my original one, and Sig. Nobili and Antinori's.—M. F.] Since this time I have obtained the spark a step nearer to the inducting magnet than in any of these cases: see onwards at date of November 1834, or Phil. Mag. 1834, v. p. 350.—December 1843.

with a copper wire in the manner before described ; to immerse the extremities of this wire in a cup of mercury, and to raise the one or the other extremity at that precise moment when the lifter was attached to or detached from the magnet. When two persons operate without any kind of machinery, it is more easy to lose than to catch this moment. But when the movements were simultaneous, which happened every now and then, we had the satisfaction of seeing a spark, which left nothing to be desired.

Such was the mode by which we saw the first spark : but as this beautiful result deserved to be produced at pleasure, it claimed an appropriate apparatus ; and after various arrangements more or less complicated, we stopped at the following, which has the advantage of being very successful and very simple.

The whole of the contrivance is attached to the lifter of the magnet. This piece, which is a parallelopiped, is surrounded in the middle by the electro-dynamic spiral, to which it is firmly attached by two pieces of brass, so that the latter can enter between the magnetic poles whilst the lifter comes in contact with the poles in the ordinary way. The extremities of the spiral come in contact one with each magnetic pole by means of two little springs in the form of wings attached to the lifter, and which press slightly against the poles when the lifter is in its place. To leave room for these springs, the lifter is narrower than usual, covering about half the poles ; the remaining space serves for the contact of the springs, which are in this way isolated as it were from the lifter ; and yet by means of the magnet itself serve to complete the electro-dynamic circuit. Suppose that the lifter is in its place, the springs touch the poles, and the circuit of the spirals is metallically closed by the magnets ; on detaching the lifter, the circuit opens in two places ; and either at the one or the other interruption the spark almost constantly appears. When the effect does not take place, it is because the separation has not been well effected ; but it is so easy to repeat the experiment, that it is useless to think of a piece of mechanism to remedy an inconvenience which is so easily remedied.

In this apparatus the spiral on the lifter was of copper. On substituting an iron wire the spark also occurred. This experiment was interesting in illustration of any influence which the ordinary power of the magnet over iron might exert upon the electro-dynamic influence.   It did not appear that the one action disturbed the other ; but before positively affirming the independence, it will be necessary to obtain other proof, which we shall endeavour to do at a more favourable opportunity (*Exp. Res.* 9. 254.).

### 3. *Terrestrial Magnetism* (*Exp. Res.* 137. 140. &c.).

We took a paper tube two inches in diameter and four inches long, a copper wire forty metres long was coiled round it, the two ends being left at liberty to connect with the galvanometer ; the tube was trimmed at the ends, so that it could be placed upright upon the table either in one direction or the other at pleasure (*Exp. Res.* 142.).   A cylinder of soft iron, as is well known, placed parallel to the dip is subject to the terrestrial magnetic influence ; the lower part becomes a north pole, the upper a south pole.   This is a phenomenon of position always occurring in the same direction with this kind of iron, which is as incapable of retaining the magnetism received, as it is disposed to receive the new magnetism to which it may be subjected.

In our latitudes the inclination of the needle is about 63°. The paper tube with its spiral was therefore arranged in that direction, and an iron cylinder introduced ; whilst in the act of introducing it, the galvanometer was seen to move (*Exp. Res.* 146.), owing to the presence of an electric current excited by the magnetism.   On taking out the cylinder the motion was reversed : there is no doubt, therefore, that terrestrial magnetism is sufficient of itself to develope currents of electricity.   It should not be concealed here, that in the above experiment the electricity is developed by the intermedium of soft iron introduced into the spiral : this without doubt is true, but it is also true that it is not essentially necessary to recur to this aid to obtain unequivocal signs of the influence of which we speak. On placing our cylindrical spiral so that its axis should be parallel to the magnetic dip, and then inverting it by a half revolution in the magnetic meridian (*Exp. Res.* 148.), we observed at the comparative galvanometer the signs of a current

excited in the spiral by the sole influence of terrestrial magnetism.

It is not even necessary for this effect to place the spiral in
the direction of the dip: the experiment will succeed in the
vertical position; the effect is less, but always so distinct as to
remove every error (*Exp. Res.* 153, &c.).

We experimented with three copper wires of different diameters; the smallest was 0·5, the second 0·66, and the third
1· millimetre in diameter. The effects increased with the size:—
the first gave deviations from 2 to 4; the second from 4 to 8;
and the third from 10 to 20. To obtain these great motions,
we operated in the usual way of inverting the current at the
most favourable moment, which is easily learned by repeating
the experiment a few times.

In the present state of science this is most certainly the simplest mode of obtaining the current[1]; all is done by terrestrial
magnetism, which is everywhere. We purpose hereafter to
study the manner of increasing the effect, and of making some
useful applications, if certain apparatus which we purpose constructing should meet our wishes (*Exp. Res.* 147. 154, &c.).
The first thought is that of using it to measure the terrestrial
magnetic intensity; but what precision the mode may be capable of, remains at present to be determined.

The galvanometer which should be used for the experiments
of this section should be very sensible. And I repeat on this
occasion what I have elsewhere said relative to these instruments : two systems may be adopted to obtain maximum effects;
the one for hydro-electric currents, the other for thermo-electric
currents. The galvanometer of my thermo-multiplicator is of
the latter kind, and precisely that which is best in the present
researches[2]. The reason will be evident, by observing that
the new currents of Faraday are entirely developed in metallic
circuits, like the thermo-electricity of Dr. Seebeck; and that,
also like those of thermo-electricity, they pass with difficulty
through humid conductors.

[1] A much more simple mode is described in my paper at (170, &c.); for
neither spiral nor soft iron is necessary.—M. F.]
[2] Nobili, Bib. Univ., Juillet 1830, p. 275.

### 4. *Electric Tension.*

The trials which we have as yet made on this new class of currents, to obtain by the electrometer the ordinary signs of tension, have not conducted us to any positive result: but the means which we have employed are far from satisfying us fully. We are preparing others for the purpose of attacking the question with more efficacious means. We shall then extend the research to thermo-electric combinations, which deserve to be studied in the same point of view, as they have never yet presented sensible signs of electric tension. We shall also try with these latter currents to obtain the spark under favourable circumstances; but we cannot but confess that at present we doubt, and consider the thermo-electric currents as in their nature the least fitted to produce either tension or a spark, as we will explain in due time and place.

### 5. *Chemical and Physiological Effects (Exp. Res. 22. 56. 133.).*

The new currents of Faraday pass, although with difficulty, through humid conductors. So says the notice; and such is the fact, as may be readily verified by introducing a conductor of that kind into the circuit of the electro-dynamic spiral (*Exp. Res.* 20. 23. 33. 56.). In the case of other known currents, I have demonstrated elsewhere that there is always chemical decomposition when they pass liquid conductors; and that however feeble they may be, the decomposition is always assured by their transit through the fluid. It is therefore very probable that the new currents will produce the phenomena of decomposition, but their distinctive character of brief duration must not be forgotten (*Exp. Res.* 59, &c.). I believe that the time, however short, is still sufficient for decomposition; but I will not venture anything before I have interrogated that grand master in everything—experiment.

The physiological effects (*Exp. Res.* 22. 56, &c.) consist, as is well known, in the shocks or contractions of the muscles, the acrid and acidulous taste on the tongue, and the light before the eyes[1]. For obtaining these effects, it is absolutely necessary that the electricity should penetrate into our organs;

[1 The sensation on the tongue and the light before the eyes I believe I have obtained. See (56) of my papers.—M. F.]

these latter belonging to humid conductors. This path, as we have seen, is very difficult for the new currents; nevertheless, the frog put into the circuit of our electro-dynamic spirals, arranged around the lifter of our magnet, was powerfully convulsed each time that the lifter was separated or attached (*Exp. Res.* 56.). The experiment is beautiful and instructive; beautiful, because of the energetic convulsions produced apparently by the immediate action of the magnet; and instructive, because it confirms the fact of the passage of these currents through humid conductors, and because also it shows that the frog is in all cases the most delicate galvanoscope[1]. This is a fit occasion to say what I have already said elsewhere, relative to the discovery of Dr. Seebeck, that it was not necessary that Œrsted's discovery and the following one of the galvanometer should be known, to arrive at the knowledge of the thermo-electric currents[2]. The frog properly prepared was sufficient for the purpose, and the same animal would have been quite sufficient to discover the new currents of Faraday. Although it is not by this road that these two discoveries have been arrived at, still it is not less true that they might have been made by the simple assistance of this interpreter, which astonished Europe in the first times of galvanism.

6. *Magnetism of Rotation* (*Exp. Res.* 81 *to* 139: 149 *to* 169: 181 *to* 192: 217 *to* 230: 244 *to* 254, &c.).

What will happen when an electro-dynamic spiral is approached to the pole of a bar magnet? A current is produced in its successive spirals, which enters upon itself in consequence of the conjunction of the extremities of the wire. But if in place of the spiral a mass of copper is submitted to the influence of the same magnetic pole, what will happen? It would appear reasonable to admit in this mass the same development of currents, with this difference only; that in the spiral they cannot re-enter upon themselves in each spire; whilst in the mass the currents will re-enter directly into themselves, on the circle or zone of matter in which they are determined by the influence of the magnet: these currents, in the present state of science, cannot be considered as other than the consequence of a movement of the same nature which takes

---

[1] Bib. Univ. xxxvii. 10.          [2] Ibid.

place around each particle of the magnetic metal. This induction seems sufficiently natural; and for its greater confirmation we have instituted the following experiment:—a ring of copper was taken, and the two conjoining wires intended to complete the communication with the galvanometer soldered to it at the extremities of one of its diameters. On placing this ring between the two poles of a horse-shoe magnet, in the place where we introduced our electro-dynamic spiral, motions were instantly manifested at the galvanometer, due to the presence of currents excited by the magnetism in the copper ring[1].

Our idea being thus fixed relative to the circular currents, which we believed ought to be produced in the mass of copper submitted to the influence of the magnetic pole, let us pass to the question of magnetism by rotation, the wonderful discovery of M. Arago. Here we have magnetic poles in presence of a disc, which instead of being quiescent as in the preceding case, is continually moving on its own axis. The latter condition is the only one added, and by it we see that the final result of the phenomena will be excessively complicated, but that in reality nothing new will happen. In all cases it is the currents developed by the magnetism at the place of the disc which is directly acted upon by this magnetism which are concerned. This part is rapidly removed by the rotation, and another comes forward, which is subjected to the same influence, which always tends to form currents in the contrary direction to those which may be supposed to exist in the magnetic pole (*Exp. Res.* 53. 255.). These currents, by their nature, tend to be inverted so soon as they are withdrawn from the presence of the cause which produced them, and are in fact inverted every time that the velocity of rotation will permit it. The theory of this species of magnetism appears mature[2]; we shall endeavour to develope its physical principles in a more detailed manner in a separate paper, being content here

[1 This experiment will bear another interpretation. I do not (as I understand the description) believe the ring to have anything particular to do with the result; the whole appears to me a repetition of the experiment I have described (*Exp. Res.* 109).—M. F.]

[2 Sig. Nobili and Antinori have mistaken the character of the acting causes in Arago's experiment altogether; the view which they have briefly expressed and mean to pursue, is precisely that which I at first entertained and pursued, to state the particular character which distinguishes it from all other kinds, and which rendered it not easily assailable before the discovery of Mr. Faraday. This character does not consist only in momentary duration, which it has in common with soft iron, but also in being a double magnetism, *inverse* and *direct*; *inverse*, at the moment of its production, opposite to the producing cause; *direct*, at the moment after, when this cause disappears.

Mr. Faraday considers Arago's magnetism of rotation as entirely connected with a phenomenon which he discovered about ten years ago (*Exp. Res.* 121.). " *He then ascertained*," so says the notice, " *that by the rotation of a metallic disc under the influence of a magnet, there may be formed, in the direction of the radii of that disc, electric currents in sufficient number to render the disc a new electric machine.*" We are quite ignorant how Mr. Faraday has ascertained this fact; and we do not know how a result of such a nature could remain so long a time generally unknown, and as it were lost in the hands of the author of the discovery[1]. Besides, there is something here very problematical to us; and before we leave the subject we will describe the experiment we have made relative to it.

---

but which I soon found experimental reason to reject. However, I need merely refer here to the fourth division of my first paper, expressly on that phenomenon, and to parts of the sixth division in the continuation of the Researches, for what I believe to be a true view of the phenomenon (see especially *Exp. Res.* 121. 122. 123.).—M. F.]

[1 Sig. Nobili and Antinori here seriously mistake the sense of my letter to M. Hachette. I did not write " I then ascertained." The French translation of my letter in *Le Lycée*, No. 35, sent to me by M. Hachette, does not say so. " M. Faraday considère le phénomène qui se manifeste dans cette expérience, comme intimement lié à celui de la rotation magnétique qu'il a eu le bonheur de trouver il y a dix ans. Il a reconnu que par la rotation du disc métallique, &c. &c." I am not Italian scholar enough to say how Sig. Nobili and Antinori themselves at first expressed it; but the phrase used in the present part of their paper is, " *Egli reconobbe fin d'allora che, &c.* ;" whilst that which they used at the head of the paper, to express the same words of my letter, is, " *Egli ha riconosciuto che, &c. &c.*" It was in consequence of the recent researches detailed in my paper that I ascertained the state of the revolving plate, and could then refer the effect in its kind to that which I had so long before discovered. The succeeding remarks of Sig. Nobili and Antinori have no reference therefore except to their mistake of my meaning.—M. F.]

A disc of copper was revolved, and two long copper wires prepared, attached at one set of ends to the galvanometer, and at the other held by the hand against the disc, the one at the centre, and the other at the circumference, in the direction of the radii.   In the rotation of the disc, the points of copper pressed against it will be heated, but unequally; that pressed against the circumference will be most heated, and that at the centre the least.   This difference is quite sufficient to determine an electric current capable of moving the needle of the galvanometer, and retaining it after a few vibrations at a certain degree of the division[1].   When the needle is thus quiescent, if a horse-shoe magnet be advanced towards the plate so as to embrace it without interrupting its motion, it will be seen that the deviation of the needle will augment or diminish according as the poles act in the one direction or the other.   This effect is a sure proof of the current manifested in the disc by the action of the magnet: but because the wires connected with the galvanometer are arranged with their ends in the direction of the radius of the disc, are we to conclude that they are exactly in the direction in which the current excited by the magnetism exists[2]?   We do not believe it, for the reasons given above; and though we should, with Mr. Faraday, admit this species of irradiating currents, there would still exist for us a great difference between this mode of exciting electricity, and the ordinary one of our common electrical machines.   There is here a great void to fill, in passing from a superlative conductor, like the metallic disc of M. Arago, to the worst, such as the glass plate of an ordinary machine[3].

[1] All these causes of error were fully guarded against in every part of my researches (*Exp. Res.* 91. 113. 186.).—M. F.]

[2] I have nowhere drawn such conclusions.—M. F.]

[3] The case of the currents tending to be formed, or really existing in the direction of the radii throughout the *whole* plate, occurs only when the axis of the magnet approached coincides with the axis of the revolving plate (*Exp. Res.* 156. 158.), or when the magnetic curves intersected by the revolving plate are of equal strength, and pass through all parts of the plate in the same direction, as happens when the earth's magnetism is used as the exciting cause (*Exp. Res.* 149. 155.).   My reasons for calling the revolving plate an electrical machine (*Exp. Res.* 154. 158.) are entirely untouched by what is said in the text.

It must not be supposed that in these notes I am criticizing Sig. Nobili and

But these our particular opinions do not in any way diminish the intrinsic merit of Mr. Faraday's discovery. It is one of the most beautiful of our time, whether it be considered in itself for the largeness of the vacancy which it serves to fill, or for the light which it throws over the various theories, and especially that of magnetism of rotation.

We hope that these our first researches will justify the lively interest which we have taken in this new branch of electro-dynamics. We have but one regret, namely, that of having entered into a path before we knew all the steps taken in it by the illustrious philosopher who threw it open.

Florence, Jan. 31, 1832.

---

*Nobili and Antinori's Errors in Magneto-electric Induction:*
in a Letter to M. Gay-Lussac[1].

MY DEAR SIR,                    Royal Institution, Dec. 1, 1832.

I AM anxious to write you a letter on Electro-magnetism, and I beg you to insert it in the Annales de Chimie et de Physique, if you can grant me that favour. I fear that this letter may occasion more controversy than I desire, but the circumstances are such as to force me to take the pen; for if I am silent the silence will be regarded as the acknowledgement of error, not only in a philosophical, but in a moral point of view, and that in cases where I believe I am exempt from both.

You doubtless comprehend that I wish to speak of the mémoire of MM. Nobili and Antinori. I write to you because you

---

Antinori for not understanding my views. It was impossible that I could put forth in a brief letter, matter which, though I have condensed it as much as possible, still occupies seventy quarto pages of the Philosophical Transactions; and I may perhaps be allowed to say, (more in reference however to what I think ought to be a general regulation than to the present case,) that had I thought that that letter to M. Hachette would be considered as giving the subject to the philosophical world for general pursuit, I should not have written it; or at least not until after the publication of my *first paper.*—M. F.]

[1] Annales de Chimie et de Physique, 1832, t. li. p. 404.

have thought so well of the matter of my paper as to introduce it into your excellent and truly philosophical journal, and because having inserted also the mémoire of MM. Nobili and Antinori, all that has been written on this subject is found in the Annales. I may therefore hope you will not refuse me that which I now desire.

On the 24th November, 1831, my first paper was read to the Royal Society ; it is that which you have done me the honour to insert in the Annales for May 1832 (t. l. pp. 5–69). This paper was the *first* announcement which I made of my researches on electricity. The 18th December, 1831, I wrote a letter to my friend M. Hachette, who did me the honour to communicate it to the Academy of Sciences the 26th of the same month[1]. This letter was also inserted in the Number of the Annales for December 1831 (t. xlviii. p. 402). The second series of my researches, dated the 21st December, 1831, was read to the Royal Society the 12th January, 1832, and found a place in the Annales for June 1832 (t. l. pp. 113–162). These are the only publications (except certain notes appended to the memoirs of others) which I have made respecting the present matter up to this time, and the *whole* of them were written and read before anything whatsoever by any other philosopher on the same subject.

In the meantime the letter which I wrote to M. Hachette, and which you did me the honour to insert in the Annales, drew the attention of MM. Nobili and Antinori, and those industrious philosophers published a mémoire, the date of which is 31st January, 1832, and consequently posterior to all my writings. This mémoire obtained a place in the Annales for December 1831 (t. xlviii. pp. 412–430). A second mémoire, entitled " *New Electro-magnetic Experiments,*" by the same philosophers, dated the 24th March, 1832, has also appeared, and has been inserted in the Annales for July (t. l. pp. 280–304).

I fear that the letter which I wrote to M. Hachette, and which in his kindness for me he did me the honour to read to the Academy of Sciences, has become a source of misunderstanding and errors, and in its result has injured rather than served the cause of philosophic truth. Nevertheless I do not know how

[1] According to the account of the sitting which is given in the Lycée, No. 35.

to explain this point and re-establish matters in their right position without having the appearance of complaining in some degree of MM. Nobili and Antinori; than which there cannot be to me a more disagreeable thing. I honour those gentlemen for all that they have done, not only for electricity but also for science in general, and if it were not that the contents and wording of their mémoires oblige me to speak and place me in the alternative of admitting or denying the correctness of their assertions, I should have put aside the scientific errors which I believe them to contain, leaving to others the care of removing them. These philosophers unfortunately had no other knowledge of my researches than the short letter which I wrote to M. Hachette, and not being careful to refer to my papers (though it appears to me they should have done so under the circumstances), they have mistaken altogether the sense of a phrase relating to the beautiful observations of M. Arago; they have presumed that I had not previously done that which they thought they had done themselves; and finally, they advance what appear to me to be erroneous ideas of magneto-electric currents and give their ideas as corrections of mine, which had not as yet come under their eyes.

First let me rectify that which I consider as the most serious error, the misinterpretation given of my words; for those committed in the experiments would have been easily removed by the course of time.

MM. Nobili and Antinori say (Annales, t. xlviii. p. 428), " Mr. Faraday considers Arago's magnetism of rotation as al- " together connected with the phenomenon which he discovered " ten years ago. *He then recognised, as the notice says, that by* " *the rotation of a metallic disc under the influence of a magnet* " *we may produce electric currents in the direction of the radii* " *of the disc in sufficient quantity to make this disc become a* " *new electric machine.* We are entirely ignorant how Mr. " Faraday had ascertained this fact, and we do not know how " a result of this nature *could remain generally unknown for* " *so* LONG A TIME, *and so to say* FORGOTTEN in the hands of the " author of the discovery; besides, &c."

Now I never said that which MM. Nobili and Antinori here impute to me. In my letter to M. Hachette, referred to at the beginning of this letter, I gave a brief account of that which I had recently discovered and read on the 24th of the preceding month to the Royal Society. This notice is found page 402 of the same Number of the Annales, and it there says: " The " fourth part of the papers considers the equally curious and " extraordinary experiment of M. Arago, which, as is known, " consists in revolving a metallic disc under the influence of a " magnet. Mr. Faraday considers the phenomena exhibited in " this experiment as *intimately connected* with that of the mag- " netic rotation which he had the good fortune to discover ten " years ago. *He has ascertained that by the rotation* of a " metallic disc under the influence of a magnet *we may* form " electric currents in the direction of the radii of the disc in " sufficient number to make the disc become a new electric ma- " chine."

I have never said, nor ever had the intention of saying, that I had obtained electric currents by the rotation of a metallic disc at a period previous to the date of the memoir which I had then just written ; but I said that the extraordinary effect dis- covered by M. Arago was connected in its nature with the electro-magnetic rotation which I had discovered several years before, for both of them are due to a tangential action ; and I said that by the rotation of a disc near a magnet I can (now) cause electric currents to pass or tend to pass in the direction of the radii, thus constituting the disc a new electric machine : and that I think is satisfactorily proved in the part of the paper of which I was giving an account, as may be seen at pp. 65–118 of vol. l. of the Annales.

I have the most earnest desire to have this error removed, for I have always admired the prudence and philosophic reserve shown by M. Arago in resisting the temptation to give a theory of the effect he had discovered so long as he could not devise one which was perfect in its application, and in refusing his assent to the imperfect theories of others. Admiring his reserve I adopted it in this respect, and perhaps for that reason had my eyes open to recognise the truth when it was presented.

I have now arrived at that which concerns the philosophy of my writings. My paper of 24th November, 1831, contains in its fourth part my opinion of the cause of Arago's phenomenon, an opinion which I *at this time* see no reason to change. MM. Nobili and Antinori, in their writings of the 31st January and

24th March, 1832, profess to remove certain errors from among my facts, and to give extensive developments of electro-magnetic phenomena. I have not been able to perceive that the writings of these philosophers add a single fact to those contained in my papers, except it may be that they make mention of the spark obtained from the ordinary magnet, a result which I had myself obtained before from the electro-magnet. On the other hand I think that the mémoires of these gentlemen contain erroneous ideas of the nature of magneto-electric currents, and that they are mistaken both as to the action and the direction of the currents in the revolving disc of Arago. These philosophers say, " *We have recently verified, extended, and perhaps* " *rectified in some parts the results of the English philoso-* "*pher, &c.*" (Annales, l. 281.) And afterwards at p. 298, in reference to what they *supposed* to be my ideas (for though they had been read, and are now published, they had not thought proper to consult them), they say, " We have already " given our opinion on this idea ; but if, at the commencement " of our researches, it appeared to us not easy to make it ac- " cord with the nature of the currents discovered by Mr. Fara- " day himself, what shall we now say after all the new obser- " vations which we have arrived at during the continuation " of our researches ? We say that we have in the galvano- " meter the competent judge, and that it is for it to resolve the " question."

With the greatest desire to be corrected when in error, it is still impossible for me to discover in the writings of these gentlemen any correction by which I can profit; but I fully admit the competence of the galvanometer, and shall proceed as briefly as possible to submit to its judgement our different notions concerning the phenomenon of Arago : and I am so satisfied at present with the facts and results contained in the papers which I have published (though I could make changes in certain parts if I had to rewrite them) that I shall have no need to go beyond the experiments which they contain.

It is not my intention to enlarge further on the first mémoire of the learned Italians. I have added correcting notes to an English translation of it which has appeared in the Philosophical Magazine[1], and I have had the honour to send some

---

[1] See page 164 of the present volume.

copies to you and to the authors.   At present my object is to compare the second part of their writings with the fourth part of my first paper and with some other portions of other papers throwing light on the general principles.   The two writings have for their object the explication of the phenomenon of Arago, and fortunately both are found in the fiftieth volume of the Annales, so that reference to them is easy.   I shall refer to my paper by the numbers thus indicated (F. 114.) and to the writings of MM. Nobili and Antinori simply by indication of the page of the Annales.

At page 281, after some general remarks, we read, " We " have recently verified, extended, perhaps rectified in some " parts the results of the English philosopher : *we then said* " that the magnetism of rotation found a true point of bearing " in the new facts of Mr. Faraday, and that consequently the " theory of magnetism *appeared to us* at present so far ad- " vanced as to deserve that we should undertake to develope " the physical principles on which it depends.   *The writing* " *which* WE *now cause to appear is destined to fill this void,* " *&c.*"   On this point I will only remark, that just four months before, the paper which I had read to the Royal Society said the same thing, and had given that which is, I hope, a true and exact exposition of the philosophy of the effect in question (F. 4. 80.).

At page 282 we read, " We have already distinguished " these currents in our first researches," that is to say, in the first paper which was inserted in the Number for December (p. 412): but I had already described these currents four months before  (F. 90.).

At page 283 are found described " the explorers or galva- " nometric sounds," which are nothing else than what I had be- fore  described and distinguished by the name of *collectors* or *conductors* (F. 86, &c.).

At the commencement of the investigation by the Italian phi- losophers of the state of Arago's disc revolving in the neigh- bourhood  of a magnet, two relative positions of the plate and magnet were chosen, one called (p. 284) the " *central arrange- ment,*" where the magnetic pole was placed vertically over the centre of the disc, the other (p. 285), " *excentric arrangement,*" in which the magnet acted out of that position.   In respect of

the central arrangement we read (p. 284), " in this case when
" the magnet acts on the centre of the disc the sounds (collectors)
" transmit no signs of a current to the galvanometer *wherever*
" *they are placed,* and if small deviations are accidentally ob-
" served it is only because of a fault in the centralization, so that
" we have only to *correct this fault,* and immediately all signs
" from this equivocal source disappear, &c. In fact, what happens
" with an electro-dynamic spiral turning on its own axis always
" in front of the same magnetic pole? *Absolutely nothing.* Its
" turning is an *indifferent circumstance.* The formation of the
" currents *belongs to an entirely different condition,* for they
" are *not produced* except at the moment the spirals are *ap-*
" *proached to* or *withdrawn from* the magnet.   As long as the
" spirals remain at a constant distance, *moving or not moving,*
" there is *no current,* just as in the same manner *there is none*
" in the case of central rotation, when the points of the disc,
" remaining constantly at the same distance from the magnetic
" pole, thus renew the combination of continual presence to
" which the *new laws* of the currents of Mr. Faraday ASSIGN
" *no effect."*

This statement is so erroneous in all its parts that I have
been obliged to copy the whole of it.   In the first place the
electric currents *tend as strongly* to be produced in the revolving disc in the case of the " central arrangement " as in any
other case (F. 149–156.), but their direction is from the centre
to the circumference or *vice versâ,* and it is at these parts that
the collectors should be applied.   It is precisely this case which
makes the revolving disc a new electric machine (F. 154.), and
it is on this point that MM. Nobili and Antinori have altogether
deceived themselves in both their mémoires.   This error is
found in every part of the mémoire which I am now comparing
with my first paper, and appears, as I think, in all the parts,
without exception, of the theory given of Arago's phenomenon
in that mémoire.

It is said at p. 284, that *absolutely nothing* happens when a
helix revolves on its axis concentric with a magnetic pole, and
that the circumstance of rotation is indifferent.   I venture to
say, though I have not made the experiment, that an electric
current will tend to pass transversely to the helix, and that the
circumstance of rotation, instead of being indifferent, contains

186        Faraday's *letter to* M. Gay-Lussac        [DEC.

in this case the only essential condition required to produce currents.   The helix in fact may be considered as analogous to a
cylinder occupying its place, except that it is by no means so
good, because it is as it were cut into a long spiral wire.   The
helix may be considered as a simple wire placed in any part of
the space occupied by the cylinder; and I have demonstrated
that such wires produce currents when they rotate, their opposed extremities being applied to a galvanometer.

It is said at p. 284, that the formation of currents " depends
" upon an *entirely different condition,* for they are not pro-
" duced except at the moment when the spirals are either ap-
" proached to or withdrawn from the magnet:  as long as
" the spirals remain at a constant distance *there is no current*
" whether they move or not, just as in the same manner there
" is no current in the case of *central rotation,* &c."

Now, in my first paper I proved that the essential condition
was, not an approximation or a recession, but simply that the
moving metal should cut the magnetic curves (F. 101. 116. 118.
&c.), and that consequently, all other things being equal, motion without change of distance is the most effectual and the most
powerful means of obtaining the current, instead of being that
condition in which *absolutely nothing* occurs.   In my second
paper *I proved* that motion across the magnetic curves was the
*only condition* necessary (F. 217.), and that far from approximation or recession being required, we might produce the currents from the magnet itself, drawing them off in the proper direction (F. 220.).

Finally, when speaking of this " central arrangement," and
the supposed absence of effect when " the parts of the disc
" remained constantly at the same distance from the magnetic
" pole," MM. Nobili and Antinori say, (p. 285) " in renewing
" thus the combination of continued presence to which the new
" laws of the currents of Mr. Faraday assign no effect," and
then we read in a note, " these laws may be reduced to three;"
which are then specified, first fully and afterwards as follows:
" 1st LAW. During the approximation: a current produced
" contrary to the producing current; repulsion between the two
" systems.  2nd LAW. Invariable distance: no effect.  3rd LAW.
" During recession: current reproduced in the same direction as
" the producing current; attraction between the two systems."

I have not myself ever given the above as the simple laws which govern the production of the currents I was so fortunate as to discover; neither can I comprehend why MM. Nobili and Antinori say they are *my* LAWS, though at p. 282, one of them is so called.    But I described three similar cases both in my first paper (F. 26. 39. 53.) and in the notice, *i. e.* in my letter to M. Hachette, as the general effects that I had observed.    It has been shown by that which I have already said, that they are not the laws of magneto-electric action, for the simple fact of obtaining electric currents by means of the revolution of a cylinder (F. 219.), or of a disc (F. 218.) attached to a magnet, or of the magnet itself (F. 220.), contradicts every one of these laws.    ONE LAW which includes the whole of the effects is given in my paper (F. 114. 116. &c.), and it simply expresses the *direction* in which the moving conducting body *intersects* the magnetic curves.    This law of direction being given I endeavoured to express the whole generally (F. 118.) in the terms which I will here repeat : " All these results show " that the power of inducing electric currents is circumferen- " tially exerted by a magnetic resultant or axis of power, just " as circumferential magnetism is dependent upon and is ex- " hibited by an electric current."

I have quoted at length the passage of the learned Italians because it contains nearly all the difference between us, as to the facts and the views of this part of our subject.    Having shown the errors which the passage contains, I may now be allowed to be more concise in showing by *the aid of the gal- vanometer* the mistakes which flowing from them, are found spread through the other parts of the mémoires.    It is in fact very curious to observe how, with galvanometric indications generally correct, these philosophers have suffered themselves to be led away under the influence of preconceived notions. For example, at pp. 287, 288, and in fig. 2, plate III. we find the result of an examination by the galvanometer of the cur- rents in a revolving disc ; these currents are represented almost with perfect accuracy by means of the arrows, nevertheless the *two conclusions* which are drawn from them accords with the theory announced, but are diametrically opposed to the facts.

" One of these conclusions (p. 287) results from the imme- " diate inspection of the arrows indicating the currents in the two

" parts of the disc (fig. 2), and it is, that *in the parts (or side)*
" *which approach (or enter), the system of currents developed*
" *is contrary to that produced on the other side.* The other
" conclusion is obtained by comparing the currents produced
" on the disc with the currents of the producing cause; and it
" is, that, *the direction of the currents on the parts of the disc*
" *which enter (or approach) is contrary to that of the pro-*
" *ducing currents, whilst on the other side there is identity of*
" *direction in the two systems.*"

Now I had demonstrated in my first paper (F. 119.) " that
" when a piece of metal passed either before a single pole, or
" between the two opposite poles of a magnet, or near electro-
" magnetic poles, whether ferruginous or not, electric currents
" are produced across the metal transverse to the direction of
" motion." This fact is proved by means of wires (F. 109.),
plates (F. 101.), and discs (F. 92, &c.), and in all these cases the
electric current was *in the same direction*, whether the metal
approximated or receded from the magnet, provided the direction of the motion did not change. In the revolving disc of
Arago the electricity which in innumerable experiments I drew
from its various parts, always accorded with this result (F. 92.
95. 96.); and consequently (F. 119, &c.) I have recapitulated
them in a short description as those presented by Arago's disc;
establishing above all (F. 123.) that the currents produced near
to or under the poles " are discharged or return in the parts of
" the plate on *each* side of and more distant from the place of
" the pole, where of course the magnetic induction is weaker."

I have represented this state of things under a general form in
the figure 2, plate V. (joined to this paper), which, as respects
the arrows, the designation of parts, &c. I have also made to correspond as well as I could with the figure 2, plate III. of the mémoire of the Italian philosophers. I will now proceed to show
how far it accords with their galvanometrical results and how
far with their *conclusions.*

As regards the galvanometric results, my figure might be used
in place of theirs without causing any difference, and I indeed
have no reason to say that their results are inaccurate.

With regard to that " one of the conclusions which result
" from the immediate inspection of the arrows indicating the
" currents in the two parts of the disc," or of any other atten-

tive and experimental examination, it is seen that the entering currents *n, n, n*, instead of being in *a contrary direction* to those in the retreating parts *s, s, s*, follow exactly the same direction ; that is to say, that as to the general motion, near the pole they go from above downwards, or from the circumference towards the centre transversely to the lines which the different parts describe in their course, and that at a greater distance (F. 92.) on each side of the pole they pass in the contrary direction.     As any point in a line described by the motion approaches the pole, a current begins to traverse it, and increases in intensity until the point has arrived at the shortest distance (or perhaps a little beyond, if time enters as an element into the effect) ; afterwards, because of increase of distance, the current diminishes in intensity, but without ever having changed its direction relative to its own course.     It is only when it arrives at parts still more distant where the excited electricity may be discharged, that a current appears either in the opposite direction, or more or less oblique.     I presume that it is quite unnecessary to speak of the partial change in the direction of the current at the parts of the disc towards the centre or the circumference ; the two or three curves which I have roughly traced will show in what direction these changes take place.

*The second conclusion* which results from the mémoire of the learned Italians (p. 288) is that " in the parts which approach " the direction of the currents is contrary to that of the pro- " ducing currents " (that is, of those which are considered as existing in the magnet), " whilst on the other side there is " identity in the direction of these two systems." This assertion is exactly the reverse of the truth (F. 117.).     By means of the arrows, fig. 2 and 1, I have indicated the direction of the currents in the magnetic pole, and it is the same as the direction given by MM. Nobili and Antinori in their figure 1, plate III.     But my figure 2, as well as the indication of the galvanometer, evidently prove the approaching parts *n, n, n*, have currents which pass across them in the *same* direction as the current in that side of the magnetic pole, and that the parts which recede *s, s, s*, have currents which follow a *contrary* direction to those which are assumed as existing in that side of the magnetic pole from which they recede.

I suppose, but am not quite sure, that MM. Nobili and Antinori imagine that circular currents are excited in the part of
the metal near to the pole, in the same manner and absolutely like
those which are formed in a helix when it is brought towards a
magnet; and that as this part of the disc recedes, the circular
currents are somehow reversed, as is the case with the helix
when it is withdrawn from the magnet.   A passage in their first
paper, and another at the end of page 284, appears to imply
that such is their notion.   This idea occurred to me more than
a year ago, but I soon saw from many experiments (I have just
quoted some of them) that it did not satisfy the facts: and when
I found that the action of the helix, in approaching to and
receding from the pole, was perfectly explained (F. 42.)
by the law (F. 114.), I was constrained to give up my previous
opinion.

The mémoire then goes on (p. 288) to explain the phenomena of Arago's revolving disc: but as I have shown that the
theory generally is founded on two conclusions, which are the
reverse of reality, it will not be necessary to make a close examination of this part.   It is not possible that it can accurately
represent the phenomena.   Those who are curious to know the
true state of things can decide for themselves, by the assistance
of a very few experiments, whether the view which I published
in the paper which first announced the discovery of these currents is the true one, or whether the learned Italians have
reason to say I was in error, and have themselves published
more correct views of the subject.

All the world knows that when M. Arago published his remarkable discovery, he said that the action of the disc on the
magnet might be resolved into three forces: the *first* perpendicular to the revolving disc, and this he found repulsive: the
*second* horizontal and perpendicular to the vertical plane containing the radius beneath the magnetic pole; this is a tangential force, and causes the rotation of the pole with the
metal: the *third* is horizontal and parallel to the same radius;
this at a certain distance from the circumference is null, nearer
the centre it tends to urge the pole towards the centre, and
nearer the circumference it tends to move it from the centre.

At p. 289, MM. Nobili and Antinori give the explanation of
the first of these forces.   As I have said, these philosophers

consider the approaching parts of the disc as having currents contrary to those which exist in that side of the pole which they are approaching, and consequently repulsive; and they consider the parts which are receding as having currents identical in their direction with those in the side of the magnet from which they recede, and consequently these parts are attractive. The amount of each of these two forces is equal the one to the other, but as concerns the needle or magnet their relation is not the same; " the repulsive forces being the nearest exist " in the disc to the part even under the needle, and thus ob- " tain a preponderance over the action of the contrary forces " which are exerted more obliquely and further off; on the " whole, it is only one part of the repulsive force which is " balanced by the attractive force; the difference finds no " opposition, and it is that portion which produces the effect."

But I have proved in this letter that the currents in the parts which either approach or recede are exactly the reverse of those supposed by the learned Italians; and that consequently where they expect attraction they should have repulsion, and for repulsion attraction; so that according to their conclusions, corrected by experiment, the result should be *attraction* instead of *repulsion*. But M. Arago was right in saying the force was repulsive, consequently the theory of the effect here given cannot be true.

In my first paper will be found my view of this effect. I have there inquired whether it was possible or probable (F. 125.) that time may be required for the development of the maximum current in the plate, in which case the resultant of all the forces would be in advance of the magnet when the plate is rotated, or in the rear of the latter when the magnet is rotated: the line joining this resultant with the pole would be oblique to the plane of rotation: and then the force directed according to this line may be resolved into two others, the one parallel and the other perpendicular to the plane of rotation: the latter would be a repulsive force, producing an effect analogous to that remarked by M. Arago.

The *second* force is that which makes the magnet and disc mutually follow each other. On referring to page 290, and fig. 1 or 2 (my figure 2 will answer the same purpose), we read " there exist in $s, s, s,$ attractive forces towards which it (the

" magnet) is drawn, and at *n, n, n* there are repulsive forces
" which push it in the same direction," consequently the magnet moves after the metal. But the currents, and consequently
the forces, are exactly the reverse of that which is supposed,
as I have just shown: the magnet and disc therefore ought to
move in opposite directions if the forces act in the manner
assumed; nevertheless as the fact is they do not move in opposite directions, it is evident that the theory which explains
their motions by reversing the facts must itself be erroneous.

The *third* force is that which tends to carry the magnetic
pole either towards the centre or towards the circumference on
each side of a neutral point in that radius above which the
magnet is placed; this effect is described at p. 281, and also
in the figure 4 which accompanies the mémoire, which latter
I believe to be quite correct. The mémoire goes on to explain
this effect by referring to the repulsive force admitted (p. 289),
to render a reason for the *first* effect observed by M. Arago,
namely, the vertical repulsion from the disc; and assuming
that this repulsive force is spread over a certain extent of the
disc under the magnet, it is concluded (p. 292, fig. 5) that if
the pole is situated very near to the circumference, the portion
of the disc from whence this force emanates is diminished, being
cut off by the circumference itself, and consequently the parts
nearer to the centre act more powerfully and push the pole outwards: whilst on the other hand, if the pole is placed nearer
to the centre, the extent of disc from whence the force emanates will reach beyond the centre, and as this part beyond
is considered (though wrongly) as inactive, so the portion
near the circumference is the most powerful and pushes the
pole towards the centre.

One or two little objections offer themselves at once to this
opinion, but they are as nothing in comparison with that
which arises when we remember that, according to the views
of the authors themselves respecting the action of these currents, the error made in giving the direction of those excited
near the pole obliges us to substitute *attraction* for *repulsion*,
as I have shown in speaking of the first of these forces; consequently all the motions connected with the *third* force
ought to be exactly the contrary of what they really are: and
the theory which when it is corrected by experiments made

with the galvanometer indicates such motions deserves to be abandoned.

At page 292 I find that the mémoire refers to the " second law" of Mr. Faraday.   As I have said, I never gave the three statements as laws.   In fact, I regret very much that a letter which was not intended to give minute details, but only certain facts gathered in haste from the hundreds previously described in the paper read to the Royal Society, I regret, I say, that this letter, which was never intended for printing, should have led the learned Italians into error.   And yet after a re-examination of all the facts I cannot see that I am in the least degree answerable for the mistakes into which they have fallen; either as having advanced erroneous results, or as concerns the paper, in not having given to the scientific world full details as soon as it was possible for me to do so.

I have not as yet published my view of the cause of the *third* force distinguished by M. Arago; but as the Italian philosophers, when giving the hypothesis which I have just now condemned as inaccurate, say (293) " in fact what other hypo-
" thesis can reconcile the *verticality* which the needle preserves
" in the two positions $n\,s$, $n''\,s''$ (fig. 4) with the other fact of
" repulsion from below upwards, which raises the needle in the
" second position $s''$, $n''$ ?"—I am tempted to offer another in this place; premising always that the directions and forms which I may trace as those of the excited electro-magnetic currents are to be considered only as general approximations.

If a piece of metal sufficiently large to contain without derangement all the currents which may be excited in its mass by a magnetic pole placed above it, moves in a rectilinear direction beneath the pole, then an electric current will pass across the line of motion in all those parts in the immediate neighbourhood of the pole and will return in the opposite direction on each side in those parts which being further from the pole are subjected to a feebler inductive force, and thus the current will be completed or discharged (fig. 3).   Let A, B, C, D, represent a plate of copper moving in the direction of the arrow E, and N the north end of a magnet placed above it, electric currents will be produced in the metal; and though they extend without doubt from the part just under the pole to a great distance round (F. 92.) and at the same time diminish

in intensity and change in direction as the distance from this
part increases, nevertheless the two circles may serve to represent the resultant of these currents : and it will be evident that
the most intense point of action is where these circles touch
and immediately beneath the magnetic pole; or, because of the
time required, a little in advance.   Hence that portion of the
force which acts parallel to the plane of the metal will carry
the pole in advance in the direction of the arrow E, because
the forces are equally powerful on the side A, B, of the pole
as on the side C, D : and that portion of the force which, because of the time necessary for the production of the excited
current, is perpendicular to the direction of the metal, as I have
already said, will be repulsive, and tend to push the pole upwards or outwards.

But suppose that instead of this plate which moves in a
rectilinear direction, we substitute a circular disc revolving on
its axis, and then consider the case of the magnetic pole placed
over its centre (fig. 4), there will then be no electric currents
produced, not because they do not tend to be produced, for
I have already said in this letter and shown in my papers
(F. 149. 156. 217.) that from the moment the disc moves, the
currents also are ready to move, tending to be formed in the
direction of radii from the circumference to the centre ; but because all the parts are equally influenced, all of them being
equally distant from the centre, so none of them can gain an
excess of power over the others, no discharge can take place,
and consequently no current can be formed. As no *current* can
exist, so none of the effects due to the action of a current on a
pole can be produced, and thus it is that there is neither *revolution* nor repulsion of the magnet.   Hence the cause of the
*verticality without repulsion* which occurs at this place.

Now let us consider the case where the pole of the magnet,
instead of being placed over the centre of the revolving metal,
is on one side, as at N, fig. 5.   The tendency to the formation
of electric currents is due to the motion of the parts of the
disc *across* the magnetic curves (F. 116. 217.), and when these
curves are of equal intensity the electric currents increase in
force in proportion to the increased velocity with which the
parts of the disc bisecting these magnetic curves move (F. 258.).
Let us therefore trace a circle, *a b*, fig. 5, round the magnetic

pole as a centre, and it will represent the projection on the disc
of magnetic curves having *equal intensity*; *a* and *b* will be those
points in the radius passing immediately under the pole, which
are at an equal distance from the pole ; but as the part *a* passes
under the pole with a much greater velocity than the part *b*,
the intensity of the electric current excited in that part is pro-
portionally greater. The same is true for points in any other
radius cutting the circle *a b*, and it will be also true for any
other circle drawn round N as a centre, and representing therefore magnetic curves of equal intensity, except that when this
circle extends beyond the centre *c* of the revolving disc, as at
*c d*, instead of a weaker current at *d* than at *c* it will be a contrary current that tends to be produced.

The natural consequence of these actions of the various parts
is, that, as the sum of the forces tending to produce an electric
current in the direction from *c* to *d* is greater on the side *c* of
the magnetic pole than on the side *d*, the curvature, or the return of these currents by the right and left, will also commence
on this side, and therefore the two circles which we may regard, as before, as representing the resultants of these currents will not touch exactly under the pole, but at a greater or
smaller distance from it towards the circumference, as in fig. 6.

This circumstance alone would give rise to no motion of the
pole constrained so as to move only in the direction of the
radius, but being combined with that which results from the
*time* necessary for the development of the current, and to which
I have already referred as explaining the *first* of the three
forces by which M. Arago represents the action of the pole
and the revolving disc, it will explain I hope perfectly all the
effects which we are examining and prove also the influence of
time as an element :—for let *c*, fig. 7, be the centre of the revolving disc, and *r c* a part of the radius under the magnetic
pole *p* : the contact of the two circles (representing the currents) is, as we have just seen, on the side of the pole furthest
from the centre *c* : but because of the element of time and the
direction of the rotation R of the disc of metal, it is also a little
to the left of the radius *r c*, so that the pole is subjected, not
symmetrically, but obliquely to the action of these two sets of
currents. The necessary consequence is that if it be free to
move in the direction of the radius, and in that only, it will

move towards the centre *c*, because the currents produced by a marked (or north) pole are precisely such as by their mutual action with the pole would push it in that direction.

This relation of the currents to the pole which produces them, is as easily proved by experiment as by calculation. I have shown (F. 100.) that when a marked (north) pole is above a disc revolving in the direction of the arrow R in the figures of the mémoire of the Italian philosophers or in mine, the currents (indicated by the circles) are as in fig. 3, 6 or 7. Upon bending a metal wire carrying a current in this double direction, fig. 8, and placing a marked (north) pole above it, limited so that it could only move parallel to *r c*, I found that whenever it was placed in the line *r c* it had not the least tendency to move. There is also another line perpendicular to this first line, and which crosses the contact of the circles, in which the pole has no tendency to move. But placed in any point out of these two lines it will move in one direction or the other, and when it is placed in the positions marked 1, 2, 3, 4, it will move in the direction of the arrows placed in these points. Now the position of the pole to the currents produced in the disc of M. Arago, when the magnet and disc are arranged as in fig. 5 or 7, is exactly that of position 1 in fig. 8, and hence the pole has a tendency towards the centre C.

Let us now direct our attention to that which will occur if we gradually carry the pole from the centre towards the circumference. Let fig. 9 represent the new condition of things at a given time, as fig. 5 represented the former state: it is evident that the velocities of the parts *b a* of the radius under the pole do not differ so much from each other as they did before, being now nearly as $1 : 1\frac{1}{2}$, instead of $1 : 6$, and with all the magnetic curves of equal intensity comprised within this circle the difference will be even less. That alone would cause that the place of the magnetic pole and the place of contact of the circles which represent the currents (fig. 7) would approach the one to the other in the direction of the line *r c*, and consequently carry the pole at 1, fig. 8, nearer to the neutral line *l i*. Casting the eyes on the second circle *d*, fig. 9, of magnetic curves of equal intensity, we perceive that as the disc does not extend to *c*, or even beyond *a*, there is nothing to add to the force of the current on that side of the pole, whilst at *d*, the radius moving across magnetic curves adds to the intensity of the current excited in *b* and everywhere else on this side of the pole, and can easily, according to the position of the pole over the plate of metal (that is, nearer to or further from the edge), render their sum equal to or greater than the sum of the forces on the other side, or towards the circumference. If the sums of the forces on the two sides of the pole are equal, then the pole will be in some part of the neutral line *l i*, as in 5, fig. 8, and will have no tendency either towards the centre or the circumference, though its tendency to move with the disc or upwards from the disc will remain unchanged. Or if the sum of the forces is greater on the side *d* than on the side *c*, then the pole will be in the position 2, fig. 8, and will be urged outwards in the direction of the radius, in conformity with Arago's results.

Besides this cause of change in the motion of the pole parallel to the radius, and which depends on the position of the pole near the circumference, there is another cause which occurs, I believe, at the same time and assists the action of the former. When the pole is placed near the edge of the disc the discharge of the currents excited near the centre is resisted at the part towards the edge in consequence of the want of conducting matter: so that instead of having the regular forms represented in figs. 7 and 8, they will, as in fig. 10, be arrested and directed in their course towards the circumference, whilst they will have all the room necessary for their motion in those places where they are directed towards the centre. That alone would cause that the point of greatest force would be a little nearer the centre than the projection of the axis of the magnetic pole, and would assist in placing the pole in the position 2, fig. 8. I have such confidence in this opinion, that though I have not had the opportunity of making the experiment myself, I venture to predict, that if instead of using a revolving disc, a band or plate of metal 5 or 6 inches wide, as A, B, C, D, fig. 11, were moved in a rectilinear direction according to the arrow under a magnetic pole placed at *a*, the pole would tend to move forward with the plate as before, but not to the right or left; whereas if the pole were placed above the point *b*, it would also tend towards the border A B ; or if it were placed over *c* it would tend to move towards the border C D.

Having thus replied to the question of " What other hypotheses," &c. put by the authors of the mémoire at p. 293,
I may now continue the examination of the mémoire.  At p. 294
the error relative to the nature of the currents (*i. e.* their supposed inversion) is repeated : such inversion is the case with a
helix and some other forms of apparatus ; but the simple and
elementary current produced by the motion of a wire before a
magnetic pole is not reversed as the wire recedes (F. 171.
111. 92.).

At page 295 it is supposed that when the rotation is slow
" the revolution of the currents is circumscribed in small limits,
" and there is *little to add* to the results which have served as a
" foundation to the whole of the (our) theory."   But when the
motion is rapid the currents envelope the whole disc, " so as to
become a kind of labyrinth."   For my part, I believe that the
currents have the same general direction which I have given
already in the figures, whether the rotation be slow or rapid,
and that the only difference is an augmentation of force with
increase of velocity.

A condition is then chosen (in the mémoire), really simple,
though it appears at first complicated, that, where the opposite
poles are placed over a plate so as to be in the same diameter,
but on opposite sides of the centre.   This condition, with the
direction of revolution, and the currents produced, is found in
fig. 7 of the mémoire of the Italian philosophers.   It is not
necessary to quote pp. 296, 297, which explains this figure,
but I will give my figure 12, which accords with my views and
experiments, and which so far corresponds with the former
figure that the two may be compared with each other.  It is very
satisfactory to me to find that in this part of the mémoire, as
well as in the first, I do not find a single *important* experimental result adverse to the views which I have published,
though I am very far from adopting the conclusions drawn
from them.

If we examine fig.12 we shall see that it results in the simplest
possible manner from the use of two contrary poles ; thus as
to the upper or north pole only, the currents are as in fig. 6.
But as with this pole the current produced by it goes from the
circumference towards the centre, so with the south pole in the
same or a corresponding position the currents will go from the

centre to the circumference (F. 100.), and consequently in
fig. 12 they will continue along the diameter N S, across the
centre of the revolving plate, to return in the direction of the
arrows at the sides E O. The points where I do not agree
with the *indications of the galvanometer* obtained by MM.
Nobili and Antinori are, first, the direction of the currents in
N and in S, which with them are contrary to those which I
obtain; and secondly, the existence of an oblique axis of power,
as at P Q of their figure 7.

The mémoire finishes, as far as I am concerned, at p. 298, in
again speaking of the error (but not as an error) relative to the
revolving disc becoming a *new electrical machine.* At the commencement the authors, but little acquainted with the principles
under the influence of which such a result is obtained, deny
it; and though they here say further, " What shall we say
" after all the *new observations* which we have made during
" the continuation of our researches ?" I am still in no degree
moved to alter anything that I have published : on the contrary,
I have more confidence than before in it; since if their conclusions had been in accordance with the results I had arrived at,
I should have had great reason, after the examination I have
just made, to fear that my own views were erroneous.

I cannot terminate this letter without again expressing the
regret I feel in having been obliged to write it : but if it be remembered that the mémoires of the Italian philosophers were
written and published *after my* original papers ; that their last
writing has appeared in the same Number of the *Annales de
Chimie et de Physique* with mine ; and that consequently they
have the *appearance* of carrying science beyond that which I
had myself done ; that both their papers accuse me of errors
in experiment and theory and, beyond that, of good faith ; that
the last of these writings bears the date of March, and has not
been followed by any correction or retraction on the part of
the authors, though we are now in December ; and that I sent
them several months ago (at the time when I sent to you and
other persons) copies of my original papers, and also copies of
notes on a translation of their first paper[1] ; and if it be remembered that after all I have none of those errors to answer for

[1] See page 164, &c.

with which they reproach me; and that the mémoires of these gentlemen are so worded that I was constrained to reply to the objections they made against me; I hope that no person will say that I have been too hasty to write that which might have been avoided; or that I should have shown my respect for the truth or rendered justice to my own writings and this branch of science, if, knowing of such important errors, I had not pointed them out.

I am, my dear Sir, yours very faithfully,

M. FARADAY.

---

*New Experiments relative to the Action of Magnetism on Electro-dynamic Spirals, and a Description of a new Electro-motive Battery.  By Signor* SALVATORE DAL NEGRO; *with Notes by* MICHAEL FARADAY, *F.R.S.*[1]

[*Addressed to* Dr. Ambrogio Fusinieri, *Director of the Annali delle Scienze, &c. &c.*]

SIR,

ON repeating the experiments relative to the action of terrestrial magnetism on electro-dynamic spirals, an action which was first observed[2] by the two illustrious Italian philosophers Nobili and Antinori, it occurred to me to examine the effect of an ordinary magnet on similar spirals at the moment when one of the poles traversed the axis of the spiral (*Exp. Res.* 39. 41. 114.), and I obtained such results as indicated the path which it would be proper for me to follow, in order to profit by this new property of magnetism.  Ultimately I succeeded in constructing a new electrometer, by means of which the efficacy of the instantaneous currents discovered by the celebrated Faraday may be augmented without limit, and obtained in succes-

[1] Lond. and Edinb. Phil. Mag., 1832, vol. i. p. 45.  That date which at the top of these pages is on the left-hand is the date of the Italian paper, that on the right-hand is the date of my notes.—M. F.

[2] [This is an error.  A long section is devoted to terrestrial magneto-electric induction in my original researches (140 to 192) of the date of December 21, 1831.  As my brief letter to M. Hachette is continually taken instead of my memoirs as representing my views of magneto-electricity, I venture to add a few notes and references to this paper, in the same manner as I have done to the paper by Signori Nobili and Antinori, at page 401, of the last volume of the Phil. Mag. and Annals.—M. F.]

sion with such celerity as to render (as it were) continual the
action of these currents [1]. He [Dr. Fusinieri] has already witnessed the principal part of these my experiments, and more
than once has been so good as to assist me faithfully in regis-
tering the results, and has solicited a description that might be
made public. I did not hesitate to make a brief exposition
that might be transmitted and inserted in the forthcoming
number of his Journal. He returned from us as quickly as
possible, and did not forget to take with him the magnet I had
promised.

His most affectionate friend,

Padua, April 20, 1832.      SALVATORE DAL NEGRO.

## *New Experiments, &c. &c.*

1. Place a cylindrical tube of paper surrounded by a spiral
of silk-covered copper wire upright upon a little table, and
connect the extremities of the spiral with a very sensible galvanometer, constructed according to the method of Signor Nobili: introduce the north pole of an ordinary horse-shoe magnet into the axis of the cylinder, and an electric current will be
obtained, which will act strongly on the galvanometer. (*Exp.
Res.* 39. 147.) On withdrawing the pole of the magnet, a current, in the contrary direction, will be obtained (*Exp. Res.* 39.).
On repeating the experiment with the south pole, currents will
be manifested in the contrary direction (*Exp. Res.* 114. &c.) to
those caused by the north pole, and less powerful, as has been
observed.

2. Introduce into the same spiral the north pole of a more
powerful magnet than the first, and the conflict will produce
a much greater effect; I say, " conflict," because the phenomena in question obey the laws of the collisions of solids.
The magnetism of rotation discovered by the celebrated Arago
has already shown what influence motion has in these phenomena. Then slowly moving the magnet, it may be introduced
and removed from the spiral without causing any sensible current. To obtain the maximum effect, it is necessary that the

[1 I have described at length a different but perfect way of obtaining a continuous current by magneto-electric induction. (*Exp. Res.* 90. 154. 155. 156.
&c.)—M. F.]

magnetic pole should make its entrance or exit with great velocity. (*Exp. Res.* 136. 153. 258.)

3. Introduce at the same time the poles of the magnet into two equal spirals, having the same direction, and two contrary currents will be obtained, which would destroy each other if the poles of the magnet were of equal strength. But as the north pole is in our latitudes more active than the south, the effect obtained will equal the difference of the two currents, and be in the direction of the greater force; exactly as happens in the collision of solids. It results from this my experiment, that henceforth we may ascertain at once with facility which is the most powerful of two magnets, and how much more active the north pole is than the opposite south pole of the same magnet[1].

4. In order to take advantage at the same moment of both the poles of the same magnet, construct two spirals turning in opposite directions, and place them as usual in connection with the galvanometer. Then on introducing the poles of the magnets, an effect will be obtained, equal to the sum of those which could be produced by the poles separately. To measure the effect produced by these two spirals with a more powerful magnet than the first, I was obliged to use a galvanometer of only one-twentieth the sensibility of the first.

5. I immediately perceived that this pair of spirals was a valuable element capable of furnishing a mode of augmenting without limit the efficacy of the instantaneous currents. I

[1] The statement that the north pole is in our latitudes more powerful than the south is a mistake. The cause of the effects obtained by Signor Negro will be found at (147) of my Exp. Research., and is dependent on the inductive force of the earth, as a magnet, upon other magnets, as well as upon soft iron. When a straight magnet is held in the dip, or even vertically with its marked pole downwards, both poles are strengthened; when held with its unmarked pole downwards, both poles are weakened. And though when a horse-shoe magnet is held with both poles downwards, as in Signor Negro's experiment, the marked pole is stronger than the unmarked one, it is only because the two limbs are affected as the single magnets just referred to, and the bend of the magnet being the upper part becomes virtually a feeble south pole. If the horse-shoe magnet be held with its poles upwards, then the contrary effect happens, and the unmarked (usually called the south) pole becomes the stronger; or if both poles are in equal relation to the magnetic dip, then both are equally strong.—M .F.]

therefore instantly constructed a second pair of spirals equal to the first, and putting both in connection with the galvanometer, I caused two magnets to enter them contemporaneously, and obtained an effect due to the sum of both pair of spirals.   On using still more powerful magnets, even the second galvanometer became useless.   The galvanometer which I substituted consists of a rhomboidal needle, about five Paris inches in length, and suspended as in the ordinary compass.   The wire which connects the extremities of the spirals passes beneath the needle distant about $3\frac{1}{2}$ lines, and is parallel to it when the latter is at rest; on obtaining this fortunate result I conceived the idea of constructing a battery of several magnets put in conflict with an equal number of pairs of spirals.

## Construction of a new Electro-motive Battery.

6. I had at command only four magnets, so that for the present I am limited in my construction to four pairs of spirals, as in the manner following : On a little table is placed one after the other four pairs of spirals, with the axes horizontal, and so that the perimeters of the cylinders shall have the same horizontal line as a common tangent, it being parallel to one of the sides of the table.   On a second table contiguous to the first, but not in contact, was placed a little carriage consisting of a rectangular table supported on four wheels, by means of which it could easily receive a motion to and fro.   The four magnets were placed upon this carriage, so that the poles of each could move horizontally towards the pairs of spirals, and enter within them.

The magnets were firmly fixed on the carriage so as not to alter in position, and the latter was so arranged as to move to and fro only in one direction.   On moving the carriage, the limbs of the magnets passed at once into all the spirals, and they could be made to enter or move out with the utmost facility, and with any required velocity.

That the battery thus disposed may give an electric current equal in force to the sum of all the currents excited in the pairs of spirals, it is necessary that all the spirals turning to the right should communicate with each other, that they may form a single metallic wire.   The same must be done with all those turning to the left.   Then these wires are to be connected in the usual well-known manner with a galvanometer, which we may suppose placed on a third little table, so far distant from the magnets that it may not be influenced by their presence. Although these electric currents are only obtained of instantaneous duration naturally, nevertheless with my battery they may be excited successively with such celerity as to produce an action, which is as it were continuous[1]. From the little I have done, and from what I have said, it follows that being able by this method to sum up the simultaneous action of an indefinite number of electric currents, this my battery may become fulminating.

I hope I have said enough to enable my readers to comprehend the mode of constructing this electro-motive battery. Hereafter, and by the help of a figure, I will describe the most useful and convenient distribution of the elementary pairs, and the mode of obtaining the maximum effect when employing the smallest possible number of elements, or of pairs of spirals.

---

*On the Magneto-electric Spark and Shock, and on a peculiar Condition of Electric and Magneto-electric Induction[2].*

*To Richard Phillips, Esq., F.R.S., &c.*

My dear Sir,

If you think well of the following facts and reasoning, you will, perhaps, favour them with a place in the Philosophical Magazine.

When I first obtained the magneto-electric spark[3], it was by the use of a secondary magnet, rendered for the time active by a principal one; and this has always, as far as I am aware, been the general arrangement. My principal was an electro-magnet; Nobili's was, I believe, an ordinary magnet; others have used the natural magnet, but in all cases the secondary magnet was a piece of soft iron.

---

[1] [See the note at page 201.—M.F.]

[2] Lond. and Edin. Phil. Mag. 1834, vol. v. p. 349.

[3] Philosophical Transactions, 1832, p. 132. [See also Phil. Mag. and Annals, N.S. vol. xi. p. 401, &c.—Edit.]

The spark is never the electricity of the principal, or even of the secondary magnet. The power in the first induces a corresponding power in the second, and that induces a motion of the electricity in the wire round the latter, which electricity produces the spark. It seemed to me, however, no difficult matter to dispense with the secondary or temporary magnet, and thus approach a step nearer to the original one; and this was easily accomplished in the following manner. About 20 feet of silked copper wire were made into a short ring helix, on one end of a pasteboard tube, through which a cylindrical magnet, an inch in diameter, could move freely; one end of the helix wire was fastened to a small amalgamated copper plate, and the other end bent round so as to touch this plate perpendicularly upon its flat surface, and also in such a manner that when the magnet was passed through the cylinder it should come against this wire, and separate the end from contact with the plate. The consequence was that whenever this action was quickly performed, the magneto-electric spark appeared at the place of disjunction.

My apparatus was placed horizontally, and a short loose plug of wood was put into the end of the cylinder, so that the disjunction at the plate should take place at the moment the end of the magnet was passing through the helix ring, that be-

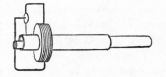

ing the most favourable condition of the apparatus. The magnet was driven with a sharp quick motion through the cylinder, its impetus being overcome, as soon as the spark was obtained, by an obstacle placed at a proper distance on the outside of the moveable wire. From the brightness and appearance of the spark, I have no doubt that if both ends of a horse-shoe magnet were employed, and a jogging motion were communicated to the light frame carrying the helices, a spark equal, if not superior, to those which down to this time have been obtained with magnets of a certain power, would be produced.

Thus the magneto-electric spark has been brought one step nearer to the exciting magnet. The much more important matter still remains to be effected of rendering that electricity which is in the magnet itself, and gives it power, evident under the form of the spark.

The next point to which I wish to direct your attention is the *magneto-electric shock*. This effect I have felt produced by Mr. William Jenkins in a manner that was new to me; and as he does not intend to work out the result any further, but has given me leave, through Mr. Newman, to make it known to you, I think the sooner it is published the better. Mr. Jenkins's apparatus consists of a helix cylinder formed of copper wire in the usual manner. An iron rod, about 2 feet long and half an inch in diameter, can be passed at pleasure into the centre of this cylinder. The helix consists of three lengths of wire, (which, however, might as well be replaced by one thick wire,) the similar ends of which are soldered to two thicker terminal wires, and on these are soldered also two short copper cylinders, to be held in the hand and give extensive contact. The electro-motor was a single pair of plates, exposing, perhaps, 3 square feet of surface on *both* sides of the zinc plate. On holding the two copper handles tightly in the hands, previously moistened with brine, and then alternately making and breaking the contact of the ends of the helix with the electro-motor, there was a considerable electric shock felt in the latter case, *i.e.* on breaking contact, provided the iron rod were in the helix; but none either on making or breaking contact when the latter was away.

This effect appears very singular at first, in consequence of its seeming to be the shock of the electricity of a single pair of plates. But in reality it is not so. The shock is not due to the electricity set in motion (through the body) by the plates, but to a current in the reverse direction, induced by the soft iron electro-magnet at the moment when, from the cessation of the original current, it loses its power. It is, however, very interesting thus to observe an original current of electricity, having a very low intensity, producing ultimately a counter (second) current having an intensity probably a hundredfold greater than its own, and the experiment constitutes one of the very few modes we have at command of converting quantity into intensity as respects electricity in currents.

It has been generally supposed that the electric spark producible by a single pair of plates can only be obtained upon breaking contact; but this, as I have shown in the Eighth Series of my Experimental Researches, is an error, and a very important one as regards the theory of voltaic electricity[1]; it is, however, true that the spark upon breaking contact can be very greatly exalted by circumstances having no such effect upon that produced at the moment of making contact.

Every experimenter on electro-magnetism is aware, that when the current from a single pair of plates is passed through a helix surrounding a piece of soft iron (to produce an electro-magnet,) the spark, upon breaking contact, is much brighter than if the soft iron were away; and because this effect occurs at the same moment with the shock in Mr. Jenkins's experiment, it might at first be supposed that the electricity producing both the spark and the shock was the same, and that the effects of both were increased, because of the increase in power of this their common cause. But the fact is not so, for the electricity producing the spark is passing in one direction, being that which the zinc plate and acid determine, whilst the electricity producing the shock is circulating in the contrary way.

From the appearance of the spark, which is always in this form of the experiment due to the electricity which is passing at the moment when contact is broken, it might seem that a greater current of electricity is circulating during the time that the contact is preserved, whilst the iron is present in the helix, than when it is away. But this is not the case; for when the quantity is measured by a very delicate galvanometer, it is found to remain unchanged after the removal or replacement of the iron, and to depend entirely upon the action at the zinc plate. Still the appearance of the spark is an evident and decisive proof, that the electricity which is passing at the moment of disjunction is of greater intensity when the iron is in the helix than when it is away, and this increased effect is evidently dependent, not upon any change in the state of things at the source of the electricity, but in a change of the condition of the conducting wire caused by the presence of the soft iron. I do not suppose that this change is *directly* connected with the magnetizing power of the current over the iron, but is due rather to the power of the iron after it becomes a magnet, to

[1] See this corrected, p. 5 of the preface of the first volume of these Researches and papers; and as to the whole paper see Exp. Res. 1048, &c.—M. F. Dec. 1843.

react upon the wire; and I have no doubt, though I have not
had time to make the experiment, that a magnet of very hard
steel, of equal force with the soft iron magnet, if put into the
helix in the same direction, would exert an equal influence over
the wire [1].

I will now notice another circumstance, which has a similar
influence in increasing the intensity of the spark which occurs
when the junction of the circuit is broken.   If a pair of zinc
and copper plates immersed in acid are connected by a short
wire, and all precautions are taken to avoid sources of inaccuracy, then, as I have already shown, the spark, upon breaking
contact, is not greater than that upon making contact.   But
if the connecting wire be much lengthened, then the spark
upon breaking contact is much increased.   Thus, a connecting
copper wire of $\frac{1}{18}$th of an inch in diameter when 12 inches
long, produced but a small spark with the same pair of plates
which the moment before or after would give a large spark
with a wire of the same diameter and 114 feet long.   Again,
12 inches in length of wire $\frac{1}{9}$th of an inch in diameter gave a
much smaller spark than 36 feet of the same wire.

In both these cases, though the long wires gave the larger
spark, yet it was the short wires which conducted the greatest
quantity of electricity in the given time; and that was very evident in the one of small diameter, for the short length became
quite hot from the quantity of electricity passing through
it, whereas the longer wire remained cold.   Still there can be
no doubt that the sparks from the long wires were of greater
intensity than those from the short wires, for they passed over
a greater interval of air; and so the paradoxical result comes
forth, that currents of electricity having the same common
source, and passing the same quantity of electricity in the same
time, can produce in this way sparks of very different intensity.

This effect, with regard to lengthened wires, might be explained by assuming a species of momentum as being acquired
by the electricity during its passage through the lengthened
conductor, and it was this idea of momentum which guided

[1] See forward, p. 211.   It does not do so, and for reasons very evident when
we consider how much less the magneto-inductive action is exerted upon hard
steel than upon soft iron (Nov. 1843).

Signori Nobili and Antinori in their process for obtaining the magneto-electric spark by means of a common magnet. Whether a current of electricity be considered as depending upon the motion of a fluid of electricity or the passing of mere vibrations, still the essential idea of momentum might with propriety be retained. But it is evident that the similar effect produced by the soft iron of increasing the intensity of the spark cannot be explained in this way, *i. e.* by momentum; and as it does not seem likely that the effects, which in these cases are identical, should have two causes, I believe that both are produced in the same way, although the means employed are apparently so different.

When the electric current passes through a wire, that wire becomes magnetic; and although the direction of the magnetism is peculiar, and very different to that of the soft iron placed in the helix of the first experiments, yet the direction of the magnetic curves, both of the wire so magnetized and of the soft iron magnet, in relation to the course which the current is pursuing (*i. e.* in the conducting wire), is the same. If, therefore, we refer the increased spark to a peculiar effect of induction exerted by the magnetism over the passing electric current, all becomes consistent. Let us, for instance, for the sake of reference, represent the magnetism by the magnetic curves: then, in the first place, the longer the wire the greater the number of magnetic curves which can exert their inductive influence; and the effect in a wire of a hundred feet in length will be nearly a hundred times greater than in a wire of the same diameter only a foot in length. The reason why a core of soft iron produces the same effect as elongation of the wire, will be that it also brings magnetic curves into inductive action exactly in the same direction as those around the wire; and the rest of the circumstances, as far as I can perceive, will accord with the cause assumed.

That the magnetic curves of the wire carrying the current shall actually affect the character of the current which gives them origin, need not excite any difficulty, for this branch of science shows many such cases. Ampère's experiment of revolving a magnet on its own axis, and the case which I have shown of drawing away electricity from the poles and equator of a magnet when it is revolved, are both instances of the same kind.

In conclusion, I wish to say that I think I see here some of
those indications of an *electro-tonic* or peculiar state, of which
I have expressed expectations in the second series of my Experimental Researches, par. 242.[1]; for though I here speak of
magnetism and magnetic curves for the sake of reference, yet
allowing Ampère's theory of the magnet, all the effects may be
viewed as effects of induction produced by electrical currents.
Hence many extensions of the experiments. I have no doubt,
for instance, that if a long wire were arranged so as to discharge a single pair of plates, and the spark occurring at the
breaking of contact were noted, and then another wire carrying a current in the same direction from another electromotor, were placed parallel and close to but without touching the
first, the spark obtained on breaking the contact at the first
wire would be greater than before. This experiment can easily
be made with a double helix; but at my present distance from
town I have no means of trying the experiment, or of examining
more closely these indications[2].

I am, my dear Sir, very truly yours,

Brighton, Oct. 17, 1834.                M. FARADAY.

---

*Additional Observations respecting the Magneto-electric*
*Spark and Shock*[3].

*To Richard Phillips, Esq., F.R.S., &c.*

MY DEAR SIR,

LIKE most things done in haste, my letter to you last month
involves several errors, some from want of attention, others
from want of knowledge. Will you do me the favour to print
the present in correction of them?

The first error consists in supposing the electricity of the shock
and the electricity of the spark (obtained at the moment of
disjunction) are due to different currents, page 207 (of this
volume). They are, as I find by careful experiments, due to the

[1] Philosophical Transactions, 1832, p. 189.
[2] See forward, p. 211.
[3] Lond. and Edin. Phil. Mag. Dec. 1834, vol. v. p. 444.

same current, namely, one produced by an inductive action at the moment when the current from the electromotor ceases.

If at p. 206, line 28, after " set in motion " be inserted " through the body ;" and at line 33 for " counter " be read " second", and if the above statement be allowed to stand for that in page 207, this error will be corrected.

The experimental results which I anticipated, page 208, lines 1—5, and page 210, lines 9—15, do not occur except under peculiar circumstances, and I am now aware why, for natural reasons, they should not. All the effects, in fact, belong to the inductive action of currents of electricity described in the first section of the first series of my Experimental Researches. I have investigated them to a considerable extent, and find they lead to some exceedingly remarkable and novel consequences. I have still some points to verify, and shall then think it my duty to lay them (in continuation of my first paper) before the Royal Society[1].

> I am, my dear Sir, very truly yours,

Royal Institution, Nov. 20, 1834.                    MICHAEL FARADAY.

---

*Reply to* Dr. John Davy's " *Remarks on certain Statements of* Mr. Faraday *contained in his* ' *Researches in Electricity* [2].' "

### *To Richard Phillips, Esq.*

MY DEAR PHILLIPS,

You know as well as most persons how great my dislike is to controversy, but you also know that upon some rare occasions I have been driven into it ; an occasion of this kind constrains me at present to ask a favour of you. On the 22nd of January of this year, two papers were read at the Royal Society, the first entitled " Remarks on certain Statements of Mr. Faraday contained in the Fourth and Fifth Series of his Experimental Researches in Electricity," by Dr. Davy; the second, " A Note

[1] This paper is in the former volume as the *Ninth* Series of the Experimental Researches, p. 322.

[2] Lond. and Edinb. Phil. Mag. May 1835, vol. vii. p. 337.

See Jameson's Edinburgh New Philosophical Journal, October 1835, p. 317-325.

in reference to the preceding Observations," by myself. These the Royal Society did not think fit to publish in the Philosophical Transactions, but the notice of the readings appears in the ' Proceedings' of the Society, No. 19, and in your Philosophical Magazine, April 1835, page 301.

I now find that Dr. Davy has published his paper in the last number of the Edinburgh New Philosophical Journal, p. 317. I was in hopes that if that paper appeared in print mine might have immediately followed it; and meeting Dr. Davy in the Royal Institution in May last, asked him to do me the favour to allow that to be the case : this, I presume for good reasons, (which, however, I do not understand,) he declined. I am thus placed in a difficult position; for, however willing Professor Jameson, the learned Editor of the Edinburgh Journal, may be to act impartially, and give me the same opportunity of publication he has given Dr. Davy, he cannot do so before the lapse of three months. Under these circumstances, and with the old adage before my eyes that "delays are dangerous," may I beg you to insert this letter and my paper in the next Number of the Philosophical Magazine? and I may still, perhaps, be indebted to the kindness of Professor Jameson for its insertion in the next Number of the Journal in which Dr. Davy's "Remarks" have appeared.

I am, my dear Sir, most truly yours,

Royal Institution, Oct. 10, 1835.        M. FARADAY.

---

The secretary of the Royal Society having mentioned to me the preceding paper, I requested a sight of it, that I might as soon as possible correct any error in the papers to which it referred, and of which it might make me conscious; and having read it, I am induced to hope the present note may accompany Dr. Davy's observations.

I do not know that I have any right to suppose Dr. Davy generally does not understand me in my papers, and yet something of this kind must have occurred; for instance, the new law of conduction referred to in my Fourth Series[1] is not even

[1 An Abstract of Mr. Faraday's Fourth Series will be found in Lond. and Edinb. Phil. Mag., vol. iii. pp. 449, 450.—EDIT.]

now evident to him, and therefore I think I cannot have erred in supposing Sir Humphry Davy unacquainted with it.    The *law* is, that *all substances* decomposable by the pile are in the fluid state conductors, and in the solid state non-conductors, of the electricity of the voltaic battery (393. 394. 404. 407. 413. 505. 676. 679. 697., &c.[1]).    The more careful examination of this law in other parts of my printed Researches shows that no bodies but electrolytes have this relation to heat and electricity, the few exceptions which seem to occur being probably only apparent (690. &c.[1]).    That the title of *law*, therefore, is merited, and that this law was not known to Sir Humphry Davy, are, I think, justifiable conclusions, notwithstanding Dr. Davy's remarks.    As to Priestley's results with the electric machine, they really have nothing to do with the matter.

I have said that Sir Humphry Davy spoke in general terms. " The mode of action by which the effects take place is stated very generally, so generally indeed that probably a dozen precise schemes of electro-chemical action might be drawn up differing essentially from each other, yet all agreeing with the statement there given (482.)."    In this and other parts of what I have written (483. 484.[2]), which Dr. Davy quotes, he thinks that I have been deficient in doing justice, or in stating Sir Humphry Davy's " hypotheses" correctly.

Dr. Davy for my word " general" substitutes " vagueness". I used *general* in contradistinction to *particular*, and I fear that vagueness cannot with propriety stand in the same relation.    I am sure that if Sir Humphry Davy were alive, he would approve of the word I have used; for what is the case? Nearly thirty years ago he put forth a *general* view of electro-chemical action, which, as a general view, has stood the test to this day; and I have had the high pleasure of seeing the Royal Society approve and print in its Transactions of last year, a laborious paper of mine in support and confirmation of that view (1834.

[1] The paragraphs here referred to belong to Mr. Faraday's Fourth and Seventh Series, and will be found reprinted in Lond. and Edinb. Phil. Mag., vol. v. p. 166–169.—EDIT.]

[2] These paragraphs belong to the Fifth Series, noticed in Lond. and Edinb. Phil. Mag., vol. iii. p. 460.—EDIT.]

214 Reply to Dr. John Davy's Remarks.

Part ii. page 448.[1] Exp. Res. Series viii.). But that it is not a particular account is shown, not merely by the manner in which Sir Humphry Davy wrote, but by the sense of his expressions, for, *as Dr. Davy says*, "he attached to them no undue importance, believing that our philosophical systems are very imperfect, and confident that they must change more or less with the advancement of knowledge[2];" and what have I done but helped with many others to advance what he began; to support what he founded?

That I am not the only one, as Dr. Davy seems to think, who cannot make out the precise (or, I would rather say, the particular) meaning of Sir Humphry Davy in some parts of his papers may be shown by a reference to Dr. Turner's excellent Elements of Chemistry, where, at page 167 of the fifth edition, the author says: "The views of Davy, both in his original essay and in his subsequent explanation (Philosophical Transactions 1826), were so *generally and obscurely* expressed that chemists have never fully agreed, as to some points of the doctrine, about his real meaning. *If* he meant that a particle of free oxygen or free chlorine is in a negatively excited state, then his opinion is contrary to the fact, that neither of these gases affect an electrometer," &c. &c. Having similar feelings, I thought that I was doing Sir Humphry Davy far more justice in considering his expressions as general, and not particular, except where they were evidently intended to be precise, as in the cases which I formerly quoted (483. 484.)[3].

Again, Dr. Davy says, "What can be more clear than this; that my brother did not consider water as essential to the for-

[1] See Lond. and Edinb. Phil. Mag., vol. vi. p. 181.—EDIT.]

[2] Phil. Trans. 1826, p. 390. Edinb. New Phil. Journ., Oct. 1835, p. 323.

[3] I may be allowed to quote in a note a passage from one of Mr. Prideaux's papers, of the date of March 1833; I was not aware of it when I wrote in answer to Dr. Davy. Mr. Prideaux says, "Sir Humphry Davy's theory assumes that 'chemical and electrical attractions are produced by the same cause; acting in one case on particles, in the other on masses : and the same property, under different modifications, is the cause of all the phenomena exhibited by different voltaic combinations.' A view so comprehensive, embracing every modification of chemical as well as electrical action, seems to include the other two, *and every one that has been or can be attempted* on the subject. But what it gains in extent it wants in distinctness." Lond. and Edinb. Phil. Mag., vol. ii. p. 215.

mation of a voltaic combination ?" &c.   If this be so clear, how
happens it that Mr. Brande, in the last edition of his Manual,
vol. i. p. 97, says that " Sir Humphry Davy further remarks
that *there are no fluids, except such as contain water*, which
are capable of being made the medium of connexion between
the metals of the voltaic apparatus ;" and Mr. Brande's observation is, " This, however, appears to me to admit of doubt."?
How happens it also that Dr. Ure, in giving his eloquent account
of Sir Humphry Davy's discoveries [1], uses the very same words
as those I have quoted from Mr. Brande, adding, " It is probable
that the power of water to receive double polarities and to
evolve oxygen and hydrogen is *necessary* to the constant operation of the connected battery."?   I ought, perhaps, rather to
ask, How could Sir Humphry Davy use such words, and mean
what Dr. Davy wishes to be considered as his meaning? Why,
*there can be no doubt that if I had proved that water was the
only substance that could perform these duties, Dr. Davy
would have claimed the discovery for his brother.*

As I cannot impute to Dr. Davy *the intention of doing injustice*, the only conclusion I can come to is that the language
of Sir Humphry Davy is obscure even to his brother, who
thinks it perfectly clear ; so obscure, indeed, as to leave on his
mind the conviction of a meaning the very reverse of that which
it bears to Mr. Brande and Dr. Ure.   Thus Dr. Davy puts his
seal to the truth of Dr. Turner's observation [2] by the very act
of denying it.

What makes the matter still more remarkable is, that Dr.
Davy charges it upon me as a fault, that I, and *I alone*, have
said what he denies in words, but proves in fact; whereas *I
have not said* it, and others have.

If Sir Humphry Davy's meaning is thus obscure to his brother,
I have no right to expect that mine should have been rightly
taken; and therefore it is that I suspect, as I said before, that
Dr. Davy generally does not understand me in my papers.

That " probably a dozen precise schemes of *electro-chemical
action* might be drawn up" differing from each other, but all
agreeing with Sir Humphry Davy's general statement, is no
exaggeration.   I have in the very paper which is the subject

[1] Chemical Dictionary, *art.* Electricity.
[2] And to that of Mr. Prideaux's also.

of Dr. Davy's remarks quoted six : 1. that of Grotthus, (481.) ; 2. of Sir Humphry Davy himself (482.); 3. of Riffault and Chompré (485.); 4. of Biot (486.); 5. of De la Rive (489.); and 6. my own (518. &c.). These refer to modes of decomposition only; but as I spoke in the passage above quoted of " electro-chemical action" in reference to chemical effects and their cause generally, I may now quote other particular views. Volta, Pfaff, Marianini, &c. consider the electricity of the voltaic pile due to contact alone. Davy considered it as excited by contact, but continued by chemical action. Wollaston, De la Rive, Parrot, Pouillet, &c. considered it as of purely chemical origin. Davy, I believe, considered the particles of matter as possessing an inherent electrical state to which their chemical properties were due ; but I am not sure of his meaning in this respect. Berzelius, according to Turner, views them as being naturally indifferent, but having a natural appetency to assume one state in preference to another[1], and this appears to be the theory of M. Fechner also[2]. Again, electro-chemical phenomena have been hypothetically referred to vibrations by Pictet, Savary, myself, and others. Now, all these views differ one from another ; and there are, I think, a dozen of them, and it is very likely that a dozen more exist in print if I knew where to look for them ; yet I have no doubt that if any one of those above could be proved by a sudden discovery to be the right one, it would be included by Dr. Davy, and, as far as I can perceive, by myself also, in Sir Humphry Davy's general statement. What ground is there, therefore, for Dr. Davy's remarks on this point?

In reference to another part of Dr. Davy's observations I may remark, that I was by no means in the same relation as to scientific communication with Sir Humphry Davy after I became a fellow of the Royal Society in 1824, as before that period, and of this I presume Dr. Davy is aware. But if it had been otherwise, I do not see that I could have gone to a fitter source for information than to his printed papers. Whenever I have ventured to follow in the path which Sir Humphry Davy has trod, I have done so with respect and with the highest admiration of his talents, and nothing gave me more pleasure

[1] Turner's Elements, Fifth Edit., p. 167.
[2] Quarterly Journal of Science, vol. xxvi. p. 428.

in relation to my last published paper, the Eighth Series, than the thought, that whilst I was helping to elucidate a *still obscure* branch of science, I was able to support the views advanced twenty-eight years ago, and for the first time, by our great philosopher.

I have such extreme dislike to controversy that I shall not prolong these remarks, and regret much that I have been obliged to make them.   I am not conscious of having been unjust to Sir Humphry Davy, to whom I am anxious to give all due honour; but, on the other hand, I feel anxious lest Dr. Davy should inadvertently be doing injury to his brother by attaching a meaning, sometimes of particularity and sometimes of extension, to his words, which I am sure he would never himself have claimed, but which, on the contrary, I feel he has disavowed in saying "that our philosophical systems are very imperfect," and in expressing his confidence "that they *must change more or less with the advancement of science."*   On these points, however, neither Dr. Davy nor myself can now assume to be judges, since with respect to them he has made us both partisans.   Dr. Davy has not made me aware of anything that I need change; and I am quite willing to leave the matter as it stands in the printed papers before scientific men, with only this request, which I am sure beforehand will be granted, that such parts of Sir Humphry Davy's papers and my own as relate to the subject in question, be considered both as to their letter and spirit before any conclusion be drawn.

Royal Institution, January 9, 1835.

---

## On the general Magnetic Relations and Characters of the Metals[1].

GENERAL views have long since led me to an opinion, which is probably also entertained by others, though I do not remember to have met with it, that *all* the metals are magnetic in the same manner as iron, though not at common temperatures or under ordinary circumstances[2].   I do not refer to a feeble mag-

[1] Lond. and Edinb. Phil. Mag., 1836, vol. viii. p. 177.

[2] It may be proper to remark, that the observations made in par. 255 of my "Experimental Researches," have reference only to the three classes of bodies there defined as existing at ordinary temperatures.

netism[1], uncertain in its existence and source, but to a distinct and decided power, such as that possessed by iron and nickel; and my impression has been that there was a certain temperature for each body, (well known in the case of iron,) beneath which it was magnetic, but above which it lost all power; and that, further, there was some relation between this *point* of temperature, and the *intensity* of magnetic force which the body when reduced beneath it could acquire. In this view iron and nickel were not considered as exceptions from the metals generally with regard to magnetism, any more than mercury could be considered as an exception from this class of bodies as to liquefaction.

I took occasion during the very cold weather of December last, to make some experiments on this point. Pieces of various metals in their pure state were supported at the ends of fine platinum wires, and then cooled to a very low degree by the evaporation of sulphurous acid. They were then brought close to one end of one of the needles of a delicate astatic arrangement, and the magnetic state judged of by the absence or presence of attractive forces. The whole apparatus was in an atmosphere of about 25° Fahr.: the pieces of metal when tried were always far below the freezing-point of mercury, and as judged, generally at from 60° to 70° Fahr. below zero.

The metals tried were,

| | |
|---|---|
| Arsenic, | Lead, |
| Antimony, | Mercury, |
| Bismuth, | Palladium, |
| Cadmium, | Platinum, |
| Cobalt, | Silver, |
| Chromium, | Tin, |
| Copper, | Zinc, |
| Gold, | |

and also Plumbago; but in none of these cases could I obtain the least indication of magnetism.

Cobalt and chromium are said to be both magnetic metals. I cannot find that either of them is so, in its pure state, at any temperatures. When the property was present in specimens supposed to be pure, I have traced it to iron or nickel.

[1] Encyclop. Metrop. 'Mixed Sciences,' vol. i. p. 761.

The step which we can make downwards in temperature is, however, so small as compared to the changes we can produce in the opposite direction, that negative results of the kind here stated could scarcely be allowed to have much weight in deciding the question under examination, although, unfortunately, they cut off all but two metals from actual comparison. Still, as the only experimental course left open, I proceeded to compare, roughly, iron and nickel with respect to the points of temperature at which they cease to be magnetic. In this respect iron is well known[1]. It loses all magnetic properties at an orange heat, and is then, to a magnet, just like a piece of copper, silver, or any other unmagnetic metal. It does not intercept the magnetic influence between a magnet and a piece of cold iron or a needle. If moved across magnetic curves, a magneto-electric current is produced within it exactly as in other cases. The point at which iron loses and gains its magnetic force appears to be very definite, for the power comes on suddenly and fully in small masses by a small diminution of temperature, and as suddenly disappears upon a small elevation, at that degree.

With nickel I found, as I expected, that the point at which it lost its magnetic relations was very much lower than with iron, but equally defined and distinct. If heated and then cooled, it remained unmagnetic long after it had fallen below a heat visible in the dark : and, in fact, almond oil can bear and communicate that temperature which can render nickel indifferent to a magnet. By a few experiments with the thermometer it appeared that the demagnetizing temperature for nickel is near 630° or 640°. A slight change about this point would either give or take away the full magnetic power of the metal.

Thus the experiments, as far as they go, justify the opinion advanced at the commencement of this paper, that all metals have similar magnetic relations, but that there is a certain temperature for each beneath which it is magnetic in the manner of iron or nickel, and above which it cannot exhibit this property. This magnetic capability, like volatility or fusibility, must depend upon some peculiar relation or condition of the particles of the body ; and the striking difference between

---

[1] See Barlow on the Magnetic Condition of Hot Iron. Phil. Trans., 1822, p. 117, &c.

the necessary temperatures for iron and nickel appears to me to render it far more philosophical to allow that magnetic capability is a general property of all metals, a certain temperature being the essential condition for the development of this state, than to suppose that iron and nickel possess a physical property which is denied to all the other substances of the class.

An opinion has been entertained with regard to iron, that the heat which takes away its magnetic property acts somehow within it and amongst its electrical currents (upon which the magnetism is considered as depending) as flame and heat of a similar intensity act upon conductors charged with ordinary electricity. The difference of temperature necessary for iron and nickel is against this opinion, and the view I take of the whole is still more strongly opposed to it.

The close relation of electric and magnetic phenomena led me to think it probable, that the sudden change of condition with respect to the magnetism of iron and nickel at certain temperatures, might also affect, in some degree, their conducting power for electricity in its ordinary form; but I could not, in such trials as I made, discover this to be the case with iron. At the same time, although sufficiently exact to indicate a great change in conduction, they were not delicate enough to render evident any small change; which yet, if it occurred, might be of great importance in illustrating the peculiarity of magnetic action under these circumstances, and might even elucidate its general nature.

Before concluding this short paper, I may describe a few results of magnetic action, which, though not directly concerned in the argument above, are connected generally with the subject [1]. Wishing to know what relation that temperature which could take from a magnet its power over soft iron, had to that which could take from soft iron or steel its power relative to a magnet, I gradually raised the temperature of a magnet, and found that when scarcely at the boiling-point of almond oil it lost its polarity rather suddenly, and then acted with a magnet as cold soft iron: it required to be raised to a full orange heat before it lost its power as soft iron. Hence the force of the steel to *retain* that condition of its particles

[1] See on this subject, Christie on Effects of Temperature, &c. Phil. Trans. 1825, p. 62, &c.

which renders it a permanent magnet, gives way to heat at a far lower temperature than that which is necessary to prevent its particles assuming the *same state* by the inductive action of a neighbouring magnet.    Hence at one temperature its particles can of themselves retain a permanent state; whilst at a higher temperature, that state, though it can be induced from without, will continue only as long as the inductive action lasts; and at a still higher temperature all capability of assuming this condition is lost.

The temperature at which polarity was destroyed appeared to vary with the hardness and condition of the steel.

Fragments of loadstone of very high power were then experimented with.    These preserved their polarity at higher temperatures than the steel magnet; the heat of boiling oil was not sufficient to injure it.    Just below visible ignition in the dark they lost their polarity, but from that to a temperature a little higher, being very dull ignition, they acted as soft iron would do, and then suddenly lost that power also.    Thus the loadstone retained its polarity longer than the steel magnet, but lost its capability of becoming a magnet by induction much sooner.    When magnetic polarity was given to it by contact with a magnet, it retained this power up to the same degree of temperature as that at which it held its first and natural magnetism.

A very ingenious magnetizing process, in which electro-magnets and a high temperature are used, has been proposed lately by M. Aimé[1].    I am not acquainted with the actual results of this process, but it would appear probable that the temperature which decides the existence of the polarity, and above which all seems at liberty in the bar, is that required.    Hence probably it will be found that a white heat is not more advantageous in the process than a temperature just above or about that of boiling oil; whilst the latter would be much more convenient in practice.    The only theoretical reason for commencing at high temperatures would be to include both the hardening and the polarizing degrees in the same process; but it appears doubtful whether these are so connected as to give any advantage in practice, however advantageous it may be to commence the process above the depolarizing temperature.

Royal Institution, Jan. 27, 1836.

[1] Annales de Chimie et de Physique, tome lvii. p. 442.

### Notice of the Magnetic Action of Manganese at Low Temperatures, as stated by M. Berthier[1].

#### To the Editors of the *Philosophical Magazine and Journal*.

GENTLEMEN,

THE following fact, stated by M. Berthier, has great interest to me, in consequence of the views I have taken of the general magnetic relations and characters of the metals. As you have done me the favour to publish these views in your Magazine[2], perhaps you will think the present note also worth a place in the next Number.

Berthier, in his *Traité des Essais par la Voie Sèche*, tome i. p. 532, has the following passage in his account of the physical properties of the metals:—"Magnetism.—There are only three metals which are habitually endowed with magnetic force: these are iron, cobalt, and nickel; *but manganese also possesses it beneath a certain degree of temperature much below zero.*" There is no reference to any account of this experimental result, and it is therefore probable that M. Berthier himself has observed the fact, in which case it cannot be doubted; but the result is so important, that any one possessing pure manganese who can verify the result and give an account of the degree of temperature at which the change takes place, will be doing a service to science. The great point will be to secure the *perfect absence* of iron or nickel from the manganese. With respect to cobalt, I have already stated that when pure, I cannot find it to possess magnetic properties at common or low temperatures.

                    I am, Gentlemen, yours, &c.,

Royal Institution, June 17, 1836.                    M. FARADAY.

---

[1] Lond. and Edinb. Phil. Mag., 1836, vol. ix. p. 65.

[2] See Lond. and Edinb. Phil. Mag., vol. viii. p. 177.—EDIT. or p. 217.

*On the general Magnetic Relations and Characters of the Metals: Additional Facts*[1].

An idea that the metals would be all magnetic if made extremely cold, as they are all non-magnetic if above a certain temperature, was put forth in March 1836[2], and some experiments were made, in which several were cooled as low as $-60°$ or $-70°$ Fahr., but without acquiring magnetic powers. It was afterwards noticed[3] that Berthier had said, that besides iron, cobalt, and nickel, *manganese also possesses magnetic force beneath a certain degree of temperature, much below zero*. Having had last May the opportunity of working with M. Thilorier's beautiful apparatus for giving both the liquid and the solid state to carbonic acid gas, I was anxious to ascertain what the extremely low temperature procurable by its means would effect with regard to the magnetic powers of metals and other substances, especially with relation to manganese and cobalt; and not having seen any account of similar trials, I send the results to the Philosophical Magazine (if it please the Editors to insert them) as an appendix to the two former notices.

The substances were cooled by immersion in the mixture of ether and solid carbonic acid, and moved either by platina wires attached to them, or by small wooden tongs, also cooled. The temperature, according to Thilorier, would be about $112°$ below $0°$ of Fahrenheit. The test of magnetic power was a double astatic needle, each of the two constituent needles being small and powerful, so that the whole system was very sensible to any substance capable of having magnetism induced in it when brought near one of the four poles. Great care was required and was taken to avoid the effect of the downward current of air formed by the cooled body; very thin plates of mica being interposed in the most important cases.

The following metals gave no indications of any magnetic power when thus cooled to $-112°$ Fahr.

| | |
|---|---|
| Antimony, | Cadmium, |
| Arsenic, | Chromium, |
| Bismuth, | Cobalt, |

[1] Lond. and Edinb. Phil. Mag., 1839, vol. xiv. p. 161.
[2] Ibid. vol. viii. p. 177, or p. 217.    [3] Ibid., vol. ix. p. 65, or p. 222.

| | |
|---|---|
| Copper, | Platinum, |
| Gold, | Rhodium, |
| Lead, | Silver, |
| Mercury, | Tin, |
| Palladium, | Zinc. |

A piece of metallic manganese given to me by Mr. Everett was very slightly magnetic and polar at *common* temperatures. It was not more magnetic when cooled to the lowest degree. Hence I believe the statement with regard to its acquiring such powers under such circumstances to be inaccurate. Upon very careful examination a trace of iron was found in the piece of metal, and to that I think the magnetic property which it possessed must be attributed.

I was very careful in ascertaining that pure *cobalt* did not become magnetic at the very low temperature produced.

The native alloy of iridium and osmium, and also crystals of titanium, were found to be slightly magnetic at common temperatures; I believe because of the presence of iron in them[1]. Being cooled to the lowest degree they did not present any additional magnetic force, and therefore it may be concluded that *iridium, osmium,* and *titanium* may be added as non-magnetic metals to the list already given.

Carbon and the following metallic combinations were then experimented upon in a similar manner, but all the results were negative : not one of the bodies gave the least sign of the acquirement of magnetic power by the cold applied.

| | |
|---|---|
| 1. Carbon. | 12. Galena. |
| 2. Hæmatite. | 13. Realgar. |
| 3. Protoxide of lead. | 14. Orpiment. |
| 4. ———————— antimony. | 15. Dense native cinnabar. |
| 5. ———————— bismuth. | 16. Sulphuret of silver. |
| 6. White arsenic. | 17. ——————— copper. |
| 7. Native oxide of tin. | 18. ——————— tin. |
| 8. ——————— manganese. | 19. ——————— bismuth. |
| 9. Chloride of silver. | 20. ——————— antimony. |
| 10. ——————— lead. | 21. Protosul. iron crystallized. |
| 11. Iodide of mercury. | 22. ——————— anhydrous. |

[1 See Dr. Wollaston's paper on this subject, Phil. Trans. 1823, Part II., or Phil. Mag. First Series, vol. lxiii. p. 15.—Edit.]

The carbon was the dense hard kind obtained from gas retorts; the substances 3. 4. 5. 6. 9. 10. 11. and some of the sulphurets had been first fused and solidified; and all the bodies were taken in the most solid and dense state which they could acquire.

It is perhaps superfluous to add, except in reference to effects which have been supposed by some to occur in northern latitudes, that the iron and nickel did not appear to suffer any abatement of their peculiar power when cooled to the very lowest degree.

Royal Institution, Feb. 7, 1839.

---

### On a supposed new Sulphuret and Oxide of Antimony[1].

### To the Editors of the Philosophical Magazine and Journal.

GENTLEMEN,

IN my Experimental Researches, paragraphs 693. 694. 695. 696., I have, in relation to antimony, described what I considered to be a new sulphuret, and expressed my belief that a new and true protoxide existed consisting of single proportions, "but could not stop to ascertain this matter strictly by analysis." Professor Rose when in London informed me that Berzelius objected to my new sulphuret, and I was induced to make more accurate experiments on that point, which showed me my error, and accorded generally with what Rose had described to me. I intended to publish these results in the first electric paper which I might have to put forth; but my friend Mr. Solly has put into my hands a translation of Berzelius's paper, and it is so clear and accurate as to the facts that I now prefer asking you to publish it, adding merely that my experiments quite agree with those described in it, as regards the sulphuret. With respect to the supposed chloride and oxide, I have not anywhere implied that I had made quantitative experiments on them.

[1] Lond. and Edinb. Phil. Mag., 1836, vol. viii. p. 476.

*On Faraday's supposed Sulphuret of Antimony and Oxide of Antimony; by* J. J. BERZELIUS.—*From his "*Jahresbericht,*"
No.* 15.

" Faraday has stated, that when sulphuret of antimony is heated with more metallic antimony, a new sulphuret of antimony is formed, which when in the fused state is distinguishable from the common sulphuret. According to a few experiments, this sulphuret of antimony is composed of Sb S, or one atom of each element. When this sulphuret is dissolved in muriatic acid, sulphuretted hydrogen is evolved, and although a little antimony is separated, yet there remains in solution a combination with chlorine Sb Cl, which when decomposed with carbonate of soda furnishes a new oxide. The mixing of this with the common oxide is said to have given rise to the contradictory views of its composition, and also to the appearance that the fused oxide of antimony is decomposed to a certain extent by the electric current only until the new oxide is reduced.

" Faraday appears convinced of the truth of this statement, but adds that he has not confirmed by analysis the composition of this oxide, because he should thereby have interrupted the course of his main experiments.

" This appeared to me to deserve a nearer investigation, as well for itself as for the importance of its influence on Faraday's electro-chemical views. I have therefore repeated the above-described experiments of Faraday on the three new combinations of antimony with sulphur, chlorine, and oxygen, and I have found that even if they do exist they cannot possibly be formed by the means which he has described, and they are therefore still to be discovered.

" The following is the substance of my examination. I mixed together very carefully and intimately sulphuret of antimony and metallic antimony in the proportions that, through melting, the combination Sb + S must be formed : the mixture was then put into a glass tube : this was drawn out to a capillary end; the air was then expelled by heat, and the tube was hermetically sealed. The tube was then placed in a vessel covered with sand, heated to a full red-heat, and then suffered to cool slowly. When the mass was taken out there was at the bottom a regulus, which contained 63 per cent. of the antimony which had been added after it had been separated from some adhering portions of sulphuret of antimony by boiling with a little muriatic acid.

" This had all the properties of pure antimony. Rubbed to powder and boiled with muriatic acid, it still evolved however a little sulphuretted hydrogen and gave some antimony to the acid. The powder when thus boiled had lost $6\frac{1}{4}$ per cent.

" From all this it is evident that though the resulting sulphuret of antimony contained more antimony after than before the process, it is not the combination which Faraday thought it was. Even in the cleavage it had not the appearance of a pure sulphuret of antimony. The upper portions had the same radiated structure as the common sulphuret of antimony, and a few larger crystals had shot up into the upper surface of the regulus, where they were surrounded with an irregular mass of a lighter colour. The upper and the lower portions of this so-formed antimony were each separately analysed, in such a manner that a weighed portion was put into muriatic acid and digested in it in the water-bath. The solution went on rapidly. From the lowermost portion crystals fell off one after another, upon which the acid did not act. The same happened likewise with the uppermost portion, only they were smaller and fewer in number. These insoluble parts when well boiled and washed were from the lowermost 15 and from the uppermost 10 per cent. It proved to be pure metallic antimony formed in feathery crystals, and shows, therefore, the interesting fact that sulphuret of antimony can dissolve at a high temperature $13\frac{1}{4}$ per cent. of metallic antimony, which when the solution is suffered to cool sufficiently slowly crystallizes out of the yet fluid sulphuret of antimony before this latter solidifies. By a more rapid cooling the whole mass congeals together, and the cleavage is then quite similar throughout.

" From what has been said it is quite evident that the muriatic acid takes up nothing but the common chloride of antimony. I have examined this behaviour further in detail, and thereby found, that by this method neither with water nor alkali is it possible to obtain any other oxide.

" The above-mentioned experiment of Faraday, that melted oxide of antimony is decomposed by the electric current, clearly proves that the law proposed by him, that similar quantities of electricity always evolve equal chemical proportions, only holds good so long as the comparison is made between combinations of proportional composition.

" As for the cause of the appearance, that the decomposition of the oxide of antimony becomes gradually weaker and weaker, and at last ceases, it is evident that Faraday has overlooked the circumstance that the oxide is decomposed into metal at the negative conductor and antimonious acid at the positive conductor, which then soon becomes encrusted with a solid substance, after which the electricity could not have any further action."

---

With respect to Berzelius's objection in the last paragraph but one of his paper, I will ask you to reprint paragraph 821. of my series. " All these facts combine into, I think, an irresistible mass of evidence, proving the truth of the important proposition which I at first laid down, namely, *that the chemical power of a current of electricity is in direct proportion to the absolute quantity of electricity which passes.* (377. 783.) They prove too that this is not merely true with one substance, as water, but generally with all electrolytic bodies; and further that the results obtained with any *one substance* do not merely agree amongst themselves, but also with those obtained from *other substances*, the whole combining together into *one series of definite electro-chemical actions.* (505.)  I do not mean to say that no exceptions will appear; perhaps some may arise, especially amongst substances existing only by weak affinity: but I do not expect that any will seriously disturb the result announced.  If, in the well-considered, well-examined, and I may surely say, well-ascertained doctrines of the definite nature of ordinary chemical affinity, such exceptions occur, as they do in abundance, yet without being allowed to disturb our minds as to the general conclusion, they ought also to be allowed, if they should present themselves at this the opening of a new view of electro-chemical action; not being held up as obstructions to those who may be engaged in rendering that view more and more perfect, but laid aside for a while, in hopes that their perfect and consistent explanation will finally appear."

With regard to my having overlooked the cause of the diminution and cessation of voltaic action on the oxide of antimony, I do not know how that can well be said, for Berzelius's statement seems in parts to be almost a copy of the reasons I have given: see paragraph 801. of the Seventh Series of my Researches. My explanation is actually referred to in the account of the action on the oxide of antimony at paragraph 693., but by a misprint 802. has been stated instead of 801[1].

           I am, Gentlemen, yours, &c.

                         M. FARADAY.

---

*On the History of the Condensation of the Gases, in reply to* Dr. Davy, *introduced by some Remarks on that of Electromagnetic Rotation*[2].

MY DEAR SIR,           Royal Institution, May 10, 1836.

I HAVE just concluded looking over Dr. Davy's Life of his brother Sir Humphry Davy. In it, between pages 160 and 164 of the second volume, the author links together some account, with observations, of the discovery of electro-magnetic rotation, and that of the condensation of the gases, concluding at page 164 with these words: " I am surprised that Mr. Faraday has not come forward to do him [Sir Humphry Davy] justice. As I view the matter, it appears hardly less necessary to his own honest fame than his acknowledgement to Dr. Wollaston, on the subject of the first idea of the rotary magnetic motion."

I regret that Dr. Davy by saying this has made that necessary which I did not before think so; but I feel that I cannot after his observation indulge my earnest desire to be silent on the matter without incurring the risk of being charged with something opposed to an *honest* character. This I dare not

---

[1] This reference is correctly made in Lond. and Edinb. Phil. Mag., vol. v. p. 170.—EDIT.

[2] Lond. and Edinb. Phil. Mag. 1836, vol. viii. p. 521.

risk; but in answering for myself, I trust it will be understood that I have been driven unwillingly into utterance.

Dr. Davy speaks of electro-magnetic rotation, and so also must I, for the purpose of showing certain coincidences in dates, &c. between the latter part of that affair and the condensation of chlorine and the gases, &c. Œrsted's experiments were published in Thomson's Annals of Philosophy for October 1820, and from this, I believe, was derived the first knowledge of them which we had in this country. At all events it was the first intimation Sir Humphry Davy and I had of them, for he brought down the Number into the laboratory on the morning of its appearance (October 1st) and we repeated the experiments together. I may remark that this is a proof that Dr. Davy, in the Life[1] as well as elsewhere[2], does not always understand the meaning of his brother's words, and I think that he would never have written the lines which have driven me to the present and a former reply[3] if he had.

Immediately upon Œrsted's great discovery, the subject was pursued earnestly, and various papers were written, amongst which is one by Sir Humphry Davy, Phil. Trans. 1821, page 7, read before the Royal Society November 16, 1820, in which, at page 17, he describes the rolling of certain wires upon knife-edges, being *attracted* when the north pole of the magnet was presented under certain conditions of current, and *repelled* under certain other conditions of current, &c.

Another paper was a brief statement by the Editor of the Quarterly Journal of Science, (Mr. Brande,) in which he announces distinctly and clearly Dr. Wollaston's view of the nature of the electro-magnetic force, and its circumferential character. It is in the tenth volume, p. 363, and may be dated according to the number of the Journal, 1st January 1821.

Then there are my historical sketches in the Annals of Philosophy, N.S., vols. ii. and iii. written in July, August, and September 1821, and the paper describing my discovery of the electro-magnetic rotation dated 11th September 1821[4], and

---

[1] Vol. ii. p. 143.

[2] Lond. and Edinb. Phil. Mag., 1835, vol. vii. p. 340; or p. 215 of this volume.

[3] Ibid. p. 337; or page 211 of this volume.

[4] Quarterly Journal of Science, vol. xii. p. 74; or page 127 of this volume.

others; but we will pass on to that of Sir Humphry Davy, read 6th March 1823[1], which with its consequents is *synchronous* with the affair of the condensation of gases. This is the paper which Dr. Davy says " he (Sir H. D.,) concludes by an act of justice to Dr. Wollaston, pointing out how the discovery of the *rotations of the electro-magnetic wire round its axis* by the approach of a magnet, realized by the ingenuity of Mr. Faraday, had been anticipated, and even attempted by Dr. Wollaston in the laboratory of the Royal Institution[2]."

I have elsewhere[3] done full justice to Dr. Wollaston on the point of electro-magnetic rotation, and have no desire to lessen the force of anything I have said, but would rather exalt it. But as Dr. Davy has connected it with the condensation of the gases, I must show the continual tendency to error which has occurred in both these matters. Dr. Davy, then, is in error when he says I realized Dr. Wollaston's expectation; nor does Sir Humphry Davy say what his brother imputes to him. *I did not realize* the rotations of the electro-magnetic wire round its axis; that fact was discovered by M. Ampère, at a later date; and even after I had discovered the rotation of the wire round the magnet as a centre, and that of the magnet round the wire, I could not succeed in causing the wire to revolve on its own axis[4]. The result which Wollaston very philosophically and beautifully deduced from his principles, and which he tried to obtain in the laboratory, was, that wires could be caused to roll, not by attraction and repulsion as had been effected by Davy[5], but by a tangential action, according to the principles which had been already made known to the public as his (Dr. W.'s) by Mr. Brande[6].

What Sir Humphry Davy says in his printed paper[7] is this: " I cannot with propriety conclude without mentioning a circumstance in the history of the progress of electro-magnetism, which, though well known to many Fellows of this Society, has, I believe, never been made public, namely, that we owe to the sagacity of Dr. Wollaston the first idea of the possibility

[1] Phil. Trans. 1823, p. 153.          [2] Life, vol. ii. p. 160.
[3] Quarterly Journal of Science, vol. xv. p. 288; or page 159 of this volume.
[4] Ibid., vol. xii. p. 79 ; or page 131 of this volume.
[5] Phil. Trans. 1821, p. 17.     [6] Quarterly Journal of Science, vol. x. p. 363.
[7] Phil. Trans. 1823, p. 158.

of *the rotations of the electro-magnetic wire round its axis by the approach of a magnet*; and I witnessed early in 1821 an unsuccessful experiment which he made to produce the effect in the laboratory of the Royal Institution." This paper being read on the 6th of March 1823, was reported on the first of the following month in the Annals of Philosophy, N.S., vol. v. p. 304; the reporter giving altogether a different sense to what is conveyed by Sir Humphry Davy's printed paper, and saying that " had not an experiment on the subject made by Dr. W. in the laboratory of the Royal Institution, and witnessed by Sir Humphry, failed, *merely through an accident* which happened to the apparatus, *he would have been the discoverer of that phenomenon*[1]."

I have an impression that this report of the paper was first made known to me by Sir Humphry Davy himself, but a friend's recollection makes me doubtful on this point: however, Sir Humphry, when first he adverted to the subject, told me it was inaccurate and very unjust; and advised me to draw up a contradiction which the Editor should insert the next month. I drew up a short note, and submitting it to Sir Humphry he altered it and made it what it appears in the May Number of the Annals of Philosophy, N.S. vol. v. p. 391, as from the Editor, all the parts from " but writing only " to the end being Sir Humphry's; and I have the manuscript in *his hand-writing* inserted as an illustration into my copy of Paris's Life of Davy.

The whole paragraph stands thus : " *\*\*\** We endeavoured last month to give a full report of the important paper communicated by the President to the Royal Society on the 5th [6th] of March[2]; but writing only from memory, we have made two errors, one with respect to the rotation of the mercury not being stopped, but produced, by the approximation of the magnet; the other in the historical paragraph in the conclusion, which, as we have stated it, is unjust to Mr. Faraday, and does not at all convey the sense of the author. We wish, therefore, to refer our readers forward to the original paper, when it shall be published, for the correction of these mistakes.—*Edit.*"

[1] In justice to the reporter, I have sought carefully at the Royal Society for the original manuscript, being the paper which he heard read; but it cannot be found in its place.

[2] So far is mine ; the rest is Sir Humphry Davy's.

From this collection of dates and documents any one may judge that I at all events was *unjustly* subject to some degree of annoyance, and they will be the more alive to this if they recollect that all these things were happening at the very time of the occurrence of the condensation of gases and its consequences, and during the time that my name was before the Royal Society as a candidate for its fellowship.  I do not believe that any one was wittingly the cause of this state of things, but all seemed confusion, and generally to my disadvantage. For instance, this very paper of Sir Humphry Davy's which contains the " act of justice," as Dr. Davy calls it, is entitled, " *On a new phenomenon of Electro-magnetism.*"  Yet what is electro-magnetic was not new, but merely another form of my rotation ; and the *new phenomenon* is purely electrical, being the same as that previously discovered by M. Ampère.  As M. Ampère's result is described for the first time in a paper of the date of the 4th of September 1822[1], and Sir Humphry Davy's paper was read as soon after as the 6th of March 1823[2], the latter probably did not know of the result which the former had obtained.

To conclude this matter : in consequence of these and other circumstances, and the simultaneous ones respecting the condensation of chlorine, I wrote the historical statement[3], to which Dr. Davy refers[4], in which, admitting everything that Dr. Wollaston had done, I claim and *prove* my right to the discovery of the rotations I had previously described. This paper before its publication I read with Dr. Wollaston ; he examined the proofs which I have adduced at p. 291 (page 161 of this volume), and after he had made a few alterations he brought it into the state in which it is printed, expressed his satisfaction at the arguments and his approval of the whole.    The copy I have preserved, and I will now insert the most considerable and important of Dr. Wollaston's corrections as an illustration. At the end of the paragraph at the bottom of page 291 (page 162 of this volume), I had expressed the sense thus : "But what I thought to be attraction and repulsion in August 1821, Dr.

---

[1] Ann. de Chim., 1822, vol. xxi. p. 47.          [2] Phil. Trans. 1823, p. 153.
[3] Quarterly Journal of Science, vol. xv. p. 288 ; or page 159 of this volume.
[4] Life, vol. ii. p. 146, bottom of the page.

Wollaston long before perceived to be an impulsion in one direction only, and upon that knowledge founded his expectations." This he altered to: " But what I thought to be attraction *to* and repulsion *from the wire* in August 1821, Dr. Wollaston long before perceived to arise from *a power not directed to or from the wire, but acting circumferentially round it as axis,* and upon that knowledge founded his expectation." The parts in Italics are in his hand-writing.

[The remainder of this letter regards the condensation of the gases, which as it has no connexion with electricity or magnetism, I omit, with the exception of the concluding paragraph, which is as follows.]

Believing that I have now said enough to preserve my own " honest fame" from any injury it might have risked from the mistakes of Dr. Davy, I willingly bring this letter to a close, and trust that I shall never again have to address you on the subject.

I am, my dear Sir, yours, &c.

*Richard Phillips, Esq., &c. &c.*                     M. FARADAY.

---

*On a peculiar Voltaic Condition of Iron, by Professor* SCHOEN- BEIN, *of Bâle ; in a Letter to* Mr. Faraday: *with further Experiments on the same subject, by* Mr. FARADAY, *communicated in a Letter to* Mr. Phillips[1].

### *To Michael Faraday, D.C.L., F.R.S., &c.*

SIR,

As our continental and particularly German periodicals are rather slow in publishing scientific papers, and as I am anxious to make you as soon as possible acquainted with some new electro-chemical phenomena lately observed by me, I take the liberty to state them to you by writing. Being tempted to do so only by scientific motives, I entertain the flattering hope that the contents of my letter will be received by you with kindness. The facts I am about laying before you seem to me not only to be new, but at the same time deserving the attention of chemical philosophers. *Les voici.*

If one of the ends of an iron wire be made red hot, and after

---

[1] Lond. and Edinb. Phil. Mag., 1836, vol. ix. p. 53.

cooling be immersed in nitric acid, sp. gr. 1·35, neither the
end in question nor any other part of the wire will be affected,
whilst the acid of the said strength is well known to act rather
violently upon common iron.  To see how far the influence of
the oxidized end of the wire goes, I took an iron wire of 50′
in length and 0‴·5 in thickness, heated one of its ends about
3″ in length, immersed it in the acid of the strength above mentioned, and afterwards put the other end into the same fluid.
No action of the acid upon the iron took place.  From a similar experiment made upon a cylindrical iron bar of 16′ in
length and 4‴ diameter the same result was obtained.  The
limits of this protecting influence of oxide of iron with regard
to quantities I have not yet ascertained ; but as to the influence
of heat, I found that above the temperature of about 75° the
acid acts in the common way upon iron, and in the same manner
also, at common temperatures, when the said acid contains
water beyond a certain quantity, for instance, 1, 10, 100, and
even 1000 times its volume.  By immersing an iron wire in
nitric acid of sp. gr. 1·5 it becomes likewise indifferent to the
same acid of 1·35.

But by far the most curious fact observed by me is, that any
number of iron wires may be made indifferent to nitric acid by
the following means.  An iron wire with one of its ends oxidized is made to touch another common iron wire ; both
are then introduced into nitric acid of sp. gr. 1·35, so as to
immerse the oxidized end of the one wire first into the fluid,
and have part of both wires above the level of the acid.
Under these circumstances no chemical action upon the wires
will take place, for the second wire is, of course, but a continuation of that provided with an oxidized end.   But no action occurs, even after the wires have been separated from each other.
If the second wire having become indifferent be now taken out
of the acid and made to touch at any of its parts not having been
immersed a third wire, and both again introduced into the
acid so as to make that part of the second wire which had previously been in the fluid enter first, neither of the wires will be
acted upon either during their contact or after their separation.
In this manner the third wire can make indifferent or passive
a fourth one, and so on.

Another fact, which has as yet, as far as I know, not been observed, is the following one. A wire made indifferent by any of the means before mentioned is immersed in nitric acid of sp. gr. 1·35, so as to have a considerable part of it remaining out of the fluid; another common wire is put into the same acid, likewise having one of its ends rising above the level of the fluid. The part immersed of this wire will, of course, be acted upon in a lively manner. If the ends of the wires which are out of the acid be now made to touch one another, the indifferent wire will instantly be turned into an active one, whatever may be the lengths of the parts of the wires not immersed. [If there is any instance of chemical affinity being transmitted in the form of a current by means of conducting bodies, I think the fact just stated may be considered as such.] It is a matter of course that direct contact between the two wires in question is not an indispensably necessary condition for communicating chemical activity from the active wire to the passive one; for any metal connecting the two ends of the wires renders the same service.

Before passing to another subject, I must mention a fact, which seems to be one of some importance. An iron wire curved into a fork is made to touch at its bend, a wire provided with an oxidized end; in this state of contact both are introduced into nitric acid of sp. gr. 1·35 and 30°, so as first to immerse in the acid the oxidized end; the fork will, of course, not be affected. If now a common iron wire be put into the acid, and one of the ends of the fork touched by it, this end will immediately be acted upon, whilst the other end remains passive; but as soon as the iron wire with the oxidized end is put out of contact with the bend of the fork, its second end is also turned active. If the parts of the fork rising above the level of the acid be touched by an iron wire, part of which is immersed and active in the acid, no communication of chemical activity will take place, and both ends of the fork remain passive; but by the removal of the iron wire (with the oxidized end) from the bend of the fork this will be thrown into chemical action.

As all the phenomena spoken of in the preceding lines are, no doubt, in some way or other dependent upon a peculiar electrical state of the wires, I was very curious to see in what manner iron would be acted upon by nitric acid when used as an electrode. For this purpose I made use of that form of the pile called the *couronne des tasses,* consisting of fifteen pairs of zinc and copper. A platina wire was connected with (what we call) the negative pole of the pile, an iron wire with the positive one. The free end of the platina wire was first plunged into nitric acid sp. gr. 1·35, and by the free end of the iron wire the circuit closed. Under these circumstances the iron was not in the least affected by the acid; and it remained indifferent to the fluid not only as long as the current was passing through it, but even after it had ceased to perform the function of the positive electrode. The iron wire proved, in fact, to be possessed of all the properties of what we have called a passive one. If such a wire is made to touch the negative electrode, it instantaneously becomes an active one, and a nitrate of iron is formed; whether it be separate from the positive pole or still connected with it, and the acid be strong or weak.

But another phenomenon is dependent upon the passive state of the iron, which phenomenon is in direct contradiction with all the assertions hitherto made by philosophical experimenters. The oxygen at the anode arising from the decomposition of water contained in the acid, does not combine with the iron serving as the electrode, but is evolved at it, just in the same manner as if it were platina, and to such a volume as to bear the ratio of $1:2$ to the quantity of hydrogen evolved at the cathode. To obtain this result I made use of an acid containing 20 times its volume of water; I found, however, that an acid containing 400 times its volume of water still shows the phenomenon in a very obvious manner. But I must repeat it, the indispensable condition for causing the evolution of the oxygen at the iron wire is to close the circuit exactly in the same manner as above mentioned. For if, *exempli gratiá,* the circuit be closed with the negative platina wire, not one single bubble of oxygen gas makes its appearance at the positive iron; neither is oxygen given out at it, when the circuit is closed, by plunging first one end of the iron wire into the nitric acid, and by afterwards putting its other end in connexion with the positive pole of the pile. In both cases a nitrate of iron is formed, even in an acid containing 400 times its volume of water; which salt may be easily observed descending from the iron wire in the shape of brownish-yellow-coloured streaks.

I have still to state the remarkable fact, that if the evolution of oxygen at the anode be ever so rapidly going on, and the iron wire made to touch the negative electrode within the acid, the disengagement of oxygen is discontinued, not only during the time of contact of the wires, but after the electrodes have been separated from each other. A few moments holding the iron wire out of the acid is, however, sufficient to recommunicate to it the property of letting oxygen gas evolve at its surface. By the same method the wire acquires its evolving power again, whatever may have been the cause of its loss. The evolution of oxygen also takes place in dilute sulphuric and phosphoric acids, provided, however, the circuit be closed in the manner above described. It is worthy of remark, that the disengagement of oxygen at the iron in the last-named acids is much easier stopt, and much more difficult to be caused again, than is the case in nitric acid. In an aqueous solution of caustic potash, oxygen is evolved at the positive iron, in whatever manner the circuit may be closed; but no such disengagement takes place in aqueous solutions of hydracids, chlorides, bromides, iodides, fluorides. The oxygen, resulting in these cases from the decomposition of water, and the anion (chlorine, bromine, &c.) of the other electrolyte decomposed combine at the same time with the iron.

To generalize these facts, it may be said, that independently of the manner of closing the circuit, oxygen is always disengaged at the positive iron, provided the aqueous fluid in which it is immersed do not (in a sensible manner) chemically act upon it; and that no evolution of oxygen at the anode in contact with iron under any circumstances takes place, if besides oxygen another anion is set free possessed of a strong affinity for iron. This metal having once had oxygen evolved at itself, proves always to be indifferent to nitric acid of a certain strength, whatever may be the chemical nature of the fluid in which the phenomenon has taken place.

I have made a series of experiments upon silver, copper, tin, lead, cadmium, bismuth, zinc, mercury, but none showed any resemblance to iron, for all of them were oxidized when serving

as positive electrodes.    Having at this present moment neither
cobalt nor nickel at my command, I could not try these magnetic metals, which I strongly suspect to act in the same manner as iron does.

It appears from what I have just stated that the anomalous
bearing of the iron has nothing to do with its degree of affinity
for oxygen, but must be founded upon something else.    Your
sagacity, which has already penetrated into so many mysteries
of nature, will easily put away the veil which as yet covers the
phenomenon stated in my letter, in case you should think it
worth while to make it the object of your researches.

Before I finish I must beg of you the favour of overlooking
with indulgence the many faults I have, no doubt, committed
in my letter.    Formerly I was tolerably well acquainted with
your native tongue; but now, having been out of practice in
writing or speaking it, it is rather hard work to me to express
myself in English.

It is hardly necessary to say that you may privately or publicly make any use of the contents of this letter.

I am, Sir, your most obedient Servant,

C. T. SCHOENBEIN,

Bâle, May 17, 1836.                          Prof. of Chem. in the University of Bâle.

DEAR PHILLIPS,

The preceding letter from Professor Schoenbein, which I received a week or two ago, contains facts of such interest in relation to the first principles of chemical electricity, that I think
you will be glad to publish it in your Philosophical Magazine.
I send it to you unaltered, except in a word or two here and
there; but am encouraged by what I consider the Professor's
permission (or rather the request with which he has honoured
me), to add a few results in confirmation of the effects described, and illustrative of some conclusions that may be drawn
from the facts.

The influence of the oxidized iron wire, the transference of
the inactive state from wire to wire, and the destruction of that
state, are the facts I have principally verified; but they are so
well described by Professor Schoenbein that I will not add a
word to what he has said on these points, but go at once to
other results.

Iron wire, as M. Schoenbein has stated, when put *alone* into strong nitric acid, either wholly or partly immersed, acquires the peculiar inactive state.    This I find takes place best in a long narrow close vessel, such as a tube, rather than in a flat broad open one like a dish.    When thus rendered quiescent by itself, it has the same properties and relations as that to which the power has been communicated from other wires.

If a piece of ordinary iron wire be plunged wholly or in part into nitric acid of about specific gravity 1·3 or 1·35, and after action has commenced it be touched by a piece of platina wire, also dipping into the acid, the action between the acid and the iron wire is instantly stopped.    The immersed portion of the iron becomes quite bright, and *remains* so, and is in fact in the same state, and can be used in the same manner as the iron rendered inactive by the means already described.    This protecting power of platina with respect to iron is very constant and distinct, and is the more striking as being an effect the very reverse of that which might have been anticipated prior to the knowledge of M. Schoenbein's results.    It is equally exerted if the communication between it and the iron is not immediate, but made by other metals; as, for instance, the wire of a galvanometer; and if circumstances be favourable, a small surface of platina will reduce and nullify the action of the acid upon a large surface of iron.

This effect is the more striking if it be contrasted with that produced by zinc; for the latter metal, instead of protecting the iron, throws it into violent action with the nitric acid, and determines its quick and complete solution.    The phenomena are well observed by putting the iron wire into nitric acid of the given strength, and touching it in the acid alternately by pieces of platina and zinc: it becomes active or inactive accordingly; being preserved by association with the platina, and corroded by association with the zinc.    So also, as M. Schoenbein has stated, if iron be made the negative electrode of a battery containing from two to ten or more pairs of plates in such acid, it is violently acted upon; but when rendered the positive electrode, although oxidized and dissolved, the process, comparatively, is extremely slow.

Gold has the same power over iron immersed in the nitric acid that platina has.    Even silver has a similar action; but from its relation to the acid, the effect is attended with peculiar and changeable results, which I will refer to hereafter.

A piece of box-wood charcoal, and also charcoal from other sources, has this power of preserving iron, and bringing it into the inactive state.   Plumbago, as might be expected, has the same power.

When a piece of bright steel was first connected with a piece of platina, then the platina dipped into the acid, and lastly the steel immersed, according to the order directed in the former cases by Professor Schoenbein, the steel was preserved by the platina, and remained clear and bright in the acid, even after the platina was separated from it, having, in fact, the proper-- ties of the inactive iron.   When immersed of itself, there was at first action of the usual kind, which, being followed by the appearance of the black carbonaceous crust, known so well in the common process of examining steel, the action immediately ceased, and the steel was preserved, not only at the part immersed, but upon introducing a further portion, it also remained clean and bright, being actually protected by association with the carbon evolved on the part first immersed.

When the iron is in this peculiar inactive state, as M. Schoenbein has stated, there is not the least action between it and the nitric acid.   I have retained such iron in nitric acid, both alone and in association with platina wire for 30 days, without change; the metal has remained perfectly bright, and not a particle has been dissolved.

A piece of iron wire in connexion with platina wire was entirely immersed in nitric acid of the given strength, and the latter gradually heated.   No change took place until the acid was nearly at the boiling-point, when it and the iron suddenly entered into action, and the latter was instantly dissolved.

As an illustration of the extent and influence of this state, I may mention, that with a little management it can be shown that the iron has lost, when in the peculiar state, even its power of precipitating copper and other metals.   A mixture of about equal parts of a solution of nitrate of copper and nitric acid was made.   Iron in the ordinary, or even in the peculiar state, when put into this solution, acted, and copper was precipitated; but if the inactive iron was first connected with a piece of platina dipping into the solution, and then its own prepared surface immersed, after a few seconds the platina might be removed, and the iron would remain pure and bright for some time. At last it usually started into activity, and began to precipitate copper, being itself rapidly corroded. When silver is the metal in solution, the effect is still more striking, and will be referred to immediately.

I then used a galvanometer as the means of connexion between the iron and other metals thus associated together in nitric acid, for the purpose of ascertaining, by the electric currents produced, in what relative condition the metals stood to each other; and I will, in the few results I may have to describe, use the relations of platina and zinc to each other as the terms of comparison by which to indicate the states of these metals under various circumstances.

The oxidized iron wire of Professor Schoenbein is, when in association with platina, exactly as another piece of platina would be. There is no chemical action, nor any electric current. The iron wire, rendered inactive either by association with the oxidized wire or in any other way, is also as platina to the platina, and produces no current.

When ordinary iron and platina in connexion by means of the galvanometer are dipped into the acid, (it matters not which first,) there is action at the first moment on the iron, and a very strong electric current, the iron being as zinc to the platina. The action on the iron is, however, soon stopped by the influence of the platina, and then the current instantly ceases, the iron now acting as platina to the platina. If the iron be lifted into the air for a moment until action recommences on it, and be then reimmersed, it again produces a current, acting as zinc to the platina; but as before, the moment the action stops, the current is stopt also.

If an active or ordinary, and an inactive or peculiar iron wire be both immersed in the nitric acid separately, and then connected either directly or through the galvanometer, the second does not render the first inactive, but is itself thrown into action by it. At the first moment of contact, however, a strong electric current is formed, the first iron acting as zinc, and the second as platina. Immediately that the chemical action is re-established at the second as well as the first, all current ceases, and both pieces act like zinc. On touching either of them in the acid with a piece of platina, both are protected, and cease to act; but there is no current through the galvanometer, for both change together.

When iron was associated with gold or charcoal, the phenomena were the same. Using steel instead of iron, like effects ensued.

One of the most valuable results in the present state of this branch of science which these experiments afford, is the additional proof that *voltaic electricity is due to chemical action, and not to contact.* The proof is equally striking and decisive with that which I was able to give in the Eighth Series of my Experimental Researches (par. 880). What indeed can show more evidently that the current of electricity is due to chemical action rather than to contact, than the fact, that though the contact is continued, yet when the chemical action ceases, the current ceases also?

It might at first be supposed, that in consequence of the peculiar state of the iron, there was some obstacle, not merely to the *formation* of a current, but to the *passage* of one; and that, therefore, the current which metallic contact tended to produce could not circulate in the system. This supposition was, however, negatived by removing the platina wire into a second cup of nitric acid, and then connecting the two cups by a compound platina and iron wire, putting the platina into the first vessel, and the iron attached to it into the second. The second wire acted at the first moment, producing its corresponding current, which passed through the first cup, and consequently through the first and inactive wire, and affected the galvanometer in the usual way. As soon as the second iron was brought into the *peculiar* condition, the current of course ceased; but that very cessation showed that the electric current was not stopped by a want of conducting power, or a want of metallic contact, for both remained unchanged, but by the absence of chemical action. These experiments, in which the current ceases whilst contact is continued, combined with those I formerly gave, in which the current is produced though contact does not exist, form together a perfect body of evidence in respect to this elementary principle of voltaic action.

With respect to the state of the iron when inactive in the nitric acid, it must not be confounded with the inactive state of amalgamated or pure zinc in dilute sulphuric acid. The distinction is easily made by the contact of platina with either in the respective acids, for with the iron such association does nothing, whereas with the zinc it developes the full force of that metal and generates a powerful electric current. The iron is in fact as if it had no attraction for oxygen, and therefore could not act on the electrolyte present, and consequently could produce no current. My strong impression is that the surface of the iron is oxidized, or that the superficial particles of the metal are in such relation to the oxygen of the electrolyte as to be equivalent to an oxidation; and that having thus their affinity for oxygen satisfied, and not being dissolved by the acid under the circumstances, there is no renewal of the metallic surface, no reiteration of the attraction of successive particles of the iron on the elements of successive portions of the electrolyte, and therefore not those successive chemical actions by which the electric current (which is definite in its production as well as in its action) can be continued.

In support of this view, I may observe, that in the first experiment described by Professor Schoenbein, it cannot be doubted that the formation of a coat of oxide over the iron when heated is the cause of its peculiar and inactive state : the coat of oxide is visible by its colour. In the next place, all the forms of experiment by which this iron, or platina, or charcoal, or other voltaic arrangements are used to bring ordinary iron into the peculiar state, are accompanied by a determination of oxygen to the surface of the iron ; this is shown by the electric current produced at the first moment, and which in such cases always precedes the change of the iron from the common to the peculiar state. That the coat of oxide produced by common means might be so thin as not to be sensible. and yet be effectual, was shown by heating a piece of iron an inch or two from the end, so that though blue at the heated part, the end did not seem in the slightest degree affected, and yet that end was in the peculiar state. Again, whether the iron be oxidized in the flame much or only to the very slight degree just described, or be brought into the peculiar state by voltaic association with other pieces or with platina, &c., still if a part of its surface were removed even in the smallest degree and then the new surface put into contact with the nitric acid, that part was at the first moment as common iron ; the state being abundantly evident by the electrical current produced at the instant of immersion.

Why the superficial film of oxide, which I suppose to be formed when the iron is brought into the peculiar state by voltaic association, or occasionally by immersion alone into nitric acid, is not dissolved by the acid, is I presume dependent upon the peculiarities of this oxide and of nitric acid of the strength required for these experiments ; but as a matter of fact it is well known that the oxide produced upon the surface of iron by heat, and showing itself by thin films of various colours, is scarcely touched by nitric acid of the given strength though left in contact with it for days together. That this does not depend upon the film having any great thickness, but upon its peculiar condition, is rendered probable from the fact, that iron oxidized by heat, only in that slight degree as to offer no difference to the eye, has been left in nitric acid of the given strength for weeks together without any change. And that this mode of superficial oxidation, or this kind of oxide, may occur in the voltaic cases, is rendered probable by the results of the oxidation of iron in nitrate of silver. When nitrate of silver is fused and common iron dipped into it, so as to be thoroughly wetted, being either alone or in association with platina, the iron does not commence a violent action on the nitrate and throw down silver, but it is gradually oxidized on the surface with exactly the same appearances of colour, uniformity of surface, &c., as if it were slowly oxidized by heat in the air.

Professor Schoenbein has stated the case of iron when acting as the positive electrode of a *couronne des tasses.* If that instrument be in strong action, or if an ordinary battery be used containing from two to ten or more plates, the positive iron instantly becomes covered in the nitric acid with a coat of oxide, which though it does not adhere closely still is not readily dissolved by the acid when the connexion with the battery is broken, but remains for many hours on the iron, which itself is in the peculiar inactive state. If the power of the voltaic apparatus be very weak, the coat of oxide on the iron in the nitric acid often assumes a blue tint like that of the oxide formed by heat. A part of the iron is however always dissolved in these cases.

If it be allowed that the surface particles of the iron are associated with oxygen, are in fact oxidized, then all the other actions of it in combination with common iron and other metals will be consistent; and the cause of its platina-like action, of its forming a strong voltaic current with common iron in the first instance, and then being thrown into action by it, will be explained by considering it as having the power of determining and disposing of a certain portion of hydrogen from the electrolyte at the first moment and being at the same time brought into a free metallic condition on the surface so as to act afterwards as ordinary iron.

I need scarcely refer here to the probable existence of a very close connexion between the phenomena which Professor Schoenbein has thus pointed out with regard to iron, and those which have been observed by others, as Ritter and Marianini, with regard to secondary piles, and A. De la Rive with respect to peculiar affections of platina surfaces.

In my Experimental Researches (par. 476.) I have recorded a case of voltaic excitement, which very much surprised me at the time, but which I can now explain. I refer to the fact stated, that when platina and iron wire were connected voltaically in association with fused nitrate or chloride of silver, there was an electric current produced, but in the reverse direction to that expected. On repeating the experiment, I found that when iron was associated with platina or silver in fused nitrate or chloride of silver, there was occasionally no current, and when a current did occur it was almost constantly as if the iron was as platina, the silver or platina used being as zinc. In all such cases, however, it was a thermo-electric current which existed. The volta-electric current could not be obtained, or lasted only for a moment.

When iron in the peculiar inactive state was associated with silver in nitric acid sp. gr. 1·35, there was an electric current, the iron acting as platina; the silver gradually became tarnished and the current continued for some time. When ordinary iron and silver were used in the nitric acid there was immediate action and a current, the iron being as zinc, to the silver as platina. In a few moments the current was reversed, and the relation of the metals was also reversed, the iron being as platina, to the silver as zinc; then another inversion took place, and then another, and thus the changes went on sometimes eight or nine times together, ending at last generally in a current constant in its direction, the iron being as zinc, to the silver as platina: occasionally the reverse was the case, the predominant current being as if the silver acted as zinc.

This relation of iron to silver, which was before referred to page 242, produces some curious results as to the precipitation of one metal by another. If a piece of clean iron is put into an aqueous solution of nitrate of silver, there is no immediate apparent change of any kind. After several days the iron will become slightly discoloured, and small irregular crystals of silver will appear; but the action is so slow as to require time and care for its observation. When a solution of nitrate of silver to which a little nitric acid had been added was used, there was still no sensible immediate action on the iron. When the solution was rendered very acid, then there was direct immediate action on the iron; it became covered with a coat of precipitated silver: the action then suddenly ceased, the silver was immediately redissolved, and the iron left perfectly clear, in the peculiar condition, and unable to cause any further precipitation of the silver from the solution. It is a remarkable thing in this experiment to see the silver rapidly dissolve away in a solution which cannot touch the iron, and to see the iron in a clean metallic state unable to precipitate the silver.

Iron and platina in an aqueous solution of nitrate of silver produce no electric current; both act as platina. When the solution is rendered a little acid by nitric acid, there is a very feeble current for a moment, the iron being as zinc. When still more acid is added so as to cause the iron to precipitate silver, there is a strong current whilst that action lasts, but when it ceases the current ceases, and then it is that the silver is redissolved. The association of the platina with the iron evidently helps much to stop the action.

When iron is associated with mercury, copper, lead, tin, zinc, and some other metals, in an aqueous solution of nitrate of silver, it produces a constant electric current, but always acts the part of *platinum*. This is perhaps most striking with mercury and copper, because of the marked contrast it affords to the effects produced in dilute sulphuric acid and most ordinary solutions. The constancy of the current even causes crystals of silver to form on the iron as the negative electrode. It might at first seem surprising that the power which tends to reduce silver on the iron negative electrode did not also bring back the iron from its peculiar state, whether that be a state of oxidation or not. But it must be remembered that the moment a particle of silver is reduced on the iron, it not only tends to keep the iron in the peculiar state according to the facts before described, but also acts as the negative electrode; and there is no doubt that the current of electricity which continues to circulate through the solution passes essentially between it and the silver, and not between it and the iron, the latter metal being merely the conductor interposed between the silver and the copper extremities of the metallic arrangement.

I am afraid you will think I have pursued this matter to a greater length than it deserves; but I have been exceedingly interested by M. Schoenbein's researches, and cannot help thinking that the peculiar condition of iron which he has pointed out will (whatever it may depend upon) enable us hereafter more closely to examine the surface-action of the metals and electrolytes when they are associated in voltaic combinations, and so give us a just knowledge of the nature of the two modes of action by which particles under the influence of the same power can produce either local effects of combination or current affinity[1].

I am, my dear Phillips, very truly yours,

Royal Institution, June 16, 1836.                    M. Faraday.

---

*Letter from* Mr. Faraday *to* Mr. Brayley *on some former Researches relative to the peculiar Voltaic Condition of Iron reobserved by Professor* Schoenbein, *supplementary to a Letter to* Mr. Phillips, *in the last Number*[2].

My dear Sir,                         Royal Institution, July 8, 1836.

I am greatly your debtor for having pointed out to me Sir John F. W. Herschel's paper on the action of nitric acid on

[1] Exp. Researches, Eighth Series, 947. 996.
[2] Lond. and Edinb. Phil. Mag., 1836, vol. ix. p. 122.

iron in the Annales de Chimie et de Physique; I read it at the time of its publication, but it had totally escaped my memory, which is indeed a very bad one now. It renders one half of my letter (supplementary to Professor Schoenbein's) in the last Number of the Philosophical Magazine, page 57 (or page 239 of this volume), superfluous; and I regret only that it did not happen to be recalled to my attention in time for me to rearrange my remarks, or at all events to add to them an account of Sir John Herschel's results. However, I hope the Editors of the Phil. Mag. will allow my present letter a place in the next Number; and entertaining that hope I shall include in it a few references to former results bearing upon the extraordinary character of iron to which M. Schoenbein has revived the attention of men of science.

" Bergman relates that upon adding iron to a solution of silver in the nitrous acid no precipitation ensued[1]."

Keir, who examined this action in the year 1790[2], made many excellent experiments upon it. He observed that the iron acquired a *peculiar or altered* state in the solution of silver; that this state was only superficial; that when so altered it was inactive in nitric acid; and that when ordinary iron was put into strong nitric acid there was no action, but the metal assumed the *altered* state.

Westlar, whose results I know only from the Annales des Mines for 1832[3], observed that iron or steel which had been plunged into a solution of nitrate of silver lost the power of precipitating copper from its solutions; and he attributes the effect to the assumption of a negative electric state by the part immersed, the other part of the iron having assumed the positive state.

Braconnot in 1833[4] observed, that filings or even plates of iron in strong nitric acid are not at all affected at common temperatures, and scarcely even at the boiling-point.

Sir John Herschel's observations are in reality the first which refer these phenomena to electric forces; but Westlar's, which do the same, were published before them. The results ob-

---

[1] Phil. Trans. 1790, p. 374.          [2] Ibid. pp. 374, 379.
[3] Annales des Mines, 1832, vol. ii. p. 322; or Mag. de l'harm. 1830.
[4] Annales de Chimie et de Physique, vol. lii. p. 288.

tained by the former, extracted from a private journal dated August 1825, were first published in 1833 [1].   He describes the action of nitric acid on iron; the altered state which the metal assumes; the superficial character of the change; the effect of the contact of other metals in bringing the iron back to its first state; the power of platina in assisting to bring on the altered or prepared state; and the habits of steel in nitric acid: he attributes the phenomena to a certain *permanent electric state of the surface of the metal.*   I should recommend the republication of this paper in the Philosophical Magazine.

Professor Daniell, in his paper on Voltaic Combinations [2] (Feb. 1836), found that on associating iron with platina in a battery charged with nitro-sulphuric acid, the iron would not act as the generating metal, and that when it was afterwards associated with zinc it acted more powerfully than platina itself. He considers the effect as explicable upon the idea of a force of heterogeneous attraction existing between bodies, and is inclined to believe that association with the platina cleanses the surface of the iron, or possibly causes a difference in the mechanical structure developed in this particular position.

In my letter, therefore, as published in the Philosophical Magazine for the present month (July), what relates to the preserving power of platina on iron ought to be struck out, as having been anticipated by Sir John Herschel, and also much of what relates to the action of silver and iron, as having been formerly recorded by Keir.   The facts relating to gold and carbon in association with iron; the experimental results as to the electric currents produced; the argument respecting the chemical source of electricity in the voltaic pile; and my opinion of the cause of the phenomena as due to a relation of the superficial particles of the iron to oxygen, are what remain in the character of contributions to our knowledge of this very beautiful and important case of voltaic condition presented to us by the metal iron.

I am, my dear Sir, yours very truly,

*E. W. Brayley, Esq.*                    M. Faraday.
      *London Institution.*

[1]  Annales de Chimie et de Physique, 1833, vol. liv. p. 87.
[2]  Phil. Trans. 1836, p. 114.

*A Letter to* Prof. Faraday, *on certain Theoretical Opinions.*
*By* R. Hare, *M.D., Professor of Chemistry in the Univer-*
*sity of Pennsylvania*[1].

DEAR SIR,

1. I HAVE been indebted to your kindness for several pamphlets comprising your researches in electricity, which I have perused with the greatest degree of interest.

2. You must be too well aware of the height at which you stand, in the estimation of men of science, to doubt that I entertain with diffidence any opinion in opposition to yours. I may say of you as in a former instance of Berzelius, that you occupy an elevation inaccessible to unjustifiable criticism. Under these circumstances, I hope that I may, from you, experience the candour and kindness which were displayed by the great Swedish chemist in his reply to my strictures on his nomenclature.

3. I am unable to reconcile the language which you hold in paragraph 1615, with the fundamental position taken in 1165. Agreeably to the latter, you believe ordinary induction to be the action of *contiguous* particles, consisting of a species of polarity, instead of being an action of either particles or masses at " *sensible distances.*" Agreeably to the former, you conceive that " assuming that a perfect vacuum was to intervene in the course of the line of inductive action, it does not follow from this theory that the line of particles on opposite sides of such a vacuum would not act upon each other." Again, supposing " it possible for a positively electrified particle to be in the centre of a vacuum an inch in diameter, nothing in my present view forbids that the particle should act at a distance of half an inch on all the particles forming the inner superficies of the bounding sphere."

4. Laying these quotations before you for reconsideration, I beg leave to inquire how a positively excited particle, situated as above described, can react " inductrically" with any particles

[1] From Silliman's American Journal of Science and Arts, vol. 38, No. 1., or Phil. Mag. 1840, vol. xvii. p. 44.

[We have taken the liberty of numbering the paragraphs of Dr. Hare's letter.—EDIT.]

in the superficies of the surrounding sphere, if this species of
reaction require that the particles between which it takes place
be contiguous.    Moreover if induction be not " an action either
of particles or masses at *sensible* distances," how can a particle,
situated as above described, " *act at the distance of half an
inch on all the particles forming the disk of the inner superficies of the bounding sphere?*"    What is a sensible distance,
if half an inch is not?

5. How can the force thus exercised obey the " well-known
law of the squares of the distances," if as you state (1375) the
rarefaction of the air does not alter the intensity of the inductive action?    In proportion as the air is rarefied, do not its
particles become more remote?

6. Can the ponderable particles of a gas be deemed contiguous, in the true sense of this word, under any circumstances?
And it may be well here to observe, that admitting induction
to arise from an affection of intervening ponderable atoms, it
is difficult to conceive that the intensity of this affection will
be inversely as their number, as alleged by you.    No such law
holds good in the communication of heat.    The air in contact
with a surface at a constant elevation of temperature, such for
instance as might be supported by boiling water, would not
become hotter by being rarefied, and consequently could not
become more efficacious in the conduction of heat from the
heated surface to a colder one in its vicinity.

7. As soon as I commenced the perusal of your researches
on this subject, it occurred to me that the passage of electricity
through a vacuum, or a highly rarefied medium, as demonstrated by various experiments, and especially those of Davy,
was inconsistent with the idea that ponderable matter could
be a necessary agent in the process of electrical induction.    I
therefore inferred that your efforts would be primarily directed
to a re-examination of that question.

8. If induction, in acting through a vacuum, be propagated
in right lines, may not the curvilinear direction which it pur-
sues, when passing through " dielectrics," be ascribed to the
modifying influence which they exert?

9. If, as you concede, electrified particles on opposite sides
of a vacuum can act upon each other, wherefore is the received
theory of the mode in which the excited surface of a Leyden jar

induces in the opposite surface a contrary state, objectionable?

10. As the theory which you have proposed gives great importance to the idea of polarity, I regret that you have not defined the meaning which you attach to this word. As you designate that to which you refer, as a " species of polarity," it is presumable that you have conceived of several kinds with which ponderable atoms may be endowed. I find it difficult to conceive of any kind which may be capable of as many degrees of intensity as the known phenomena of electricity require; especially according to your opinion that the only difference between the fluid evolved by galvanic apparatus and that evolved by friction, is due to opposite extremes in quantity and intensity; the intensity of electrical excitement producible by the one being almost infinitely greater than that which can be produced by the other. What state of the poles can constitute quantity—what other state intensity, the same matter being capable of either electricity, as is well known to be the fact? Would it not be well to consider how, consistently with any conceivable polarization, and without the assistance of some imponderable matter, any great difference of intensity in inductive power can be created?

11. When by friction the surface is polarized so that particles are brought into a state of constraint from which they endeavour to return to their natural state, if nothing be superadded to them, it must be supposed that they have poles capable of existing in two different positions. In one of these positions, dissimilar poles coinciding, are neutralized; while in the other position, they are more remote, and consequently capable of acting upon other matter.

12. But I am unable to imagine any change which can admit of gradations of intensity, *increasing* with remoteness. I cannot figure to myself any reaction which increase of distance would not lessen. Much less can I conceive that such extremes of intensity can be thus created, as those of which you consider the existence as demonstrated. It may be suggested that the change of polarity produced in particles of electrical inductions, may arise from the forced approximation by reciprocally repellent poles, so that the intensity of the inductive force, and of their effort to return to their previous situation,

may be susceptible of the gradation which your electrical doctrines require.    But could the existence of such a repellent
force be consistent with the mutual cohesion which appears
almost universally to be a property of ponderable particles?
I am aware that, agreeably to the ingenious hypothesis of Mossotti[1], repulsion is an inherent property of the particles which
we call ponderable ; but then he assumes the existence of an
imponderable fluid to account for cohesion; and for the necessity of such a fluid to account for induction it is my ultimate
object to contend.    I would suggest that it can hardly be expedient to ascribe the phenomena of electricity to the polarization of ponderable particles, unless it can be shown, that if
admitted, it would be competent to produce all the known
varieties of electric excitement, whether as to its nature or
energy.

13.  If I comprehend your theory, the opposite electrical state
induced on one side of a coated pane, when the other is directly electrified, arises from an affection of the intervening
vitreous particles, by which a certain polar state caused on one
side of the pane, induces an opposite state on the other side.
Each vitreous particle having its poles severally in opposite
states, they are arranged as magnetized iron filings in lines ;
so that alternately opposite poles are presented in such a
manner that all of one kind are exposed at one surface, and all
of the other kind at the other surface.    Agreeably to this or
any other imaginable view of the subject, I cannot avoid considering it inevitable that each particle must have at least two
poles.    It seems to me that the idea of polarity requires that
there shall be in any body possessing it, two opposite poles.
Hence you correctly allege, that agreeably to your views it
is impossible to charge a portion of matter with one electric
force without the other.    (See par. 1177.)    But if all this be
true, how can there be a " positively excited particle?" (See
par. 1616.)    Must not every particle be excited negatively, if
it be excited positively?    Must it not have a negative, as well
as a positive pole?

14.  I cannot agree with you in the idea, that consistently
with the theory which ascribes the phenomena of electricity to

[1] [See Scientific Memoirs, vol. i. p. 448.—EDIT.]

one fluid, there can ever be an isolated existence either of the positive or negative state. Agreeably to this theory, any excited space, whether minus or plus, must have an adjoining space relatively in a different state. Between the phenomena of positive and negative excitement there will be no other distinction than that arising from the direction in which the fluid will endeavour to move. If the excited space be positive, it must strive to flow outward; if negative, it will strive to flow inward. When sufficiently intense, the direction will be shown by the greater length of the spark, when passing from a small ball to a large one. It is always longer when the small ball is positive, and the large one negative, than when their positions are reversed[1].

15. But for any current it is no less necessary that the pressure should be on one side, comparatively minus, than that on the other side, it should be comparatively plus; and this state of the forces must exist whether the current originates from a hiatus before or from pressure behind. One current cannot differ essentially from another, however they may be produced.

16. In paragraph 1330, I have been struck with the following query, " What then is to separate the principle of these extremes, perfect conduction and perfect insulation, from each other; since the moment we leave the smallest degree of perfection at either extremity, we involve the element of perfection at the opposite ends?" Might not this query be made with as much reason in the case of motion and rest, between the extremes of which there is an infinity of gradations? If we are not to confound motion with rest, because in proportion as the former is retarded, it differs less from the latter; wherefore should we confound insulation with conduction, because in proportion as the one is less efficient, it becomes less remote from the other?

17. In any case of the intermixture of opposite qualities, may it not be said in the language which you employ, " the moment we leave the element of perfection at one extremity, we involve the element of perfection at the opposite "? Might it not be

---

[1] See my Essay on the causes of the diversity in the length of the sparks, erroneously distinguished as positive and negative, in vol. v. American Philosophical Transactions.

said of light and darkness, or of opakeness and translucency? in which case, to resort to your language again, it might be added, " especially as we have not in nature a case of perfection at one extremity or the other." But if there be not in nature any two bodies, of which one possesses the property of perfectly resisting the passage of electricity, while the other is endowed with the faculty of permitting its passage without any resistance; does this affect the propriety of considering the qualities of *insulation* and conduction in the abstract, as perfectly distinct, and inferring that so far as matter may be endowed with the one property, it must be wanting in the other?

18. Have you ever known electricity to pass through a pane of sound glass. My knowledge and experience create an impression that a coated pane is never discharged through the glass unless it be cracked or perforated. That the property by which glass resists the passage of electricity, can be confounded with that which enables a metallic wire to permit of its transfer, agreeably to Wheatstone's experiments, with a velocity greater than that of the solar rays, is to my mind inconceivable.

19. You infer that the residual charge of a battery arises from the partial penetration of the glass by the opposite excitements. But if glass be penetrable by electricity, why does it not pass through it without a fracture or perforation?

20. According to your doctrine, induction consists " in a forced state of polarization in contiguous rows of the particles of the glass" (1300); and since this is propagated from one side to the other, it must of course exist equally at all depths. Yet the partial penetration suggested by you, supposes a collateral affection of the same kind, extending only to a limited depth. Is this consistent? Is it not more reasonable to suppose that the air in the vicinity of the coating gradually relinquishes to it a portion of free electricity, conveyed into it by what you call " *convection* "? The coating being equally in contact with the air and glass, it appears to me more easy to conceive that the air might be penetrated by the excitement, than the glass.

21. In paragraph 1300, I observe the following statement: " *When a Leyden jar is charged, the particles of the glass are forced into this polarized and constrained condition by the electricity of the charging apparatus. Discharge is the return of the particles to their natural state, from their state of ten-*

*sion, whenever the two electric forces are allowed to be disposed of in some other direction.*" As you have not previously mentioned any particular direction in which the forces are exercised during the prevalence of this constrained condition, I am at a loss as to what meaning I am to attach to the words " some other direction." The word *some,* would lead to the idea that there was an uncertainty respecting the direction in which the forces might be disposed of; whereas it appears to me that the only direction in which they can operate, must be the opposite of that by which they have been induced.

22. The electrified particles can only " return to their natural state" by retracing the path by which they departed from it. I would suggest that for the words " *to be disposed of in some other direction,*" it would be better to substitute the following, " *to compensate each other by an adequate communication.*"

23. Agreeably to the explanation of the phenomenon of coated electrics afforded in the paragraph above quoted (1300), by what process can it be conceived that the opposite polarization of the surfaces can be neutralized by conduction through a metallic wire? If I understand your hypothesis correctly, the process by which the polarization of one of the vitreous surfaces in a pane produces an opposite polarization in the other, is precisely the same as that by which the electricity applied to one end of the wire extends itself to the other end.

24. I cannot conceive how two processes severally producing results so diametrically opposite as insulation and conduction, can be the same. By the former, a derangement of the electric equilibrium may be permanently sustained, while by the other, all derangement is counteracted with a rapidity almost infinite. But if the opposite charges are dependent upon a polarity induced in contiguous atoms of the glass, which endures so long as no communication ensues between the surfaces; by what conceivable process can a perfect conductor cause a discharge to take place, with a velocity at least as great as that of the solar light? Is it conceivable that all the lines of " contra-induction" or depolarization can concentrate themselves upon the wire from each surface so as to produce therein an intensity of polarization proportioned to the concentration; and that the opposite forces resulting from the polarization are thus reciprocally compensated? I must confess, such a concentra-

tration of such forces or states, is to me difficult to reconcile with the conception that it is at all to be ascribed to the action of rows of *contiguous ponderable particles.*

25. Does not your hypothesis require that the metallic particles, at opposite ends of the wire, shall in the first instance be subjected to the same polarization as the excited particles of the glass; and that the opposite polarizations, transmitted to some intervening point, should thus be mutually destroyed, the one by the other? But if discharge involves a return to the same state in vitreous particles, the same must be true in those of the metallic wire. Wherefore then are these dissipated, when the discharge is sufficiently powerful? Their dissipation must take place either while they are in the state of being polarized, or in that of returning to their natural state. But if it happen when in the first-mentioned state, the conductor must be destroyed before the opposite polarization upon the surfaces can be neutralized by its intervention. But if not dissipated in the act of being polarized, is it reasonable to suppose that the metallic particles can be sundered by returning to their *natural state* of polarization?

26. Supposing that ordinary electrical induction could be satisfactorily ascribed to the reaction of ponderable particles, it cannot, it seems to me, be pretended that magnetic and electro-magnetic induction is referable to this species of reaction. It will be admitted that the Faradian currents do not for their production require intervening ponderable atoms.

27. From a note subjoined to page 37 of your pamphlet[1], it appears that " on the question of the existence of one or more imponderable fluids as the cause of electrical phenomena, it has not been your intention to decide." I should be much gratified if any of the strictures in which I have been so bold as to indulge, should contribute to influence your ultimate decision.

28. It appears to me that there has been an undue disposition to burden the matter, usually regarded as such, with more duties than it can perform. Although it is only with the properties of matter that we have a direct acquaintance, and the existence of matter rests upon a theoretical inference that since we perceive properties, there must be material particles to which those properties belong; yet there is no conviction which the

[1] Page 409 of the former volume of these papers.

mass of mankind entertain with more firmness than that of the existence of matter in that ponde͏ ͏le form, in which it is instinctively recognised by people of ͏ɔɪ ͏.on sense.  Not perceiving that this conviction can only be supported as a theoretic deduction from our perception of the properties ; there is a reluctance to admit the existence of other matter, which has not in its favour the same instinctive conception, although theoretically similar reasoning would apply.  But if one kind of matter be admitted to exist because we perceive properties, the existence of which cannot be otherwise explained, are we not warranted, if we notice more properties than can reasonably be assigned to one kind of matter, to assume the existence of another kind of matter ?

29.  Independently of the considerations which have heretofore led some philosophers to suppose that we are surrounded by an ocean of electric matter, which by its redundancy or deficiency is capable of producing the phenomena of mechanical electricity, it has appeared to me inconceivable that the phenomena of galvanism and electro-magnetism, latterly brought into view, can be satisfactorily explained without supposing the agency of an intervening imponderable medium by whose subserviency the inductive influence of currents or magnets is propagated.   If in that wonderful reciprocal reaction between masses and particles, to which I have alluded, the polarization of condensed or accumulated portions of intervening imponderable matter, can be brought in as a link to connect the otherwise imperfect chain of causes ; it would appear to me a most important instrument in lifting the curtain which at present hides from our intellectual vision, this highly important mechanism of nature.

30.  Having devised so many ingenious experiments tending to show that the received ideas of electrical induction are inadequate to explain the phenomena without supposing a modifying influence in intervening ponderable matter, should there prove to be cases in which the results cannot be satisfactorily explained by ascribing them to ponderable particles, I hope that you may be induced to review the whole ground, in order to determine whether the part to be assigned to contiguous ponderable particles, be not secondary to that performed by the imponderable principles by which they are surrounded.

31. But if galvanic phenomena be due to ponderable (*imponderable*?) matter, evidently that matter must be in a state of combination. To what other cause than an intense affinity between it and the metallic particles with which it is associated, can its confinement be ascribed consistently with your estimate of the enormous quantity which exists in metals? If "a grain of water, or a grain of zinc, contain as much of the electric fluid as would supply eight hundred thousand charges of a battery containing a coated surface of fifteen hundred square inches," how intense must be the attraction by which this matter is confined! In such cases may not the material cause of electricity be considered as latent, agreeably to the suggestion of Œrsted, the founder of electro-magnetism? It is in combination with matter, and only capable of producing the appropriate effects of voltaic currents when in act of transfer from combination with one atom to another; this transfer being at once an effect and a cause of chemical decomposition, as you have demonstrated.

32. If polarization in any form can be conceived to admit of the requisite gradations of intensity, which the phenomena seem to demand; would it not be more reasonable to suppose that it operates by means of an imponderable fluid existing throughout all space, however devoid of other matter? May not an electric current, so called, be a progressive polarization of rows of the electric particles, the polarity being produced at one end and destroyed at the other incessantly, as I understood you to suggest in the case of contiguous ponderable atoms?

33. When the electric particles within different wires are polarized in the same tangential direction, the opposite poles being in proximity, there will be attraction. When the currents of polarization move oppositely, similar poles coinciding, there will be repulsion. The phenomena require that the magnetized or polarized particles should be arranged as tangents to the circumference, not as radii to the axis. Moreover, the progressive movement must be propagated in spiral lines in order to account for rotary influence.

34. Between a wire which is the mean of a galvanic discharge and another not making a part of a circuit, the electric matter which intervenes may, by undergoing a polarization,

become the medium of producing a progressive polarization in the second wire moving in a direction opposite to that in the inducing wire; or in other words, an electrical current of the species called Faradian may be generated.

35. By progressive polarization in a wire, may not stationary polarization or magnetism be created; and reciprocally by magnetic polarity may not progressive polarization be excited?

36. Might not the difficulty, above suggested, of the incompetency of any imaginable polarization to produce all the varieties of electrical excitement which facts require for explanation, be surmounted by supposing intensity to result from an accumulation of free electric polarized particles, and quantity from a still greater accumulation of such particles, polarized in a latent state or in chemical combination?

37. There are it would seem many indications in favour of the idea that electric excitement may be due to a forced polarity, but in endeavouring to define the state thus designated, or to explain by means of it the diversities of electrical charges, currents and effects, I have always felt the incompetency of any hypothesis which I could imagine. How are we to explain the insensibility of a gold-leaf electroscope to a galvanized wire, or the indifference of a magnetic needle to the most intensely electrified surfaces?

38. Possibly the Franklinian hypothesis may be combined with that above suggested, so that an electrical current may be constituted of an imponderable fluid in a state of polarization, the two electricities being the consequence of the position of the poles, or their presentation. Positive electricity may be the result of an accumulation of electric particles, presenting poles of one kind; negative, from a like accumulation of the same matter with a presentation of the opposite poles, inducing of course an opposite polarity. The condensation of the electric matter, within ponderable matter, may vary in obedience to a property analogous to that which determines the capacity for heat, and the different influence of dielectrics upon the process of electrical induction may arise from this source of variation.

With the highest esteem, I am yours truly,

ROBERT HARE.

*An Answer to* Dr. Hare's *Letter on certain Theoretical Opinions.*

MY DEAR SIR,

i. YOUR kind remarks have caused me very carefully to re-
vise the general principles of the view of *static induction* which
I have ventured to put forth, with the very natural fear that as
it did not obtain your acceptance, it might be founded in error;
for it is not a mere complimentary expression when I say I have
very great respect for your judgement. As the reconsideration
of them has not made me aware that they differ amongst themselves or with facts, the resulting impression on my mind is, that
I must have expressed my meaning imperfectly, and I have a
hope that when more clearly stated my words may gain your
approbation. I feel that many of the words in the language
of electrical science possess much meaning; and yet their interpretation by different philosophers often varies more or less,
so that they do not carry exactly the same idea to the minds
of different men: this often renders it difficult, when such words
force themselves into use, to express with brevity as much as,
and no more than, one really wishes to say.

ii. My theory of induction (as set forth in Series xi. xii. and
xiii.) makes no assertion as to the nature of electricity, or at all
questions any of the theories respecting that subject (1667.).
It does not even include the origination of the developed or
excited state of the power or powers; but taking that as it is
given by experiment and observation, it concerns itself only
with the arrangement of the force in its communication to a
distance in that particular yet very general phenomenon called
*static induction* (1668.). It is neither the nature nor the
amount of the force which it decides upon, but solely its mode
of distribution.

iii. Bodies whether conductors or non-conductors can be
*charged*. The word *charge* is equivocal: sometimes it means
that state which a glass tube acquires when rubbed by silk, or
which the prime conductor of a machine acquires when the
latter is in action; at other times it means the state of a Leyden jar or similar inductive arrangement when it is said to be
charged. In the first case the word means only the peculiar

condition of an electrified mass of matter considered by itself, and does not apparently involve the idea of induction; in the second it means the whole of the relations of two such masses charged in opposite states, and most intimately connected by inductive action.

iv. Let three insulated metallic spheres A, B and C be placed in a line, and not in contact: let A be electrified positively, and then C uninsulated; besides the general action of the whole system upon all surrounding matter, there will occur a case of inductive action amongst the three balls, which may be considered apart, as the type and illustration of the whole of my theory: A will be charged positively; B will acquire the negative state at the surface towards A, and the positive state at the surface furthest from it; and C will be charged negatively.

v. The ball B will be in what is often called a polarized condition, *i. e.* opposite parts will exhibit the opposite electrical states, and the two sums of these opposite states will be exactly equal to each other. A and C will not be in this polarized state, for they will each be, as it is said, charged (iii.), the one positively, the other negatively, and they will present no polarity as far as this particular act of induction (iv.) is concerned.

vi. That one part of A is more positive than another part does not render it polar in the sense in which that word has just been used. We are considering a particular case of induction, and have to throw out of view the states of those parts not under the inductive action. Or if any embarrassment still arise from the fact that A is not uniformly charged all over, then we have merely to surround it with balls, such as B and C, on every side, so that its state shall be alike on every part of its surface (because of the uniformity of its inductive influence in all directions) and then that difficulty will be removed. A therefore is charged, but not polarly; B assumes a polar condition; and C is charged inducteously (1483.), being by the prime influence of A brought into the opposite or negative electrical state through the intervention of the intermediate and polarized ball B.

vii. Simple charge therefore does not imply polarity in the body charged. Inductive charge (applying that term to the sphere B and all bodies in a similar condition (v.)) does (1672.). The word charge as applied to a Leyden jar, or to the *whole* of any inductive arrangement, by including *all* the effects, comprehends of course both these states.

viii. As another expression of my theory, I will put the following case. Suppose a metallic sphere C, formed of a thin shell a foot in diameter; suppose also in the centre of it another metallic sphere A only an inch in diameter; suppose the central sphere A charged positively with electricity to the amount we will say of 100; it would act by induction through the air, lac, or other insulator between it and the large sphere C; the interior of the latter would be negative, and its exterior positive, and the sum of the positive force upon the whole of the external surface would be 100. The sphere C would in fact be polarized (v.) as regards its inner and outer surfaces.

ix. Let us now conceive that instead of mere air, or other insulating dielectric, within C between it and A, there is a thin metallic concentric sphere B six inches in diameter. This will make no difference in the ultimate result, for the charged ball A will render the inner and outer surfaces of this sphere B negative and positive, and it again will render the inner and outer surfaces of the large sphere C negative and positive, the sum of the positive forces on the outside of C being still 100.

x. Instead of one intervening sphere let us imagine 100 or 1000 concentric with each other, and separated by insulating matter, still the same final result will occur; the central ball will act inductrically, the influence originating with it will be carried on from sphere to sphere, and positive force equal to 100 will appear on the outside of the external sphere.

xi. Again, imagine that all these spheres are subdivided into myriads of particles, each being effectively insulated from its neighbours (1679.), still the same final result will occur; the inductric body A will polarize all these, and having its influence carried on by them in their newly acquired state, will exert precisely the same amount of action on the external sphere C as before, and positive force equal to 100 will appear on its outer surface.

xii. Such a state of the space between the inductric and inducteous surfaces represents what I believe to be the state of an insulating dielectric under inductive influence; the particles

of which by the theory are assumed to be conductors individually, but not to one another (1669.).

xiii. In asserting that 100 of positive force will appear on
the outside of the external sphere under all these variations, I
presume I am saying no more than what every electrician will
admit. Were it not so, then positive and negative electricities
could exist by themselves, and without relation to each other
(1169. 1177.), or they could exist in proportions not equivalent to each other. There are plenty of experiments, both old
and new, which prove the truth of the principle, and I need
not go further into it here.

xiv. Suppose a plane to pass through the centre of this spherical system, and conceive that instead of the space between
the central ball A and the external sphere C being occupied
by a uniform distribution of the equal metallic particles, three
times as many were grouped in the one half to what occurred
in the other half, the insulation of the particles being always
preserved : then more of the inductric influence of A would
be conveyed outwards to the inner surface of the sphere C,
through that half of the space where the greater number of
metallic particles existed, than through the other half: still the
exterior of the outer sphere C would be uniformly charged
with positive electricity, the amount of which would be 100 as
before.

xv. The actions of the two portions of space, as they have
just been supposed to be constituted (xiv.), is as if they possessed two different *specific inductive capacities* (1296.) ; but
I by no means intend to say, that *specific inductive capacity*
depends in all cases upon the number of conducting particles
of which the dielectric is formed, or upon their vicinity. The
full cause of the evident difference of inductive capacity of different bodies is a problem as yet to be solved.

xvi. In my papers I speak of all induction as being dependent
on the action of contiguous particles, *i. e.* I assume that insulating bodies consist of particles which are conductors individually (1669.), but do not conduct to each other provided the
intensity of action to which they are subject is beneath a given
amount (1326. 1674. 1675.) ; and that when the inductric body
acts upon conductors at a distance, it does so by polarizing
(1298. 1670.) all those particles which occur in the portion of

dielectric between it and them. I have used the term *contiguous* (1164. 1673.), but have I hope sufficiently expressed the meaning I attach to it; first by saying at par. 1615, " the next existing particle being considered as the contiguous one"; then in a note to par. 1665, by the words, "I mean by contiguous particles those which are next to each other, not that there is no space between them;" and further by the note to par. 1164. of the octavo edition of my Researches, which is as follows : " The word contiguous is perhaps not the best that might have been used here and elsewhere, for as particles do not touch each other it is not strictly correct. I was induced to employ it because in its common acceptation it enabled me to state the theory plainly and with facility. By contiguous particles, I mean those which are next."

xvii. Finally, my reasons for adopting the molecular theory of induction were the phenomena of electrolytic discharge (1164. 1343.), of induction in curved lines (1166. 1215.), of specific inductive capacity (1167. 1252.), of penetration and return action (1245.), of difference of conduction and insulation (1320.), of polar forces (1665.), &c. &c., but for these reasons and any strength or value they may possess I refer to the papers themselves.

xviii. I will now turn to such parts of your critical remarks as may require attention. A man who advances what he thinks to be new truths, and to develope principles which profess to be more consistent with the laws of nature than those already in the field, is liable to be charged, first with self-contradiction; then with the contradiction of facts; or he may be obscure in his expression, and so justly subject to certain queries; or he may be found in non-agreement with the opinions of others. The first and second points are very important, and every one subject to such charges must be anxious to be made aware of, and also to set himself free from or acknowledge them; the third is also a fault to be removed if possible; the fourth is a matter of but small consequence in comparison with the other three; for as every man who has the courage, not to say rashness, of forming an opinion of his own, thinks it better than any from which he differs, so it is only deeper investigation, and most generally future investigators, who can decide which is in the right.

xix. I am afraid I shall find it rather difficult to refer to your letter. I will, however, reckon the paragraphs in order from the top of each page, considering that the first which has its *beginning* first in the page[1]. In referring to my own matter I will employ the usual figures for the paragraphs of the Experimental Researches, and small Roman numerals for those of this communication.

xx. At paragraph 3, you say, you cannot reconcile my language at 1615, with that at 1165. In the latter place I have said I believe *ordinary induction* in all cases to be an action of *contiguous* particles, and in the former assuming a very hypothetical case, that of a vacuum, I have said nothing in my theory forbids that a charged particle in the centre of a vacuum should act on the particle next to it, though that should be half an inch off. With the meaning which I have carefully attached to the word contiguous (xvi.) I see no contradiction here in the terms used, nor any natural impossibility or improbability in such an action. Nevertheless all *ordinary* induction is to me an action of contiguous particles, being particles at insensible distances: induction across a vacuum is not an ordinary instance, and yet I do not perceive that it cannot come under the same principles of action.

xxi. As an illustration of my meaning, I may refer to the case, parallel with mine, as to the extreme difference of interval between the acting particles or bodies, of the modern views of the radiation and conduction of heat. In radiation the rays leave the hot particles and pass occasionally through great distances to the next particle, fitted to receive them: in conduction, where the heat passes from the hotter particles to those which are contiguous and form part of the same mass, still the passage is considered to be by a process precisely like that of radiation; and though the effects are, as is well known, extremely different in their appearance, it cannot as yet be shown that the principle of communication is not the same in both.

xxii. So on this point respecting contiguous particles and induction across half an inch of vacuum, I do not see that I am in contradiction with myself or with any natural law or fact.

[1] We shall change Prof. Faraday's references for the numbers which we have attached to Dr. Hare's letter, and refer thus, par. 23, &c.—Ed. Phil. Mag.

xxiii. Paragraph 4 is answered by the above remarks and by viii. ix. x.

xxiv. Paragraph 5 is answered according to my theory by viii. ix. x. xi. xii. and xiii.

xxv. Paragraph 6 is answered, except in the matter of opinion (xviii.), according to my theory by xvi. The conduction of heat referred to in the paragraph itself, will, as it appears to me, bear no comparison with the phenomenon of electrical induction:—the first refers to the distant influence of an agent which travels by a very slow process, the second to one where distant influence is simultaneous, so to speak, with the origin of the force at the place of action:—the first refers to an agent which is represented by the idea of one imponderable fluid, the second to an agency better represented probably by the idea of two fluids, or at least by two forces:—the first involves no polar action, nor any of its consequences, the second depends essentially on such actions;—with the first, if a certain portion be originally employed in the centre of a spherical arrangement, but a small part appears ultimately at the surface; with the second, an amount of force appears instantly at the surface (viii. ix. x. xi. xii. xiii. xiv.) exactly equal to the exciting or moving force, which is still at the centre.

xxvi. Paragraph 13 involves another charge of self-contradiction, from which, therefore, I will next endeavour to set myself free. You say I " correctly allege that it is impossible to charge a portion of matter with one electric force without the other (see par. 1177). But if all this be true, how can there be a *positively excited particle*? (see par. 1616). Must not every particle be excited negatively if it be excited positively? Must it not have a negative as well as a positive pole?" Now I have not said exactly what you attribute to me; my words are, " it is impossible, experimentally, to charge a portion of matter with one electric force *independently* of the other: charge always implies *induction*, for it can in no instance be effected without (1177.)." I can, however, easily perceive how my words have conveyed a very different idea to your mind, and probably to others, than that I meant to express.

xxvii. Using the word *charge* in its simplest meaning (iii. iv.), I think that a body *can* be charged with one electric force without the other, that body being considered in relation to itself only.    But I think that such charge cannot exist without induction (1178.), or independently of what is called the development of an equal amount of the other electric force, not in itself, but in the neighbouring consecutive particles of the surrounding dielectric, and through them of the facing particles of the uninsulated surrounding conducting bodies, which, under the circumstances, terminate as it were the particular case of induction.    I have no idea, therefore, that a particle when charged must itself of necessity be polar; the spheres A B C of iv., v., vi., vii., fully illustrate my views (672.).

xxviii. Paragraph 20 includes the question, " is this consistent?" implying self-contradiction, which, therefore, I proceed to notice.    The question arises out of the possibility of glass being a (slow) conductor or not of electricity, a point questioned also in the two preceding paragraphs.    I believe that it is.    I have charged small Leyden jars made of thin flint glass tube with electricity, taken out the charging wires, sealed them up hermetically, and after two and three years have opened and found no charge in them.    I will refer you also to Belli's curious experiments upon the successive charges of a jar and the successive return of portions of these charges[1].    I will also refer to the experiments with the shell lac hemisphere, especially that described in 1237. of my Researches; also the experiment in 1246.    I cannot conceive how, in these cases, the air in the vicinity of the coating could gradually relinquish to it a portion of free electricity, conveyed into it by what I called convection, since in the first experiment quoted (1237.), when the return was gradual, there was *no coating*; and in the second (1246.), when there was *a coating*, the return action was most sudden and instantaneous.

xxix. Paragraphs 21 and 22 perhaps only require a few words of explanation.    In a charged Leyden jar I have considered the two opposite forces on the inductric and inducteous surfaces as being directed towards each other through the glass of the jar, provided the jar have no projection of its inner coating, and is uninsulated on the outside (1682.).    When discharge by a wire or discharger, or any other of the many arrangements used for that purpose is effected, these supply the " some other directions" spoken of (1682. 1683.).

[1] Bibliotheca Italiana, 1837, lxxxv. p. 417.

xxx.  The inquiry in paragraph 23, I should answer by saying,
that the process is the same as that by which the polarity of the
sphere B (iv., v.,) would be neutralized if the spheres A and C
were made to communicate by a metallic wire; or that by which
the 100 or 1000 intermediate spheres (x.) or the myriads of polarized conducting particles (xi.) would be discharged, if the
inner sphere A, and the outer one C, were brought into communication by an insulated wire; a circumstance which would
not in the least affect the condition of the power on the exterior of the globe C.

xxxi.  The obscurity in my papers, which has led to your remarks in paragraph 25, arises, as it appears to me (after my
own imperfect expression), from the uncertain or double meaning of the word discharge.  You say, " if discharge involves a
return to the same state in vitreous particles, the same must
be true in those of the metallic wire.  Wherefore then are
these dissipated when the discharge is sufficiently powerful?"
A jar is said to be discharged when its charged state is reduced by any means, and it is found in its first indifferent condition.  The word is then used simply to express the state of
the apparatus; and so I have used it in the expressions cri-
ticised in paragraph 21, already referred to.  The process of
discharge, or the mode by which the jar is brought into the
discharged state, may be subdivided, as of various kinds; and
I have spoken of conductive (1320.), electrolytic (1343.), disruptive (1359.), and convective (1562.) discharge, any one of
which may cause the discharge of the jar, or the discharge of
the inductive arrangements described in this letter (xxx.), the
action of the particles in any one of these cases being entirely
different from the mere return action of the polarized particles
of the glass of the jar, or the polarized globe B (v.), to their
first state.  My view of the relation of insulators and conductors, as bodies of one class, is given at 1320. 1675. &c. of the
Researches; but I do not think the particles of the good conductors acquire an intensity of polarization anything like that
of the particles of bad conductors; on the contrary, I conceive
that the contiguous polarized particles (1670.) of good conductors discharge to each other when their polarity is at a very
low degree of intensity (1326. 1338. 1675.).  The question of
why are the metallic particles dissipated when the charge is

sufficiently powerful, is one that my theory is not called upon at present to answer, since it will be acknowledged by all, that the dissipation is not necessary to discharge. That different effects ensue upon the subjection of bodies to different degrees of the same power, is common enough in experimental philosophy; thus, one degree of heat will merely make water hot, whilst a higher degree will *dissipate* it as steam, and a lower will convert it into ice.

xxxii. The next most important point, as it appears to me, is that contained in paragraphs 16 and 17. I have said (1330.), " what then is to separate the principle of these two extremes, perfect conduction and perfect insulation, from each other, since the moment we leave in the smallest degree perfection at either extremity we involve the element of perfection at the opposite end?" and upon this you say, might not this query be made with as much reason in the case of motion and rest?—and in any case of the intermixture of opposite qualities, may it not be said, the moment we leave the element of perfection at one end, we involve the element of perfection at the opposite?—may it not be said of light and darkness, or of opakeness and translucency? and so forth.

xxxiii. I admit that these questions are very properly put; not that I go to the full extent of them all, as for instance that of motion and rest; but I do not perceive their bearing upon the question, of whether conduction and insulation are different properties, dependent upon two different modes of action of the particles of the substances respectively possessing these actions, or whether they are only differences in *degree* of one and the same mode of action? In this question, however, lies the whole gist of the matter. To explain my views, I will put a case or two. In former times a principle or force of levity was admitted, as well as of gravity, and certain variations in the weights of bodies were supposed to be caused by different combinations of substances possessing these two principles. In later times, the levity principle has been discarded; and though we still have imponderable substances, yet the phenomena causing weight have been accounted for by one force or principle only, that of gravity; the difference in the gravitation of different bodies being considered due to differences in *degree* of this *one force* resident in them all. Now no one can for a moment suppose that it is the same thing philosophically to assume either the two forces or the one force for the explanation of the phenomena in question.

xxxiv. Again, at one time there was a distinction taken between the principle of heat and that of cold : at present that theory is done away with, and the phenomena of heat and cold are referred to the same class, (as I refer those of insulation and conduction to one class,) and to the influence of different degrees of the same power. But no one can say that the two theories, namely, that including but one positive principle, and that including two, are alike.

xxxv. Again, there is the theory of one electric fluid and also that of two. One explains by the difference in degree or quantity of one fluid, what the other attributes to a variation in the quantity and relation of two fluids. Both cannot be true. That they have nearly equal hold of our assent, is only a proof of our ignorance ; and it is certain, whichever is the false theory, is at present holding the minds of its supporters in bondage, and is greatly retarding the progress of science.

xxxvi. I think it therefore important, if we can, to ascertain whether insulation and conduction are cases of the same class, just as it is important to know that hot and cold are phenomena of the same kind. As it is of consequence to show that smoke ascends and a stone descends in obedience to one property of matter, so I think it is of consequence to show that one body insulates and another conducts only in consequence of a difference in degree of one common property which they both possess ; and that in both cases the effects are consistent with my theory of induction.

xxxvii. I now come to what may be considered as queries in your letter which I ought to answer. Paragraph 8 contains one. As I concede that particles on opposite sides of a vacuum may perhaps act on each other, you ask, " wherefore is the received theory of the mode in which the excited surface of a Leyden jar induces in the opposite surface a contrary state, objectionable ?" My reasons for thinking the excited surface does not directly induce upon the opposite surface, &c., is, first, my belief that the glass consists of particles conductive in themselves, but insulated as respects each other (xvii.); and next, that in the arrangement given iv., ix., or x., A does not induce directly on C, but through the intermediate masses or particles of conducting matter.

xxxviii. In the next paragraph, the question is rather implied than asked—what do I mean by polarity? I had hoped that the paragraphs 1669. 1670. 1671. 1672. 1679. 1686. 1687. 1688. 1699. 1700. 1701. 1702. 1703. 1704. in the Researches, would have been sufficient to convey my meaning, and I am inclined to think you had not perhaps seen them when your letter was written. They, and the observations already made (v., xxvi.), with the case given (iv., v.), will, I think, be sufficient as my answer. The sense of the word *polarity* is so diverse when applied to light, to a crystal, to a magnet, to the voltaic battery, and so different in all these cases to that of the word when applied to the state of a conductor under induction (v.), that I thought it safer to use the phrase " species of polarity," than any other, which being more expressive would pledge me further than I wished.

xxxix. Paragraph 11 involves a mistake of my views. I do not consider bodies which are charged by friction or otherwise, as polarized, or as having their particles polarized (iii., iv., xxvii.). This paragraph and the next do not require, therefore, any further remark, especially after what I have said of polarity above (xxxviii.).

xl. And now, my dear sir, I think I ought to draw my reply to an end. The paragraphs which remain unanswered refer, I think, only to differences of opinion, or else, not even to differences, but opinions regarding which I have not ventured to judge. These opinions I esteem as of the utmost importance; but that is a reason which makes me the rather desirous to decline entering upon their consideration, inasmuch as on many of their connected points I have formed no decided notion, but am constrained by ignorance and the contrast of facts to hold my judgment as yet in suspense. It is, indeed, to me an annoying matter to find how many subjects there are in electrical science, on which, if I were asked for an opinion, I should have to say, I cannot tell,—I do not know; but, on the other hand, it is encouraging to think that these are they which if pursued industriously, experimentally, and thoughtfully, will lead to new discoveries. Such a subject, for instance, occurs in the currents produced by dynamic induction, which you say

it will be admitted do not require for their production intervening ponderable atoms.   For my own part, I more than half
incline to think they do require these intervening particles, that
is, where any particles intervene (1729. 1733. 1738.).   But on
this question, as on many others, I have not yet made up my
mind.   Allow me, therefore, here to conclude my letter; and
believe me to be, with the highest esteem,

My dear Sir,<br>
Your obliged and faithful Servant,

Royal Institution, April 18, 1840.                    M. Faraday.

---

A second letter was written by Dr. Hare to Mr. Faraday on
the same subject, which may be found in the American Journal
of Science, vol. xli. p. 2, or the Lond. and Edinb. Phil. Mag.
1841, vol. xviii. p. 465.

---

## *On* Dr. Hare's *Second Letter, and on the Chemical and Contact Theories of the Voltaic Battery*[1].

### *To R. Taylor, Esq.*

My dear Sir,

You are aware that considerations regarding health have
prevented me from working or reading in science for the last
two years.   This will account to you for my ignorance of the
circumstance that you had reprinted Dr. Hare's second letter
to me[2]; and I believe I knew it only for the first time a week
or two ago, on beginning to read up.   As some persons think
a letter unanswered is also unanswerable, I write merely to say,
that when it was sent to me as printed in Silliman's Journal, I
sent a brief letter back, declining to enter into discussion, since
I had nothing more to say than had been said, and still thought
that that was sufficient to enable my own mind to rest in the
view it had taken of static induction, &c.   My reason for declining was no want of respect to Dr. Hare, but a strong conviction that controversial reply and rejoinder is but a vain occu-

<hr>

[1] Lond. and Edinb. Phil. Mag., 1843, vol. xxiii.
[2] Ibid. 1841, vol. xviii. p. 465.

pation. Professor Silliman wrote me word that he had very unfortunately lost my brief note, but hoped to find it and print it[1]. Since then I have forgotten the matter, and only renew it

---

[1] I have recently found the rough copy of this letter and venture to print it as a note.—M. F., June 1844.

Royal Institution, London, 6th May 1841.

My dear Sir,

I received a week or two ago the printed copy of your second letter, dated January 1, 1841, and am greatly obliged by it, both as it is another expression of your kindness, and also an evident proof that you think the views I have ventured to put forth on Electrical Induction are worthy of notice.

You must excuse me however for several reasons from answering it at any length: the first is my distaste for controversy, which is so great, that I would on no account our correspondence should acquire that character. I have often seen it do great harm, and yet remember few cases in natural knowledge where it has helped much either to pull down error or advance truth. Criticism, on the other hand, is of much value ; and when criticism, such as yours, has done its duty, then it is for other minds than those either of the author or critic to decide upon and acknowledge the right.

A second reason is, that I do not wish to be drawn into statements more precise than are my thoughts, and this I have already expressed in my former letter (xl.).

A third is, that I do not find anything in your last communication which creates any difficulty in my mind with respect to my view of electrical induction, nor any important point which is not answered by my papers generally, or by my former letter to you. In saying this, I keep in mind paragraphs i., xviii., and also xvii. and xxxi. of mine to you. Do not think however that I have the vanity to suppose that this my opinion is of any importance to the scientific world, or any answer to your letter ; it is merely of consequence as giving a reason why I need not go further into the statement of that which at present appears to me already correctly stated.

The fourth reason is, that judging from what I have been able to observe, I do not perceive that the statement I have endeavoured to give of my theory leads other persons to apprehend its principles in a manner seriously different from that which I should desire ; and such being the case, I can have nothing more to say, since they are the judges, and have the evidence as fairly before them as present facts and circumstances permit.

I am, my dear Sir, your obliged and faithful Servant,

*Dr. Hare, &c. &c. &c.* M. Faraday.

Dear Sir,

Will you let me trouble you with the above for your Journal, as my answer to Dr. Hare's second letter to me?

Ever your obliged Servant,

*Professor Silliman, &c. &c. &c.* M. Faraday.

to give the same sort of answer to the letter as contained in your Journal.

I perceive also in your Magazine several attacks, from Germany, Italy and Belgium, upon the chemical theory of the voltaic battery, and some of them upon experiments of mine. For my own part I refrain from publicly noticing these arguments, simply because there is nothing in them which suggests to my mind a new thought illustrative of the subject, or gives any ground for a change in my opinion. But whilst speaking on this point I cannot help expressing a wish that some of the advocates of the contact theory would touch upon the consideration which, up to this time, seems to have been most carefully avoided, namely the unphilosophical nature of the assumed contact force, as I have endeavoured to express it in par. 2065 to 2073 of my "Experimental Researches," and as Dr. Roget has expressed it in words which I have appended in a note to my paper. Such a consideration seems to me to remove the *foundation itself* of the contact theory. I wish you could be persuaded to think it worth while to reprint those three pages in your Magazine [1]. As far as I can perceive, they express a fundamental principle which cannot be set aside or evaded by a philosophical mind possessing only a moderate degree of strictness in its reasonings; and I must confess, that until some answer, or some show of answer in the form of assumption or otherwise, is made to that expression of what I believe to be a law of nature, I shall feel very little inclined to attach much importance to facts which, though urged in favour of the contact theory, are ever found by the partisans of the chemical theory just as favourable to, and consistent with, their peculiar views.

I am, my dear Sir,
Very faithfully yours,
M. FARADAY.

Royal Institution, March 11, 1843.

[1] We purpose to insert these pages in our next Number.—ED. Phil. Mag.

*On some supposed forms of Lightning*[1].

*To the Editors of the Philosophical Magazine and Journal.*

Gentlemen,

THE magnificent display of lightning which we had on the evening of the 27th of last month, and its peculiar appearance to crowds of observers at London, with the consequent impressions on their minds, induce me to trouble you with a brief letter on certain supposed appearances and forms of lightning, respecting which the judgment of even good observers is often in error.

When, after a serene sky, or one that is not overcast, thunder-clouds form in the distance, the observer sees the clouds and the illumination of the lightning displayed before him as a magnificent picture; and what he often takes to be forked lightning (*i. e.* the actual flash, and not a reflexion of it), appears to run through the clouds in the most beautiful manner. This was the case on that evening to those who, being in London, observed the storm in the west, about nine o'clock, when the clouds were at a distance of twenty miles or more; and I have very frequently observed the same effect from our southern coasts over the sea.   In many of these cases, that which is thought to be the electric discharge is only the illuminated edge of a cloud, beyond and behind which the real discharge occurs.   It is in its nature like the bright enlightened edge which a dark well-defined cloud often presents when between the sun and the observer; and even the moon also frequently produces similar appearances.   In the case of its production by lightning and distant clouds, the line is so bright by comparison with the previous state of the clouds and sky, so sudden and brief in its existence, so perfectly defined, and of such a form, as to lead every one at the first moment to think it is the lightning itself which appears.

But the forms which this line assumes, being dependent on the forms of the clouds, vary much, and have led to many mistakes about the shape of the lightning flash.   Often, when the lightning is supposed to be seen darting from one cloud to another, it is only this illuminated edge which the observer

[1] Lond. and Edinb. Phil. Mag., 1841, vol. xix. p. 104.

sees.  On other occasions, when he was sure he saw it ascend,
it was simply this line more brilliant at its upper than at its
lower part.   Some writers have described curved flashes of
lightning, the electric fluid having parted from the clouds,
gone obliquely downwards to the sea, and then turned upwards
to the clouds again: this effect I have occasionally seen, and
have always found it to be merely the illuminated edge of a
cloud.

I have seen cases of this kind in which the flash appeared
to divide in its course, one stream separating into two; and
when flashes seen at a distance are supposed to exhibit this
rare condition, it is very important the observer should be
aware of this very probable cause of deception.

I have also frequently seen, and others with me, a flash
having an apparently sensible duration, as if it were a momentary stream, rather than that sudden, brief flash which the
electric spark always presents, whose duration even Wheatstone could not appreciate.   This I attribute to two or three
flashes occurring very suddenly in succession at the same place,
or nearly so, and illuminating the same edge of a cloud.

The effect I have described can frequently be easily traced
to its cause, and when thus traced best prepares the mind to
appreciate the mistakes it may lead, and has led, to in the
character, shape and condition of the lightning flash.   It often
happens at the sea-side, that, after a fine day, clouds will towards evening collect over the sea on the horizon, and lightning will flash about and amongst them, recurring at intervals
as short as two or three seconds, for an hour or more together.
At such times the observer may think he sees the lightning of
a flash; but if he waits till the next illumination, or some future
one, takes place, he will perceive that the flash appears a second time in the same place, and with the same form; or perhaps it has travelled a little distance to the left or right, and
yet has the same form as before.   Sometimes an apparent flash,
having the same shape, has occurred three or four times in
succession; and sometimes it has happened that a certain
shaped flash having appeared in a certain place, other flashes
have appeared in other places, then the first has reappeared in
its place, and even the others again in their places.   Now in all
these cases it was simply the illuminated edges of clouds that

were seen, and not the real flashes of lightning.    These forms frequently exist in the cloud, and yet are not distinguishable till the lightning occurs.    It is easy, however, to understand why they are then only developed, for that which appears in the distance to be one dull mass of cloud, distinguishable in figure only at its principal outline, often consists of many subordinate and well-shaped masses, which, when the lightning occurs amongst or beyond them, present forms and lines before unperceived.

The apparent duration, which I before spoke of, is merely a case of very rapidly recurring flashes, and may, by a careful observer, be easily connected with that which I have now proposed as the best test of the nature of the phenomena.

There are some other circumstances which will help to distinguish the effect I have thus endeavoured to describe from the true appearance of the lightning flash, as the apparent thickness, sometimes, of the supposed flash, and its degree of illumination; but I have, I think, said enough to call attention to the point; and, considering how often the philosopher is, in respect to the character of these appearances, obliged to depend upon the report of casual observers, the tendency of whose minds is generally rather to give way to their surprise than to simplify what may seem remarkable, I hope I have not said too much.

I am, Gentlemen, your obedient Servant,

M. Faraday.

June 22, 1841.

---

### On Static Electrical Inductive Action[1].

### *To R. Phillips, Esq., F.R.S.*

Dear Phillips,

Perhaps you may think the following experiments worth notice; their value consists in their power to give a very precise and decided idea to the mind respecting certain principles of inductive electrical action, which I find are by many accepted with a degree of doubt or obscurity that takes away

---

[1] Lond. and Edinb. Phil. Mag., 1843, vol. xxii.

much of their importance: they are the expression and proof of certain parts of my view of induction[1].   Let A in the diagram represent an insulated pewter ice-pail ten and a half inches high and seven inches diameter, connected by a wire with a delicate gold-leaf electrometer E, and let C be a round brass ball insulated by a dry thread of white silk, three or four feet in length, so as to remove the influence of the hand holding it from the ice-pail below. Let A be perfectly discharged, then let C be charged at a distance by a machine or Leyden jar, and introduced into A as in the figure.  If C be positive, E also will diverge positively; if C be taken away, E will collapse perfectly, the apparatus being in good order.  As C enters the vessel A the divergence of E will increase until C is about three inches below the edge of the vessel, and will remain quite steady and unchanged for any greater depression.   This shows that at that distance the inductive action of C is entirely exerted upon the interior of A, and not in any degree directly upon external objects.  If C be made to touch the bottom of A, *all* its charge is communicated to A; there is no longer any inductive action between C and A, and C, upon being withdrawn and examined, is found perfectly discharged.

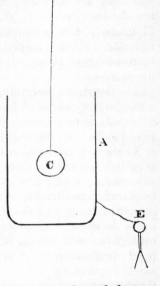

These are all well-known and recognised actions, but being a little varied, the following conclusions may be drawn from them.   If C be merely suspended in A, it acts upon it by induction, evolving electricity of its own kind on the outside of A; but if C touch A its electricity is then communicated to it, and the electricity that is afterwards upon the outside of A

---

[1] See Experimental Researches, Par. 1295, &c., 1667, &c., and Answer to Dr. Hare, Phil. Mag., 1840, N. S. vol. xvii. p. 56. viii. (or page 264 of this volume.)

may be considered as that which was originally upon the carrier C. As this change, however, produces no effect upon the leaves of the electrometer, it proves that the electricity *induced* by C and the electricity *in* C are accurately equal in amount and power.

Again, if C charged be held equidistant from the bottom and sides of A at one moment, and at another be held as close to the bottom as possible without discharging to A, still the divergence remains absolutely unchanged, showing that whether C acts at a considerable distance or at the very smallest distance, the amount of its force is the same. So also if it be held excentric and near to the side of the ice-pail in one place, so as to make the inductive action take place in lines expressing almost every degree of force in different directions, still the sum of their forces is the same constant quantity as that obtained before; for the leaves alter not. Nothing like expansion or coercion of the electric force appears under these varying circumstances.

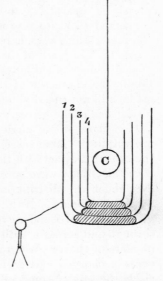

I can now describe experiments with many concentric metallic vessels arranged as in the diagram, where four ice-pails are represented insulated from each other by plates of shell-lac on which they respectively stand. With this system the charged carrier C acts precisely as with the single vessel, so that the intervention of many conducting plates causes no difference in the amount of inductive effect. If C touch the inside of vessel 4, still the leaves are unchanged. If 4 be taken out by a silk thread, the leaves perfectly collapse; if it be introduced again, they open out to the same degree as before. If 4 and 3 be connected by a wire let down between them by a silk thread, the leaves remain the same, and so they still remain if 3 and 2 be connected by a similar wire; yet all the electricity originally on the carrier and acting at a considerable distance, is now on the outside of 2, and acting through only a small non-conducting space. If at last it be communicated to the outside of 1, still the leaves remain unchanged.

Again, consider the charged carrier C in the centre of the system, the divergence of the electrometer measures its inductive influence; this divergence remains the same whether 1 be there alone, or whether all four vessels be there; whether these vessels be separate as to insulation, or whether 2, 3 and 4 be connected so as to represent a very thick metallic vessel, or whether all four vessels be connected.

Again, if in place of the metallic vessels 2, 3, 4, a thick vessel of shell-lac or of sulphur be introduced, or if any other variation in the character of the substance within the vessel 1 be made, still not the slightest change is by that caused upon the divergence of the leaves.

If in place of one carrier many carriers in different positions are within the inner vessel, there is no interference of one with the other; they act with the same amount of force outwardly as if the electricity were spread uniformly over one carrier, however much the distribution on each carrier may be disturbed by its neighbours. If the charge of one carrier be by contact given to vessel 4 and distributed over it, still the others act through and across it with the same final amount of force; and no state of charge given to any of the vessels 1, 2, 3 or 4, prevents a charged carrier introduced within 4 acting with precisely the same amount of force as if they were uncharged. If pieces of shell-lac, slung by white silk thread and excited, be introduced into the vessel, they act exactly as the metallic carriers, except that their charge cannot be communicated by contact to the metallic vessels.

Thus a certain amount of electricity acting within the centre of the vessel A exerts exactly the same power externally, whether it act by induction through the space between it and A, or whether it be transferred by conduction to A, so as absolutely to destroy the previous induction within. Also, as to the inductive action, whether the space between C and A be filled with air, or with shell-lac or sulphur, having above twice the specific inductive capacity of air; or contain many concentric shells of conducting matter; or be nine-tenths filled with

conducting matter, or be metal on one side and shell-lac on the
other; or whatever other means be taken to vary the forces,
either by variation of distance or substance, or actual charge
of the matter in this space, still the amount of action is precisely the same.

Hence if a body be charged, whether it be a particle or a
mass, there is nothing about its action which can at all consist
with the idea of exaltation or extinction; the amount of force
is perfectly definite and unchangeable: or to those who in their
minds represent the idea of the electric force by a fluid, there
ought to be no notion of the compression or condensation of
this fluid within itself, or of its coercibility, as some understand that phrase. The only mode of affecting this force is
by connecting it with force of the same kind, either in the
same or the contrary direction. If we oppose to it force of
the contrary kind, we may *by discharge* neutralize the original
force, or we may *without discharge* connect them by the
simple laws and principles of static induction; but away from
induction, which is *always of the same kind*, there is no other
state of the power in a charged body; that is, there is no state
of static electric force corresponding to the terms of *simulated*
or *disguised* or *latent* electricity away from the ordinary principles of inductive action; nor is there any case where the
electricity is *more latent* or *more disguised* than when it exists
upon the charged conductor of an electrical machine and is
ready to give a powerful spark to any body brought near it.

A curious consideration arises from this perfection of inductive action. Suppose a thin uncharged metallic globe two or
three feet in diameter, insulated in the middle of a chamber,
and then suppose the space within this globe occupied by myriads of little vesicles or particles charged alike with electricity
(or differently), but each insulated from its neighbour and the
globe; their inductive power would be such that the outside
of the globe would be charged with a force equal to the sum of
*all* their forces, and any part of this globe (not charged of
itself) would give as long and powerful a spark to a body
brought near it as if the electricity of all the particles near and
distant were on the surface of the globe itself. If we pass
from this consideration to the case of a cloud, then, though we
cannot altogether compare the external surface of the cloud to

the metallic surface of the globe, yet the previous inductive effects upon the *earth* and its buildings are the same; and when a charged cloud is over the earth, although its electricity may be diffused over every one of its particles, and no important part of the *inductric* charge be accumulated upon its under surface, yet the induction upon the earth will be as strong as if all that portion of force which is directed towards the earth *were* upon that surface; and the state of the earth and its tendency to discharge to the cloud will also be as strong in the former as in the latter case. As to whether lightning-discharge begins first at the cloud or at the earth, that is a matter far more difficult to decide than is usually supposed[1]; theoretical notions would lead me to expect that in most cases, perhaps in all, it begins at the earth.   I am,

My dear Phillips, ever yours,

Royal Institution, Feb. 4, 1843.       M. FARADAY.

---

*A speculation touching Electric Conduction and the Nature of Matter*[2].

*To Richard Taylor, Esq.*

DEAR SIR,       Royal Institution, Jan. 25, 1844.

LAST Friday I opened the weekly evening-meetings here by a subject of which the above was the title, and had no intention of publishing the matter further, but as it involves the consideration and application of a few of those main elements of natural knowledge, facts, I thought an account of its nature and intention might not be unacceptable to you, and would at the same time serve as the record of my opinion and views, as far as they are at present formed.

The view of the atomic constitution of matter which I think is most prevalent, is that which considers the atom as a something material having a certain volume, upon which those powers were impressed at the creation, which have given it, from that

[1] Experimental Researches, Par. 1370, 1410, 1484.
[2] Lond. and Edinb. Phil. Mag., 1844, vol. xxiv. p. 136.

time to the present, the capability of constituting, when many atoms are congregated together into groups, the different substances whose effects and properties we observe. These, though grouped and held together by their powers, do not touch each other, but have intervening space, otherwise pressure or cold could not make a body contract into a smaller bulk, nor heat or tension make it larger; in liquids these atoms or particles are free to move about one another, and in vapours or gases they are also present, but removed very much further apart, though still related to each other by their powers.

The atomic doctrine is greatly used one way or another in this, our day, for the interpretation of phenomena, especially those of crystallography and chemistry, and is not so carefully distinguished from the facts, but that it often appears to him who stands in the position of student, as a statement of the facts themselves, though it is at best but an assumption; of the truth of which we can assert nothing, whatever we may say or think of its probability. The word atom, which can never be used without involving much that is purely hypothetical, is often *intended* to be used to express a simple fact; but good as the intention is, I have not yet found a mind that did habitually separate it from its accompanying temptations; and there can be no doubt that the words definite proportions, equivalents, primes, &c., which did and do express fully all the *facts* of what is usually called the atomic theory in chemistry, were dismissed because they were not expressive enough, and did not say all that was in the mind of him who used the word atom in their stead; they did not express the hypothesis as well as the fact.

But it is always safe and philosophic to distinguish, as much as is in our power, fact from theory; the experience of past ages is sufficient to show us the wisdom of such a course; and considering the constant tendency of the mind to rest on an assumption, and, when it answers every present purpose, to forget that it is an assumption, we ought to remember that it, in such cases, becomes a prejudice, and inevitably interferes, more or less, with a clear-sighted judgment. I cannot doubt but that he who, as a wise philosopher, has most power of penetrating the secrets of nature, and guessing by hypothesis at her mode of working, will also be most careful, for his own safe progress and that of others, to distinguish that knowledge which consists of assumption, by which I mean theory and hypothesis, from that which is the knowledge of facts and laws; never raising the former to the dignity or authority of the latter, nor confusing the latter more than is inevitable with the former.

Light and electricity are two great and searching investigators of the molecular structure of bodies, and it was whilst considering the probable nature of conduction and insulation in bodies not decomposable by the electricity to which they were subject, and the relation of electricity to space contemplated as void of that which by the atomists is called matter, that considerations something like those which follow were presented to my mind.

If the view of the constitution of matter already referred to be assumed to be correct, and I may be allowed to speak of the particles of matter and of the space between them (in water, or in the vapour of water for instance) as two different things, then space must be taken as the only continuous part, for the particles are considered as separated by space from each other. Space will permeate all masses of matter in every direction like a net, except that in place of meshes it will form cells, isolating each atom from its neighbours, and itself only being continuous.

Then take the case of a piece of shell-lac, a non-conductor, and it would appear at once from such a view of its atomic constitution that space is an insulator, for if it were a conductor the shell-lac could not insulate, whatever might be the relation as to conducting power of its material atoms; the space would be like a fine metallic web penetrating it in every direction, just as we may imagine of a heap of siliceous sand having all its pores filled with water; or as we may consider of a stick of black wax, which, though it contains an infinity of particles of conducting charcoal diffused through every part of it, cannot conduct, because a non-conducting body (a resin) intervenes and separates them one from another, like the supposed space in the lac.

Next take the case of a metal, platinum or potassium, constituted, according to the atomic theory, in the same manner. The metal is a conductor; but how can this be, except space be a conductor? for it is the only continuous part of the metal, and the atoms not only do not touch (by the theory), but as we shall see presently, must be assumed to be a considerable way apart. Space therefore must be a conductor, or else the metals could not conduct, but would be in the situation of the black sealing-wax referred to a little while ago.

But if space be a conductor, how then can shell-lac, sulphur, &c. insulate? for space permeates them in every direction. Or if space be an insulator, how can a metal or other similar body conduct?

It would seem, therefore, that in accepting the ordinary atomic theory, space may be proved to be a non-conductor in non-conducting bodies, and a conductor in conducting bodies, but the reasoning ends in this, a subversion of that theory altogether; for if space be an insulator it cannot exist in conducting bodies, and if it be a conductor it cannot exist in insulating bodies. Any ground of reasoning which tends to such conclusions as these must in itself be false.

In connexion with such conclusions we may consider shortly what are the probabilities that present themselves to the mind, if the extension of the atomic theory which chemists have imagined, be applied in conjunction with the conducting powers of metals. If the specific gravity of the metals be divided by the atomic numbers, it gives us the number of atoms, upon the hypothesis, in equal bulks of the metals. In the following table the first column of figures expresses nearly the number of atoms in, and the second column of figures the conducting power of, equal volumes of the metals named.

| Atoms. | | Conducting power. |
|---|---|---|
| 1·00 | gold | 6·00 |
| 1·00 | silver. | 4·66 |
| 1·12 | lead | 0·52 |
| 1·30 | tin | 1·00 |
| 2·20 | platinum | 1·04 |
| 2·27 | zinc | 1·80 |
| 2·87 | copper | 6·33 |
| 2·90 | iron | 1·00 |

So here iron, which contains the greatest number of atoms in a given bulk, is the worst conductor excepting one; gold, which contains the fewest, is nearly the best conductor. Not that these conditions are in inverse proportions, for copper, which contains nearly as many atoms as iron, conducts better

still than gold, and with above six times the power of iron.
Lead, which contains more atoms than gold, has only about
one-twelfth of its conducting power; lead, which is much
heavier than tin and much lighter than platina, has only half
the conducting power of either of these metals.    And all this
happens amongst substances which we are bound to consider,
at present, as elementary or simple.    Whichever way we consider the particles of matter and the space between them, and
examine the assumed constitution of matter by this table, the
results are full of perplexity.

Now let us take the case of potassium, a compact metallic
substance with excellent conducting powers, its oxide or hydrate a non-conductor; it will supply us with some facts having
very important bearings on the assumed atomic construction
of matter.

When potassium is oxidized an atom of it combines with an
atom of oxygen to form an atom of potassa, and an atom of
potassa combines with an atom of water, consisting of two
atoms of oxygen and hydrogen, to form an atom of hydrate of
potassa, so that an atom of hydrate of potassa contains four
elementary atoms.    The specific gravity of potassium is 0·865,
and its atomic weight 40; the specific gravity of cast hydrate
of potassa, in such state of purity as I could obtain it, I found
to be nearly 2, its atomic weight 57.    From these, which may
be taken as facts, the following strange conclusions flow.    A
piece of potassium contains less potassium than an equal piece
of the potash formed by it and oxygen.    We may cast into
potassium oxygen atom for atom, and then again both oxygen
and hydrogen in a twofold number of atoms, and yet, with all
these additions, the matter shall become less and less, until it
is not two-thirds of its original volume.    If a given bulk of potassium contains 45 atoms, the same bulk of hydrate of potassa
contains 70 atoms nearly *of the metal potassium,* and besides
that, 210 atoms more of oxygen and hydrogen.    In dealing
with assumptions I must assume a little more for the sake of
making any kind of statement; let me therefore assume that in
the hydrate of potassa the atoms are all of one size and nearly
touching each other, and that in a cubic inch of that substance
there are 2800 elementary atoms of potassium, oxygen and hydrogen; take away 2100 atoms of oxygen and hydrogen, and

the 700 atoms of potassium remaining will swell into more than a cubic inch and a half, and if we diminish the number until only those containable in a cubic inch remain, we shall have 430, or thereabout.   So a space which can contain 2800 atoms, and amongst them 700 of potassium itself, is found to be entirely filled by 430 atoms of potassium as they exist in the ordinary state of that metal.   Surely then, under the suppositions of the atomic theory, the atoms of potassium must be very far apart in the metal, *i. e.* there must be much more of space than of matter in that body : yet it is an excellent conductor, and so space must be a conductor ; but then what becomes of shell-lac, sulphur, and all the insulators ? for space must also by the theory exist in them.

Again, the volume which will contain 430 atoms of potassium, and nothing else, whilst in the state of metal, will, when that potassium is converted into nitre, contain very nearly the same number of atoms of potassium, *i. e.* 416, and also then seven times as many, or 2912 atoms of nitrogen and oxygen besides.   In carbonate of potassa the space which will contain only the 430 atoms of potassium as metal, being entirely filled by it, will, after the conversion, contain 256 atoms more of potassium, making 686 atoms of that metal, and, in addition 2744 atoms of oxygen and carbon.

These and similar considerations might be extended through compounds of sodium and other bodies with results equally striking, and indeed still more so, when the relations of one substance, as oxygen or sulphur, with different bodies are brought into comparison.

I am not ignorant that the mind is most powerfully drawn by the phenomena of crystallization, chemistry and physics generally, to the acknowledgement of centres of force.   I feel myself constrained, for the present hypothetically, to admit them, and cannot do without them, but I feel great difficulty in the conception of atoms of matter which in solids, fluids and vapours are supposed to be more or less apart from each other, with intervening space not occupied by atoms, and perceive great contradictions in the conclusions which flow from such a view.

If we must assume at all, as indeed in a branch of knowledge like the present we can hardly help it, then the safest course appears to be to assume as little as possible, and in that respect the atoms of Boscovich appear to me to have a great advantage over the more usual notion.   His atoms, if I understand aright, are mere centres of forces or powers, not particles of matter, in which the powers themselves reside.   If, in the ordinary view of atoms, we call the particle of matter away from the powers *a*, and the system of powers or forces in and around it *m*, then in Boscovich's theory *a* disappears, or is a mere mathematical point, whilst in the usual notion it is a little unchangeable, impenetrable piece of matter, and *m* is an atmosphere of force grouped around it.

In many of the hypothetical uses made of atoms, as in crystallography, chemistry, magnetism, &c., this difference in the assumption makes little or no alteration in the results, but in other cases, as of electric conduction, the nature of light, the manner in which bodies combine to produce compounds, the effects of forces, as heat or electricity, upon matter, the difference will be very great.

Thus, referring back to potassium, in which as a metal the atoms must, as we have seen, be, according to the usual view, very far apart from each other, how can we for a moment imagine that its conducting property belongs to it, any otherwise than as a consequence of the properties of the space, or as I have called it above, the *m*? so also its other properties in regard to light or magnetism, or solidity, or hardness, or specific gravity, must belong to it, in consequence of the properties or forces of the *m*, not those of the *a*, which, without the forces, is conceived of as having no powers.   But then surely the *m* is the *matter* of the potassium, for where is there the least ground (except in a gratuitous assumption) for imagining a difference in kind between the nature of that space midway between the centres of two contiguous atoms and any other spot between these centres? a difference in degree, or even in the nature of the power consistent with the law of continuity, I can admit, but the difference between a supposed little hard particle and the powers around it I cannot imagine.

To my mind, therefore, the *a* or nucleus vanishes, and the substance consists of the powers or *m*; and indeed what notion can we form of the nucleus independent of its powers? all our perception and knowledge of the atom, and even our fancy, is limited to ideas of its powers: what thought remains on which to hang the imagination of an *a* independent of the acknowledged forces? A mind just entering on the subject may consider it difficult to think of the powers of matter independent of a separate something to be called *the matter*, but it is certainly far more difficult, and indeed impossible, to think of or imagine that *matter* independent of the powers. Now the powers we know and recognize in every phenomenon of the creation, the abstract matter in none; why then assume the existence of that of which we are ignorant, which we cannot conceive, and for which there is no philosophical necessity?

Before concluding these speculations I will refer to a few of the important differences between the assumption of atoms consisting merely of centres of force, like those of Boscovich, and that other assumption of molecules of something specially material, having powers attached in and around them.

With the latter atoms a mass of matter consists of atoms and intervening space, with the former atoms matter is everywhere present, and there is no intervening space unoccupied by it. In gases the atoms touch each other just as truly as in solids. In this respect the atoms of water touch each other whether that substance be in the form of ice, water or steam; no mere intervening space is present. Doubtless the centres of force vary in their distance one from another, but that which is truly the matter of one atom touches the matter of its neighbours.

Hence matter will be *continuous* throughout, and in considering a mass of it we have not to suppose a distinction between its atoms and any intervening space. The powers around the centres give these centres the properties of atoms of matter; and these powers again, when many centres by their conjoint forces are grouped into a mass, give to every part of that mass the properties of matter. In such a view all the contradiction resulting from the consideration of electric insulation and conduction disappears.

The atoms may be conceived of as highly *elastic*, instead of being supposed excessively hard and unalterable in form; the mere compression of a bladder of air between the hands can alter their size a little; and the experiments of Cagniard de la Tour carry on this change in size until the difference in bulk at one time and another may be made several hundred times. Such is also the case when a solid or a fluid body is converted into vapour.

With regard also to the *shape* of the atoms, and, according to the ordinary assumption, its definite and unalterable character, another view must now be taken of it. An atom by itself might be conceived of as spherical, or spheroidal, or where many were touching in all directions, the form might be thought of, as a dodecahedron, for any one would be surrounded by and bear against twelve others, on different sides. But if an atom be conceived to be a centre of power, that which is ordinarily referred to under the term *shape* would now be referred to the disposition and relative intensity of the forces. The power arranged in and around a centre might be uniform in arrangement and intensity in every direction outwards from that centre, and then a section of equal intensity of force through the radii would be a sphere; or the law of decrease of force from the centre outwards might vary in different directions, and then the section of equal intensity might be an oblate or oblong spheroid, or have other forms; or the forces might be disposed so as to make the atom polar; or they might circulate around it equatorially or otherwise, after the manner of imagined magnetic atoms. In fact nothing can be supposed of the disposition of forces in or about a solid nucleus of matter, which cannot be equally conceived with respect to a centre.

In the view of matter now sustained as the lesser assumption, matter and the atoms of matter would be mutually penetrable. As regards the mutual penetrability of matter, one would think that the facts respecting potassium and its compounds, already described, would be enough to prove that point to a mind which accepts a fact for a fact, and is not obstructed in its judgement by preconceived notions. With respect to the mutual penetrability of the atoms, it seems to me to present in many points of view a more beautiful, yet equally probable and philosophic idea of the constitution of bodies than the other hypotheses, especially in the case of chemical combination. If we suppose an atom of oxygen and an atom of potassium about to combine and produce potash, the hypothesis of solid unchangeable impenetrable atoms places these two particles side by side in a position easily, because mechanically, imagined, and not unfrequently represented; but if these two atoms be centres of power they will mutually penetrate to the very centres, thus forming one atom or molecule with powers, either uniformly around it or arranged as the resultant of the powers of the two constituent atoms; and the manner in which two or many centres of force may in this way combine, and afterwards, under the dominion of stronger forces, separate again, may in some degree be illustrated by the beautiful case of the conjunction of two sea waves of different velocities into one, their perfect union for a time, and final separation into the constituent waves, considered, I think, at the meeting of the British Association at Liverpool. It does not of course follow, from this view, that the centres shall always coincide; that will depend upon the relative disposition of the powers of each atom.

The view now stated of the constitution of matter would seem to involve necessarily the conclusion that matter fills all space, or, at least, all space to which gravitation extends (including the sun and its system); for gravitation is a property of matter dependent on a certain force, and it is this force which constitutes the matter. In that view matter is not merely mutually penetrable, but each atom extends, so to say, throughout the whole of the solar system, yet always retaining its own centre of force. This, at first sight, seems to fall in very harmoniously with Mossotti's mathematical investigations and reference of the phenomena of electricity, cohesion, gravitation, &c. to one force in matter; and also again with the old adage, " matter cannot act where it is not." But it is no part of my intention to enter into such considerations as these, or what the bearings of this hypothesis would be on the theory of light and the supposed æther. My desire has been rather to bring certain facts from electrical conduction and chemical combination to bear strongly upon our views regarding the nature of atoms and matter, and so to assist in distinguishing in natural philosophy our real knowledge, *i. e.* the knowledge of facts and laws, from that, which, though it has the form of knowledge, may, from its including so much that is mere assumption, be the very reverse.

I am, my dear Sir, yours, &c.,<br>Michael Faraday.

# INDEX TO VOLUME II

N.B. A dash rule represents the *italics* immediately preceding it. The references are sometimes to the individual paragraph, and sometimes to that and such as succeed it. Those which follow *p* or *pp* are to pages, the others to the paragraphs of the Experimental Researches.

*A*CIDS, effect of dilution, 1977.
——, their effect on electricity of steam, 2091, 2121.
—— *and metals*, their thermo currents, 1934, 1939.
—————— with heat, 1946, 1949, 1956, 1963.
*Active voltaic circles* without metallic contact, 2017.
—— with sulphuret of potassium, 1877, 1881, 1907.
Air, its effect on excitement, 1921.
*Air compressed, electricity evolved by*, 2129.
——, due to moisture in it, 2130, 2132.
——, double excitements, 2139.
——, *with* sulphur, 2138, 2140.
——, —— silica, 2138, 2140.
——, —— gum, 2138, 2139.
——, —— resin, 2138, 2139.
Alcohol, its effect on the electricity of steam, 2115.
*Alkalies*, their effect on electricity of steam, 2092, 2094, 2121, 2126.
—— and metals with heat, 1945, 1948, 1956, 1962, 1966.
Ammonia, its effect on the electricity of steam, 2094.
*Animal electricity*, 1749.
——. *See* Gymnotus.
Anomalous character of contact force, 1862, 1864, 1871, 1888, 1989, 2056.
*Antimony*, on a supposed new oxide of, *p.* 225.
—— in sulphuret of potassium, 1902.
Apparatus for electricity from steam and water, 2076, 2087.
*Arago's magnetic phenomena*, *pp.* 176, 182.
——, third force in, *pp.* 190, 193.
*Assumption of the contact theory, as regards* solids, 1809, 1844, 1870, 1888, 1982, 2014.

*Assumption of the contact theory, as regards* fluids, 1810, 1835, 1844, 1860, 1865, 1870, 1888, 1982, 1992, 2006, 2014, 2060.
Atmosphere, its electricity, no relation to that of steam, 2145.
Atomic hypothesis of matter, *p.* 284.
*Atoms*, their hypothetical nature, *pp.* 285, 291.
——, their shape, *p.* 292.
—— of metals and conducting power, *p.* 287.
—— *of potassium*, *pp.* 288, 290.
—————, their penetrability, *pp.* 289, 290, 292.
Attraction, cohesive, of mercury affected by the electric current, *p.* 156.

Batteries, voltaic, without metallic contact, 2024.
*Bismuth with sulphuret of potassium*, 1894.
—— shows excitement is not due to contact, 1895.
Boscovich, his atoms, *p.* 290.
Breaking contact, spark, *p.* 207.

Cadmium with sulphuret of potassa, 1904.
Cathode, excitement at, 2016, 2045, 2052.
Centres of force, *p.* 289.
Charge, state, defined, *p.* 262.
Chemical and contact excitement compared, 1831, 1836, 1844.
Chemical theory of the voltaic pile, 1801, 1803, 2017, 2029.
*Chemical action* evolves electricity, 2030, 2039.
—— being changed, electricity changes with it, 2031, 2036, 2040.
—— the source of voltaic power, 1796, 1884, 1875, 1956, 1982, 2029, 2053.
——. *See* Voltaic pile, source of its power.

Plates to Volume II

PLATE I (Vol. II, see description on p. 126)

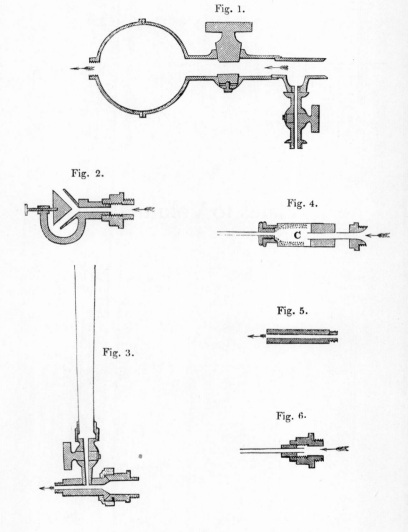

Fig. 1.

Fig. 2.

Fig. 4.

Fig. 3.

Fig. 5.

Fig. 6.

PLATE II (Vol. II, see pp. 127-147)

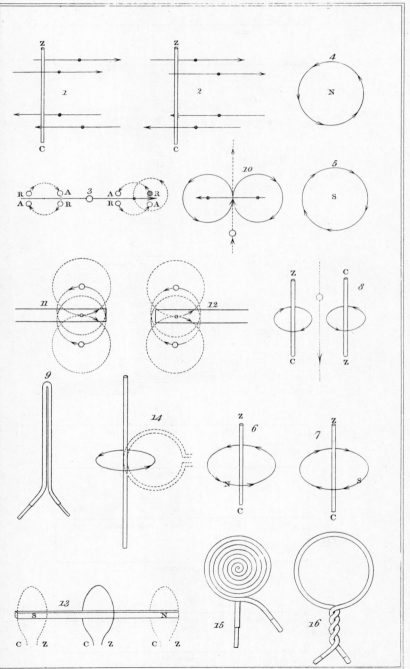

J<sup>s</sup> Basire sc.

PLATE III (Vol. II, Series XVI and XVII)

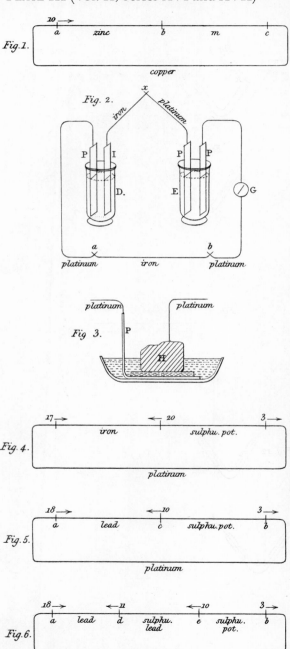

Fig.1.

10 →
a    zinc    b    m    c

copper

Fig. 2.    x

iron    platinum

P    I    P    P

D.    E    G

a    b

platinum    iron    platinum

platinum    platinum

Fig 3.    P

H

17 →    ← 20    3 →
iron    sulphu. pot.

Fig. 4.

platinum

18 →    ← 10    3 →
a    lead    c    sulphu. pot.    b

Fig. 5.

platinum

18 →    ← 11    ← 10    3 →
a    lead    d    sulphu.    e    sulphu.    b
lead    pot.

Fig. 6.

platinum

# PLATE III (continued)

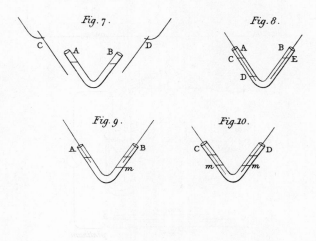

*Fig. 7.*          *Fig. 8.*

*Fig. 9.*          *Fig. 10.*

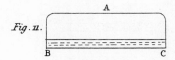

*Fig. 11.*

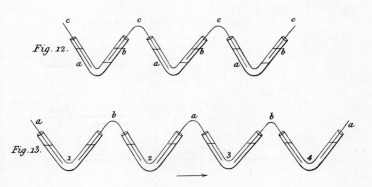

*Fig. 12.*

*Fig. 13.*

PLATE III (concluded)

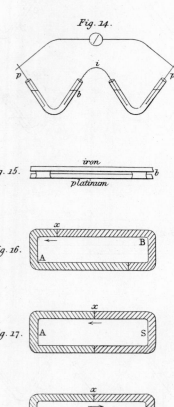

*Fig. 14.*

*Fig. 15.*

*Fig. 16.*

*Fig. 17.*

*Fig. 18.*

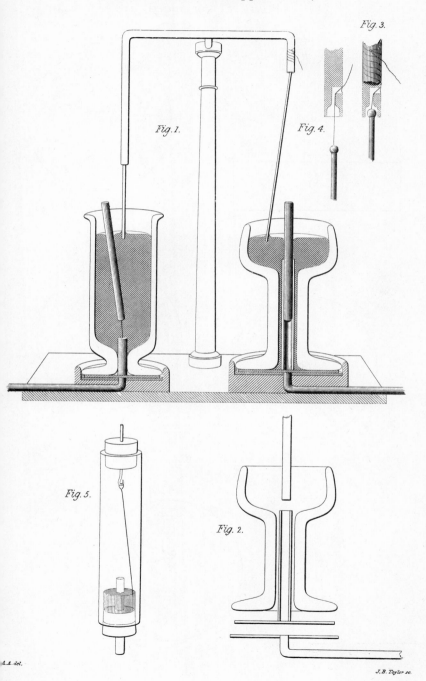

PLATE IV (Vol. II, see pp. 148-151)

Fig. 3.

Fig. 1.

Fig. 4.

Fig. 5.

Fig. 2.

A.A. del.

J. B. Taylor sc.

# PLATE V (Vol. I, Series VI and VII)

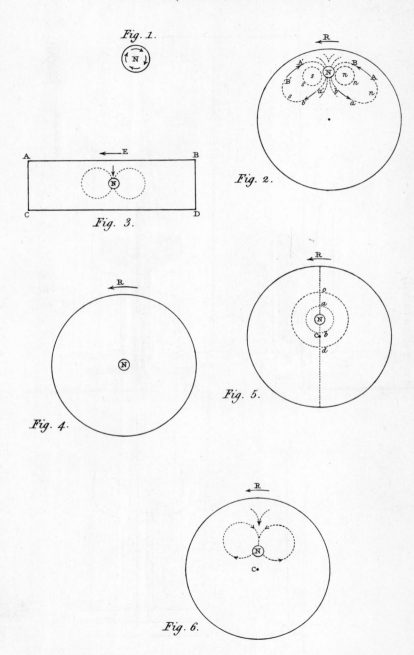

*Fig. 1.*

*Fig. 2.*

*Fig. 3.*

*Fig. 4.*

*Fig. 5.*

*Fig. 6.*

PLATE V (concluded)

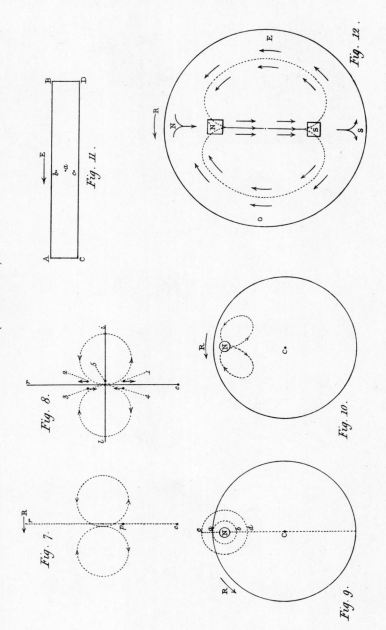

Fig. 7.

Fig. 8.

Fig. 9.

Fig. 10.

Fig. 11.

Fig. 12.

## DATE DUE

| | | |
|---|---|---|
| 5/17/13 | | |
| | | |
| | | |
| | | |
| | | |
| | | |
| | | |
| | | |
| | | |
| | | |
| | | |
| | | |
| | | |
| | | |
| | | |
| | | |

GAYLORD     #3523PI     Printed in USA